536·49

50/-

METALLURGY AND METALLURGICAL ENGINEERING SERIES

ROBERT F. MEHL, PH.D., D.Sc., *Consulting Editor*

PROPERTIES OF METALS
AT
ELEVATED TEMPERATURES

PROPERTIES OF METALS
AT
ELEVATED TEMPERATURES

BY

GEORGE V. SMITH

Research Laboratory, United States Steel
Corporation of Delaware, Kearny, New Jersey

WITH A FOREWORD AND APPENDIX
BY DR. R. F. MILLER
Assistant to Vice President, Research and Technology, Carnegie-Illinois Steel Corporation

FIRST EDITION

New York   Toronto   London
McGRAW-HILL BOOK COMPANY, INC.
1950

PROPERTIES OF METALS AT ELEVATED TEMPERATURES

FOREWORD

Shortly after the First World War, the fuel economy resulting from higher steam temperature and the increased yield of gasoline obtained by thermal cracking of petroleum resulted in a demand for metals which would withstand higher temperatures and pressures and for more information on the properties of the materials of construction. Research work was begun, and technical articles describing the investigations began to appear in considerable number. As a result of new alloys and of better use of the materials, based on improved knowledge of their properties, steam temperatures were increased steadily from about 650°F in 1920 to 1050°F at the present time. In this thirty-year period, the amount of coal required to produce a given amount of electricity by steam power was cut in half, resulting in a decrease in the average cost of residential electric service from 7.4 cents per kilowatt hour in 1920 to 3.4 cents at the present time.

This and other equally startling advances drew increasing attention to this field. Many testing programs were initiated to determine the strength of metals at elevated temperatures and to develop new materials, and much valuable engineering data were obtained and published. These results have been correlated and summarized, both in the advertising literature of the producers and in the publications of various technical societies, such as the ASME-ASTM Creep Compilation published in 1938 and in the tables of allowable working stresses published by the ASME Boiler Code and the API.

While somewhat smaller in number than the investigations being conducted to obtain engineering data, considerable research work has been devoted to the fundamental mechanisms of plastic deformation under stress at elevated temperatures and to the effect of grain size, recrystallization, distribution of the phases, and phase changes. All these metallurgical problems have a direct bearing on the use of metals at elevated temperatures, yet no correlation of these numerous investigations has been attempted in this country. It is to this task that Dr. Smith has addressed himself.

The present volume brings together the results of the research work carried out on metals at elevated temperatures since this subject first began to receive attention some twenty-five years ago and correlates these results at elevated temperatures. While far from complete, present knowledge of this field is sufficient to permit successful use of metals under such conditions. The survey shows all too clearly the numerous gaps in our knowledge of this vitally important subject, and it points the way to future research. This book is therefore commended to students, metallurgists, and engineers interested in the properties of metals at elevated temperatures.

R. F. MILLER

PITTSBURGH, PA.

PREFACE

Many engineers, and metallurgists as well, who have the responsibility of applying metals to service at elevated temperatures lack a full appreciation of the nature of the phenomena involved. This may be attributed in part to the rapidly expanding commercial interest in this use of metals which has brought many engineers newly into the field, and in part to the relative complexity of the behavior. The aim of this book is to present a comprehensive summary of available knowledge on the effect of temperature on the properties of metals which at the same time will prove useful to the student just encountering this field of interest and to the graduate metallurgist or engineer actively engaged in the development, evaluation, and application of metals for service at elevated temperatures.

The initial chapters of the book are of a fundamental character, and deal from a metallurgical point of view with the nature of plastic deformation and fracture of metals—first at ordinary temperature and then at elevated temperature. Next, the test apparatus and test procedures employed in evaluating metals for service at elevated temperatures are described. This is followed by chapters which summarize available knowledge on the effects of such variables as chemical composition, manufacturing practice, and heat-treatment. A separate chapter is devoted to the question of scaling of metals and to the nature of the changes in microstructure which may be expected to occur during service. A final chapter deals with the problem of design for service at elevated temperatures, particularly with the choice of working stress. An appendix provides useful information on the so-called "superalloys" of recent and current interest.

Inasmuch as this book deals with a field of interest in which rapid advances are being made, it could not have been written without drawing heavily on the work of others. Appropriate acknowledgments of the sources of such information are given throughout the book. The author is grateful to Dr. John Johnston, former director, and to Dr. J. B. Austin, present director, Research Laboratory, U.S. Steel Corp. of Delaware, for providing stenographic and photographic assistance in the preparation of the manuscript and for permission to use certain unpublished data.

The manuscript was read by Dr. R. F. Mehl, director of Metals Research Laboratory, Carnegie Institute of Technology, and by Dr. R. F. Miller, assistant to the vice-president, Research and Technology, Carnegie-Illinois Steel Corp., both of whom offered valued criticism and suggestions, and to whom the author expresses his thanks. He is especially indebted to Dr. Miller, who pointed out the need for the present book, and who, except for the press of other work, would have joined in its preparation. Grateful acknowledgment is also due Dr. Miller for preparing the Appendix.

GEORGE V. SMITH

KEARNY, N.J.
March, 1950

CONTENTS

Slipping and Twinning—Deformation by Slip—Effect of Temperature
and Rate of Deformation on the Slip Process—Effect of Alloying on
the Slip Process—The Critical Resolved Shear Stress—Effect of
Alloying Elements on Critical Resolved Shear Stress—Effect of Rate
of Stressing on Critical Shear Stress—Effect of Temperature on
Critical Shear Stress—Strain Hardening—The Stress-Strain Curve—
Effect of Alloying Elements on the Stress-Strain Curve—Effect of
Rate of Stressing on the Stress-Strain Curve—Effect of Temperature
on the Stress-Strain Curve—Recovery and Recrystallization—Lattice
Rotation—Deformation Bands—Deformation (or Mechanical) Twin-
ning—The Twinning Elements—Critical Shear Stress for Twinning
—Influence of Temperature and Deformation Velocity on Twinning
—Effect of Twinning on Strain Hardening—Creep of Single Crystals
—Summary.

The Nature and Effects of Grain Boundaries—The Amorphous
Cement Grain Boundary—The Equicohesive Temperature—Viscous
Nature of Grain Boundaries—Transitional Lattice Grain Boundary
—Plastic Yielding of Polycrystalline Metal—The Flow Curve and
Strain Hardening—Lattice Rotation during Deformation of Poly-
crystalline Metals-Preferred Orientation—Taylor's Theory of Flow
in Polycrystalline Aggregates—The Bauschinger Effect and the
Elastic Aftereffect—Internal Friction—The Influence of Alloying
Elements on Flow of Polycrystalline Metals—Homogeneous Alloys
(Solid Solutions)—Heterogeneous Alloys—The Influence of Rate of
Deformation and Temperature—Summary.

The Creep Curve at Constant Load—The Period of Decreasing Creep
Rate (Primary Creep)—The Minimum Creep Rate (Secondary Creep)
—The Accelerating Creep Rate (Tertiary Creep)—Mathematical
Expressions for the Creep-time Curve—Relation between Stress and
Intercept of Constant Creep-rate Slope on Strain Ordinate—Relation
between Temperature and Intercept of Constant Creep-rate Slope on
Strain Ordinate—Relation between Stress and Minimum Creep Rate
—Relation between Temperature and Minimum Creep Rate—The
Velocity-modified Temperature for Flow—Generalized Expressions
for Constant-rate Creep—The Mechanical Equation of State—Re-
laxation—Summary.

CHAPTER I

INTRODUCTION

When a metal used for structural purposes, such as steel or duralumin, is stressed at ambient temperature beyond its elastic limit, plastic deformation occurs; that is, the metal undergoes a permanent change in shape, as contrasted with the elastic or recoverable deformation which occurs when the metal is stressed below the elastic limit. The amount of this plastic deformation depends upon the applied stress, and for practical purposes, as long as the stress is not increased further, no additional extension will occur unless the stress is of a relatively large magnitude relative to the tensile strength. Figures 1 and 2 illustrate this behavior. The elastic limit is represented (Fig. 2) by the stress S_1 and corresponding extension E_1; S_2 represents an applied stress in excess of the elastic limit and E_2 the corresponding strain (in part an elastic and in part a plastic extension), which for practical purposes will remain fixed so long as the stress is not further increased. The design of statically loaded structures is usually based on an arbitrary fraction of the tensile strength or elastic limit (or oftener, on the more readily measured yield strength) as determined from the ordinary stress-strain curve such as that in Figs. 1 and 2.

A familiar exception to the behavior described in the preceding paragraph is that of the metal lead. When lead is stressed at atmospheric temperature to only slightly above its elastic limit, the extension does not cease after stressing. Rather, extension continues to occur with time, at a rate dependent upon the applied stress, as illustrated in Fig. 3. A somewhat, though not exactly, similar phenomenon is the flow of baker's dough or of tar when warmed slightly. Detailed study would show that the stress-strain curve of lead in contrast with steel or duralumin is also more affected by testing conditions, such as the rate of stressing.

Duralumin or steel on one hand and lead on the other differ in their apparent behavior only when they are compared at the same temperature. Comparison at the same temperature, however, has no real scientific value, for, as has been shown clearly by many investigators, generalizations regarding the properties and behavior of metals can be

1

made to a greater degree when comparison is made at the same fraction of the melting points.   When this is done, steel or duralumin behave quite similarly to lead in their reaction to an applied stress.   This change in behavior becomes evident if the same metal is tested, as in the simple tension test, over a range of temperature.

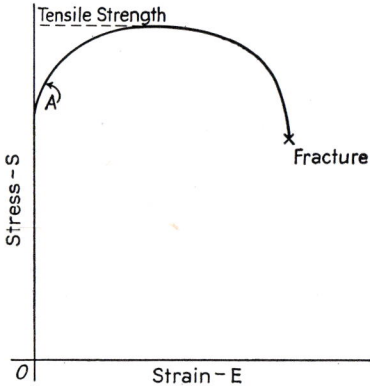

Fig. 1. Schematic stress-strain curve for a metal tension tested at atmospheric temperature. (Note: Steels often exhibit inhomogeneous plastic yielding, characterized by a sudden drop in load, in contrast to the gradual and homogeneous yielding illustrated here.)

The extension with time under constant stress has been termed "creep." It occurs in all metals under the appropriate conditions of temperature and stress. It is economically undesirable (and sometimes impossible) to employ a design stress so low that no creep occurs. Consequently, when metals are used under conditions in which creep occurs, the behavior must be recognized and accounted for in the design of the structure. No longer are the tensile or yield strengths of the simple tension test adequate for design, and no longer can design be made for an indefinite period.

The creep behavior of a metal used in service at elevated temperatures is the single most important factor and generally is the controlling factor in any particular application.   The greater part of this book will therefore be devoted to this subject.   There are other important factors, however, perhaps the chief of which is resistance to oxidation or other chemical attack under the service conditions; in particular instances such physical properties as thermal expansivity may be of concern.   These subjects will receive attention.

There are many uses of metals and alloys at elevated temperatures, and the number of applications is constantly increasing as new processes and methods are developed; simultaneously, the temperatures at which established processes are carried out are being pushed higher and higher, thus producing severer requirements which must be met by the materials engineer.   Often, it is a lack of suitable material that prevents the use of an even higher temperature.

Processes are carried out at elevated temperatures for two reasons: the process could not otherwise be done, or the process is thereby done more efficiently. An example illustrating the first reason is the commercial manufacture of silicon carbide; an example illustrating the second is the steam turbine, in which case, as is generally true of heat engines, the higher the temperature of operation, the greater the efficiency.

The first interest in the properties of metals at high temperatures must date back to shortly after the discovery of fire and its use for heating metals to aid in shaping them into weapons, cooking utensils, and tools. This matter of formability is still of interest and will receive some attention in this book. However, the principal concern will be with the properties of metals as they relate to the serviceability at elevated temperatures, generally for the purpose of containing other substances or of

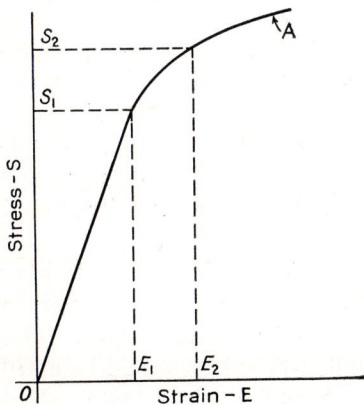

FIG. 2. Initial portion (OA) of stress-strain curve in Fig. 1.

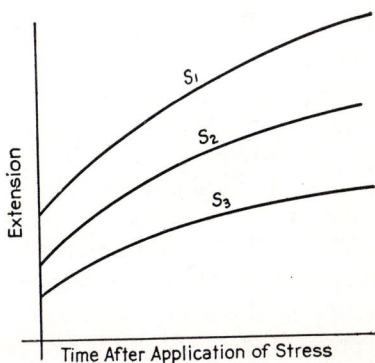

FIG. 3. Schematic creep curves for lead at room temperature under constant stresses S_1 (greatest), S_2, and S_3 (least).

supporting other structural members under some degree of stress. The first use of metals for this purpose involved relatively low stress and temperature, and it was probably not until the beginning of the industrial age, sired by the steam-engine inventions of Watts during the latter half of the eighteenth century, that the service requirements imposed upon metals for use at high temperatures became of any concern.

Since that time, advances in technology have appeared in rapid succession. In the field of power production, there has been the development of the central power-generating station to its present-day high-temperature, high-pressure, efficient operation; the more recently developed steam-turbine drive for both marine and land purposes; the invention of the diesel and gas or gasoline engines; the development of the gas turbine, which is still in its early days of development, comparatively speaking, and generally familiar owing to its well-publicized use in airplane super-chargers as well as for its use as a prime mover in central-station power production and now in locomotives; the very recent development of jet propulsion; and finally, the crowning achievement of science, nuclear fission, which opens up entirely new vistas extending so far in advance in so many fields that it is impossible to foresee even the near future.

In the interrelated oil and chemical industries, which is the other major category into which the uses of metals at high temperatures can be divided, equally important advances have been made. The oil industry uses metals in service at high temperatures for such equipment as stills, cracking units, hot oil pumps, and tubing. Recent years have been marked by the development and perfection of catalytic processes and the use of higher temperatures. In the chemical industry a majority of processes are carried out at only moderate temperatures, less than perhaps 500°F, and under such conditions, resistance to corrosion is perhaps the major concern. However, certain processes, such as the manufacture of sulfuric acid or of caustic soda and the synthesis of certain chemicals such as ammonia, require higher temperatures, and undoubtedly the future will see both the use of high temperatures and pressure in other chemical processes and of even higher temperatures for present processes.

The similarity between creep and the viscous flow characterizing viscous fluids was early recognized, and Andrade[1]* in 1911 reported the results of short-time studies of this nature for several metals. This represents the first recorded "creep" studies, though it should be noted that Andrade's investigations were carried out for only relatively short duration and were of more theoretical than practical interest. Prior to this, study seems to have been confined largely to the short-time, continuous-loading tensile test.

When the phenomenon of extension at constant stress was recognized and engineers realized that under design stresses based on the results of ordinary tension tests, even when made at the service temperature, their structures continued to distort with time, they began seeking a "limiting creep stress," a stress below which no sensible creep could be detected. Much early effort was expended in this search, and it was expected that this stress would correspond to the proportional limit of the tensile test, provided this latter quantity were measured with an extensometer of sufficient sensitivity. However, it was soon found that the more sensitive the measuring instrument, the lower the proportional limit, and that sensible creep occurred, under certain conditions of temperature,

---

* Superior numbers refer to works cited in the Bibliography.

even at stresses below a proportional limit determined by the most sensitive means available. Among the early investigators reporting in this field were Chevenard[2] in 1919, Dickenson[3] in 1922, Lea[4] in 1924, Tapsell[5] in 1925, and French *et al.*[6] in 1925. Their work was soon followed by that of others, and progress in the understanding of creep phenomena has since been quite rapid. As understanding increased, it became evident that instead of seeking a stress below which no creep would occur, it would be better to recognize that creep would occur and to design only to a stress which would cause no more than a certain, permissible, predetermined distortion. French[7] probably drew attention to this fact first. According to this view, a power-generating station is designed for 20 years, or 30 years, after which time it is slated for replacement. To design on such a basis is dictated by economics, if for no other reason, and it requires that "creep data" be obtained by the materials engineer for the various materials used at high temperatures.

The methods of obtaining, interpreting, and using such data, and other required data, and the practical and theoretical characteristics of metals at high temperatures will be the subject matter of this book.

CHAPTER II

PLASTIC DEFORMATION OF SINGLE CRYSTALS

Plasticity and strength are the individually most important character-istics of metals and alloys. By virtue of their plasticity, metals may be formed into desirable shapes, and the degree of plasticity under various conditions is therefore of considerable practical importance. Some metals possess high plasticity over a wide range of conditions, while others may be of such restricted plasticity that for practical purposes they cannot be effectively shaped by plastic deformation. The plasticity of a metal or alloy depends upon many variables—crystal structure, bonding forces, purity, composition of the alloy, heat-treatment, tem-perature, kind of stress or deformation, and rate of deformation.

The strength of metals and alloys, or the ability to support loads, is quite intimately related to plasticity through the phenomenon of strain hardening. The term "strain hardening" describes the increase with plastic deformation of the stress required for further plastic deformation. In this sense, then, strength is synonymous with the stress for plastic flow. The term "strength" can mean other things also and must be defined in each case. For example, it may be applied to fracture with-out plastic deformation, or, in the case of creep, it may apply to the stress to cause a specific rate of deformation, or to the stress which will cause failure in some specific time interval.

While this book treats primarily the creep properties of metals at high temperatures, it should be clearly recognized, as pointed out in Chap. I, that temperature is a relative term, lead at atmospheric temperature being analogous to steel at perhaps 1500°F. Furthermore, an under-standing of the phenomena of creep encountered at "elevated" tempera-tures is dependent on an understanding of the plasticity and strength of metals in general. In fact, the creep behavior of metals may be con-sidered as a special category under the general heading of Plasticity and Strength. Accordingly, this chapter, as well as the one that follows, will present first a general treatment—in some cases necessarily brief—of the subject of strength and plasticity, which will serve as a springboard for a more extensive treatment of the particular aspects of interest which can be grouped under the heading Creep Phenomena.

One of the characteristics of a metal is that it is crystalline, that is, the atoms of which it is composed are arranged in a regular three-dimensional pattern or lattice. Figure 4 illustrates several of the most common space lattices. This is in contrast to amorphous materials, such as glass, in which such definite regularity does not exist. Because metals are crystalline, their properties are frequently anisotropic, that is, dependent upon the direction of measurement (Fig. 5). However, almost all metals

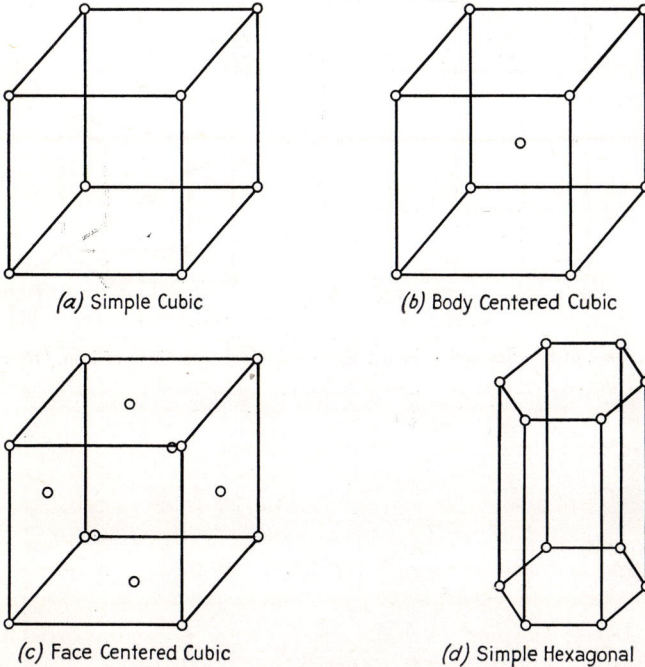

(a) Simple Cubic   *(b)* Body Centered Cubic

(c) Face Centered Cubic   *(d)* Simple Hexagonal

Fig. 4. Examples of crystallographic space lattices.

or alloys, as applied commercially, are polycrystalline, or composed of many crystals or grains; this is revealed by examination of a polished and etched section such as that shown in Fig. 6. If the individual grains of the polycrystalline aggregates are randomly oriented, the gross-scale properties will be invariant with the direction of test. Thus the elastic modulus of single crystals of iron may vary between 20,000,000 psi and 40,000,000 psi, but the polycrystalline aggregate, with randomly oriented grains, will show a modulus of about 30,000,000 psi in all directions.

Our knowledge of the behavior of polycrystalline metals and alloys has been greatly enhanced by the study of single crystals. This is true not only for the deformation and strength characteristics but for other physical characteristics. Accordingly, we shall attempt to summarize the pertinent behavior of single crystals before advancing to polycrystalline metals and then lastly to discuss the specific phases of plasticity and strength of principal interest of this book, that is, creep behavior.

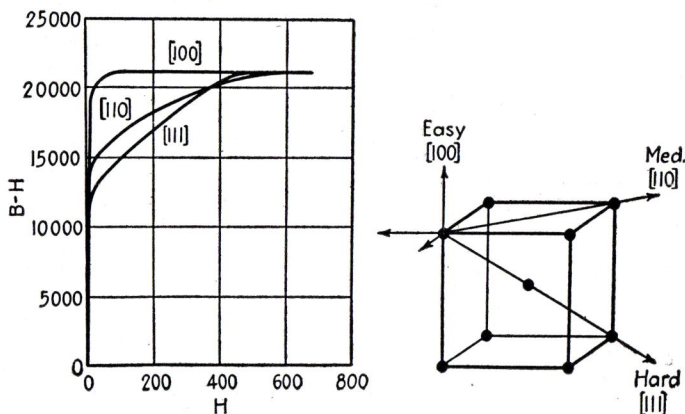

FIG. 5. Ease of magnetization in the three principal directions of iron. (*Barret.*[10])

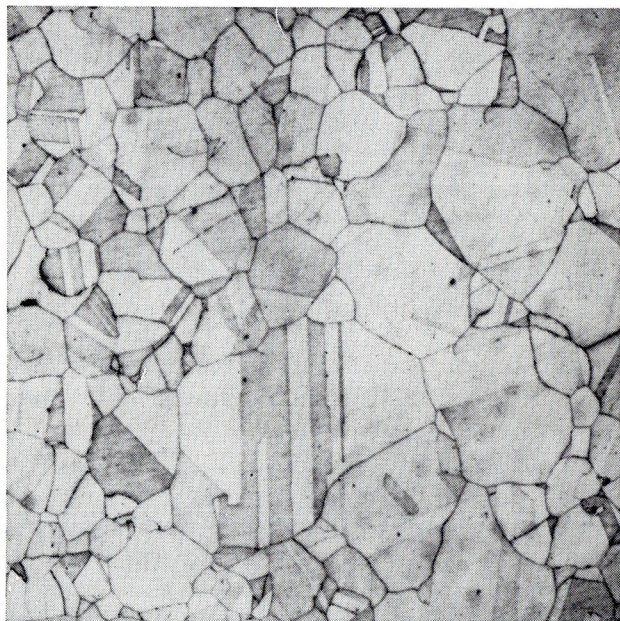

FIG. 6. Polycrystalline metal; austenitic stainless steel; ×100. Each grain is of different crystallographic orientation.

When stressed, single crystals at first extend elastically—as do poly-crystalline aggregates—until some limit is reached at which they either deform plastically, that is, acquire a permanent distortion, or fracture. However, even though the crystal deforms plastically, it will eventually fracture if the stressing is continued. Accordingly, two broad categories of plastic deformation, often called "flow" and "fracture," may be designated in which to encompass this subject. The conditions under which each may occur in any instance depend upon the temperature and upon the type and rate of stressing, and of course upon the prior history of the metal or alloy.

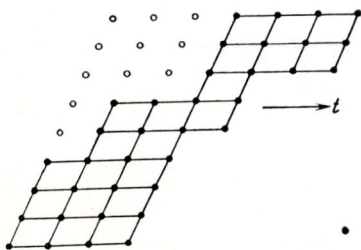

FIG. 7.   FIG. 8.

FIG. 7. Shear of atoms in slip. Open circles represent atoms before slip. The direction of slip *t* lies in the plane of slip which is perpendicular to the plane of the page. (*Schmid and Boas.*[8])

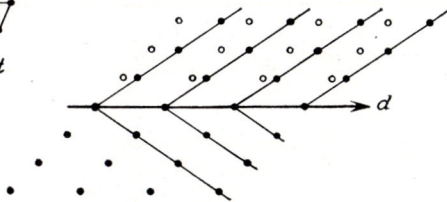

FIG. 8. Shear of atoms in deformation twinning. The twinning direction *d* lies in the twinning plane which is perpendicular to the plane of the page. Open circles represent atoms before twinning. (*Schmid and Boas.*[8])

Slipping and Twinning

Plastic deformation may occur either by slip or by twinning, but slip is the principal mode of deformation in the common metals. Both of these phenomena are quite complex on an atomistic basis, but super-ficially they may be illustrated as in Figs. 7 and 8. Both processes represent shear movements of atoms in a specific plane and direction in this plane, the essential difference between the two being that twinning is characterized by a specific degree of shear, and in such a manner that there exists a twin relation, that is, a definite crystallographic relation, between the undeformed and deformed regions. Twinning thus results from a homogeneous shear. Slip, on the other hand, represents merely a displacement or gliding of two portions of the crystal with respect to one another, the individual parts retaining their original orientation. Thus slip "lines" which appear on a surface when a sample is deformed (Fig. 9) are not ordinarily apparent if the surface is subsequently polished, whether etched or not,* while the boundaries of a twin, since it represents a difference in orientation, will be apparent after polishing and etching (Fig. 10). It might be noted that deformation twins such as those shown do not generally have the straight-edged appearance or the appreciable width of the so-called "annealing" twins common in such alloys as brass or austenitic stainless steel, some of which are to be observed in Fig. 6.

Deformation twinning may sometimes be difficult to distinguish from deformation banding, which results when two portions of a single crystal

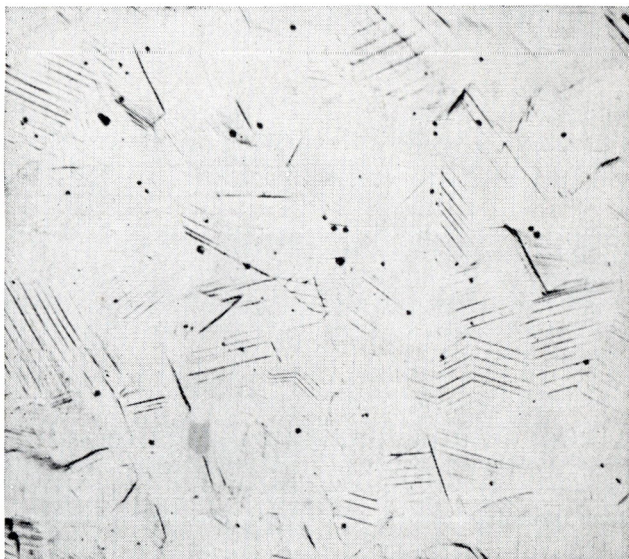

Fɪɢ. 9. Slip traces on polished surface of polycrystalline 18 Cr–8 Ni stainless steel, deformed by squeezing in a vise; unetched; ×250.

slip on different planes and directions and therefore rotate in different directions, as discussed below. In this case the difference in orientation is not the exactly fixed one of the twin relation, but is a variable one increasing gradually with deformation.

Deformation by Slip

The physical process of slip has often been compared to the gliding of groups of playing cards upon one another when the pack is subjected to shear (Fig. 11). The plane and direction of slip are generally, not al-

* In some metals, at least, refined techniques of polishing and etching have revealed slip "lines." The likelihood of thus revealing slip increases with the degree of plastic deformation.

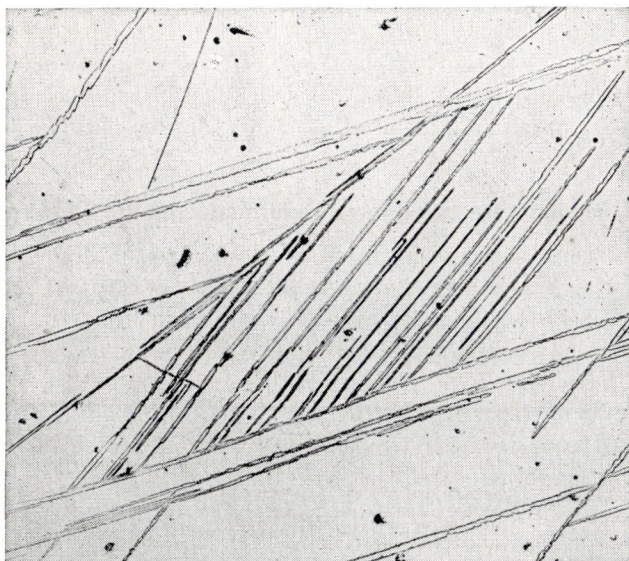

FIG. 10. Neumann bands formed in iron by rapid deformation; ×100. These are generally considered to be deformation twins.

ways, those of closest packing of the atoms, or to state it differently, of greatest atomic density. Thus in close-packed hexagonal zinc, slip is on the basal (001) plane* and in one of the three diagonal [101] directions, while in face-centered cubic copper, slip is on the octahedral {111} planes in the [110] directions. Body-centered cubic iron, an exception to the simplicity indicated by zinc and copper, will slip on any of three families of planes {110}, {112}, and {123} in the [111] di-

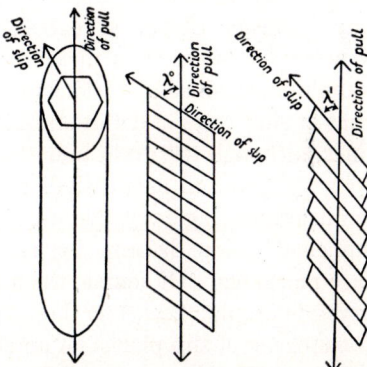

FIG. 11. Slip in a hexagonal metal. Note the rotation of the lattice with respect to the axis of pull. (*Elam.*[9])

* Miller indices notation. The Miller indices of a crystallographic plane (*hkl*) are obtained by taking the reciprocals of the intercepts, measured in terms of the unit cell dimensions, of the plane on the three crystal axes and reducing these to the smallest integers proportional to the reciprocals. The indices of a direction [*uvw*] are the smallest integers proportional to the difference in coordinates, measured in terms of the unit cell dimensions, between points lying on the direction line.

rection. The generally wavy character of slip lines in iron, incidentally, is attributed to the multiplicity of possible slip systems, several combining to produce the waviness. Barrett[10] has recently compiled the results of experimental determinations of slip systems for different metals.

Effect of Temperature and Rate of Deformation on the Slip Process

The influence of temperature on the plane and direction of slip of metal crystals has not been studied as extensively as is to be desired. In the few instances studied, it has frequently been observed that with increasing temperature, additional slip systems become active. This is illustrated in Fig. 12, which shows that iron (silicon ferrite) slips on a single family of planes at subatmospheric temperature but slips on three families at room or higher temperature. Many other of the common metals slip on only one family of planes at atmospheric temperature, but utilize additional planes at elevated temperatures. There is no reason to believe that the deformation of crystals at elevated temperatures does not occur by a crystallographic mechanism.

The influence of the rate of deformation upon the slip process has received very inadequate attention, although there is little reason to expect any influence except at extremely fast or slow rates. Hanson and Wheeler[11] have made a metallographic study of polished specimens of aluminum strained at various rates and temperatures, and have reported that at slow rates of deformation, polycrystalline samples showed no slip lines, although the grain boundaries became apparent (owing no doubt to grain rotation as we shall note when we consider creep), while at similar rates single crystals showed profuse slip markings. However, at sufficiently slow deformation rates even single crystals showed no surface markings. Of course, the absence of slip lines does not mean noncrystallographic flow, but there is indicated that there is a difference in the spacing of slip planes, of amount of shear on each plane, or of other difference worthy of detailed experimental study in the hope that it would contribute to understanding of the slip mechanism.

Effect of Alloying on the Slip Process

It has generally been observed that the plane and direction of slip do not change with addition of alloying elements. Thus the type of crystal lattice—face-centered or body-centered cubic, etc.—appears to be the determining factor. However, the decrease in number of possible slip planes in iron with increasing addition of silicon, as shown in Fig. 12, is an interesting effect of alloying, possibly attributable to a uniqueness of conditions of temperature and composition.

The Critical Resolved Shear Stress

Since slip occurs only on certain very specific planes and directions, it is to be expected that the stress necessary to initiate slip will depend upon the direction of stressing. This has been found to be true, as may be observed from the experimental points plotted in Fig. 13. However, if the applied stress required to initiate slip is resolved into the plane and direction of slip, the resulting so-called "critical resolved shear stress" is observed to be independent of direction. Thus the solid curve of Fig. 13 represents the variation of the yield point to be expected when the

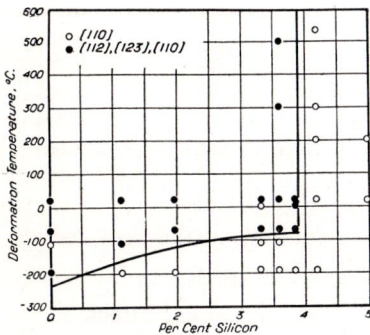

FIG. 12.   FIG. 13.

FIG. 12. Dependence of slip mechanism on temperature and silicon concentration in silicon ferrite. (*Barrett, Ansel, and Mehl.*[162])

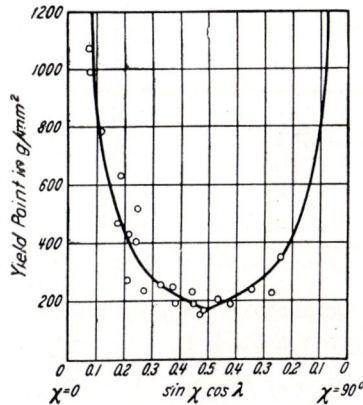

FIG. 13. Variation of yield point of single crystals of magnesium with orientation expressed as the function $\sin \chi \cos \lambda$, where χ and λ are the angles between the axis of pull and the slip plane and slip direction. The circles represent experimental observations and the solid curve the variation to be expected if there exists a critical resolved shear stress for yielding. (*Schmid and Siebel.*[219])

applied stress is resolved into the plane and direction of active slip. In the case of magnesium shown in Fig. 13, which has only one slip plane (the basal plane) the yield stress varies greatly with orientation. The cubic metals, on the other hand, show a variation in yield strength of less than twice, owing to the greater number of possible slip systems, and the accordingly closer proximity of a possible system to the plane of maximum shear stress.

The critical resolved shear stress as a criterion of plastic flow of single crystals has proved to be a far-reaching generality and a useful concept in the understanding of the deformation of metals. As will be seen when flow of polycrystals is considered, the active slip system of the individual grains in polycrystalline metals is influenced by the restraint imposed by neighboring grains, and as a consequence, the stress for plastic yielding differs somewhat from that demanded by the simple shear stress theory.

The critical resolved shear stress for yielding depends, naturally, upon the metal being considered, owing to different bonding energies. A

TABLE I.   CRITICAL RESOLVED SHEAR STRESS FOR SLIP AT ATMOSPHERIC TEMPERATURE IN SINGLE CRYSTALS OF SEVERAL METALS*

Metal	Impurities, %	Slip plane	Slip direction	Critical shear stress, kg/mm²
Cu	0.1	(111)	[10$\bar{1}$]	0.10
Ag	0.01	(111)	[10$\bar{1}$]	0.060
Au	0.01	(111)	[10$\bar{1}$]	0.092
Al	0.1	(111)	[10$\bar{1}$]	0.120
Al	0.05	(111)	[10$\bar{1}$]	0.060
Ni	0.2	(111)	[10$\bar{1}$]	0.58
Mg	0.05	(0001)	[11$\bar{2}$0]	0.083
Zn	0.04	(0001)	[11$\bar{2}$0]	0.094
Zn	0.001	(0001)	[11$\bar{2}$0]	0.004

* Data from Schmid and Boas[8] and Miller.[12]

compilation of the critical shear stress for several different metals is given in Table I.

Effect of Alloying Elements on Critical Resolved Shear Stress

The critical resolved shear stress for yielding of crystals is greatly affected by the presence of impurities, as has been indicated in Table I. The addition of alloying elements to a metal, single- or polycrystalline,

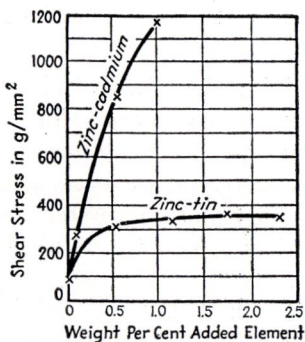

FIG. 14.   FIG. 15.

FIG. 14. Effect of cadmium and tin on the critical shear stress for plastic yielding of zinc crystals. Within the range shown, cadmium is soluble in zinc, but tin is practically insoluble. (*Rosbaud and Schmid.*[220])

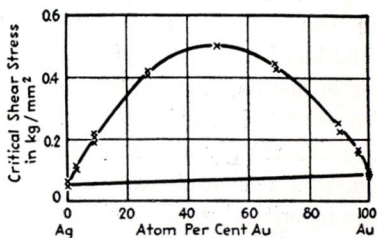

FIG. 15. Effect of composition in the silver-gold system on the critical shear stress for plastic yielding. Silver and gold are completely intersoluble. (*Sachs and Weerts*[221].)

increases its strength, the increase being dependent upon the nature and amount of the addition, whether it enters into solution or results in the occurrence of a new phase, and the microstructure. The data available for single crystals are not as abundant as for polycrystalline metals, and accordingly this subject will be more fully treated when we consider polycrystalline metals. However, Figs. 14 to 16 illustrate the nature of the effects. Figure 14 shows the difference in the effects of cadmium and tin on the critical shear stress of zinc, the former being soluble, the latter insoluble in the percentages considered. It is to be noted that the soluble element causes the greater strengthening; this is generally true, except if and when advan-

tage can be taken of a "critical dispersion" of the new phase, such as in precipitation hardening systems. Figure 15 shows maximum strengthening at about 50 atom per cent in the completely intersoluble solid solution series of the gold-silver system. Figure 16 shows the influence of zinc in single crystals of alpha brass.

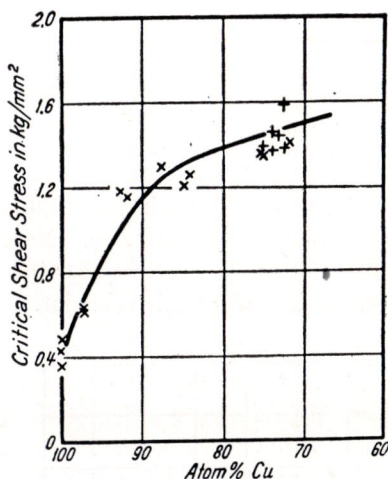

Fig. 16. Variation with composition of critical shear stress for plastic yielding of single crystals of alpha brass (Cu–Zn). (*Göler and Sachs.*[222])

Effect of Rate of Stressing on Critical Shear Stress

The rate of deformation is an important variable among those influencing plasticity and strength, particularly at high temperatures. Not much experimental study has been expended on the influence of this variable on yielding of single crystals, but the results reproduced in Fig. 17 may be presumed to be typical. These show a rather pronounced increase of critical shear stress with increase of speed, but this increase does not appear to be sensitive to temperature, as might be expected. Miller[12] has shown a qualitative dependence of the apparent elastic limit (analogous to critical shear stress) of zinc crystals on rate of deformation at or above room temperature.

Effect of Temperature on Critical Shear Stress

The critical shear stress for yielding decreases as the temperature increases, as shown in Fig. 17 for cadmium at three rates of stressing and

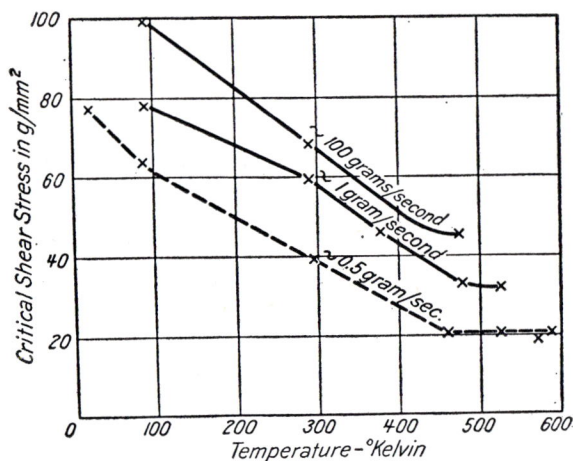

Fig. 17. Influence of speed of testing (and temperature) on the critical shear stress for plastic yielding of single crystals of cadmium. (*Boas and Schmid.*[223])

in Fig. 18 which also includes the other common hexagonal metals, bismuth, magnesium, and zinc. Noteworthy in Fig. 18 is the leveling off of the critical shear stress near the melting point. No explanation has been advanced for this behavior.

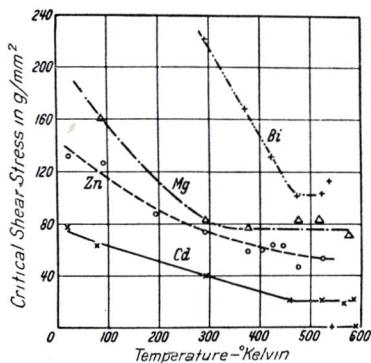

Fig. 18. Effect of temperature on the critical shear stress for plastic yielding of single crystals of cadmium, zinc, magnesium, and bismuth. (*Schmid and Boas.*[8])

Miller[12] has reported that the critical shear stresses of aluminum and silver crystals decrease rapidly above the respective recrystallization temperature, while in crystals of pure zinc this limit was so low as to be immeasurable. Miller's results, however, appear erratic, showing in some cases an increase of critical shear stress with increase of temperature, an effect which could not be explained.

Burghoff and Mathewson[13] observed that the critical resolved shear stress of single crystals of 70 per cent copper–30 per cent zinc brass in slow tension tests ranged from 1,300 to 1,465 gm/sq mm at atmospheric temperature, and was not substantially changed at 300, 500, and 700°F. The absence of a temperature variation of critical shear stress is rather surprising and is akin to the invariant regions of Figs. 17 and 18.

Strain Hardening—The Stress-Strain Curve

When in the course of stressing a crystal the critical shear stress is reached and slip occurs, the glide or shear does not continue indefinitely, but stops, because of an ill-understood but very fortunate phenomenon which has aptly been designated strain hardening. That is, the crystal is strengthened by deformation. It is this strain hardening which permits the development, for example, of cold-drawn wire with a tensile strength of several hundred thousand pounds per square inch.

The stress-strain curve (sometimes termed the "flow curve") is a reflection of strain hardening, and in fact may be regarded as the variation

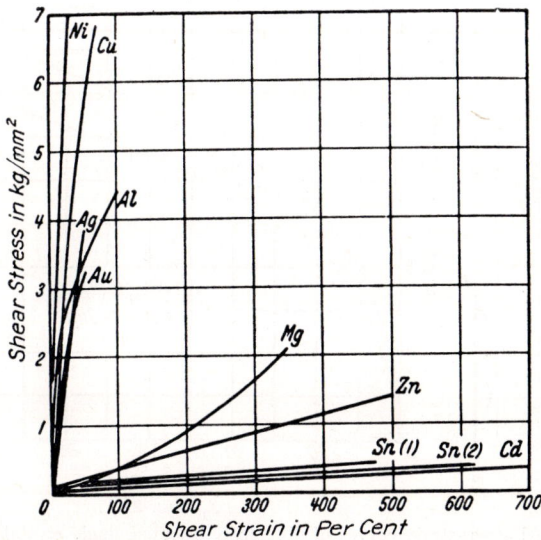

FIG. 19. Shear-stress–shear-strain curves for single crystals of different metals. The two curves for tin correspond to different operative slip systems. (*Schmid and Boas.*[8])

of the instantaneous stress to produce slip with the amount of slip itself. Shear-stress–shear-strain plots for pure single crystals of nickel, copper, aluminum, silver, and gold (all of face-centered cubic lattice structure), of magnesium, zinc, and cadmium (all hexagonal), and of tetragonal tin are shown in Fig. 19, after Schmid and Boas.[8] These plots of Fig. 19 divide readily into two natural groups, the face-centered cubic crystals on one hand, having relatively steep stress-strain curves, and the remaining crystals on the other, having relatively flat curves.

It is to be noted that the plots in Fig. 19 are for shear stress and shear strain, so that each metal can be represented by a single curve, for just as the normal stress (as opposed to shear stress) to cause slip depends

upon the orientation of the crystal with respect to the direction of stressing, so does the entire normal-stress–normal-strain curve depend upon
orientation.   Figure 20 shows the wide variation encountered in such
plots for single crystals of aluminum, and Fig. 21 shows the relatively
narrow band which represents the strain hardening of these crystals, if
the plot is made in terms of shear stress and shear strain.   These two
plots are thus analogous to Fig. 13 showing the critical resolved shear

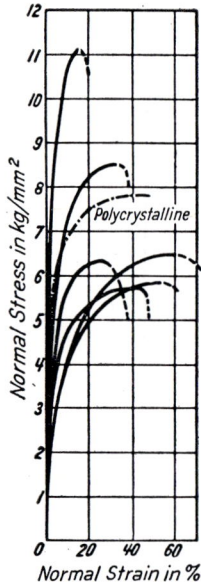

Fig. 20.   Fig. 21.

FIG. 20. Normal stress-strain curves of differently oriented single crystals of aluminum
and for a polycrystalline sample.   Compare with Fig. 21.   (*Karnop and Sachs.*[23])
FIG. 21. Shear-stress–strain curves for differently oriented single crystals of aluminum.
Compare with Fig. 20.   (*Karnop and Sachs.*[23])

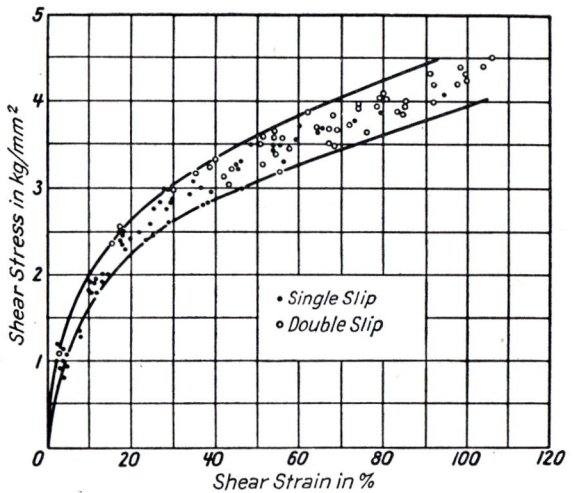

stress to be independent of orientation.   The single and double slip indicated in Fig. 21 refer to slip on one plane or on two different planes
simultaneously and will be discussed in a subsequent section.

Effect of Alloying Elements on the Stress-Strain Curve

The addition of alloying elements to a metal affects not only the critical
shear stress as we have already seen, but influences the entire stress-
strain curve.   The influence exerted by any specific addition naturally
depends upon its nature—whether it enters into solid solution, or if not,

upon the size, shape, and distribution of the new phase, etc. Figures 22 and 23 show, respectively, shear-stress–shear-strain curves for crystals of magnesium with additions of aluminum and crystals of copper with additions of zinc (alpha brasses). In the first case the entire stress-strain curve is observed to lie at a higher level the greater the alloy addition up to some 8 atom per cent aluminum, but in the brasses the

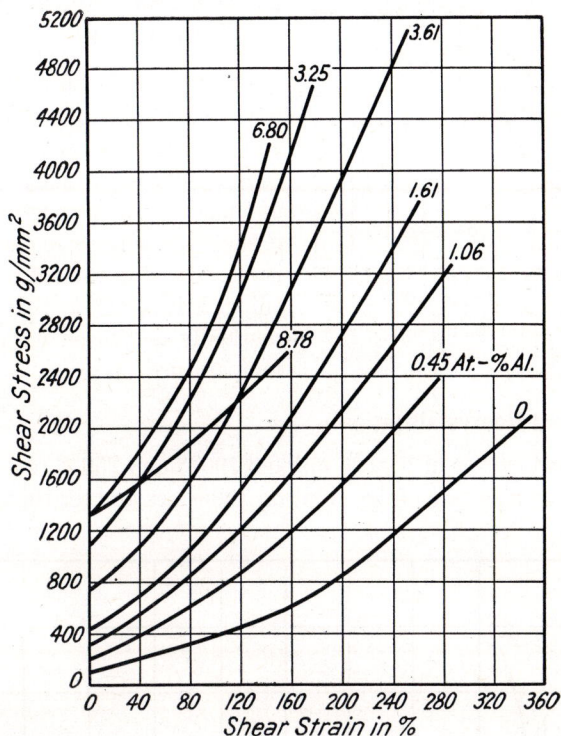

Fig. 22. Effect of aluminum on the shear-stress–strain curve of single crystals of magnesium. (*Schmid and Seliger.*[224])

opposite is true, except for the very initial portions of the stress-strain curves. The weakening effect of zinc on copper is not generally encountered in single crystals, and not in polycrystalline brass.

Effect of Rate of Stressing on the Stress-Strain Curve

The entire stress-strain curve is raised to a higher level as the rate of deformation is increased. Little work has been expended on the influence of strain rate on the flow curve of single crystals, though as we shall find, considerable such work has been done on polycrystalline aggregates. In fact, the analogous effect of the stress on the rate of creep is one of the primary interests in the study of creep. Some few data showing the influence of rate of straining on single crystals of magnesium are shown in Fig. 26, and will be discussed later.

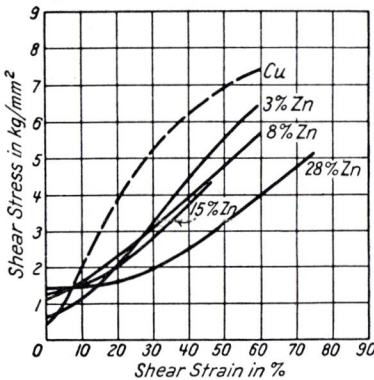

Fig. 23. Effect of zinc on the shear-stress–strain curve of single crystals of copper. (*Göler and Sachs.*[222])

Effect of Temperature on the Stress-Strain Curve

Figures 24 to 26 show the pronounced weakening effect of increased temperature on the stress-strain curves of zinc, aluminum, and magnesium, respectively. Thus, if the slope of the stress-strain curve is taken as the rate of strain hardening, it is apparent that this rate is markedly decreased with increased temperature.

Recovery and Recrystallization

The dashed curves in Fig. 26 marked 100°S and 250°S represent tests reported to be at a rate of deformation 100 times greater than the corre-

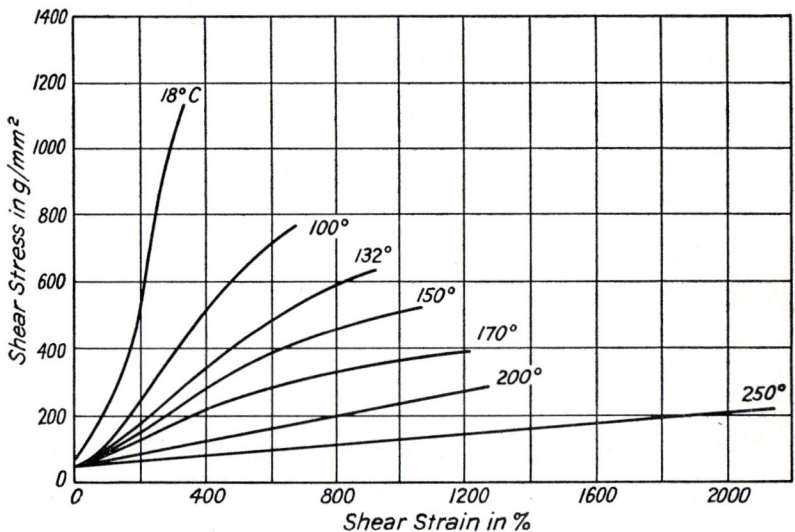

Fig. 24. Effect of temperature (in degrees centigrade) on the shear-stress–strain curve of single crystals of zinc. (*Fahrenhorst and Schmid.*[225])

sponding solid curve, and illustrate a very important interrelation of strain rate and temperature. That is, the influence of strain rate is much more important at high than at low temperatures. In fact, the influence of rate is so great at 250°C that the faster rate test at this temperature results in a stress-strain curve lying higher than the slower rate test at 200°C.

This effect is treated in this section because it is very intimately related to the phenomena of recovery and recrystallization. These two terms refer to changes occurring with time in a plastically deformed metal, changes which are in the direction of returning the metal to the properties in its undeformed state. The rate and degree of change in

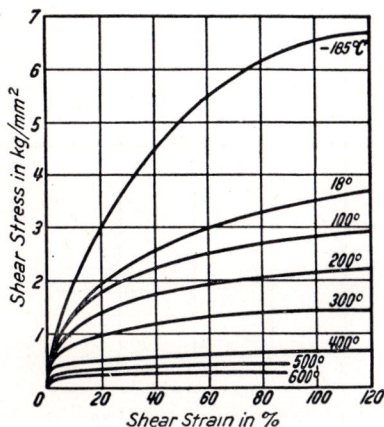 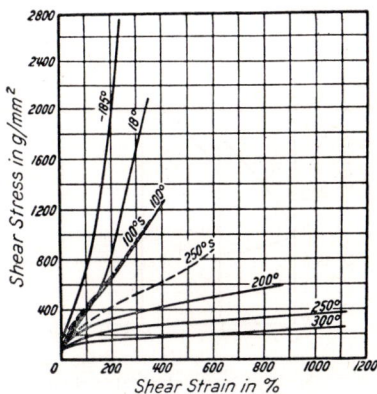

FIG. 25.　　　　　　　　　　　FIG. 26.

FIG. 25. Effect of temperature (in degrees centigrade) on the shear-stress–strain curve of single crystals of aluminum. (*Boas and Schmid.*[226])

FIG. 26. Effect of temperature (in degrees centigrade) on the shear-stress–strain curve of single crystals of magnesium. The dashed curves represent a rate of deformation 100 times greater than the solid curves. (*Schmid and Siebel.*[219])

properties depend upon a number of variables, the principal ones of which are the amount of the deformation and the temperature of holding.

The terms "recovery" and "recrystallization" define differences in the degree of return to the original properties, the former representing only a partial return, and the latter generally a complete return. This latter, as the term recrystallization implies, involves the nucleation and growth of new grains until the whole has been replaced by strain-free new grains. In the case of recovery, the process stops short of the formation of new grains, either because a certain minimum deformation has not been exceeded for the particular temperature of holding, or conversely the temperature is not higher than a certain minimum, depending on the degree of deformation.

Recovery and recrystallization unquestionably play an important role in the use of metals in service at high temperatures, and although they have been treated in a somewhat cursory fashion in this section, this is in part because they have been little studied in single crystals and in part because they are more adequately treated elsewhere in this book.*

The exact roles, if any, played by the processes of recovery and recrystallization in the influence of temperature and rate of straining on the flow curve, such as in Figs. 24 to 26, has not been determined. It has been generally assumed that with increasing temperature, or decreasing rate of straining, the tendency to strain hardening becomes overshadowed by the tendency to recovery or recrystallization, although this

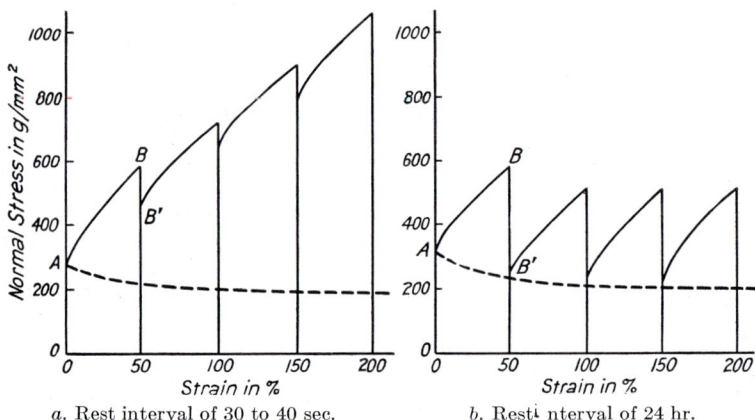

a. Rest interval of 30 to 40 sec.   b. Rest interval of 24 hr.

FIG. 27. Influence of the time of interruption of straining on the stress-strain curves of crystals of zinc at atmospheric temperature. (*Haase and Schmid.*[227])

concept is unquestionably oversimplified. However this may be, Fig. 27 shows the influence of the time of interruption of the straining of crystals of zinc at atmospheric temperature, at which temperature it is capable of recovery and recrystallization. If after straining to point B (Fig. 27a) the specimen is unloaded and allowed to rest for 30 to 40 sec, the flow stress is lowered to B', etc., which represents a partial recovery, while if the time of interruption is extended to 24 hr (Fig. 27b) complete recovery is effected.

Lattice Rotation

Accompanying the slip deformation of metals is another phenomenon of considerable importance, namely, lattice rotation. By this term is meant literally a rotation of the lattice, a change in orientation, which

* See, for example, the section on Microstructural Changes.

depends upon the type of deformation. In tension, the rotation is in such a manner that the plane and direction of slip move toward the axis of tension (Fig. 11). This would not occur if the crystal were free, but results from the restraint imposed by the need of grips to effect the deformation.

The change in orientation with deformation would in itself result in an apparent strengthening, since the resolved shear stress is less the more nearly the active slip system coincides with the axis of deformation, but this should not be confused with strain hardening which is a real and separate phenomenon, as proved by the plots of shear stress versus shear strain, described in previous sections.

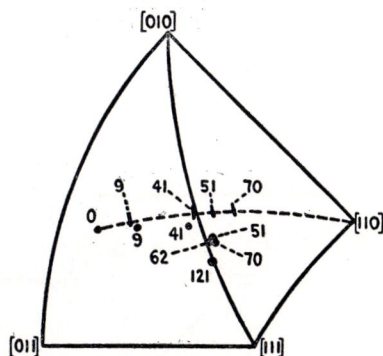

FIG. 28. Change in orientation of a single crystal of aluminum with deformation. Points represent specimen axis. Numbers above points refer to calculated positions and those below to measured positions. (*Elam.*[9])

As the orientation of the crystal changes with deformation, the resolved shear stress on another slip system (plane and direction) may become greater than on the initially active one, in which case slip is transferred to the former and ceases on the latter. But as slip proceeds on the new system, the further change in orientation may result in the resolved shear stress on the initial system again becoming the greater. Thus there arises the phenomenon of slip on two or more systems simultaneously, with the further change in orientation which preserves the symmetry of the slip systems with respect to the deformation axis and leads eventually to an equilibrium orientation. The treatment of lattice rotation presented here is somewhat oversimplified, but it serves to emphasize the occurrence of the phenomena. Actually, however, experiments have shown a more complicated state, the calculated changes in orientation seldom agreeing exactly with the measured (Fig. 28).* It

* Figure 28 represents a method of charting orientations of crystals by the stereographic projection, a technique whose description is beyond the scope of this book. The reader is referred to Barrett[10] for such a treatment. However, the reader may grasp in a general way the meaning of Fig. 28 if it is stated that the plotted points represent the axis of stressing, which changes with deformation from a position near the plane containing the [011] and [010] directions to a position in the plane including the [010] and [111] directions, in which position it is symmetrically oriented midway between the two slip directions [011] and [110], and is thus subject to double slip.

may be noted in Fig. 28 that when the axis reaches the symmetrical position midway between the two [110] slip directions, double slip occurs and the direction of change in orientation alters. Another frequently encountered complexity of the lattice rotation process is that although the latent slip systems strain-harden to approximately the same degree as the active one, the extent is generally not identical, so that double slip may or may not immediately begin when the resolved shear stresses

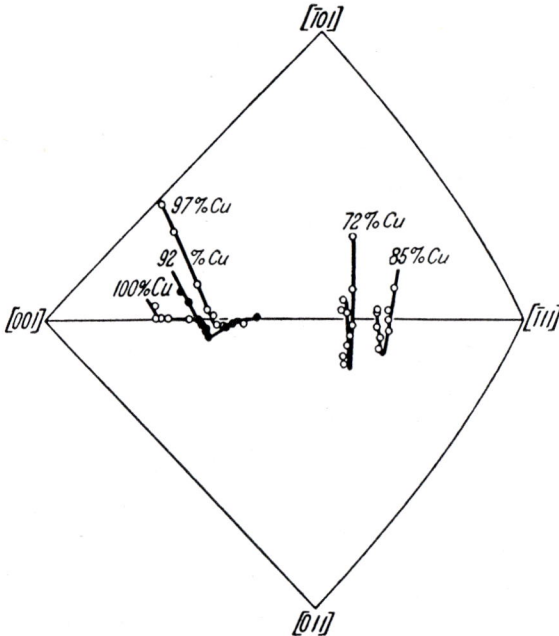

Fig. 29. Dependence of strain hardening of active and latent slip systems on composition in single crystals of alpha brass (Cu–Zn). Points represent measured positions of specimen axis. (*Göler and Sachs.*[222])

on two systems are identical. This is illustrated in Fig. 29, which reveals an influence of alloying on the effect.

Thus as deformation progresses, the orientation of the crystal changes, and this is also true when the crystal is one of a polycrystalline aggregate. These changes result in the preferred orientations, sometimes desirable, sometimes undesirable, developed during the commercial fabrication of metals by deformation processes. In polycrystalline metals the changes in orientation of the individual crystals composing the aggregate are rather complex.

Deformation Bands

As mentioned earlier, different portions of a crystal, whether alone or in a polycrystalline aggregate, sometimes slip on different systems and accordingly rotate in different directions, giving rise to deformation bands. The deformation bands would naturally be expected to have a crystallographic character, but their nature is not altogether clear. Presumably in order for different portions of a crystal to slip on different systems, the resolved shear stresses of the active slip systems must not be too unlike, owing either to suitable initial orientation of the crystal or to the fact that initial uniform rotation results in such a condition. On the other hand, some orientations, at least of single crystals, do not form deformation bands.

Deformation bands have been observed in many metals including most of the common face-centered or body-centered cubic ones. In polycrystalline metals, deformation banding would be expected to be of rather complex nature, as is slip, owing to the restraints imposed by neighboring grains.

Deformation (or Mechanical) Twinning

As stated in the introductory portion of this chapter, plastic deformation of metals occurs by two processes, slip, which has been examined already, and twinning, which will now be considered.

Twinning, as illustrated in Fig. 8, is a process of deformation characterized by homogeneous shear, such that the twinned portion bears a definite crystallographic relation to the untwinned or original portion. It thus differs from slip in which the two portions of the crystal on either side of the shear plane are identically oriented, having suffered merely a translation in the slip direction. Among the commercial metals, deformation by mechanical twinning appears to be nonexistent in the face-centered cubic metals* and relatively uncommon in body-centered cubic metals (Neumann bands in rapidly deformed iron), but is quite common in close-packed hexagonal metals such as zinc and magnesium. However, deformation twinning probably plays a very minor role even in these latter metals during creep, since, as we shall see, the critical stress necessary for twinning is much greater than for slip and the deformation of interest in creep is generally rather slight. Even in single crystals of

---

* So-called "annealing" twins, characteristic of some face-centered cubic metals, such as copper or the gamma iron alloys (Fig. 6), should not be confused with deformation twins. Annealing twins are formed by growth during recrystallization.

the hexagonal metals, deformation twinning may be relatively uncommon except in certain orientations unfavorable to slip.

The Twinning Elements

Since the twinned and untwinned portions of a crystal bear a fixed crystallographic relation to one another, it is not unexpected that the plane of the twinning shear, as well as direction, will be of relatively simple crystallographic index, analogous to shear by slip.

Geometrically, the crystallography and degree of shear may be defined in terms of the relations shown in Fig. 30, which represents a section of a unit sphere prior to and after twinning shear. The plane of the page is the plane of shear and n_1 the direction of shear lying in the twinning plane K_1 (perpendicular to the plane of the paper). In twinning, the unit sphere deforms to an ellipsoid, represented in the section by an ellipse; as a result of the shear S, point A shears to point A_1, etc. If now

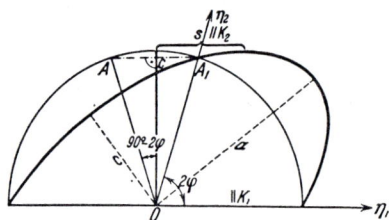

Fig. 30. Geometry of the shear of deformation twinning (see text). (*Schmid and Boas.*[8])

the angle between n_1 and n_2, which lies in a second plane K_2 perpendicular to the plane of shear, is defined as 2φ, it can be shown that $S = \dfrac{2}{\tan 2\varphi}$. The significance of the plane K_2, of course, is that it, like the twinning plane itself, remains undeformed by the twinning, line OA shearing to OA_1. Thus the crystallography of twinning is conveniently defined in terms of the two planes K_1 and K_2.

TABLE II. CRYSTALLOGRAPHY OF TWINNING

Metal	Type of crystal lattice	Twin planes		Amount of shear
		K_1	K_2	
α-Fe	Body-centered cubic	(112)	(11$\bar{2}$)	0.707
Zn	Close-packed hexagonal	(10$\bar{1}$2)	(10$\bar{1}$2)	0.143
β-Sn	Tetragonal	(331)	(1$\bar{1}\bar{1}$)	0.120
Sb	Rhombohedral	(011)	(100)	0.146

Table II, from data compiled by Schmid and Boas[8] and Elam,[9] gives the twinning planes K_1 and K_2 and the amount of shear in the deformation twinning of some metals of different crystal lattice. Metals of similar crystal lattice have similar twinning elements. Thus beryllium, magnesium, and cadmium, all close-packed hexagonal, have the same twinning elements as zinc. The amount of shear, however, differs, depending upon the unit cell dimensions.

The absence of deformation twinning in face-centered cubic metals is quite interesting, for nearly all such metals show annealing twins (on the {111} planes). It has been suggested that in some cases deformation bands, much like the Neumann bands of alpha iron, may form in certain face-centered cubic metals and that these are the origin of the annealing twins. This remains to be substantiated.

Critical Shear Stress for Twinning

Little is known about the stresses required for deformation twinning, but there is some evidence for the existence of a critical shear stress for twinning. Unfortunately, twinning is nearly always preceded by slip deformation, and this, as shown by Miller,[14] exerts an influence on the resolved shear stress to cause twinning. Miller observed that the threshold stress for twinning of zinc single crystals varied inversely with the amount of preceding slip deformation. This observation probably explains the difficulty of other investigators in failing to find a constant twinning stress. The critical resolved shear stress observed by Miller ranged from 300 to 600 gm/sq mm, which is, of course, many times greater than the critical shear stress for slip (see Table I) in zinc and is of the same order of magnitude previously observed for cadmium.[8]

It is of interest to note that when twinning occurs during a tension test of a single crystal, the process is generally accompanied by an audible click and a corresponding abrupt decrease in load, and the latter may result in a serrated stress-strain curve.

Influence of Temperature and Deformation Velocity on Twinning

Generally, decrease in temperature or increase in the rate of deformation increases the prevalence of deformation twinning, though the subject has not been adequately studied and there are exceptions. It is well known that Neumann bands (deformation twins) may be readily produced in alpha iron at ordinary temperatures only by rapid or "shock" deformation. However, as shown in Fig. 31, twinning may occur during slow torsion deformation of iron at very low temperatures. Figure 31, representing one of the very few studies of the simultaneous influences of composition and temperature, shows that with increasing silicon con-

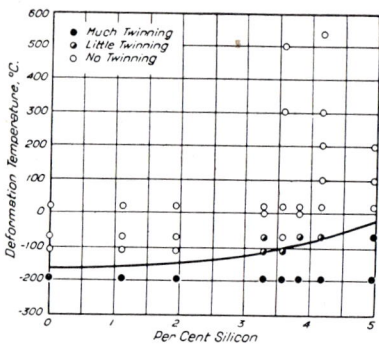

FIG. 31. Dependence of twinning of silicon ferrite single-crystal strips, deformed slowly in torsion, on the temperature and silicon concentration. (*Barrett, Ansel, and Mehl.*[162])

tent, twinning may occur at a slightly higher temperature than in pure iron.

Schmid and Boas[8] report that increase of temperature tends to suppress twinning in zinc and cadmium, but Bakarian and Mathewson[15] report that in compression tests at an elevated temperature (570°F), single crystals of magnesium showed greater twinning than at a lower temperature.

Miller[14] observed that twinning did not occur in zinc crystals during creep at constant load when the load was applied slowly, even after long durations at loads corresponding to those which resulted in twinning during conventional tensile testing.

Effect of Twinning on Strain Hardening

Deformation twinning does not result in general strain hardening as does slip, but it does cause severe local stresses, as shown by Barrett,[16] at the twin boundaries; these frequently act as centers of nucleation for recrystallization when deformed metal is annealed.[14]

Creep of Single Crystals

The creep of metals has been most extensively studied in the polycrystalline state, but there have been several studies of this phenomenon in single crystals. By creep is meant, it will be recalled, continuing deformation under constant load. In this section an effort will be made to review the important investigations of creep of single crystals.

Hanson and Wheeler[11] studied the flow and fracture of single crystals of aluminum, but without consideration for the orientation, in both short- and long-time loading over a range of temperatures from atmospheric to 400°F. Tests were also conducted on polycrystalline samples for comparison. The surfaces of the specimens were polished to permit observation of the metallographic features of the deformation. Particularly interesting was the observation that on slow deformation at temperatures as low as 400°F no slip lines were apparent, as at faster rates of deformation; the actual rates were not reported in either case. This type of deformation was termed "slipless," but the authors were careful not to infer that deformation was viscous, except possibly at very high temperatures. The possibility was suggested that slipless flow may result from the slip lines being irresolvably close to one another. In tests of polycrystalline samples under similar conditions, the boundaries between grains became quite prominent, even though no slip markings were observed. This suggested a uniform deformation within the grains and a more complex distortion in the neighborhood of the boundaries.

With increasing rate of deformation, single crystals showed profuse slip lines at rates which resulted in slipless flow of the aggregate specimens. In samples containing both small and large crystals, the latter would show slip markings and the former not.

The elongation-time curves for the single crystals were not reproduced, though from the manner in which the tests were made (by adding successively higher stresses after the creep rate had become quite small at any specific stress), it may be inferred that after an initial stage, the rate of creep gradually decreased and approached zero in a manner similar to that observed by subsequent investigators of the creep of iron and brass crystals described below.

Betty[17] studied the creep characteristics of three single crystals of lead with small amounts of impurities (different in each crystal) at atmospheric temperature. Creep occurred only at shearing stresses greater than 250 psi as resolved on the most suitably oriented octahedral {111} plane. The creep curves of the three crystals are reproduced in Fig. 32, with comparison data for polycrystalline specimens. It is to be noted that the creep rates of the single crystals ranged from approximately 0.0025 per cent per hour for crystal B to about 0.00004 per cent per hour for crystal C. It should also be pointed out that each crystal had been tested at a series of successively higher stresses before the tests shown in Fig. 32 were made.

Slip markings on the octahedral {111} planes were observed on crystals B and C, but not on A. The direction of slip was not determined. The absence of slip markings on crystal A was thought to be attributable to either or both a poor initial surface and a similarity of resolved shear stress on the four sets of possible slip planes, so that no one set would be clearly defined.

Miller[12] tested single crystals of high-purity zinc in creep tests at room temperature and at elevated temperatures, although his principal concern was with the existence or nonexistence of a true elastic range. In relation to this latter possibility, the observations indicated that there was no measurable elastic limit at or above room temperature. That is, plastic deformation occurred with the smallest stress which could be applied.

The loads necessary to produce similar creep rates in different specimens was reported to vary with the orientation, and this was held to demonstrate the crystallographic nature of the creep. Whether this variation was a quantitative one or only qualitative was not reported,

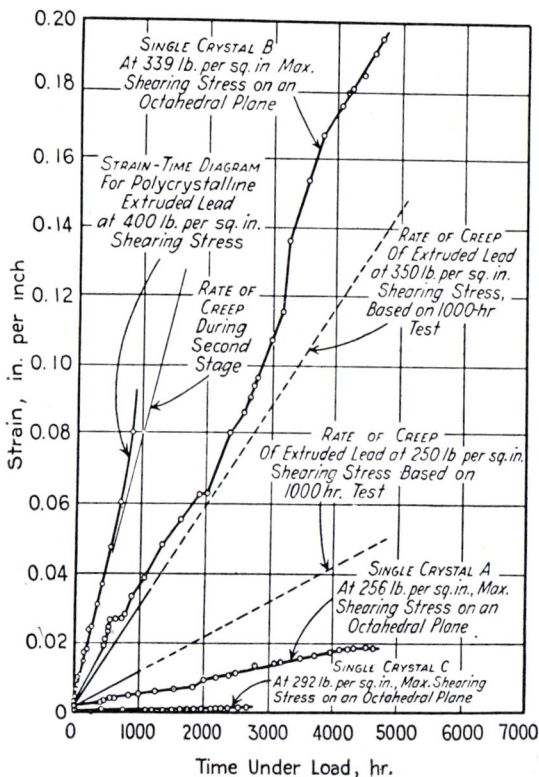

Fig. 32. Creep of single crystals in comparison with polycrystalline lead at atmospheric temperature. (*Betty.*[17])

apparently the testing not being sufficiently extensive to attempt a correlation. Creep occurred under very small resolved shearing stresses, thus at 3.7 psi at 390°F and at 11.2 psi at room temperature. The experimental plots for these two tests are shown in Figs. 33 and 34, respectively. The rather odd shape of the latter curve is to be noted. Slip markings were observed to accompany the deformation, but it is to be noted that the rates of creep are relatively rapid.

Boas and Schmid[18] made tests of single crystals of bismuth, tin, zinc, and cadmium under constant load both in a range of temperature near atmospheric and also at a subatmospheric level, with particular reference to the change in initial flow velocity with temperature. This velocity increased with temperature as would be expected, but the tests were continued for only 2 min, and therefore are of little interest here.

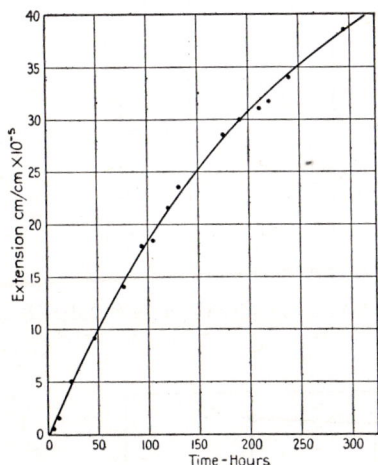

Fɪɢ. 33.   Fɪɢ. 34.

Fɪɢ. 33. Creep of a single crystal of high-purity zinc at 390°F under a resolved shear stress of 3.7 lb/sq in. (*Miller*.[12])

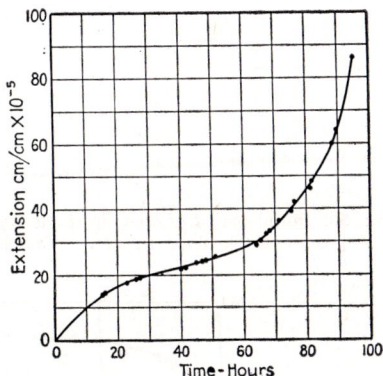

Fɪɢ. 34. Creep of a single crystal of high-purity zinc at room temperature under a resolved shear stress of 11.2 lb/sq in. (*Miller*.[12])

Chalmers[19, 20] has subjected single crystals of high-purity beta (tetragonal) tin to tension tests and discovered by means of very high-sensitivity strain measurements a type of plastic deformation occurring below the stress usually considered as the yield point; this phenomenon was designated microplasticity. The extensometer was of the optical interferometer type having a sensitivity 10^{-7} cm/cm. The specimen temperature was controlled by means of a water bath to 0.05°C. Since beta tin has four different sets ({110}, {100}, {101}, and {121}) of possible slip planes, the variation in orientation could result in only minor differences in normal, that is, unresolved into the slip plane, yield stress. Typical plots showing the initial portion of the length-time relation for tests at 20 gm/sq mm (*a*) and 10 gm/sq mm (*b*), respectively, are shown in Fig. 35. (The periodic variation apparent in the plots was observed to coincide with the bath-temperature fluctuations.) The rate of extension, which appears constant in Fig. 35, was not actually so, but decreased continuously in a roughly exponential manner.   The variation of the initial rate of creep with stress is shown in Fig. 36.   In the low-

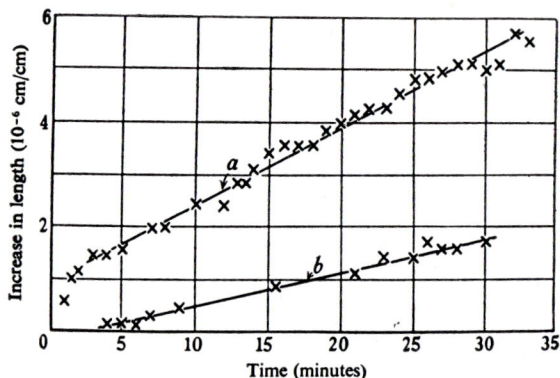

FIG. 35. Initial period of creep in single crystals of high-purity tin at 70°F under (*a*) 20 gm/sq mm and (*b*) 10 gm/sq mm.   (*Chalmers.*[19])

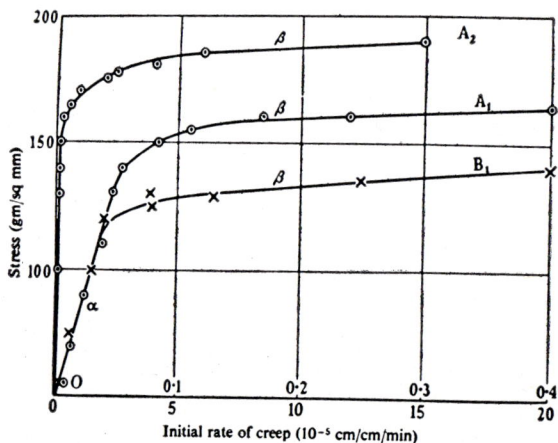

FIG. 36. Variation of initial creep rate with stress for two grades *A* and *B* of high-purity tin at 70°F.   The upper abscissas scale applies to series A_1 and B_1 and the lower to A_2. (*Chalmers.*[19])

stress portion of each plot, designated α, the rate of creep, designated microcreep, is directly proportional to the stress, and this is, of course, the relation demanded for viscous materials.   It is interesting to note that both types of tin show the same slope in the alpha range, but have a different yield point.   If in this alpha range, the stress was maintained for a sufficiently long time, the creep rate reached an apparently constant value on the order of 10^{-9} cm/cm/min, but the experiments could not be continued long enough to determine whether this rate continued indefinitely. The total extension obtained was on the order of 10^{-5} cm/cm and apparently was independent of the stress. No recovery was noted on removal of stresses in the microcreep region.

Once the small final creep rate (10^{-9} cm/cm/min) was established, no increase in rate of creep was observed if the stress were suddenly increased to another value still within the alpha range. The ability to creep could be recovered if the specimen were either allowed to rest under no stress for several hours or stressed for a short time in the beta range (Fig. 36) where another mechanism of flow designated "macrocreep" is operative.

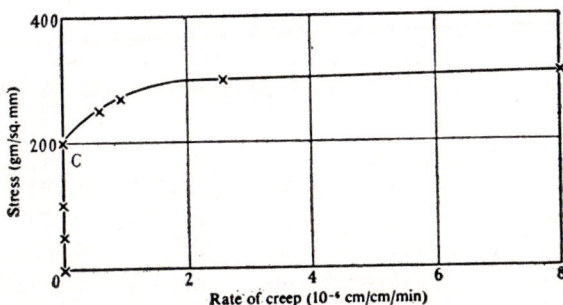

Fig. 37. Effect of stress on the rate of creep of a bicrystal, having a longitudinal grain boundary, of high-purity tin at 70°F, showing an absence of microcreep. (*Chalmers.*[19])

When stresses corresponding to the beta range (Fig. 36) were applied, much greater creep rates were obtained, which remained essentially constant, rather than showing the exponential decrease characteristic of microcreep, and it was clear that the change from the alpha region corresponds to the ordinary yield point. No recovery was observed after the removal of a stress in the beta range. Apparently primary creep, generally considered as that occurring before the rate becomes essentially constant and generally observed to be recoverable on release of stress, was absent or of small magnitude in these tests. This subject is discussed in greater detail in respect to the behavior of polycrystals. Recovery has not been adequately studied in single crystals tested in creep.

Similar tests on specimens containing two crystals with a longitudinal boundary showed no microcreep and required a considerably higher stress for yielding (Fig. 37). The influence of the boundary on the lower limit of creep varied with the difference of orientation between the crystals, as discussed in greater detail in a later section on the nature of grain boundaries.   In passing, it is also of interest to note that Chalmers observed a small degree of recovery in these large crystal specimens and a considerably greater degree in tests of small crystal specimens.   This associates the recovery process with the polycrystalline state.   Interestingly, the specimens of small crystal size showed a stress limit for macrocreep well below the limit for macrocreep in the single crystal specimen.

Chalmers explained the observed phenomena of microcreep in terms of the "dislocation" theory, discussed later, the microcreep resulting from dislocations already existant in the sample; these were caused to migrate, and thus cause extension of the specimen, by applied shear stresses of small magnitude, but actual macroyielding did not occur until the applied stress was sufficient to generate new dislocations.

Baker, Betty, and Moore[21] have made creep tests at ambient temperature on single crystals of very pure commercial lead.   Twelve tests at different magnitudes of resolved shear stress were made.   Figure 38 shows the typical elongation-time curves for four crystals tested under different resolved shear stresses, and except possibly for crystal 2, whose behavior is difficult to judge, all show a decreasing creep rate with time. Companion tests on polycrystalline samples showed much smoother creep curves than for the single crystals; it was suggested that the erratic behavior of the single crystals might be attributable to shifting from one active slip system to another.

All specimens were examined for slip markings, which as Betty[17] showed are on the octahedral {111} planes.   These were observed in only a portion of the crystals.   It was suggested that the instances in which slip markings were observed may have been those in which the resolved shear stress on one slip system was much greater than on the others, so that slip was confined to one system.

Unfortunately, discussion of this paper indicated some question as to the lattice orientation determinations for the crystals; therefore the resolved shear stresses in Fig. 38 may be somewhat in error.   In view of this uncertainty, it seems undesirable to relate the resolved shear stress to creep rate, a relation for which there is great need.

Tests of a few polycrystalline specimens indicated these to be weaker in creep than single crystals.   This is similar to the relation earlier observed by Chalmers[20] for tin.   It might be pointed out here that both tin and lead, when reasonably pure, may recrystallize at room temperature, and according to the "equicohesive temperature" theory, which is discussed in greater detail elsewhere in this book, both as to its limitation and its possibilities, it is to be expected that the fine-grained specimens should be the weaker.

Gensamer and Mehl[22] have reported creep tests at room temperature of single crystals of decarburized mild steel. The crystals were subjected to incremental (6 hr to 5 days, and 200 psi or less) dead-weight

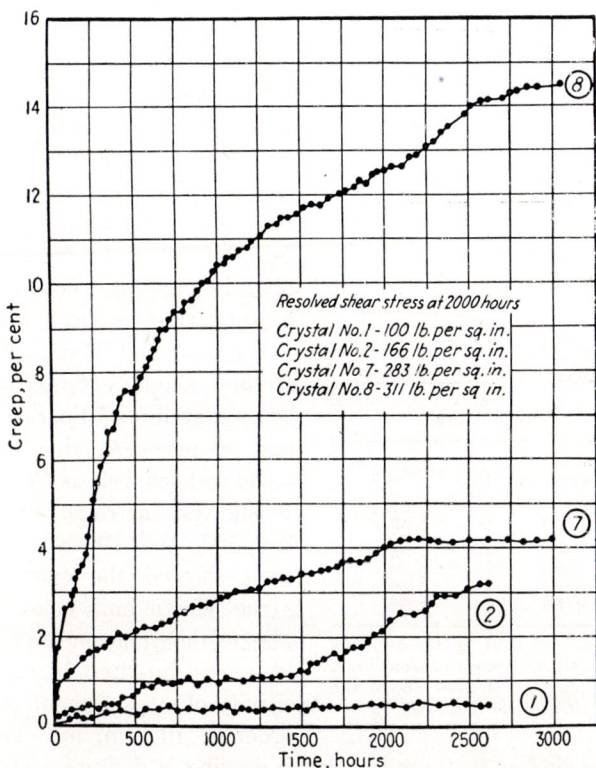

Resolved shear stress at 2000 hours

Crystal No.1 - 100 lb. per sq. in.
Crystal No.2 - 166 lb. per sq. in.
Crystal No 7 - 283 lb. per sq. in.
Crystal No.8 - 311 lb. per sq in.

FIG. 38. Creep-time curves for four single crystals of pure lead at atmospheric temperature. (*Baker et al.*[21])

loading in tension. All crystals exhibited a well-defined yield point, which ranged from 3,600 to 5,200 psi because of the different orientations. This yield point marked the limit below which creep in excess of 10^{-5} in./in. was not observed. The elongation under constant load characterizing plastic yielding was not detected immediately upon application of the "yield" load; rather, after a variable time, probably associated with the increment, the rate of creep would increase to a maximum and then decrease again to zero. After extension had ceased, further increments of load would result in a similar type of yielding, as illustrated in Fig. 39, which shows six creep curves for the same specimen. It is to be observed that the rates of elongation vary widely even with approximately equal increments of stress. Depending upon the magnitude of the stress increment, one or more additions of load had to be made to cause further yielding.

It was suggested that the characteristic type of yielding similar to that observed by Miller[12] for zinc (Fig. 34) resulted from stress concentration arising from the initial flow, this concentration accelerating the rate of slip in regions already slipping; flow eventually ceases owing to strain hardening.

Burghoff and Mathewson[13] have studied single crystals of alpha brass containing 70 per cent copper and 30 per cent zinc in tension creep tests as well as in short-time tensile tests at room temperature, 300, 500, and 700°F. The creep tests showed the existence of a "true" elastic limit below which no plastic deformation was observed in several hundred hours; the sensitivity of measurement was on the order of 10^{-6} in./in. Thus these crystals are similar to those for iron in having a definite yield point.[22] This limit corresponded to a resolved shear stress of about 1,400 psi in the range of room temperature to 500°F, being surprisingly invariant, but at 700°F appreciable creep occurred for a resolved shear stress of 280 psi. The resolved shear stress for yielding in short-time tensile test was about 1,800 psi throughout the range of room temperature to 700°F. This nonvariance is also rather surprising.

The creep curves of these single crystals, like those of Gensamer and Mehl for single crystals of iron[22] and of Miller[12] for zinc, showed that flow occurred initially at an increasing rate and then at a decreasing

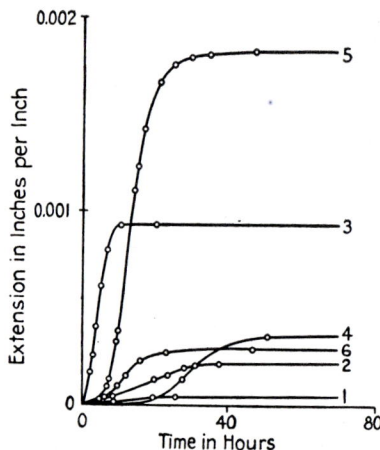

Curve	Increment of stress, psi	Stress, psi
1	248	4,420
2	270	4,690
3	273	4,960
4	309	5,270
5	318	5,590
6	292	5,890

FIG. 39. Constant-load extension-time curves for a single crystal of iron, for a sequence of loads at stresses above the yield point. (*Gensamer and Mehl.*[22])

rate, which for the lower temperatures appeared to approach zero. This behavior is illustrated in Fig. 40. It is to be noted that the time scale is considerably longer than with the iron crystals in Fig. 39.

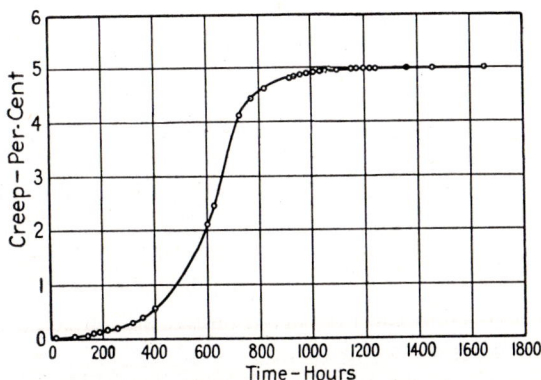

Fig. 40. Creep-time curve at room temperature for a single crystal of alpha brass (70 Cu–30 Zn) under a resolved shear stress of 1100 gm/sq mm. (*Burghoff and Mathewson.*[13])

Observations of the number of slip markings visible on the surface of the specimen whose creep curve is shown in Fig. 40 correlated quite well with the amount of creep which occurred, as shown in Fig. 41, increasing directly with the extension, at least until the slip markings became too numerous to count. These slip markings corresponded with the octa-hedral {111} plane of greatest re-solved shear stress, and when the deformation was sufficient, the change in orientation was that demanded by slip in a [101] direc-tion. Creep tests at 300 and 500°F also showed slip markings corresponding to the {111} plane of maximum resolved shear stress. At 700°F, no slip markings were visible on the blackened (scaled) surface but a limited X-ray diffrac-tion analysis based on a slight change from circular to elliptical

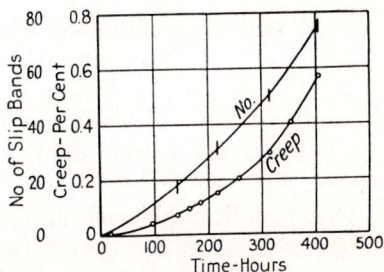

Fig. 41. Variation of number of visible slip markings with amount of creep during in-itial period of creep of specimen of Fig. 40. (*Burghoff and Mathewson.*[13])

cross section indicated, as with the lower temperature, no new or differ-ent type of deformation than that of conventional crystallographic slip.

Summary

Plastic deformation in metal single crystals occurs by means of slipping or twinning. Slip occurs by a shearing of one portion of the crystal past another on a specific crystallographic plane and in a specific crystallographic direction, generally of closest atomic packing. There is some evidence that with increasing temperature, additional planes and directions may be employed for slip, while at sufficiently slow rates of deformation, expecially at relatively high temperatures, the surface markings associated with slip are absent.

When the stress required to cause plastic yielding of single crystals is resolved into the plane and direction of active slip, the "resolved shear stress" thus obtained is independent of the orientation of the crystals. This critical shear stress for plastic yielding is generally increased by alloying, by increasing the rate of straining, and in some instances, at least, by decreasing the temperature.

As a metal single crystal is strained beyond its yield point, it undergoes strain hardening, that is, further plastic deformation does not occur without a further increase in stress. This is revealed by the stress-strain curve (or flow curve) whose slope represents the rate of strain hardening. If this curve is plotted in terms of shear stress and shear strain, a single curve, independent of the orientation, is obtained. The stress-strain curve is generally raised to higher stress level with increasing rate of straining and with decreasing temperature.

When a metal which has been plastically deformed at relatively low temperatures, that is, has been "cold-worked," is heated, it undergoes recovery and recrystallization, whereby the properties of the metal tend to revert to values characteristic of unstrained metal. This is effected in the case of recrystallization by the nucleation and growth of new strain-free grains which absorb the distorted metal. In recovery, these new grains do not develop and the reversion to original properties is only partial.

The crystallographic orientation of a crystal changes with plastic deformation as a result of the external restraints imposed upon it. Different portions of a crystal may rotate in different directions, owing to slip on different crystallographically equivalent slip systems, giving rise to deformation bands.

In deformation twinning, a homogeneous shear of one portion of a crystal with respect to another occurs in such a way that the twinned portion bears a definite crystallographic relation to the original lattice. Deformation twinning seems to be absent in face-centered cubic metals, relatively uncommon in body-centered cubic metals, but quite common in close-packed hexagonal metals.   There is evidence for the existence of a critical shear stress for twinning.   Generally, deformation twinning increases with decrease in temperature or increase in rate of deformation.

At sufficiently high temperature and stress, single crystals undergo creep, that is, continue to flow plastically under constant stress.   When this flow occurs at relatively slow rate, slip markings are absent from the surface; whether this means that flow is no longer crystallographic in character is not known with certainty.   In many of the reported creep tests of single crystals (made in tension), there is a characteristic relation between elongation and time: immediately after load application, no creep occurs, that is, there is an "incubation period"; then creep begins, the rate accelerates, passing through a maximum value, then decelerates, and creep finally ceases.

CHAPTER III

PLASTIC DEFORMATION OF POLYCRYSTALLINE METAL

The behavior of polycrystalline metals is in some respects simpler, at least superficially, and in other respects more complex than that of single crystals. The differences in behavior, whatever their aspect, are, of course, associated with the presence of grain boundaries and the restraints imposed upon any individual grain by its variously oriented neighbors. The anisotropic properties of single crystals are not apparent in the flow of aggregates of randomly oriented grains; thus the tensile modulus of elasticity of fine-grained iron is practically invariant at 30,000,000 psi, and the nominal yield and tensile strengths of the same batch of material do not differ from specimen to specimen. In these respects, and others, the flow of aggregate metals is simpler than with single crystals; but these are rather superficial concerns, and we shall find that the actual processes of deformation are less readily understood than in single crystals.

The Nature and Effects of Grain Boundaries

Since the differences between the behavior of polycrystalline and single-crystal metals are, in part, attributable to the presence of grain boundaries, it will be worth while to examine the nature of grain boundaries and to note some of the effects which they produce.

It was early realized that polycrystalline metal generally has greater hardness or strength than single crystals; there are important exceptions, however. For example, the creep strength at sufficiently high temperatures is greater with coarse grains, though possibly not with a single crystal, than with fine grains. This is discussed in greater detail in a later section on the effect of grain size on creep. Another important exception occurs in aluminum which at ordinary temperatures has a stress-strain curve for the aggregate condition lying in the midst of stress-strain curves for single crystals of different orientation, as illustrated in Fig. 20 from the studies of Karnop and Sachs.[23] However, other data, by Carpenter and Elam[24] showed the strongest of a series of single crystals of aluminum to be some 15 per cent less strong than the corresponding polycrystalline metal. In tests of the influence of grain

40

size, it is important that the metal be not different in respects other than grain size, since strength is a structure-sensitive property; this is not always readily accomplished, and some of the data in the literature are of questionable value for this reason. Too, the size of specimen has not always been properly considered in relation to the grain size, this being particularly important in the relatively coarse grain sizes.

The increased strength of polycrystalline over single-crystal metals at relatively low temperatures seems to be particularly pronounced, for the few instances in which data are available, for the close-packed hexagonal metals, if the data for zinc and magnesium are representative; Fig. 42 shows stress-strain curves for magnesium in the single and polycrystalline states.

Generally, the effect of grain size is most pronounced in the region of coarse sizes and shows a decreasing rate of change with decreasing grain size. Illustrative of the influence of grain size are the data in Fig. 43, showing tensile stress-strain curves for annealed brasses of various grain sizes according to Hollomon.[59]

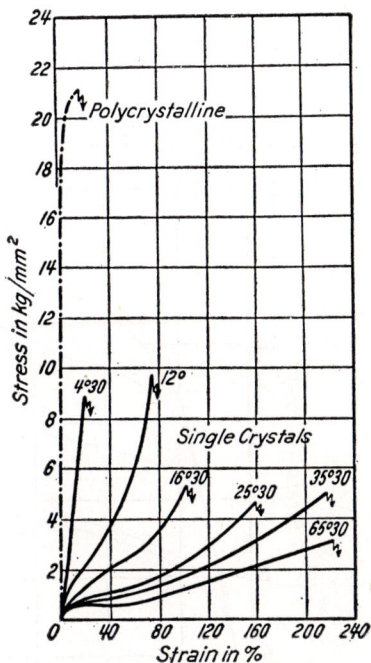

Fig. 42. Normal stress-strain curves of polycrystalline metal in contrast to differently oriented single crystals of magnesium. The original angle between the basal slip plane and the specimen axis is given on the curve for each crystal. (*Schmid and Siebel.*[219])

The Amorphous Cement Grain Boundary

The generally greater strength of polycrystalline metal was early attributed to the presence of a hard, amorphous cement surrounding the individual grains and cementing them together. The term "amorphous" applies to a noncrystalline condition, that is, without regular or orderly arrangement of atoms and lacking directional characteristics. Amorphous substances are essentially fluids of very high viscosity. The concept of an amorphous state of metals was first advanced by Beilby[26] as a result of studies of the nature of polished surfaces. The amorphous state of a metal was regarded as harder and stronger at ordinary temperatures than the crystalline state, since the former condition does not possess the regular array of atoms with which are associated natural planes of weakness, that is, planes of slip.   Thus Beilby attributed the increased hardness of polished surfaces to the formation of an amorphous layer.   The amorphous layer was furthermore presumed to be quite mobile at the moment of formation, but to "set" instantaneously.   Corroborative evidence of the amorphous surface was afforded by the isotropy (independence of direction of test) of hardness of the surface layer in contrast to the anisotropy of the underlying crystal.

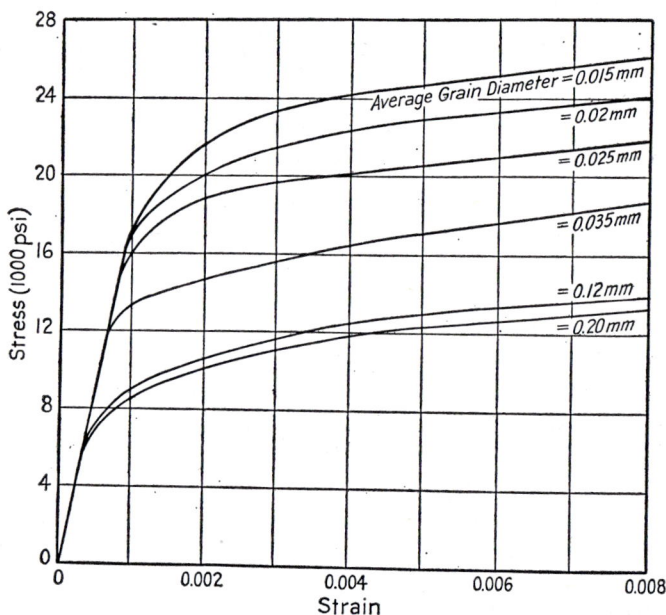

FIG. 43. Initial portion of stress-strain curves of annealed alpha brass (Cu– Zn) of different grain sizes.   (*Hollomon.*[59])

In further development of the theory, Beilby proposed that the strain hardening of metals was a result of the formation of amorphous metal in the slip planes, as the portions of the crystal across the slip planes rubbed against one another during deformation.   Again, the amorphous phase was considered to possess high mobility momentarily but then to solidify in a highly viscous state which, cementing the portions of the crystal together, made further slip on the initially active slip planes more difficult.   Thus slip was transferred to other planes in turn, requiring always greater applied stress for further deformation and thus strain hardening.   The softening of strain-hardened metals on annealing was a natural consequence, according to the amorphous theory, of the recrystallization (in the sense of devitrification of glasses) of the amorphous metal.

The existence of amorphous metal at grain boundaries, cementing the grains together, was a natural extension of Beilby's theory and was proposed almost simultaneously by Bengough[27] and Rosenhain,[28, 29, 33] and was intensively studied by the latter. The impetus for this extension was provided by the observation that the path of fracture of metals at elevated temperatures followed the grain boundaries, that is, fracture was intergranular (or intercrystalline) in contrast to the transgranular (or intracrystalline) mode of fracture commonly observed at ordinary temperature. The intergranular type of fracture was also observed to occur at a lower temperature the slower the rate of deformation. Further the intergranular mode of failure involved little or no general deformation of the metal. (It is now known, however, that considerable deformation may precede intergranular failure.) The difference in mode of fracture at normal and elevated temperatures was attributed by the proponents of the amorphous metal hypothesis to the change in relative strength of crystalline and amorphous metal with temperature; at low temperatures, amorphous metal is the stronger and accordingly fracture is transgranular, while at elevated temperatures crystalline material is the stronger and fracture follows the grain boundaries. Thus, with increasing temperature, a level is reached at which, according to the theory, the amorphous metal becomes weaker than the crystalline metal which it cements together and the type of failure changes from trans- to intergranular.

The Equicohesive Temperature

A natural corollary of the change in type of fracture with temperature is that at ordinary temperatures the metal will be stronger, the greater the amount of grain-boundary material, that is, the smaller the grain size, while at elevated temperatures, the metal will be stronger the less the amount of grain-boundary material, that is, the larger the grain size. This was recognized by Jeffries[30, 31] who studied the influence of grain size on the strength, particularly at elevated temperatures, of tungsten, iron, silver, gold, copper, and platinum. These tests showed that coarse-grained metal was indeed stronger at elevated temperatures. Jeffries coined the term "equicohesive" to characterize the temperature, or more properly the range of temperature, above which fracture follows the grain boundaries and coarse-grained material is stronger, and below which fracture is transgranular and fine-grained material is stronger.

Jeffries also proposed that the equicohesive temperature corresponded very nearly with the lowest recrystallization temperature (a rather indefinite term, since recrystallization is a progressive change dependent upon time, temperature, and degree of deformation).   This association was an outgrowth of the amorphous theory of strain hardening, which as it will be recalled, explained the softening of strain-hardened metal on annealing as a devitrification of the amorphous cement along the slip planes. A diagram illustrating schematically the influence of temperature as well as rate of deformation on crystalline and amorphous metal is given in Fig. 44.

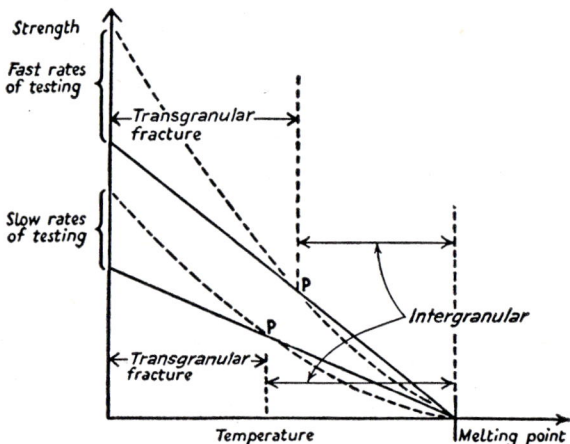

FIG. 44. Schematic illustration of the effect of temperature and rate of deformation on the strength of crystalline (—) and amorphous (---) metal and of the change in type of fracture.   *P* represents the alleged equicohesive temperature.   (After *Elam.*[9])

The experimental evidence in relation to the existence of an equicohesive temperature is reviewed in another section on the influence of grain size on creep behavior.   It is shown there that although unquestionably fracture tends to be intergranular at high temperatures (and at slow rates of deformation) and fine grains to be less strong than coarse, the transition is not sharply defined and is not clearly related to recrystallization.

Viscous Nature of Grain Boundaries

Although grain boundaries certainly appear to possess viscous characteristics, as will be discussed in more detail below, the concept of an amorphous cement has not received general acceptance.   Of course, as Zener[32] has recalled to attention, the fact that grain boundaries may appear to behave viscously does not require that they be amorphous. Before proceeding to a discussion of the arguments advanced against the amorphous theory, it may be well to mention briefly the types of evidence for viscous grain boundaries.* These fall into several categories. Perhaps the most striking evidence is that of the rotation of grains at high temperatures and slow rates of deformation, as revealed by delineation of grain boundaries owing to a relative displacement normal to the surface of different grains. This rotation was observed by Rosenhain and Humphrey,[33] Hanson and Wheeler,[11] and Moore, Betty, and Dollins[34]; Moore *et al.* noted that parallel, straight scratches on the surface of lead specimens tested in creep remained straight and parallel within any individual grain, but altered their direction from grain to grain. Neither effect was observed at low temperatures and fast rates of deformation. This influence of time and temperature on the flow of grain boundaries is of the sort to be expected for a viscous material, inasmuch as such material characteristically differs from crystalline material in having a much greater coefficient of change of strength with changing temperature or/and speed of deformation. The rotation of grains during creep will be considered further in the section on metallographic aspects of creep.

Another characteristic of metals which argues in support of viscous grain boundaries is the elastic aftereffect. Several related phenomena, discussed later in this book, fall in this category but of particular interest here is the recovery of primary creep in polycrystalline metal, but not in single crystals, as observed by Chalmers[20] for tin. Such effects can only be interpreted in terms of relaxation of stress at grain boundaries.

A third and related phenomenon is that of internal friction whose dependence on temperature and grain size has been interpreted in terms of viscous grain boundaries by Zener *et al.*[35] Kê[123, 124] has obtained additional positive evidence of the viscous nature of grain boundaries. Studying anelastic phenomena (departure from the unique dependence of strain on stress demanded by the well-known Hooke's law of elasticity) at low stress levels and low frequencies of torsional vibration in single crystals and polycrystalline aluminum of high purity, Kê observed (1) that the internal friction was a maximum at an intermediate temperature in polycrystalline but not in single-crystal samples, and was of considerably lower magnitude in these latter samples; (2) that the elastic moduli of polycrystalline aluminum showed a rapid decrease with increasing temperature, not observed in single crystals, above some 400°F; (3) that creep of polycrystalline aluminum under the conditions of test was recoverable on removal of the stress; and (4) that stress relaxation

* These are reviewed in some detail by Zener.[32]

(the decrease in stress at constant strain resulting from the exchange of creep for elastic strain) occurred in the polycrystalline but not in the single-crystal aluminum.   The nature of these phenomena are all consistent with the concept of viscous grain boundaries and the effect of temperature on viscosity.   Thus at low temperatures, the energy (force times displacement) expended in viscous flow at the grain boundaries is slight owing to high viscosity (and thus little displacement), while at high temperatures, this energy is again slight owing to low viscosity (and thus little force).

Transitional Lattice Grain Boundary

As stated earlier, the concept of amorphous cement holding the grains together has not received wide acceptance.   Instead most scientists regard the grain boundary merely as a transitional region (at the most 5-interatom distances thick, according to an estimate of Seitz and Read[36]) in which the atoms are located in strained positions intermediate between and accommodating those in the two grains joined, in an attempt at coherency.   The grain boundary is thus considered to be a highly strained and distorted crystalline bond.

Several arguments have been advanced against the amorphous cement concept and in support of the transitional lattice theory.   In the first place, it has been impossible to create an entirely amorphous sample of metal by any means including very severe cold deformation.   There is some evidence, of a controversial nature, of the existence of the amorphous phase in thin surface films, but not when they are of the apprecible thickness demanded by the amorphous theory; and in any event, it would be dangerous to compare grain boundaries with surface films. One of the most powerful arguments against the amorphous theory arises from the fact that, as described in preceding sections, latent slip planes (those not actively participating in the deformation) are strengthened to a degree equal to and sometimes greater than the active slip planes; in the latter case, when the lattice rotates into position for slip on a second plane, this slip may not occur when the resolved shear stresses are equal.   According to the amorphous theory the latent slip planes should not have been strengthened.

Several experiments other than those already described have been carried out which give a clue as to the nature of a grain boundary, or at least to the effects which may be associated with it.   Several investigators have examined experimentally the influence of grain boundaries on the process of plastic deformation.   The early work on aluminum of Hanson and Wheeler[11] *et al.*, already reported, showed that in creep the distortion at grain boundaries was of a different sort than within the grains. Irregularities near the boundary of coarse-grained samples were also observed at faster strain rates. This is a common observation of anyone who has worked with relatively large-grained samples, but was perhaps first described by Aston[37] who reported measurements of stressed tensile samples showing that the strain indicated by the relative changes in lattice orientation is less near grain boundaries than within the grain.

Miller[38] made an interesting study of the effect of a boundary between a single crystal and a polycrystalline region of a specimen of zinc upon slip in the single crystal. The sample was deformed by dead weights at 350°F in order to avoid certain "irregular cold-working effects" encountered at atmospheric temperature. During the test, the polycrystalline section did not extend measurably. Miller found the boundary to exert a pronounced restraining force on slip in the single crystals; stresses sufficient to cause slip on planes remote from the boundary did not cause slip in the immediate vicinity of the boundary. This was considered to mean that in the stressing of polycrystalline aggregates, plastic deformation of the most favorably oriented grains would be restricted

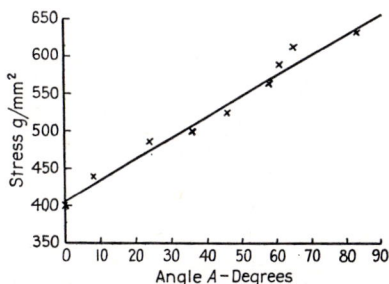

Fig. 45. Variation of yield stress with angle A between [001] axes of bicrystals of high-purity tin having a common longitudinal orientation and grain boundary. (*Chalmers.*[39])

by their neighbors until these latter had attained a sufficiently high resolved shear stress to yield.

Somewhat similar experiments have been made by Chalmers[39] in attempting to distinguish between the amorphous and transitional grain-boundary theories. Chalmers prepared and tension-tested cylindrical bicrystals of high-purity tin having a longitudinal boundary between the crystals. By means of "seed crystals," the two crystals of each specimen were oriented similarly with respect to the longitudinal axis of the specimen, but were oriented in the normal direction in such a way that rotation through an angle A about the longitudinal axis would bring one crystal into coincidence with the others. Crystallographically, the [001] axis was normal and the [101] axis at 45 deg to the specimen axis. Thus for a given load the resolved shear stresses on equivalent slip planes in the two crystals were identical. With such specimens, Chalmers determined the variation of critical yield stress with the angle A between

[001] axes of the two crystals.   Chalmers' results are reproduced in Fig. 45; the yield stress increases continuously with increasing angle A starting at zero angle (single crystal).   This latter fact indicated that grain boundaries have no inherent strength.   Chalmers concluded that the results were evidence against the existence of a thick amorphous cement at the grain boundary, as demanded by the amorphous theory, and were best explained as the effect of a transitional lattice.

Seitz and Read[36] have reviewed the literature and speculated on the nature of grain boundaries, pointing out that in the transitional type of boundary the atoms cannot be so tightly bound as within the grain and accordingly possess greater mobility at a given temperature.   In this relation, it is interesting that Chalmers[40] determined that the grain boundaries of very pure tin melted at a temperature 0.14°C below that of the remainder.   This determination was based on the observation that grains separated at their boundaries at a temperature below the melting point.   The difference in temperature was observed to be independent of the amount of impurity not in excess of 0.02 per cent and of the relative orientation of the separating crystals.

Since the forces between atoms are considered, according to the modern viewpoint, to be of short-range nature, that is, extending over only a few interatom distances, Seitz and Read[36] concluded that the width of the grain boundary cannot be more than 5-atom distances, except possibly for materials with insoluble impurities.   Presumably also, the actual width of a grain boundary will vary with the difference in orientation at the grains joined.   A thickness of 5-atom distances, of course, would mean no inherent strength to the boundary in a polycrystalline aggregate, in accordance with the observation of Chalmers.[39]   Seitz and Read further point out that the fact that fracture is normally transgranular at a low temperature does not necessarily mean that the grain-boundary material is stronger but only that once failure has started, possibly in a boundary, it is more readily propagated through the crystal, owing to the changed state of stress associated with the crack.

That grain boundaries are a site for segregation of impurities, for preferential nucleation in phase transformation, etc., is quite well known to metallurgists, and it need not be discussed here further except to point out that these effects must inevitably exert an influence on the plasticity and strength of metals.

Plastic Yielding of Polycrystalline Metal

In an earlier section it was shown that single crystals flow plastically when a critical value of the shear stress, resolved into the active slip plane and direction, is attained. This seems to be true no matter what the type of stressing—whether tensile, torsion, etc. That is, yielding is independent of the normal stress* acting on the slip plane. Accordingly, this criterion of flow—that plastic yielding occurs when the maximum shear stress reaches a critical value—is generally known as the "maximum-shear-stress law." The maximum-shear-stress concept was first proposed by Tresca[44] many years before the extensive study of single crystals described in preceding sections. A modification of the maximum-shear-stress theory by Mohr,[41, 43] for whom the theory is sometimes named,† in 1900, has generally usurped the position of the earlier theory. Mohr proposed that in addition to the requirement that the maximum shearing stress attain a critical value, the shearing stress in the planes of slip reaches a maximum value dependent upon the normal stress acting on the same planes.‡ The maximum-shear-stress theory is thus simply a special case of the Mohr proposal.

It is desirable to determine a general law governing plastic yielding in polycrystalline as well as single-crystal metals in order to know from an experimental determination of this critical value in one type of test (state of stress) the yielding under another state of stress without the necessity of an experimental determination. Considerable practical importance attaches to this ability in the commercial usage of metals.

Experimental observations have shown that the maximum-shear-stress concept fails to predict the yielding behavior of polycrystalline

---

* By normal stress is meant one acting normal to a reference plane in a body and tending to separate it across this plane by translation in the normal direction. The ordinary tensile stress-strain plot is thus a plot of normal stress versus normal strain. Of course, in this case, the normal stress varies with direction from a maximum in the direction of loading to zero in the perpendicular direction. A shear stress, on the other hand, is one which acts (in a specific direction) in the reference plane and tends to separate the body by glide of the two portions past one another along this plane. In simple tension, the shear stress varies from zero in the direction of loading through a maximum at an angle of 45 deg to zero again in the perpendicular direction. Its maximum value, at 45 deg, is one-half of the maximum normal stress. The ratio of maximum shear to maximum normal stress varies with the state of stress. Thus, in torsion, the maximum shear stress is equal to the maximum normal stress, but at the base of a notch the maximum normal stress may be many times the maximum shear stress, depending on the specific notch.

† It is also sometimes known as Guest's law.[42]

‡ Mohr was concerned with rupture as well as the initiation of yielding and introduced the normal stress dependency referred to in an effort to account for the observation that in brittle materials failure does not begin on the planes of maximum shear stress and different tensile and compressive strengths are obtained.

aggregates.   This is perhaps not too surprising when the restraints of the aggregate grains upon one another are considered.   Yielding of poly-crystalline metals is a gross process involving the yielding of individual grains, and therefore shows different macrocharacteristics.   One of the most striking illustrations of this may be seen in the yielding of mild steel, which is characterized by an inhomogeneous deformation at the initiation of plastic flow.   Associated with the inhomogeneous flow is the appearance of strain markings, generally called Lüders' lines, which are oriented approximately in the plane or planes of maximum shear stress, for example 45 deg to the specimen axis in tension or compression.   Since only fortuitously would an individual grain within the aggregate be oriented with a slip plane in this plane of maximum shear stress, it is evident that the Lüder's lines represent a summation of slip on planes and directions approximating but not actually coincident with the planes of maximum shear stress.   Moreover, as Taylor[54] has shown, the restraints imposed by neighboring grains coupled with the crystal-lographic character of slip requires that slip occur on five sets of crystal-lographically equivalent planes, rather than on one or two, in order to effect an arbitrary strain of an individual grain of an aggregate.

In a polycrystalline aggregate, consisting of randomly oriented grains, the yield stress is independent of direction of test (that is the material is isotropic) in a test involving any specific state of stress.   This con-trasts with the variation with direction in a single crystal.   Therefore, since the ratio of maximum shear stress to maximum normal stress remains fixed for a test involving one state of stress, a criterion of plastic yielding of polycrystalline metals can be determined only by comparing the yield process under different states of stress, wherein different ratios of maximum normal to maximum shear stress exist.

The failure of the simple maximum shear-stress hypothesis and of the Mohr modification for the plastic yielding of polycrystalline metals (except possibly for metals, such as mild steel, which yield inhomogene-ously) has been clearly shown by extensive tests under various types or combinations of types of deformation, such as combined internal pressure and axial tension, or torsion.*   At the same time the validity of another criterion known generally as the shear-strain energy theory, which postulates that yielding occurs when the work of deformation, exclusive of the volume change, attains a critical value, has been estab-

---

* Under a multiaxial state of stress, the maximum shearing stress τ_{max} is given by the following expression: $\tau_{max} = \frac{1}{2} (\sigma_1 - \sigma_3)$, where σ_1 and σ_3 are, respectively, the greatest and least principal stresses; the principal stresses are the normal stresses acting on the three mutually perpendicular planes (principal planes), which it is possible to choose for any state of stress, on which no shearing stresses act.

lished.* This theory was proposed by von Mises[46] and Hencky.[47] The shear-strain energy as the criterion of plastic yielding may be represented mathematically by the following expression:

$$\text{Shear-strain energy} = \frac{(\sigma_1 - \sigma_2)^2 + (\sigma_2 - \sigma_3)^2 + (\sigma_3 - \sigma_1)^2}{12G} \quad (1)$$

where σ_1, σ_2, and σ_3 are the three principal stresses and G is the shearing modulus of elasticity. Essentially the same criterion of plastic yielding has been proposed by Nadai[48] as the so-called "octahedral" shear stress, which is the shear stress in those planes which are equally inclined to the three principal directions. The octahedral shear stress is represented mathematically by the expression

$$\text{Octahedral shear stress} = \tfrac{1}{3}\sqrt{(\sigma_1 - \sigma_2)^2 + (\sigma_2 - \sigma_3)^2 + (\sigma_3 - \sigma_1)^2} \quad (2)$$

This is proportional to the square root of the shear-strain energy, and the two may therefore be considered equivalent.

The experimentation, referred to earlier, which was performed to test the criteria of yielding was carried out principally by Lode[49] on thin-walled metal tubes subjected simultaneously to internal pressure and axial tension and by Taylor and Quinney[50] on thin-walled metal tubes subjected simultaneously to torsion and axial tension. In either case, by varying independently the magnitude of the two types of loading, biaxial stress with varying ratio of the principal stresses was obtained. Taylor and Quinney's experimental results under combined internal pressure and torsion are reproduced in Fig. 46, which also shows by the curves the values to be expected

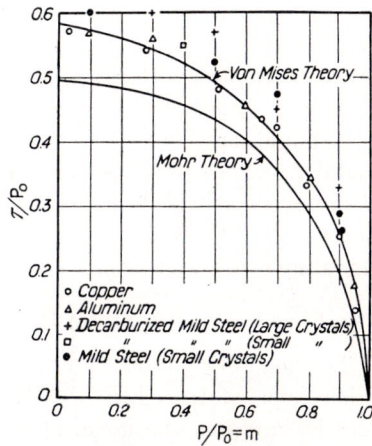

FIG. 46. Comparison of Mohr (maximum shear stress) and von Mises (maximum shear-strain energy) theories of plastic yielding with experimental observations under combined torsion and axial tension. (*Taylor and Quinney.*[50])

on the basis of the Mohr and von Mises theories. Special precautions were taken to obtain samples free from directionality (preferred ori-

---

* Various other criteria have been suggested from time to time, but, because they have been disproved, need not be discussed here. Among these proposals are the so-called "maximum stress," the maximum strain (St. Venant), and the constant energy of deformation theories. Their names are descriptive, and the reader is referred to Mohr[43] or Nadai[45] for a more complete description.

entation), and, with the exception of the mild steel, excellent agreement with the requirements of the shear-strain energy theory was observed. The disagreement of the mild steel was attributed to unavoidable anisotropy. The mild-steel samples were also prestrained in order to avoid the discontinuous flow characterizing yielding in this material. In the coordinates of the plot of Fig. 46, τ is the applied shearing stress, P_0 the tensile yield stress in pure tension, and m the ratio of the applied tensile stress P to the tensile yield strength, that is, P/P_0.*

It is to be noted that the data of Fig. 46 supporting the shear-strain energy law represent uniaxial or biaxial stressing exclusively. The experimental difficulties associated with the satisfactory study of triaxial states of stress are enormous, but Bridgman[53] has presented some data of this kind which indicate a slight effect of hydrostatic pressure.

The difference in the yielding of single crystals, which is governed by the simple maximum-shear-stress law, and of polycrystals, governed by the shear-strain energy law, has been rationalized by Sachs[51] who showed that if the yield stress of single crystals is averaged over all orientations, the corresponding averaged shear stress is nearly identical with that demanded by the von Mises theory.

It might be pointed out that the maximum difference between the yield stresses as predicted by the two theories is only 15 per cent. For many applications, particularly those in which the actual stresses are not known precisely, this difference is not of great consequence, and the simple maximum-shear-stress criterion is sufficiently accurate.

The Flow Curve and Strain Hardening

The load-elongation plot obtained in the ordinary tension test, or other type of test, has been generally converted into a stress-strain plot by dividing the instantaneous load by the original cross-sectional area and the instantaneous total elongation by the original gauge length; stress and strain thus become independent of the dimensions of the specimen. Thus, the stress S and the strain E are given by

$$S = \frac{L}{A_0} \qquad \text{and} \qquad E = \frac{l - l_0}{l_0} = \frac{\Delta l}{l_0}$$

---

* These were chosen for convenience, since as Taylor and Quinney[50] show, the variation of yield surface by the Mohr theory is given by $\dfrac{\tau}{P_0} = \left(\dfrac{1 - m^2}{4}\right)^{\frac{1}{2}}$ and by the von Mises theory by $\dfrac{\tau}{P_0} = \left(\dfrac{1 - m^2}{3}\right)^{\frac{1}{2}}$.

where L and l refer to the instantaneous load and gauge length and A_0 and l_0 refer to the original area and gauge length.

It has become more and more generally recognized that this method of defining stress and strain is fallacious, for as the specimen extends (in the tension test), its dimensions continuously change, and it is unreasonable to expect the reaction of the specimen at any instant to be dependent upon any dimensions other than the instantaneous ones. Thus the ordinary nominal stress-strain curve (Fig. 47) indicates that the stress rises to a maximum value* and then diminishes; this is only apparent, since the cross-sectional area is decreasing proportionately

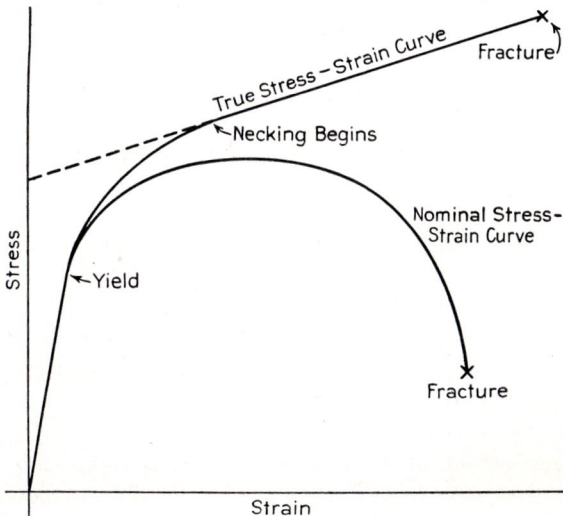

Fig. 47. Schematic illustration of nominal and true stress-strain curves.

faster than the load. Furthermore, the desirability of being able to predict the stress-strain relation for any type of deformation from a single experimental determination obviously requires a precise definition of the quantities involved. Such shortcomings as these were early recognized (though they continue to be perpetuated) and Ludwik[52] suggested in the first decade of this century the so-called "true" stress-strain curve in which the stress and strain are defined in terms of the instantaneous dimensions of the specimens. That is, stress is defined

* Commonly called the tensile strength, but having no real significance other than marking the cessation of uniform or homogeneous flow and the beginning of "necking."

as

$$\sigma = \frac{L}{A} \tag{3}$$

where σ is the true stress, L and A are the instantaneous load and cross-sectional area, and strain is defined as

$$\delta = \int_{l_0}^{l} \frac{dl}{l} = \ln \frac{l}{l_0} \tag{4}$$

where δ is the true or natural strain, l and l_0 are the instantaneous and original lengths, and dl is a small increment of strain. Or, since the volume may be considered to remain constant during plastic deformation, the strain may be defined in terms of the areas:

$$\delta = \ln \frac{A_0}{A} \tag{5}$$

since

$$A_0 l_0 = Al$$

or

$$\ln \frac{l}{l_0} = \ln \frac{A_0}{A}$$

It might be noted that with the onset of local necking deformation, the gauge length undergoing deformation is rather indeterminate, and it is accordingly desirable to make area measurements.

A true stress-strain, or flow, curve is shown schematically in Fig. 47. The results of tension tests using the concept of the true stress-strain curve have been presented by a number of investigators.[55-59] It has been shown by these investigators that approximately from the stress corresponding to the maximum load in the tensile test (at which inhomogeneous or local necking deformation sets in) to fracture, the average true strain is a linear function of the average true stress for all but a few metals and alloys. The expressions "average true strain" and "average true stress" are used because with necking the stress is no longer uniform across the specimen or uniaxial.

Illustrative of true stress-strain plots are those shown in Fig. 48 for various materials. In these plots, the true stress corresponding to the maximum load is indicated by a large, solid triangle, and the linearity from this point to fracture is evident. The anomalous sudden fall-off of cold-drawn pure copper was also observed in pure aluminum, and was attributed to the formation and propagation of a crack from the center of the specimen. True stress-strain curves for a 12 per cent chromium steel at several temperatures are shown in Fig. 49, after MacGregor,[57] although the influence of temperature on strength will be discussed in more detail in a subsequent section.

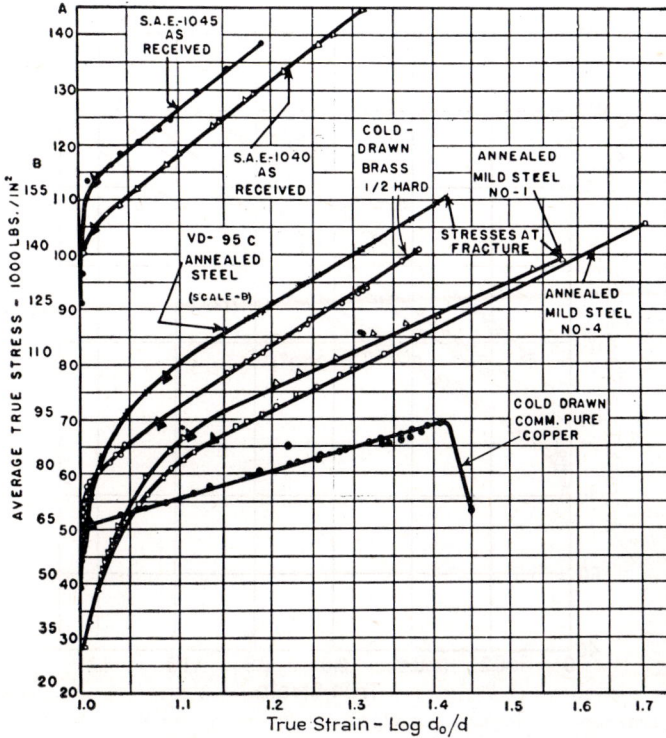

FIG. 48. True stress-strain curves for several materials. (*MacGregor.*[55])

It has been further observed[52, 59] that for a large number of metals the true stress-strain curve can be represented quite well in the plastic range by a power function (except for the initial plastic flow of materials which yield inhomogeneously like soft steel):

$$\sigma = K\delta^n \tag{6}$$

where σ and δ are again the true stress and strain and K and n are material constants. This function plots to a straight line of slope n if the logarithm of the stress is plotted against the logarithm of the strain, since

$$\log \sigma = \log K + n \log \delta \tag{7}$$

Thus the constant n is sometimes referred to as the strain-hardening coefficient, since it is a measure of the steepness of the stress-strain plot. The constant K, on the other hand, is evidently indicative of the height of the curve and thus of the relative strength; by inspection, K is numerically equal to the stress when the strain is unity.

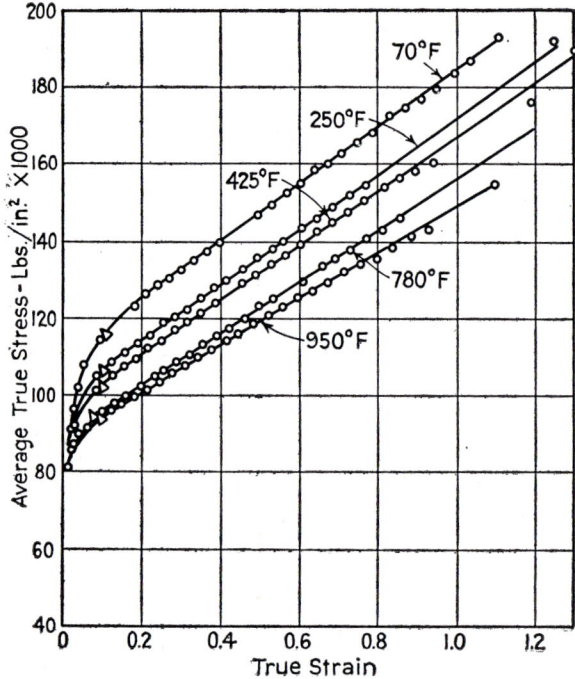

FIG. 49. True stress-strain curves for 12 per cent chromium steel at various temperatures. (*MacGregor and Welch.*[57])

Gensamer[60] has shown that the slope of the true stress-strain curve at the point at which necking begins is numerically equal to the stress, and Hollomon[59] has shown further that the strain-hardening coefficient of the exponential relation is identical with the strain at the maximum load. These relations may be developed as follows:

At the maximum load, the rate of change of the load L is zero and since the load $L = A\sigma$

$$dL = 0 = A\,d\sigma + \sigma\,dA \qquad \text{and} \qquad \frac{d\sigma}{\sigma} = -\frac{dA}{A} \qquad (8)$$

but from Eq. (7)

$$\frac{d\sigma}{\sigma} = n\,\frac{d\delta}{\delta} \qquad (9)$$

Substituting Eq. (9) in Eq. (8)

$$n\frac{d\delta}{\delta} = -\frac{dA}{A} \tag{10}$$

but by definition $d\delta = \frac{dl}{l}$, and since $Al = $ constant,

$$\frac{dl}{l} = -\frac{dA}{A} \tag{11}$$

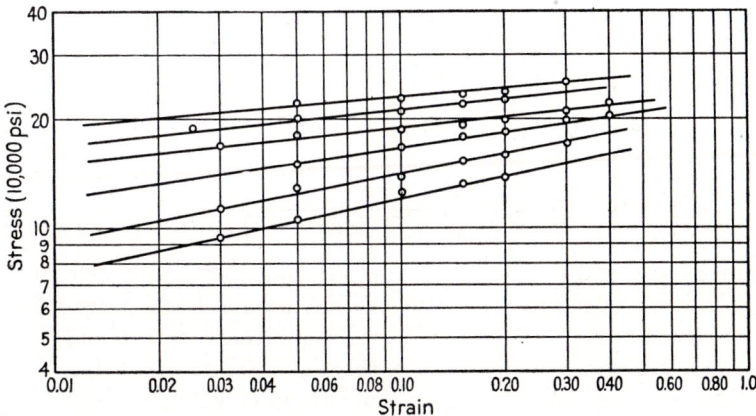

Fig. 50. True stress-strain curves plotted to logarithmic coordinates. Data of Gensamer et al.[56] for isothermally transformed plain carbon eutectoid steel. (*After Hollomon.*[59])

Substitution of Eq. (11) in Eq. (8) gives

$$\frac{d\sigma}{d\delta} = \sigma \tag{12}$$

and substitution of Eq. (11) in Eq. (10) gives

$$n = \delta \tag{13}$$

Examples of logarithmic true stress-strain plots are shown in Fig. 50, after Hollomon from data of Gensamer et al.[56] These plots are for specimens of a eutetectoid plain carbon steel isothermally transformed at different temperatures. Not all plots are straight lines throughout their course, the curve frequently turning upward on approaching the fracture strain, while, curiously, copper seems to show two straight-line portions,[59] the slope of the final portion being about 5 times that during the first period. It should be emphasized that after necking begins, the stress and strain shown in the illustration are no longer strictly "true." Bridgman[61] has considered the problem of the true state of stress in the neck of tension specimens, attempting to correct the true stress-strain plot for the deviations from simple tension.

While the data presented here have all been for simple tension and have illustrated the usefulness of the true stress-strain concept in the study of strain hardening in metals, it has been found that certain functions of stress and strain can be defined* which accurately describe the plastic flow of metals under multiaxial stress states, although, as with yielding under combined stresses, there is evidence that the hydrostatic component exerts a small effect on the flow (but a major one on fracture as we shall see later).

These functions of stress and strain may be described as follows:

$$\bar{\sigma} = \sqrt{\tfrac{1}{2}[(\sigma_1 - \sigma_2)^2 + (\sigma_2 - \sigma_3)^2 + (\sigma_3 - \sigma_1)^2]} \tag{14}$$

and

$$\bar{\delta} = \sqrt{\tfrac{2}{3}(\delta_1^2 + \delta_2^2 + \delta_3^2)} \tag{15}$$

where σ_1, σ_2, and σ_3 and δ_1, δ_2, and δ_3 are the true principal stresses and strains, respectively, and the two invariants $\bar{\sigma}$ and $\bar{\delta}$ are referred to as "generalized," "effective," or "significant" stress and strain. In simple tension $\bar{\sigma}$ and $\bar{\delta}$ reduce to σ_1 and δ_1, respectively. If the relation between effective stress and strain is valid, the flow curve should be identical no matter what the state of stress, and conversely, the behavior of a metal under any combination of stresses should be determinable from a test under a single state of stress; this in practice would be the tension test owing to the ease with which it is made.

The results of experimental tests of the validity of the invariant functions of stress and strain are shown in Figs. 51 and 52 after Jackson[63] and Lankford *et al.*,[64] respectively. The data of Fig. 51 for copper and steel were obtained by Davis[65, 66] in tests of tubes under various combinations of axial tension and internal pressure. The Lankford data for the aluminum alloy 24S in the annealed O and precipitation-hardened T conditions were obtained in simple tension or compression and biaxial tension tests. Both sets of data confirm the validity of the concept of the invariant stress and strain functions.

With the introduction and use of the concepts which have been described, the science of the plastic deformation of metals has made great strides, and it is to be expected that this will continue. In sub-

* The reader is referred to Jelinek, Latter, Thomsen, and Dorn[62] for details concerning various proposed functions and their derivations.

sequent sections of this book, we shall see some of the ways these concepts have proved fruitful in such varied fields as in the influence of alloying elements, microstructure, deformation speed, and temperature on the resistance of metals to flow and fracture.

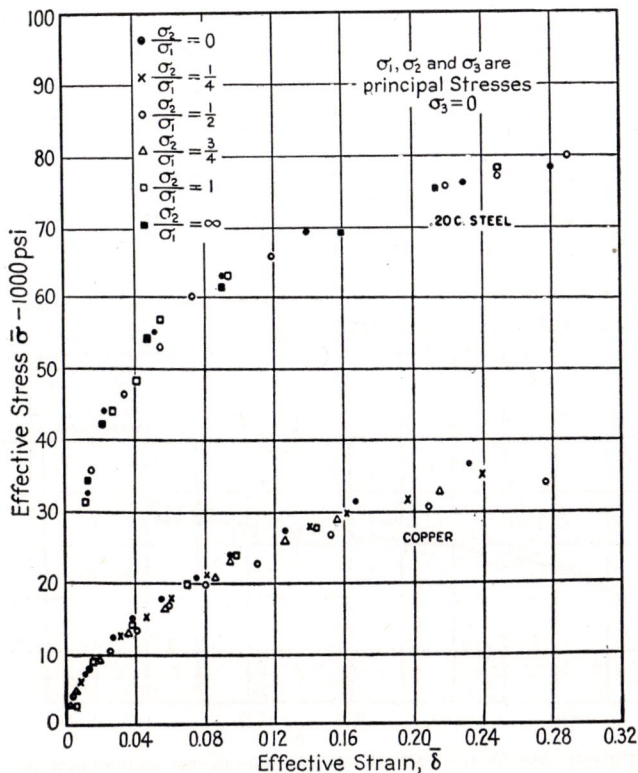

FIG. 51. Effective stress versus effective strain plots for copper and steel for various states of biaxial stress. Data of Davis[65],[66]. The invariant stress and strain functions are defined in the text.   (*After Jackson.*[63])

Lattice Rotation during Deformation of Polycrystalline Metals—Preferred Orientation

Aside from the important effects of the restraints of neighboring grains upon one another, and of the possible influences of the grain boundaries per se in at least certain instances, the deformation of the individual grains of an aggregate occurs in the same manner as in single crystals, that is, slip occurs on the same crystallographic planes and in the same directions.   Moreover, individual grains develop twins and deformation bands and undergo progressive lattice rotation as deformation proceeds.   These processes are not well understood in polycrystalline metals owing to the complex nature of the influence of one grain upon another.

As deformation is continued, the individual grains tend to rotate into one or more preferred positions, giving rise to the sometimes desirable, sometimes undesirable preferred orientations (deformation textures or fibers), but in either event of considerable practical im-

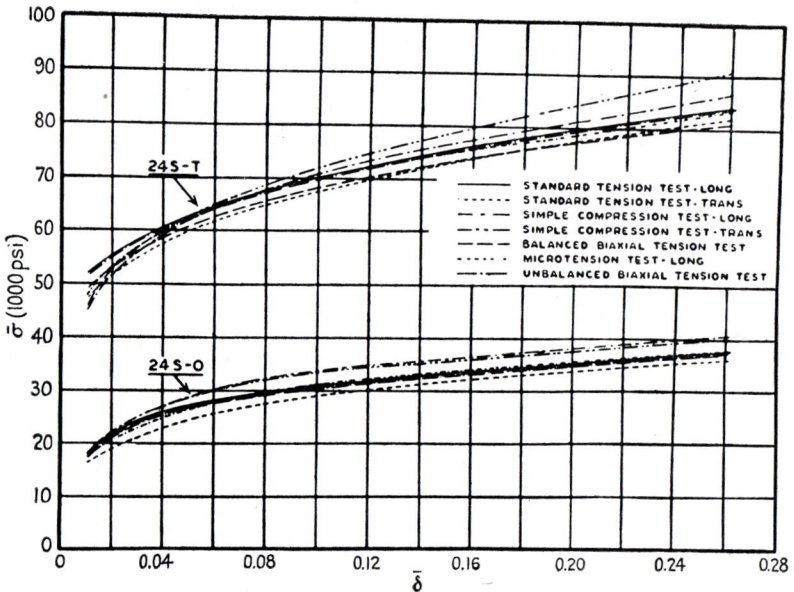

Fig. 52. Effective stress versus effective strain plots for the aluminum alloy 24S in two initial states under various types of uniaxial and biaxial stress.   (*Lankford et al.*[64])

portance.   These preferred orientations exist after recrystallization annealing, although, depending upon various factors such as the nature of the material, deformation texture, and temperature of recrystallization, the recrystallization textures are less perfectly developed than the deformation textures.   The recrystallization texture may be, but generally is not, identical with the deformation texture.

Wrought metals are seldom without some degree of preferred orientation, and the resultant anisotropy in properties is of considerable commerical importance.   Not only do the properties vary with direction of test, but the relations described in the preceding sections for defining yielding and plastic flow of polycrystalline aggregates are inapplicable to the extent that isotropy does not exist.

Preferred orientations have been extensively studied, and the textures developed by different processes of deformation have been experimentally determined for many of the common metals and alloys. No completely satisfactory accounting of the development of preferred orientations has been advanced, with the possible exception of Taylor's theory of flow in polycrystalline aggregates,[54] which also attempts a calculation of the aggregate stress-strain curve from the single-crystal behavior. A review of these theories, with the exception of Taylor's which is discussed in the next section, is beyond the scope of this book and for such a review the reader is referred to a book by Barrett.[10]

TABLE III. PREFERRED ORIENTATIONS DEVELOPED BY COLD ROLLING AND BY SUBSEQUENT RECRYSTALLIZATION*

Metal	Crystal structure	After cold rolling		After subsequent recrystallization	
		Rolling direction	Rolling plane	Rolling direction	Rolling plane
Al	Face-centered-cubic	[112], [111]	(110), (112)	[100]	(001)
Cu	Face-centered-cubic	[112], [111]	(110), (112)	[100]	(001)
Ni	Face-centered-cubic	[112], [111]	(110), (112)	[100]	(001)
85Cu–15Zn	Face-centered-cubic	[112]	(110)	[112]	(311)
Fe	Body-centered-cubic	[110]	(100), (112)	[110], [112]	(001), (11$\bar{1}$)
Mo	Body-centered-cubic	[110]	(100), (112)		
Zn	Close-packed-hexagonal	[100]	(001)		

* Data from Barrett.[10]

Table III, after Barrett,[10] compiles the deformation texture after rolling and after subsequent recrystallization, for several metals and alloys, and shows that the textures tend to be but are not always the same for a specific crystal structure.

Taylor's Theory of Flow in Polycrystalline Aggregates

As many scientists have noted, the restraints of neighboring grains exert an important influence on the deformation of an individual grain of an aggregate, and in the general case impose conditions that require the grain to slip on more than one plane simultaneously in order that it shall undergo essentially the same change in shape as its neighbors. It remained, however, for Taylor[54] to attempt a rigorous solution of the problem. Applying the principle of least work, which specifies that of the possible means of accomplishing a given end that means will be selected which requires the least expenditure of energy, Taylor showed that in the general case a crystal within an aggregate must slip on at least five slip systems (plane and direction) simultaneously in order to undergo the arbitrary change in shape imposed upon it and that of the possible groups of five slip systems the one group involving the least total work of deformation would operate.

Taylor considered the case of aluminum which has 12 possible slip systems (four {111} planes and three [110] directions) and computed

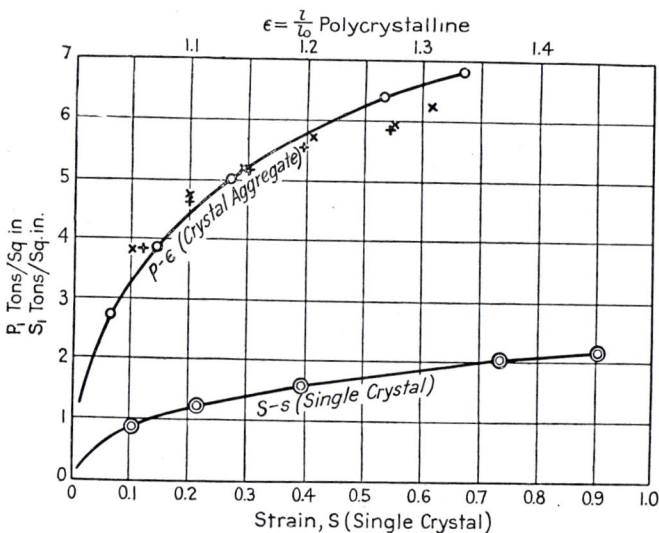

Fig. 53. Comparison of measured and calculated stress-strain curves of polycrystalline aluminum, the calculated curve being derived from the measured single-crystal stress-strain curve. (*Taylor*.[54])   ○—calculated from single crystal measurements, ✕+—aggregate, ◎—single crystal.

for 44 differently oriented single crystals the work involved for each possible grouping of 5 slip systems out of the 12 possible slip systems. There are a total of 792 ways of choosing 5 from a group of 12, but from geometry and symmetry considerations, this reduced to 24 combinations of 5 shears. Taylor calculated the work involved in deformation for each of these combinations to determine that one involving the least work; this combination was considered operative for the particular crystal orientation considered.

Taylor further suggested that each grain of an aggregate necessarily undergoes the identical strain which the sample as a whole undergoes, if voids are not to be developed. Accordingly, by taking a number of orientations representing a random orientation of the aggregate and applying the principle, observed for single crystals, that the strain hardening in a crystal undergoing multiple slip depends upon the sum of the shears in the same way as for single slip, Taylor was able to calculate the stress-strain curve of an aggregate from the stress-strain curve of a single crystal. The result shown in Fig. 53 reveals remarkably good agreement with experiment. It should be pointed out,

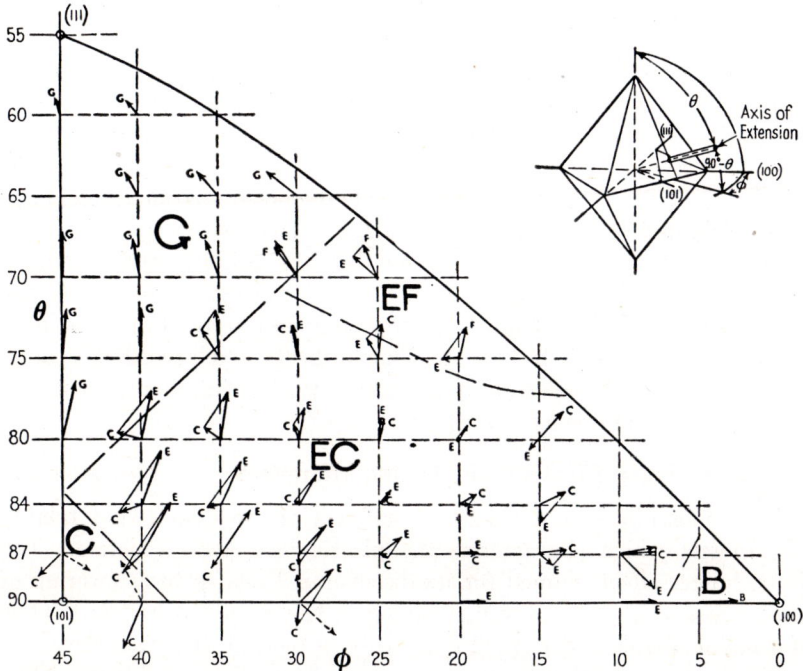

Fig. 54. Changes in lattice orientation of individual crystals within a polycrystalline aggregate for a tensile strain of 2.37 per cent as calculated by Taylor.[54]

however, that Taylor's theory does not take into account the influence of grain size on the stress-strain curve, as observed for most metals, although apparently not for aluminum (Fig. 20).

Knowing the shears involved in the deformation of crystals of an aggregate, Taylor was also able to calculate the changes in lattice orientation accompanying deformation. The results of such a calculation for 2.37 per cent tensile strain are shown in Fig. 54, the arrows representing the direction of change and the arrowhead the end position. The angles θ and ϕ are the angles of the specimen axis from the

[010] and [100] directions, respectively. The two arrows shown in many instances mean that two different combinations of five shears involve the same outlay of work. In such cases, either or both combination in any proportion were considered to be possibly operative. The heavy letters **G**, **EC**, etc., denote regions in which one or two combinations of five shears may occur. As indicated by the arrows, the aggregate will tend to a final preferred orientation in which the [111] or [100], but no [101], directions will coincide with the direction of tension which is in agreement with the experimental determination of this texture by X-ray diffraction means.

Barrett and Levenson[68] have experimentally studied the direction of rotation in compression (for strains of 11 and 31 per cent) of individual grains in an aluminum aggregate for comparison with the predictions of Taylor. These determinations showed that about one-third of the grains rotate in directions not predicted. This discrepancy was attributed to a nonuniform strain in each crystal (for which deformation bands are evidence) rather than the uniform strain assumed by Taylor. Thus although Taylor's theory predicts qualitatively the directions of rotation of most of the grains and accounts for the final preferred orientation, it fails in some respects and accordingly must be modified; nevertheless it represents a worth-while contribution to knowledge of the flow of aggregates.

The Bauschinger Effect and the Elastic Aftereffect

The Bauschinger and elastic aftereffects are two somewhat related phenomena which characterize the plastic behavior of metals. The Bauschinger effect, named for its discoverer,[69] relates to a lowering of flow stress by a prior plastic straining in the reverse direction. Thus if a metal sample is deformed plastically in tension, the yield stress for a subsequent straining in compression is lower than its virgin value. The elastic aftereffect, apparently first observed by Weber,[70] relates to a time-dependent recovery of strain after removal of load. Thus, if the load is removed from a specimen which has been creeping in tension, an immediate elastic contraction attends the unloading, but this is followed by a further contraction which occurs at a decreasing rate with time. This effect is sometimes termed "creep recovery." Elastic hysteresis, in which the elastic changes on loading and unloading do not follow the same path, is a somewhat related effect. Both the Bauschinger and elastic aftereffects appear to be related to the development of residual stresses, as discussed below.

The Bauschinger effect may be illustrated by the data of Fig. 55, after Nadai,[45] which show the stress-strain relations for torsion of mild steel first twisted in one direction and then in the reverse direction to *R*. The marked lowering of the yield strength for the reversed twisting is apparent—without the prior twisting the yield strength would be identical no matter in which direction twisted. The Bauschinger effect is of considerable practical importance in some uses of metals.

The Bauschinger effect and the elastic aftereffect have generally been explained as having their origin in residual stresses developed in polycrystalline aggregates owing to the anisotropy of properties of the individual crystals.* Thus since differently oriented crystals have different elastic moduli and yield under different loads, it is held that the state of stress developed by straining is highly inhomogeneous on a microscopic scale, that is, from grain to grain, or even in different portions of a grain. Of course, the individual crystals of an aggregate are prevented by their neighbors from yielding at the loads at which they would in the free state, as we have seen in the preceding sections, and moreover are not strained to the same degree as in the free state

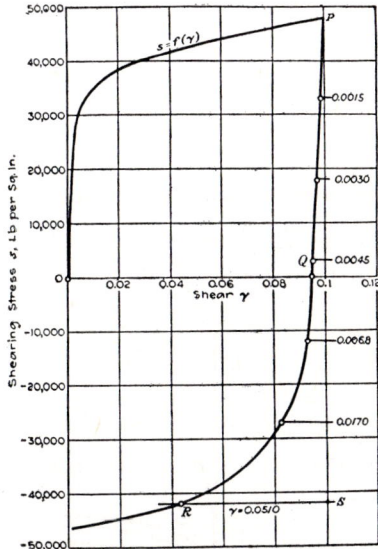

FIG. 55. The Bauschinger effect in mild steel. The specimen was stressed in pure shear to *P*, then unloaded to *Q*, and finally stressed in the reverse sense to *R*. (*Nadai.*[45])

by the same stress, since the elastic modulus of the aggregate is an average of those for the individual single crystals. Provided that none of the grains is strained plastically during loading, the inhomogeneous stress state essentially disappears with release of the load. However, if plastic deformation is attained in the initial straining, the highly inhomogeneous state of stress prior to plastic flow will tend to be relieved in some degree, and when the load is removed from such a sample, the microscopic stresses will build up further as the load is reduced to

* This explanation and a similar one for the elastic aftereffect or recovery were proposed by Heyn[71] and Masing[72] but have been modified in minor respects.

zero. In this state, the metal will have a highly inhomogeneous distribution of stresses with some grains in effect under compressive and some under tensile stresses, though the average stress is zero. Accordingly, as stressing proceeds in the direction opposite to that initially employed, the flow stress is observed to be less than in the virgin state, to a greater degree, the greater the initial straining.

If after the load had been reduced to zero, the sample had been permitted to rest, the residual stresses would have tended to relax with time at a rate dependent for any material upon the temperature, and

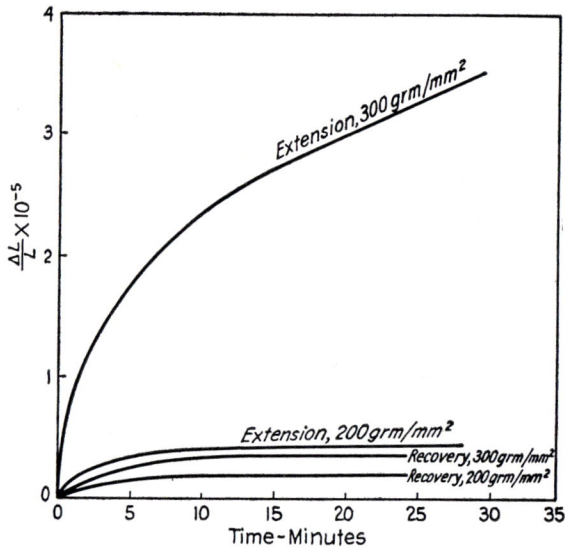

Fig. 56. Recovery after creep of large-grained tin. (*Chalmers.*[20])

the phenomenon of the elastic aftereffect or recovery would have been noted. This effect is illustrated by Figs. 56 and 57 which show recovery in tin for two different grain sizes. In these illustrations, which are for creep tests, the initial creep extension under a specific load and the time-dependent recovery contraction observed after release of the load are shown. The immediate contraction corresponding to unloading is not plotted. The recovery is of opposite sign to the initial strain since those crystals which had been plastically strained the least initially would have residual stresses of the opposite sign and having been strain-hardened less would be in a favorable state for creep.

The explanation developed above would require that in metals in which anisotropy is not pronounced, the Bauschinger and elastic aftereffects should be correspondingly less pronounced, while single crystals should not show either effect. The data to test these possibilities are not plentiful, but the few that are available are in part contradictory and in part corroboratory. Chalmers' data of Figs. 56 and 57 show very clearly that the magnitude of creep recovery is greater in the tests of small-grained tin than of coarse-grained tin.* In creep tests of single crystals Chalmers found no evidence of recovery. Wartenburg[75] found no elastic aftereffect in crystals of tungsten and zinc. These data would seem to bear out the explanation advanced earlier.

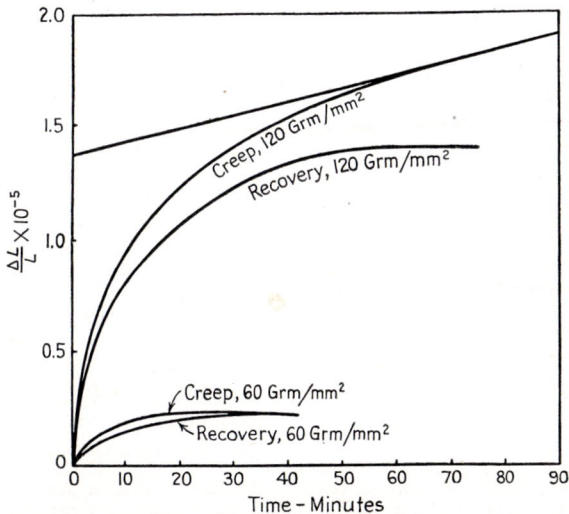

FIG. 57. Recovery after creep of fine-grained tin. (*Chalmers.*[20])

On the other hand, studies of Sachs and Shoji[74] have shown the existence of the Bauschinger effect in brass single crystals (Fig. 58). In this experiment, a single crystal of brass was first strained in tension at A, then unloaded to B, compressed at C, unloaded, and finally again strained in tension at D, thus tracing out a hysteresis loop. The lowering of the yield for reversed straining is apparent. Seitz[67] has suggested that although single crystals generally do not show the Bauschinger effect, its occurrence in brass crystals may be a result of the relatively great anisotropy of brass crystals coupled with inhomogeneities in

* The portion of creep strain recovered appears to be that known as primary creep, or that occurring prior to the essentially constant rate creep. Johnson[73] has shown that the major portion of primary creep, especially at low stresses, is recoverable.

plastic flow.   Whether or not this is true, the dearth of available data suggests that further experimentation is desirable.

An effect mentioned earlier which is akin to, or another manifestation of, the elastic aftereffect is that known as elastic hysteresis. This effect, which is illustrated in Fig. 59 for polycrystalline mild steel, results when the elastic changes on loading and unloading do not follow exactly the same path, but trace out a small hysteresis loop, that is, the metal does not show perfect elasticity. Sachs and Shoji[74] observed elastic hysteresis in brass single crystals. The effect is probably best explained as a result of residual stresses, as discussed earlier.

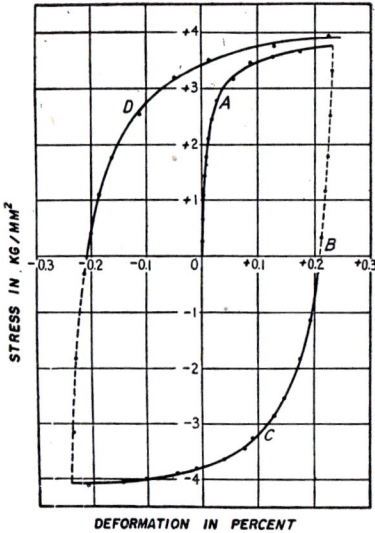

Fig. 58. The Bauschinger effect in a single crystal of brass stressed first in tension *A*, then into compression *BC*, and finally again in tension *D*.   (*Sachs and Shoji.*[74])

Internal Friction

The dissipation or damping of vibrational energy in a solid which has been set into vibration, for example, a tuning fork, is said to result from internal friction within the solid.   The ability to dissipate vibrations has also been termed damping capacity.   The quantitative measure of the internal friction of a metal is generally expressed in terms

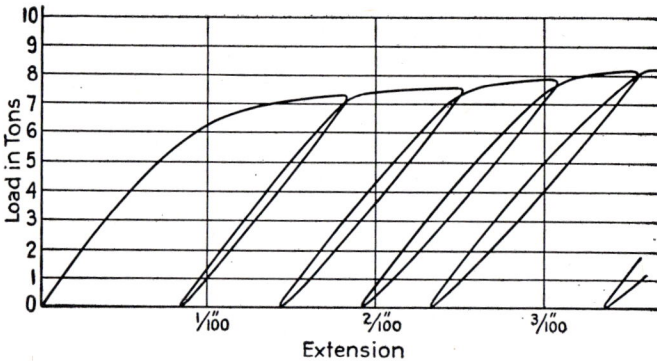

Fig. 59. Elastic hysteresis in mild steel.   (*Dalby.*[76])

of the decrement of energy (or of amplitude), that is, the ratio of energy dissipated per cycle to the instantaneous total vibrational energy.

There are several sources of internal friction in solids, and it is beyond the scope of this book to review them in any detail.* The principal sources of internal friction may be considered to be (1) plastic flow; (2) thermal diffusion both within the specimen (from one portion to another and occurring only in polycrystalline materials) and between the specimen and the surrounding environment; (3) concentration diffusion. Of these, the first two are the most important. Thermal diffusion results from the thermoelastic effect, that is, temperature increase and decrease with compression and extension, respectively.

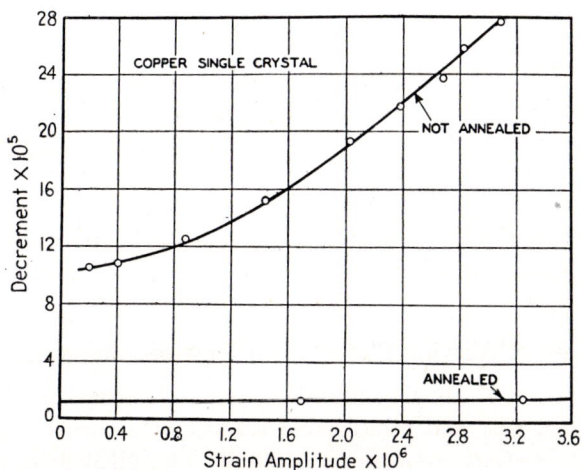

Fig. 60. Effect of annealing on the variation of internal friction with strain amplitude of a single crystal of copper. (*Read.*[77])

In ferromagnetic materials such as iron, nickel, and cobalt, an additional source of internal friction arises in eddy currents resulting from diffusion of magnetic flux.

The internal friction of plastic origin has been extensively studied by Read[77] in single crystals, where it is in a sense isolated, since intraspecimen thermal diffusion is absent. Read showed a striking effect of annealing in reducing the internal friction of single crystals of copper prepared from the melt, as illustrated in Fig. 60. In this case, the un-

* Zener and his associates have made extensive studies and have published many papers dealing with this subject. Of these, reference 32 is of a summary nature, and also discusses other inelastic effects.

annealed crystal had a much higher decrement which varied with the amplitude. In the opposite sense, the internal friction was increased by straining an annealed crystal. Read explained the effect of annealing in terms of dislocations (which will be discussed later), and in fact the internal friction of plastic flow is generally held to have its origin in movement of dislocations.

By studying the variation of the damping decrement at different strain amplitudes in different crystallographic directions of zinc crystals, Read was able to relate internal friction to plastic flow on slip planes. The internal friction increased markedly as the basal plane (which it will be recalled is the only slip plane in zinc) approached the angle (45 deg.) of maximum resolved shear stress or, in other words, as the resolved shear stress on the slip plane increased. A dependence of internal friction on crystallographic orientation has also been shown by Found[79] for brass crystals.

Internal friction of plastic origin may be expected to and does occur in polycrystalline samples, according to Zener, Clarke, and Smith,[78] but its study is made difficult owing to the need for separating away the internal friction of thermoelastic origin. Cold working increases the internal friction but the effect may be reversed by annealing, even though no change in hardness occurs, all of which conforms with dislocation theory.

The Influence of Alloying Elements on Flow of Polycrystalline Metals

The influence of alloying additions on the strength and plasticity of metals is a vast and complicated subject, which was only touched upon in the section on single crystals, and we shall have space here only to note the more important underlying principles and to review a few of the more definitive publications. Specific investigations relating to the influence of chemical composition on the high-temperature properties of metals are reviewed in Chap. VIII. As we shall see in that chapter, the strength at elevated temperatures bears little relation to that at ordinary temperatures for several reasons, although certain general principles are the same. For this reason it is important that consideration first be given to the effects of alloying additions at ordinary temperatures before considering the ways in which these effects are modified by temperature. For either atmospheric or elevated temperatures, the microstructure is of paramount importance in determining strength, and although this has been only inadequately studied, particular attention will be paid to this aspect of the problem.

The influence of alloying elements on the strength of metals has been generally studied in terms of hardness (or occasionally tensile strength) or in terms of the flow curve (true stress-strain curve) which we have discussed in preceding sections. Unfortunately, analysis of the hardness test in terms of fundamentals is relatively complex in spite of the simplicity with which the test can be made, and it is much more profitable to study the flow curve which reveals all that the hardness test shows and more. That is, since the flow curve is the locus of the instantaneous flow strengths, it describes the entire course of resistance to deformation, while at the same time indicating the rate of strain hardening and the strength and ductility at fracture. Moreover, hardness tests alone may reveal one alloy to be stronger than another, when in reality this is true only in the later stages of deformation as a consequence of different rates of strain hardening. This possibility is strikingly illustrated in Fig. 61, which will be discussed later. It might be pointed out that a measure of the work hardening may be, but only infrequently is, determined from the hardness test by performing a so-called Meyer analysis.[82] In this method of analysis, a series of hardness impressions made with a ball indenter at increasing loads are related according to the expression $L = ad^n$, where L is the load, d

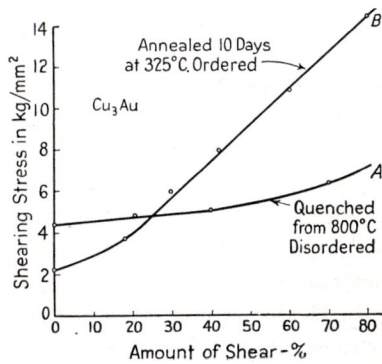

FIG. 61. Shear-stress–strain curves for single crystals of Cu_3Au in the disordered and ordered states. (*Siegel.*[80])

the diameter of the recovered impression, and a and n material constants of which n is a measure of work hardening.

When an alloying addition is made to a metal, one of two things may, in general, occur. The atoms of the added element may enter into the matrix, or parent metal lattice, forming thus a solid solution or single-phase microstructure. This may be of either the substitutional or interstitial type. Or, the added atoms may result in the formation of a new phase so that the alloy is multiphase, or heterogenous. This difference is important, for as we shall see there is little or nothing that can be done to enhance the strength* of solid solutions, while the strength of a multiphase alloy can be varied within wide

* The term "strength" is employed here in the sense of the complete flow (stress-strain) curve.

limits by heat-treatments which change the size and distribution of the microconstituents. Of course, it should be made clear that the phases of heterogeneous alloy systems may possess extended solid solubility regions either in the solid solutions which merge at either end with the pure components (terminal solid solutions) or in intermediate solutions separated from the pure components by heterogeneous fields. In view of these great differences, it will be convenient for subsequent discussion to consider the influence of alloying elements under two separate heads—homogeneous and heterogeneous alloys.

Homogeneous Alloys (Solid Solutions)

We have already seen in our brief survey of the influence of alloying elements on the strength of single crystals that elements entering into solid solution strengthen a metal. The strengthening thus conferred may be of greater magnitude than when the added element does not enter into solid solution, provided the resulting new phase is distributed in a relatively inefficacious manner. Otherwise the heterogeneous alloy may be of equal or greater strength.

Although we have yet to consider the physical mechanism of deformation by slip, it may not seem unreasonable to expect that when an atom of one kind enters in solid solution in the lattice of another element, the perfectly regular arrangement of the solvent lattice is to some degree altered and that it is this alteration which results in the increased resistance to slip, that is, increased strength, in solid solutions. The greater this alteration, the greater is the strengthening. Several studies have been made of this subject, both for nonferrous and ferrous-base alloys, to show that the strengthening effects of various elements in a common solvent differ according to their chemical and physical nature.

One of the first of these studies was made by Ludwik[83] who observed that the increase in hardness of lead by solid solution alloying was roughly related in an inverse fashion to the solid solubility of the added element; this is evident in Table IV. These data may be rationalized in terms of the differences in the chemical and physical properties of the solute atoms by the correlations of Hume-Rothery[84] of solid solubility with the size and the chemical character of the solute atom in relation to the solvent atom.

Norbury,[85] Brick *et al.*,[86] and Frye and Caum[87] have all considered the influence of different solutes on the hardness of copper, while Frye and Hume-Rothery[88] have studied the hardness of solid solutions of silver. The results of Brick *et al.* are typical of the data on copper.

It was observed that the increase in hardness varied inversely with the solid solubility and directly with the difference in size of solvent and solute atoms as well as with the change in lattice parameter.* For small additions, the increase in hardness was observed to be linear

TABLE IV. RELATION BETWEEN DEGREE OF SOLID SOLUTION HARDENING AND SOLUBILITY OF ADDED ELEMENT IN LEAD*

Solute	Solid solubility in lead	Hardness increase per atom per cent
Bi	30.	0.5
Sn	10.	1.8
Cd	5.	4.8
Sb	2.5	10.0
Mg	0.5	11.0

* Data from Ludwik.[83]

with solute concentration. The variation of hardening with change in lattice parameter is shown in Fig. 62. Magnesium and cobalt, which were also studied and found to be intermediate in hardening power between arsenic and tin, were not included in Fig. 62 owing to lack of data in regard to the influence of these elements on lattice param- eter. No explanation was offered for the appearance of silicon above the smooth curve, but this was also observed by Norbury. Brick *et al.* also made diamond pyra- mid hardness tests on the identical alloys after two different degrees of cold rolling and observed (Fig. 63) a linear relation to exist be- tween the solution hardening and the work-hardening coefficients. Thus in this series of alloys, a solute which exerts a strong influence on the solid solution hardness also exerts a strong influence on the rate of strain hardening.

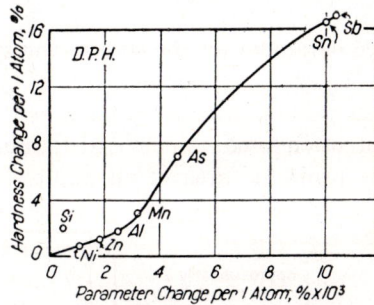

FIG. 62. Relation between the change in lattice parameter and the increase in hard- ness resulting from the solid solution of various elements in copper. (*Brick et al.*[86])

Frye and Hume-Rothery[88] found, interestingly, that the increase in hardness for a given atom per cent of solute is linearly related to the square of the lattice distortion (or the difference between the lat-

* The change in lattice parameter has also been called the lattice distortion.

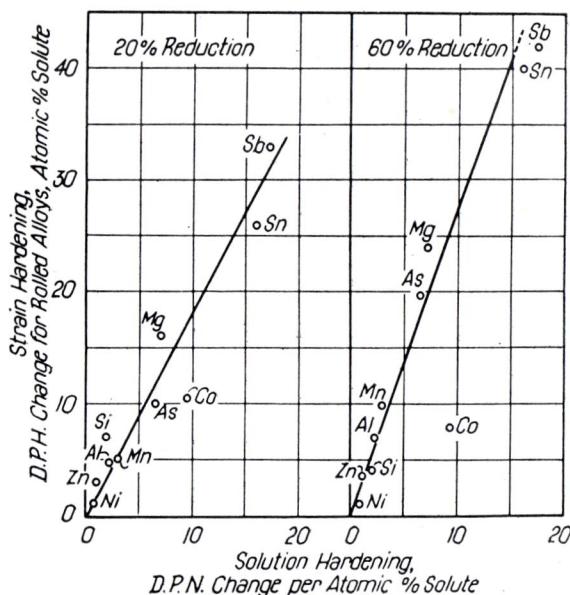

FIG. 63. Linear relation between strain hardening by cold rolling and solution hardening characteristic of copper alloys. (*Brick et al.*[86])

tice parameter of the solvent metal and the solid solution) for elements in the same row in the periodic table, as shown in Fig. 64. The hardness value plotted as ordinate is the so-called ultimate Meyer hardness, not often used, which is determined by dividing the applied load by the projected area of an impression having the same diameter as the

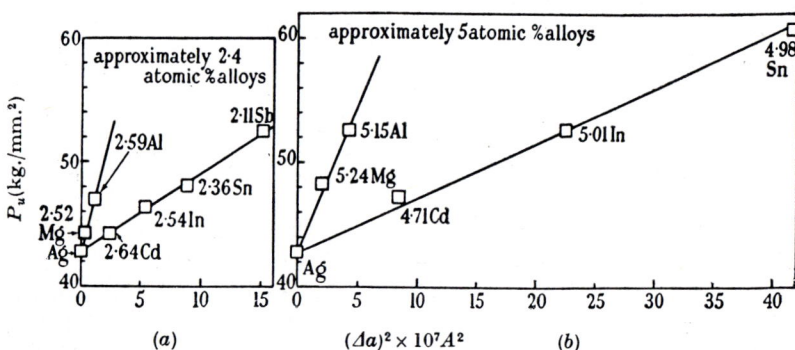

FIG. 64. Linear relation between ultimate Meyer hardness Pu and the squares of the change in lattice parameter Δa for elements of the same row of the periodic table in solid solution in silver. (*Frye and Hume-Rothery.*[88])

test ball. In relation to the observed variation, the authors pointed out that in the same row of the periodic table the underlying ions of the solute are of the same structure and the quantum numbers of the valency electrons are identical.

Frye *et al.*[89] have reported an empirical correlation between increase in hardness and increase in "lattice stress" calculated on the basis that the solute atoms produce a homogeneous lattice expansion, but the significance of this is not clear.

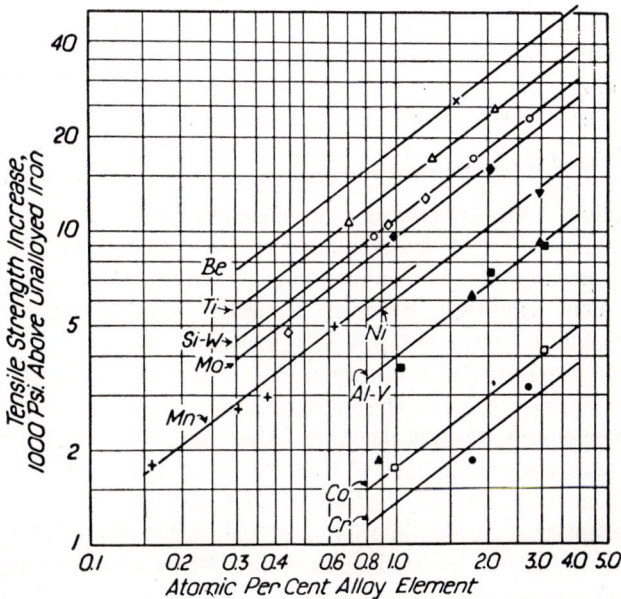

FIG. 65. Relation between increase in tensile strength and the addition of various elements in solid solution in iron. (*Lacy and Gensamer.*[91])

Austin[90] and Lacy and Gensamer[91] have conducted extensive investigations of the influence of various elements in the solid solution hardening of iron. Of these, the latter was more comprehensive, including a greater number of addition elements and employing true stress-strain rather than hardness tests so that both the strength and rate of strain hardening could be determined.

Lacy and Gensamer used low-metalloid iron as a base for alloying. The alloys were all deformed and recrystallized to a uniform grain structure and then treated in wet hydrogen to minimize aging effects. On plotting the logarithm of the increase in tensile strength against the logarithm of atom per cent of alloying element, a straight line was obtained for each element, and these lines were parallel for the different elements (Fig. 65).   This may be represented by the relation.

$$S = S_0 + k(X)^n$$

or

$$\log (S - S_0) = \log k + n \log X \tag{16}$$

where S is the tensile strength of an alloy, S_0 the tensile strength of unalloyed iron, X the concentration, and k and n material constants; of these constants n is the slope of the lines in Fig. 65, being the same (0.75) for all series, and k the intercept at 1 atom per cent, and therefore an index of the strengthening effect of an element.   The order of decreasing effectiveness in strengthening iron is accordingly: Be, Ti, W, Si, Mo, Mn, Ni, Al, V, Co, and Cr.   The yield strengths were observed to vary almost directly with the tensile strengths, but cobalt and vanadium were interchanged at concentrations less than 2 atom per cent.   The order of strengthening of the elements in iron varied, with some exceptions (particularly silicon), inversely with the corresponding solid solubility; however, it was pointed out that many of the solid solubilities are not precisely known.

Lacy and Gensamer also observed that if the logarithm of the "unstrained strength," that is, the increase of the intercept at zero strain of the extrapolated straight portion of the true stress-strain curve (see Fig. 47), was plotted against the logarithm of the atom per cent of alloying element, a similar relation to that shown in Fig. 65 was obtained, except that n was in this case 0.71 rather than 0.75.   If this unstrained strength is plotted against the slopes of the straight part of the true stress-strain curves (the rate of strain hardening) for all alloys (Fig. 66) a straight line is obtained which represents the data reasonably well.   (The identity of the symbols in Fig. 66 is the same as in Fig. 65.)   Thus, the rate of strain hardening increases with the unstrained strength (and also with the tensile strength).   It may also be deduced from Fig. 66 that the true stress-strain curves, except in so far as fracture is concerned, are independent of the alloying elements per se, the same curve being obtained by different amounts of different elements.

Study of several ternary and quaternary alloys indicated to a good approximation that the strengthening resulting from simultaneous additions of several elements is additive; that is, the increase in strength is the sum of the increases corresponding to the specific additions in the binary alloys.

Heterogeneous Alloys

As stated earlier, the strength of heterogeneous alloys is markedly influenced by variation in size and distribution of the microconstituents, in other words upon the microstructure; this is in turn determined by heat-treatment. This subject is so vast and complex that it cannot be adequately dealt with here. For example, the subject of precipitation hardening, of which our understanding has greatly increased in recent years, and the whole field of heat-treatable ferrous alloys belongs under

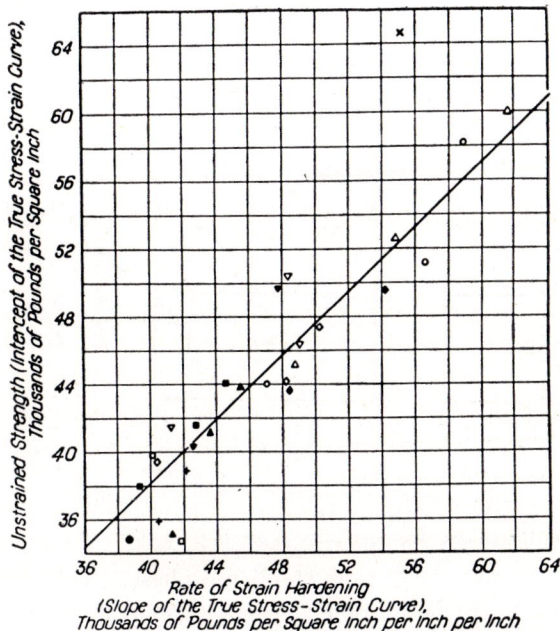

Fig. 66. Relation between the slope and the intercept on the stress axis of the true stress-strain curves of all investigated solid solution alloys of iron. Symbols are identical with those in Fig. 65. (*Lacy and Gensamer.*[91])

this heading. The hardening of steels by the formation of martensite might be considered a special case, but since this product is almost universally tempered before being put to service, hardenable steels are here considered to be heterogeneous.

Perhaps the simplest case of heterogeneous alloys is that of two metals which though soluble in one another in all proportions in the liquid state are completely insoluble in the solid state. This is illustrated by the simple eutectic system of Fig. 67a; the lead-arsenic system is one in which the two pure metals are completely insoluble or very nearly so in the solid state. The microstructure of an alloy of A and B (Fig. 67a) will then consist of a mixture of particles of A and B. If the proportions of A and B are such that the composition is that at E, the eutectic composition, the microstructure is a fine intimate mixture of the two components; while if the composition is to either side of E, the microstructure will contain, in addition to the intimate eutectic structure, larger particles (primary crystals) of the pure metal A or B, respectively, if to the left or right of E. The strength of the mixture will depend, of course, upon the relative amounts of A and B, which determines the amount of primary constituent and eutectic mixture, and upon the relative strengths of A and B, but also upon the size and distribution of the particles. These will, in general, be finer and more uniformly distributed, and the alloy will have greater strength, the

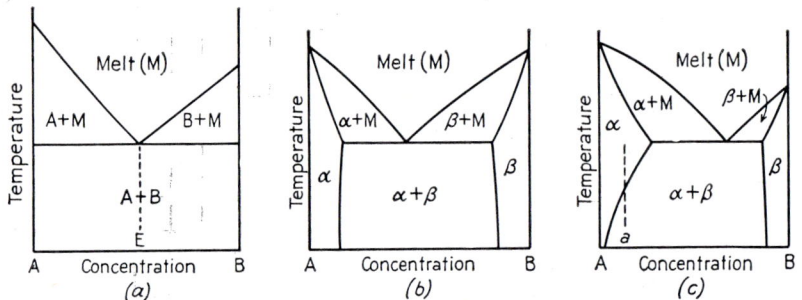

Fig. 67. Schematic equilibrium diagrams illustrating several possible types of binary equilibriums: (a) Simple eutectic with no solid solubility; (b) eutectic with terminal solid solutions; and (c) same as (b) but with the solid solubility decreasing with decreasing temperature so that there exists the possibility of precipitation hardening as in alloy a.

greater the rate of cooling from the liquid phase. The distribution of the microconstituents is in some respects inherent in the system and to that extent beyond external control. For example, the continuous phase of a heterogeneous alloy, which as its name indicates is the phase which may be traced continuously throughout the microstructure and which obviously exerts a primary influence on the strength characteristics, cannot be changed at will. The degree to which the strength of a simple eutectic alloy can be increased by refinement of microstructure is limited and, in general, is considerably less than can be attained by precipitation hardening, discussed below.

Frequently, the two metals of a binary system are not completely insoluble in one another in the solid state, giving rise to equilibrium diagrams of the kind illustrated in Fig. 67b and c. In this case the components of the eutectic mixture are not pure A and pure B but rather the solid solutions of B in A (alpha) and of A in B (beta) of the specific concentrations given by the solid-solubility curves. If the solubility curves do not decrease with decreasing temperature (Fig. 67b) the circumstances are quite similar to that of Fig. 67a, except that the components of the eutectic mixture as well as the primary particles are solid solutions rather than pure metals. When the equilibrium diagram is like that shown in Fig. 67c, in which the solid solubility decreases with decreasing temperature, the basic requirement of precipitation hardening is satisfied (although hardening may not necessarily occur). If an alloy of composition a is heated within the region of existence of the alpha phase, it will consist at equilibrium only of the single phase alpha. On cooling sufficiently slowly that equilibrium is maintained, particles of the beta solid solution precipitate as soon as the two-phase field alpha plus beta is reached, with consequent depletion of B in the alpha solid solution. This beta precipitate is relatively coarse and may or may not result in an increase in strength, depending upon the exact size and dispersion of the precipitate and upon the relative strengths of alpha and beta.

If, instead of slow cooling, the alloy is rapidly cooled to atmospheric temperature the precipitation of the beta phase may be suppressed and the alloy consist only of homogeneous alpha solid solution. This condition is thermodynamically unstable, and with time the beta phase will proceed to precipitate; the alloy is said to age. This precipitate, in contrast to that forming under conditions of near-equilibrium, is of relatively fine size and may exert a tremendous strengthening effect. The strength increases as the precipitation progresses, but generally passes through a maximum as "overaging" occurs. The aluminum-alloy duralumin (containing about 4 per cent copper, 0.5 per cent manganese, and 0.5 per cent magnesium) is a well-known example of an alloy amenable to precipitation hardening. In this case, the alpha phase of Fig. 67c is the alpha solid solution of aluminum, while the beta phase of Fig. 67c is the intermetallic compound $CuAl_2$.*

The rate of precipitation increases with increasing temperature, but the particle size of the precipitate phase also increases; the particle size also increases with time at constant temperature. If the particle size grows beyond an optimum size, the phenomena of overaging occurs, and the hardness and strength decrease. Accordingly there results a characteristic behavior in which (Fig. 68) the maximum strength develops in a shorter time with increasing temperature, but the strength level at this maximum decreases with increasing temperature.

* Although in this case the $CuAl_2$ does not have its normal lattice structure.[229]

The exact mechanism by which strengthening results from the precipitation of a finely dispersed phase is not understood, although great strides have been made in recent years with the discovery (in several aluminum alloys) of the thin submicroscopic regions a few atom distances in thickness by perhaps a hundred in diameter known as Guinier-Preston zones after their discoverers.*   The early suggested mechanism, in which the precipitate particles were pictured as simply exerting a keying effect on the slip planes is now known to be oversimplified, and it really does not represent a mechanism at all but merely a loose description of the phenomena.   The more recent studies of precipitation hardening have suggested that the hardening results from strain existing across the interface between the matrix and precipitate phases owing to a striving of the new lattice, with a different lattice size and density, to

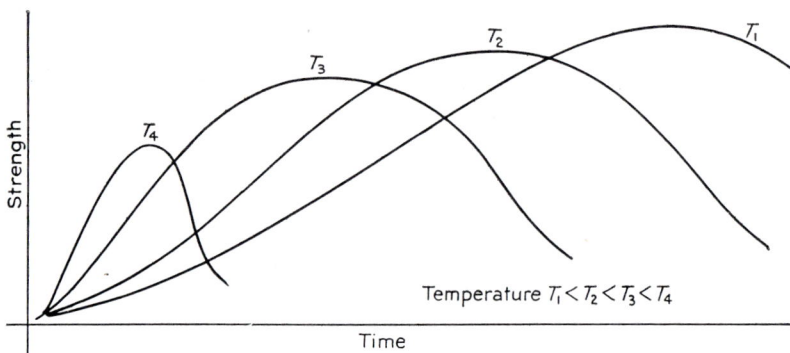

FIG. 68. Schematic illustration of the effect of temperature on precipitation hardening.

conform to that of the old.   This concept has been discussed by Nabarro[92] and experimental support is afforded by the Guinier-Preston zones as well as by the recent X-ray microscopy studies of Barrett.[16] Thus the new lattice is considered to be still in registry with the old in the stage of maximum strengthening.[229]

The varied and complex structures observed in heat-treatable ferrous alloys represent a field of study which, because of outstanding commercial importance, has received several attacks in recent years.   By heat-treatable ferrous alloys are meant those which at high temperatures consist either partially or wholly of the face-centered cubic solid solu-

* Geisler, Barrett, and Mehl[229] have provided an excellent review of this subject.

tion, commonly called austenite, of carbon and of other alloying elements in gamma iron, and which at low temperatures consist of the various products of the partial or complete transformation of austenite.

Among the first of the systematic investigations of the influence of microstructure of heterogeneous ferrous alloys on their strength characteristics were those of Gensamer *et al.*[56, 93] By means of true stress-strain measurements in tension, and in one case of fatigue tests, the properties of two plain carbon steels of eutectoid carbon content and of two manganese steels, one of eutectoid and the other of hypoeutectoid carbon content, were determined after isothermal transformation, or quenching and tempering to various microstructures. These microstructures ranged through various degrees of coarseness of pearlite, bainite, and tempered martensite (spheroidite).

The variation of properties with isothermal reaction temperature was similar in the various steels and the results for one of the plain carbon steels (Fig. 69) may be considered representative. It is to be noted that with decreasing reaction temperature in the illustration, the microstructure grows finer, commencing with very coarse pearlite at the highest temperature, and the strength increases, although not continuously. The change in slope and scatter in the range 600 to 500°C is associated with the change in type of reaction product from pearlite to bainite. The microstructure of bainite is of somewhat uncertain nature, although it is generally considered to be an aggregate (except possibly when it is first formed) which increases in fineness with decreasing reaction temperature.

In an analysis of the various microstructures tested, Gensamer *et al.*[93] developed a linear relation between the resistance to deformation and the logarithim of a quantity, "the mean ferrite path." This relation appears to hold true whether the microstructure is pearlite or spheroidite, as shown in Fig. 70, and on extrapolation to the fine dispersion of carbide in tempered martensite does not yield unreasonable values. The mean ferrite path is the mean distance in the ferrite which can be traversed without encountering a carbide platelet or spheroid, that is, the average distance from one carbide particle to another, and it was determined by drawing and measuring lines at random on photomicrographs. For the pearlites, the mean ferrite path was 1.9 times the interlamellar spacing.

Gensamer *et al.* suggested that the observed relation might apply for the mechanical properties of aggregate structures consisting of a hard constituent dispersed in another soft and continuous one. A reasonable though perhaps oversimplified explanation was advanced for the semi-logarithmic relation, shown in Fig.70, on the basis of dislocation theory, discussed in a later portion of this book.

In a subsequent summary, Gensamer[94] has assembled the data reproduced in Fig. 71, which shows a general relation between the strain-

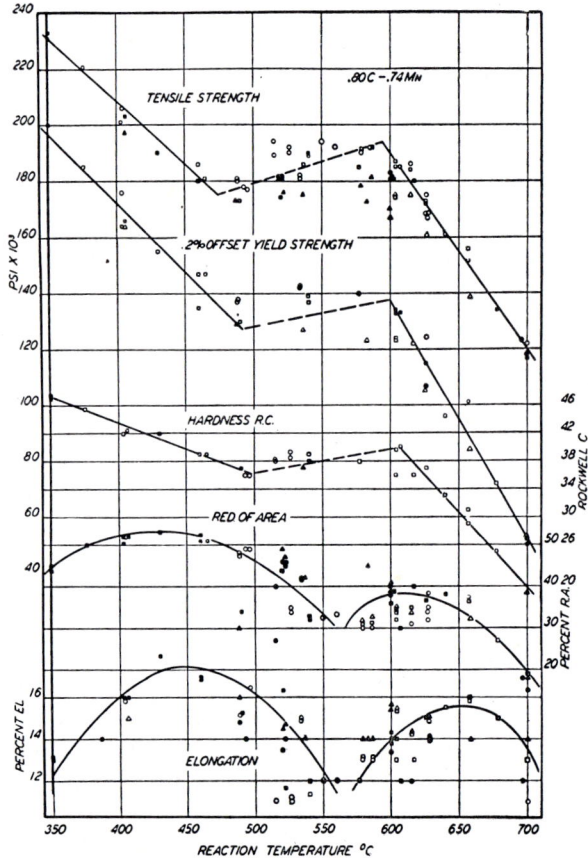

FIG. 69. Variation of mechanical properties of a plain carbon eutectoid steel with reaction temperature. (*Gensamer et al.*[93])

hardening exponent of the expression relating true stress to true strain ($\sigma = K\delta^n$) and the true stress at a true strain of 0.2 for various ferrous alloys, with and without carbon and in various conditions of heat-treatment and microstructure. Although the general relation is apparent, it is doubtful, as the author points out, that the exponent n is invariant at any strength level.   In further consideration of the influence of alloying on the solid solution strengthening of iron (ferrite), Gensamer employed an "equivalent nickel concentration" for calculating the strength of alloys containing more than one alloying element.   In using this concept, the effectiveness of each element was rated relative to the effectiveness of nickel (thus 1 per cent of chromium might be equivalent to 0.22 per cent nickel) and all added to yield the nickel

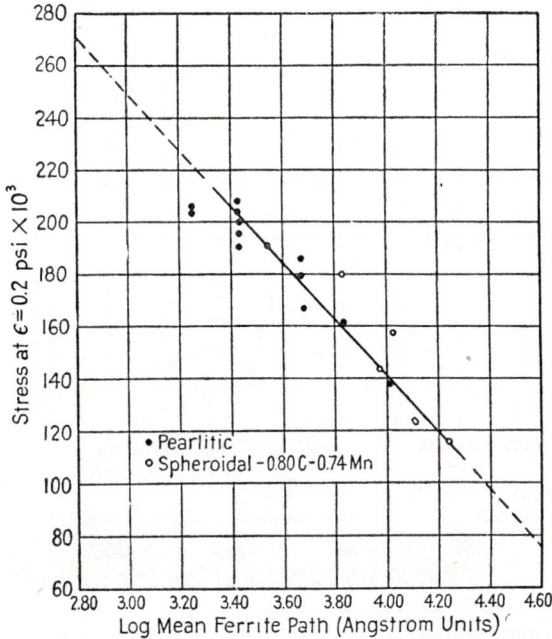

FIG. 70. Variation of the true stress for a true strain (ϵ) of 0.2 with the logarithm of the mean ferrite path for a plain carbon eutectoid steel in both the pearlitic and spheroidal conditions.   (*Gensamer et al.*[93])

equivalent.   The success of this technique in calculating the strength of alloys containing more than one alloying element is apparent in Fig. 72.

Hollomon *et al.*[95, 59, 96] have also considered the influence of microstructure on the strength of ferrous alloys.   These investigations have confirmed the relation shown by Gensamer in Fig. 71, namely, that the strain-hardening exponent n is substantially unaffected by differences in microstructures for any strength level, but that it decreases with increasing strength level.

The various investigations relating to the influence of alloying on the strength of metals which have been reviewed here have been conducted at atmospheric temperature. There is, however, no reason to believe that the fundamental behaviors would change with temperature except in so far as temperature exerts an influence on the stability of the microstructure and on recovery or recrystallization. These are important exceptions, however, and separate sections (see Chap. XI) will be devoted to the changes in microstructure which may occur at elevated temperatures.

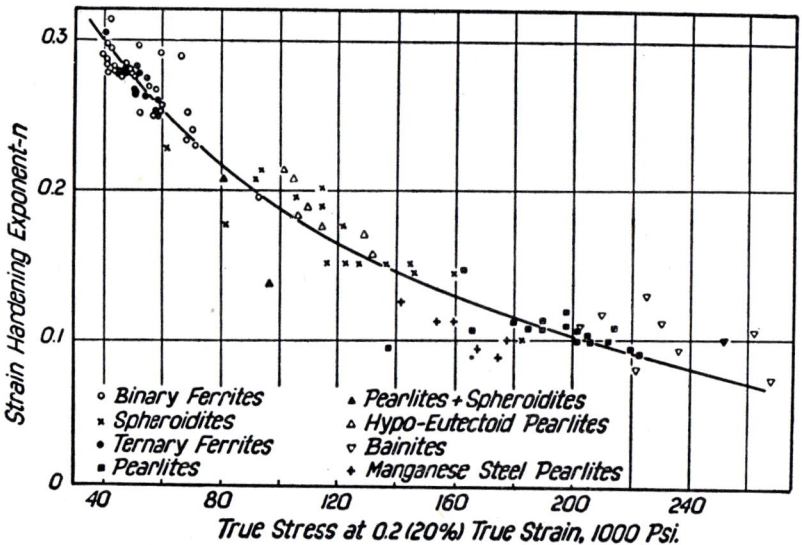

Fig. 71. Variation of the strain-hardening exponent with true stress for a true strain of 0.2 for a wide variety of steels in various microstructures. (*Gensamer.*[94])

Also, because of the importance of this subject in relation to this book, the various investigations which have been made to determine the influence of alloying on creep strength are treated in a separate section (Chap. VIII). These investigations have generally been of less fundamental character than those just described.

The Influence of Rate of Deformation and Temperature

The rate of deformation and the test temperature are two somewhat related variables which are of considerable importance in the use of metals under creep conditions. In fact, the creep strength is generally expressed in terms of the stress corresponding to a specific rate of defor-

mation at constant temperture. The variation of the rate of deformation with stress increases greatly (in a roughly exponential manner)
with increasing temperature. Thus creep testing generally involves the
study of the interrelation of stress, strain rate (and of time for rupture),
and temperature.

At moderate temperatures—atmospheric for metals used for structural purposes—the effects of speed and temperature are not of great
magnitude. The effects of speed and temperature are in general of
opposite sign, increasing speed or decreasing temperature increasing the
flow stress.

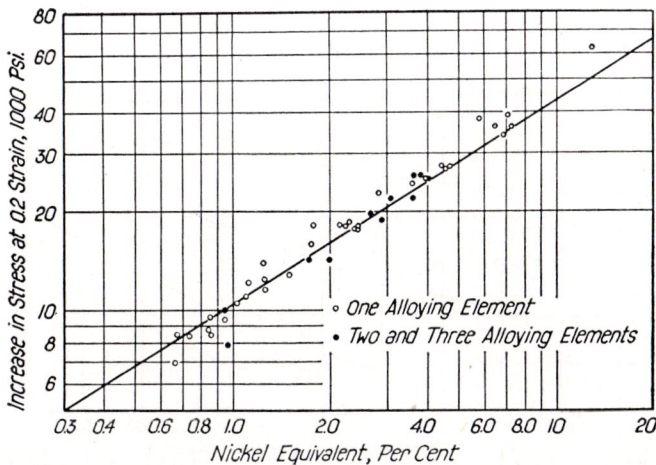

Fig. 72. Increase of flow strength with alloying addition expressed in terms of a nickel
equivalent, as described in text. (*Gensamer*.[94])

In this section we shall consider the influence of strain rate and temperature under what might be termed short-time conditions, reserving
detailed consideration of creep behavior for a subsequent section. An
additional difference in this somewhat arbitrary separation is that long-
time or creep behavior is generally studied under constant load, while
the short-time tests generally involve continuously increasing load. The
arbitrary nature of this distinction should be emphasized for as we shall
see later, short-time and long-time tests as well as continuous loading
and constant-load tests may be related with one another. Constant-
load testing for creep is, of course, a natural consequence of the manner
in which metals are used in service.

Many investigators have studied the influence of the rate of straining on the strength of metals in short-time tests. Outstanding among

the early investigators was Ludwik,[52] who considered various functional relations between strength and strain rate and concluded that the relation which best fitted the data was one in which the flow stress varies linearly with the logarithm of the strain rate. Such a relation has since been employed by Nadai *et al.*[97, 98] and by Miller *et al.*[101] as well as by others although, as illustrated in Fig. 73, the resulting curve is not always linear over a wide range of rates. In this case the variation of the tensile strength of aluminum was determined at several temperatures over a very wide range of rates. It is to be noted that at the slower strain rates the rate of change of strength is not very great, par-

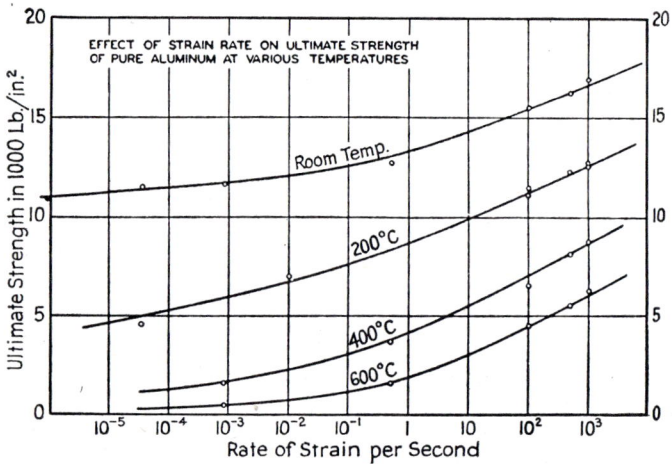

Fig. 73. Variation of ultimate tensile strength of pure aluminum with strain rate at several temperatures. (*Nadai and Manjoine.*[98])

ticularly at room temperature, but that the rate of change accelerates at faster strain rates.

Gensamer[99] has successfully employed a power function (which plots linearly on a log-log plot) to represent the relation between the maximum force developed in extrusion and the resulting extrusion rate for tin alloys (Fig. 74); but this relation had earlier been widely used for creep data, as we shall see when we consider the problem of creep. Hollomon[100] has examined the available data on the effect of strain rate on strength and concluded that the power function represents as well as any the functional relation between the two quantities. Hollomon replotted on log-log coordinates (Fig. 75) the data of Nadai and Manjoine shown in Fig. 73 and found the power relation to represent the data quite well.

Mathematically, the power relation may be expressed as follows:

$$\dot{\delta} = a\sigma^b \tag{17}$$

where σ is the flow stress, $\dot{\delta}$ the strain rate, and a and b material constants. As we shall see later a similar relation is widely used to represent the results of creep tests. Hollomon has concluded that the strain-rate exponent, b of Eq. (17), decreases with increasing strain or decreasing temperature.

As Hollomon points out, Eq. (17) is valid only at constant temperature and strain. The latter variable is generally not considered, as, for

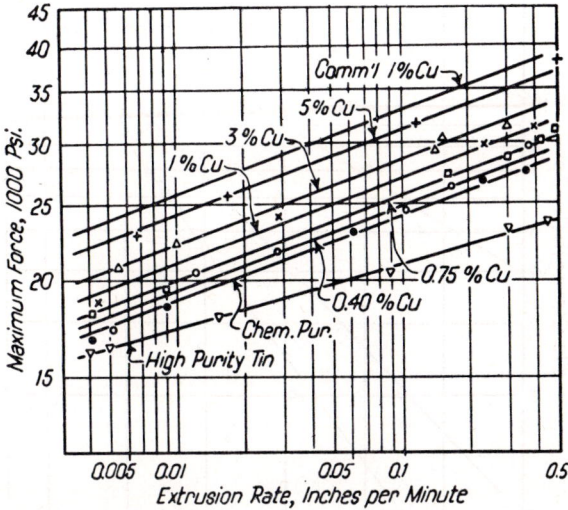

Fig. 74. Variation of the logarithm of the maximum force developed during extrusion with the logarithm of the extrusion rate for various tin alloys. (*Data of Stewart reported by Gensamer.*[99])

example, in the tests summarized in Fig. 73 relating to the tensile strength; in this case, however, it is to be expected that the strain at the tensile strength will not vary greatly with the strain rate, particularly at atmospheric temperature.

Complete nominal stress-strain curves obtained at several controlled strain rates (constant speed of crosshead movement) by Miller, Smith, and Kehl[101] are reproduced in Fig. 76 to show for one material, in two conditions of heat-treatment, the effect of increased strain rate in raising the level of the entire stress-strain curve. The plain 0.15 per cent carbon–0.50 per cent molybdenum type of steel tested has been widely used at moderately elevated temperature for creep service. The slowest strain rates employed in these tests, as well as those in Figs. 73 and 75, bridge the gap between conventional short-time tests and relatively fast creep tests.

Several of the foregoing illustrations, particularly Figs. 73 or 75, have also shown the effect of temperature on the strength of metals. Although with increasing temperature the height of the flow curve as well as the magnitude of the strain-hardening exponent generally decrease, this is not always true, one of the most outstanding exceptions being that of mild steel. As illustrated in Fig. 77, mild steel may actually

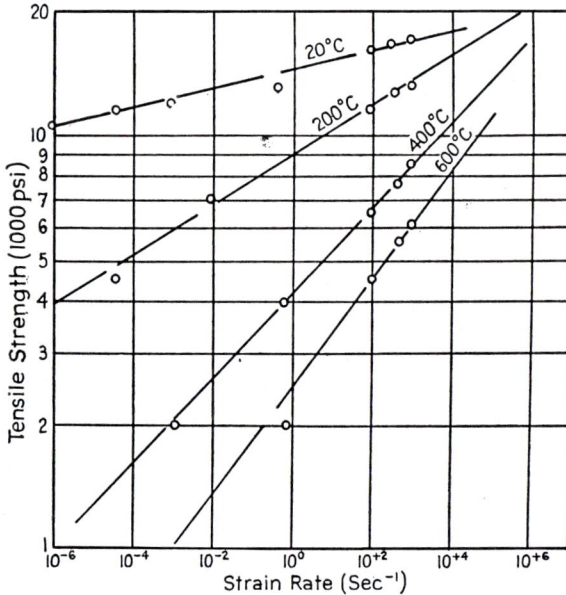

FIG. 75. Variation of the logarithm of the tensile strength of pure aluminum with logarithm of the strain rate at several temperatures. (*Data of Nadai and Manjoine*, plotted to semilogarithmic coordinates in Fig. 73; *Hollomon*.[100])

show an increase in tensile strength with increasing temperature up to some 400 to 500°F* as a result of strain aging occurring during test. As discussed more fully in the section on microstructural changes (Chap. XI), strain aging is an embrittlement phenomenon characteristic of low-carbon steel, not thoroughly deoxidized, although it may also occur in nonferrous metals. Since plastic strain is required for the aging, the yield-strength curve in Fig. 77 does not reveal its occur-

---

* Frequently termed the "blue brittle" range because of the blue temper film (oxide) which develops on heating in this range.

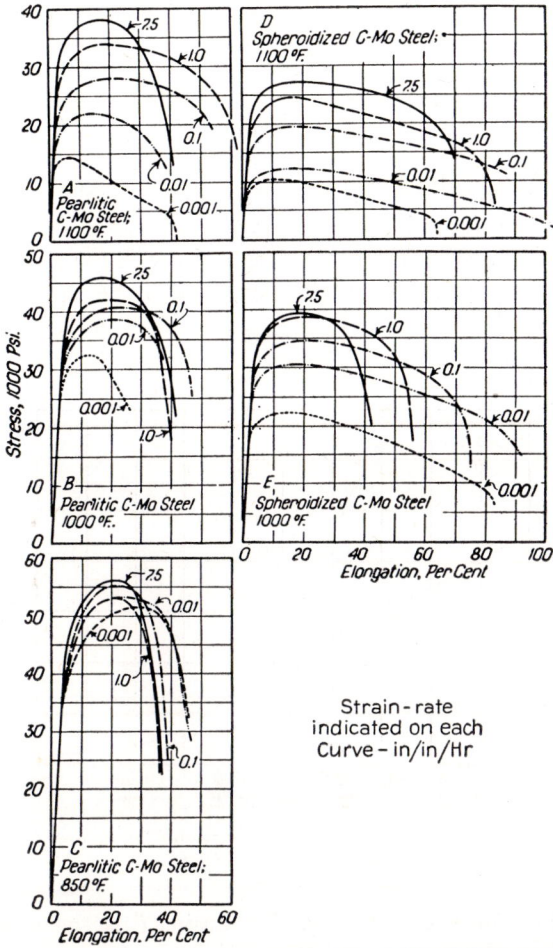

Fig. 76. Stress-strain curves for controlled strain rate tensile tests of pearlitic and spheroidized carbon-molybdenum steel at 850, 1000, and 1100°F. (*Miller, Smith, and Kehl.*[101])

rence. The temperature of maximum strain-aging embrittlement is shifted to a higher level as the rate of straining is increased, and may be in the range of 1000 to 1100°F for very fast rates, such as in impact loading.

The more generally observed relation between strength and temperature, indicated by the yield-strength curve in Fig. 77, may be illustrated by Fig. 78, after Nadai and Manjoine,[98] for pure copper and pure aluminum tested at several strain rates.   On the cartesian coordinates employed, the decrease in strength with increasing temperature is at first linear, but the slope of the curve decreases, except at the highest strain rate employed for copper, as the melting point is approached. The discontinuous change indicated to occur at the melting point is of interest.

No mathematical expression has been found which relates flow strength and temperature for widely varying temperature, although an exponential relation seems to fit the data quite well for a limited range. Hollomon[100] has suggested the following form of the equation:

$$\sigma_\delta = Ke^{Q/RT} \tag{18}$$

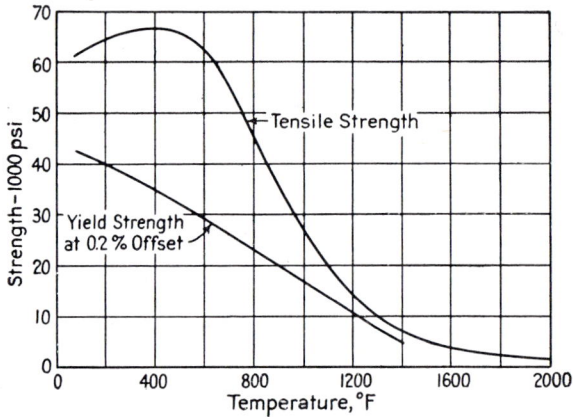

FIG. 77. Variation of yield and tensile strength of 0.10 to 0.20 per cent carbon steel with temperature.   Average of data reported in the literature.

where σ_δ is the flow stress for a specific strain, T is the absolute temperature, R the gas constant, and K and Q material constants, the latter of which may depend on the strain.   Data for several pearlitic steels at subatmospheric temperatures were observed to conform quite well to this relation, while for aluminum in the temperature range from subatmospheric to near the melting point two straight lines are obtained when the logarithm of the flow stress is plotted against the reciprocal of the absolute temperature (Fig. 79).   The significance of this change in slope is not apparent, but it may possibly be associated with a change in the fundamental mechanism of deformation.

The study of the influence of temperature on the strength of metals is complicated by the occurrence of "structural instability," that is, of changes in the microstructure. Such changes, while largely absent at low temperatures, are very prevalent at high temperatures. Structural instability is not absent in pure metals, for these may undergo recrystallization, while in multiphase alloys additional changes may include precipitation (as we have already seen in the strain aging of mild steel) and other phase changes, such as the inversion of carbide to

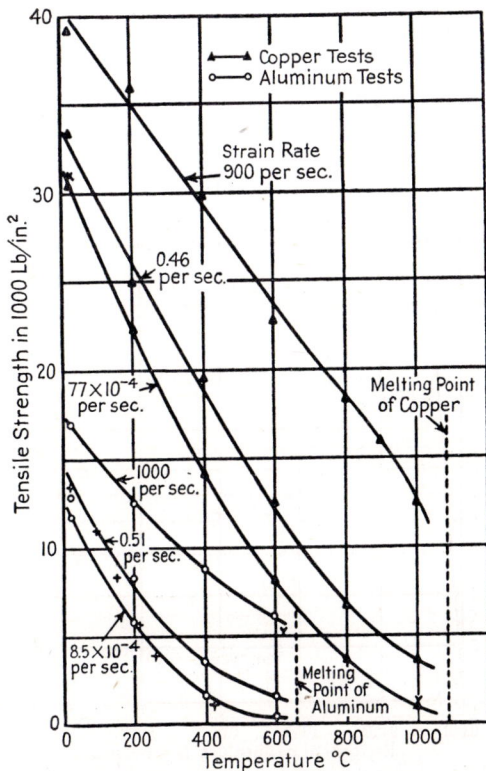

Fig. 78. Variation of tensile strength of pure copper and pure aluminum with temperature at several strain rates. (*Nadai and Manjoine.*[98])

graphite, as well as changes in the size and distribution of the microconstituents (spheroidization of carbide). These changes are treated in another portion of this book (see Chap. XI), and we shall see that they play a very important role in the use of metals at elevated temperatures.

The qualitatively similar effects of increasing strain rate and decreasing temperature on the flow strength suggested to Zener and Hollomon[102] that it might be possible to develop a single-valued quantitative rela-

tion between the two variables. Such a relation would have great
value, for with this relation it would be possible to explore by means of
one variable into a realm of variation of the other variable which could
not be directly explored owing to insuperable experimental difficulties.
Thus the effect of extremely high velocity of deformation might be

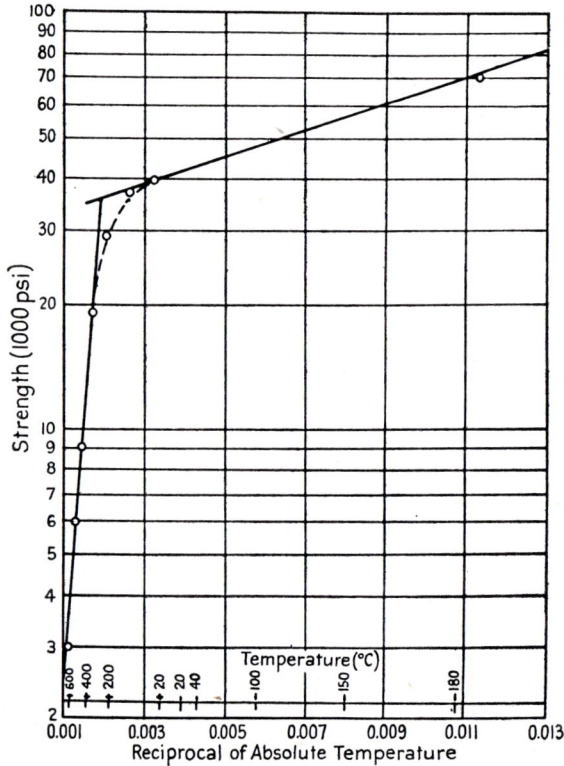

Fɪɢ. 79. Variation of the logarithm of the strength (at 20 per cent elongation) of aluminum with the reciprocal of the absolute temperature (strength in terms of original area). (*Hollomon.*[100])

gleaned from studies at very low temperatures. Zener and Hollomon
were successful in developing a relation which held true for copper
below some 750°F and a range of variation of strain rate of 10^6, as illustrated in Fig. 80 using data of Nadai and Manjoine.[98] The parameter p
whose logarithm plots linearly in Fig. 80 as a function of the stress—
in this case the true stress at the maximum load—was proposed, on the
basis of theoretical arguments, to have the form:

$$p = \frac{\dot{\delta}}{f_0} e^{Q/RT} \qquad (18a)$$

where $\dot{\delta}$ is the strain rate, Q an activation energy, R the gas constant, T the absolute temperature, and f_0 a constant. This parameter enters into the expression relating stress (σ) and strain (δ) as follows:

$$\sigma = f(\delta, p) \qquad (18b)$$

or in other words the flow stress is a function of the strain and the parameter p.

Summary

The plastic flow of polycrystalline metals is more complex than that of single crystals owing largely to the restraints imposed upon the in-

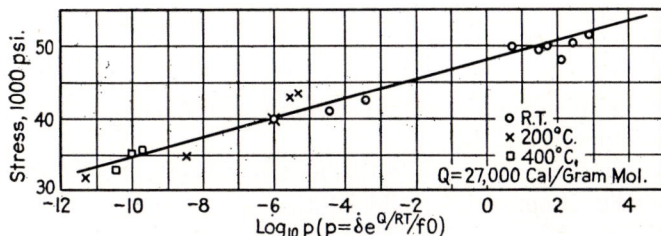

Fig. 80. Illustrating the equivalence of increasing strain rate and decreasing temperature, as discussed in the text, in increasing the tensile strength of copper. (*Zener and Hollomon.*[102])

dividual grains by their surrounding neighbors. According to modern viewpoint, the grain boundary is considered to be simply a region of transition, perhaps 5-atom distances thick, from the lattice of one grain to that of the other, and not to contain the amorphous cement proposed many years ago. Whatever their exact nature, grain boundaries behave in a viscous manner, as revealed by different types of experiments. At relatively low temperatures, fine-grained metal is stronger than coarse-grained, while at relative high temperatures the reverse is true. This transition was formerly thought to occur at a specific temperature, the equicohesive temperature, but now is more properly considered to occur within a range of temperatures, influenced by the rate of straining.

The simple maximum shear-stress criterion of plastic flow observed to apply for single crystals does not hold for polycrystalline metals. The proper criterion in this case is the so-called shear-strain energy, or equivalently, the octahedral shear stress.

The flow of polycrystalline metals is best considered in terms of the true-stress–true-strain curve (the flow curve), in which the variables are defined in terms of the instantaneous dimensions of the test specimen. True stress is related to true strain, for many instances, by an empirically observed power function. Invariant functions defined in terms of the three principal stresses and strains have been devised for defining the flow of metals under multiaxial states of stress, and these are valuable for predicting the behavior of a metal under any state of stress from its behavior under one state of stress, such as simple tension.

The individual grains of an aggregate change in orientation with plastic deformation, tending to a limiting number of orientations and giving rise thus to preferred orientation. A theory developed by Taylor predicts qualitatively the change in orientation of many but not all the grains.

As a result of the Bauschinger effect, the flow stress of a metal may be lowered by a prior plastic straining in the reverse direction. This and the somewhat similar elastic aftereffect, related to a time-dependent recovery of strain on unloading a plastically deformed metal, are considered to result from the heterogeneous state of stress which develops on straining polycrystals.

The effect of an alloying addition on the strength of a metal depends upon whether it enters into solid solution or results in the formation of a new phase. The unit strengthening effect of a metal entering solid solution varies inversely with its solid solubility and directly with the difference in size of solvent and solute atoms or the change in lattice parameter. In heterogenous alloys, the strengthening depends upon the quantity and more importantly on the distribution of the new phase; in steels, the flow strength appears to vary inversely with the average distance between the carbide particles or plates.

The flow stress of a metal increases with increasing rate of straining and with decreasing temperature. At ambient temperature, the magnitudes of the effects are not great; they become more important with increasing temperature.

CHAPTER IV

CREEP OF POLYCRYSTALLINE METALS

In the preceding chapters, we have, in effect, laid the foundation for a consideration of the creep flow of metals at elevated temperatures. As pointed out in Chap. I, the problem of creep is encountered as a continuous, generally slow, deformation occurring at relatively high temperatures under essentially constant stress, even when this stress does not exceed the yield strength or proportional limit as determined by the usual short-time tensile test. When creep was first encountered, efforts were exerted to determine "creep limits," which for any material would be the stress (at the temperature of interest) below which no creep would occur. With greater and greater refinement of the extension-measuring devices and slower and slower rates of deformation, this limit was found to lie at lower and lower stress. And at least for the more elevated temperatures, this limit was, in effect, never found, for although the laboratory test revealed a limit, long-time service under a constant load would generally show creep; this simply meant that the measuring apparatus and rates of deformation were not sufficiently sensitive or slow to detect creep.

When it became clear that a real limit below which creep is absent either does not exist or is at such a low level as to be economically impractical for design, the modern philosophy of design for creep service came into existence. With this philosophy of design, the occurrence of creep during service was recognized, and applied stresses were chosen to result in no more than certain specific limiting deformations during the contemplated life of the vessels. These limiting deformations differed from one application to another. Thus in a steam-turbine power-generating station designed to last for 20 years, the permissible distortion of the turbine blades might be limited to a total deformation of 1 per cent (beyond which they would rub against the housing) while the steam pipe might tolerate a deformation of 5 per cent.

In order for the engineer to design so that no more than certain specific deformations might occur, it became necessary to know the relations among stress, strain, time, and temperature. Thus creep testing came into existence. Because, in many cases, metals at elevated temperatures are used under essentially constant stress, these tests have almost universally consisted of measuring the creep as a function of the time under constant load and temperature. A contributing factor in this method of testing is, of course, the experimental difficulties of continuous loading tests at very slow rates. Because of this, most creep data are in regard to constant-load conditions. We shall find however, that such data may be related to continuous loading tests, at least qualitatively. It should be noted that at large deformations, constant load is not synonymous with constant stress, owing to the change in cross-sectional area.

Although we shall consider the subject in more detail in Chap. XII on Design, it should be made clear at the outset of our consideration of the creep of metals that the most important practical aspect of the commercial use of metals under creep conditions is concerned with the extrapolation of data obtained in short-time laboratory tests to the long times of interest in practice. Thus, it is impossible for obvious reasons to run an acceptance test lasting 20 years before placing a vessel into operation. A preoccupation with extrapolation will color a great deal of our treatment of creep.

It should also be pointed out at this time that in addition to requiring information about the dependence of creep on time, it is necessary to have another type of information which is unrelated, except in a very general way, to the rate and total amount of deformation, namely, that relating to fracture. This is needed, because in a design based on extrapolation to long time, the metal may rupture before attaining the contemplated strain. Thus, the relation between time for rupture and stress is required, and in design a compromise is effected if necessary between the two limits, deformation and rupture. The subject of rupture is treated in a later section.

The Creep Curve at Constant Load

The creep curve at constant load and constant temperature as obtained in the conventional creep test is shown schematically, with linear coordinates, in Fig. 81 for several different loads (or alternatively different temperatures). In general the creep curve may be considered to be comprised of four stages or periods as perhaps first pointed out by Tapsell.[104] These may be described in reference to Fig. 81, as follows:

1. The strain occurring immediately, or almost so, on application of the load (OA). This strain is comprised partly of an elastic strain and partly of a plastic strain.*

---

* These may be differentiated by an independent determination of the elastic modulus which permits computation of the elastic strain, or alternatively by an unloading experiment since the elastic strain is immediately recoverable.

2. A period which is characterized by decreasing creep rate (*AB*).
3. A period of substantially uniform creep rate which is also the minimum occurring during test (*BC*).
4. A period of increasing creep rate and ending in rupture (*CD*).

By considering only extension which occurs after the initial elastic extension, as many have done especially in this country, the creep curve may be considered as made up of three stages. This has some advantages, since strictly speaking all the plastic extension is time dependent.

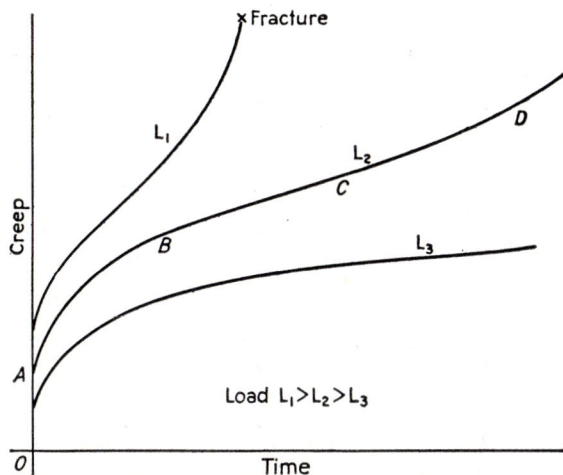

Fig. 81. Schematic representation of creep curves under different loads at constant temperature; cartesian coordinates. In reference to curve L_2, OA represents the elastic and plastic deformation on application of load; AB represents the period of decreasing rate; BC the period of substantially constant creep rate; and CD the period of accelerating creep rate which would end in fracture if the test were continued.

With this classification the terms primary and secondary creep are frequently employed to denote, respectively, creep occurring prior to the constant-rate stage, that is, prior to point *B* in Fig. 81, and that occurring in the constant-rate stage, *BC*.

All creep curves have this same general character (test L3 in Fig. 81 was discontinued prior to the beginning of stage 4), though certain portions may be accentuated or minimized or absent under some circumstances. Important among these are extremes of temperature or load and structural instability. Thus at a relatively low stress and temperature, creep may cease, for practical purposes, although it may be argued theoretically that this is only apparent, owing to insufficient sensitivity of measurement. At a relatively high temperature and stress, on the other hand, creep tests may show no period of decreasing creep rate, but rather may exhibit an accelerating rate from the outset.

The effect of structural instability, which includes phase transformation phenomena, recrystallization, and grain growth, on the creep curve is of far-reaching importance, and we shall devote a separate section (Chap. XI) to a consideration of the nature of these changes. However, in view of the influence of these changes on the character of the creep curve and therefore of the possibility of misinterpretation, we shall

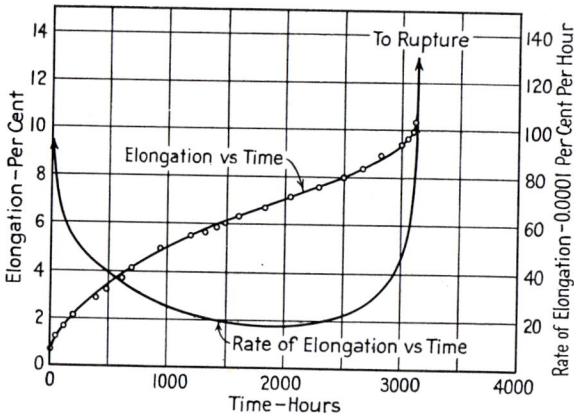

Fig. 82a. Dependence of creep and rate of creep on time; 18Cr–8Ni–Ti steel (AISI Type 321); 1500°F; 2,800 psi. (*U.S. Steel Corp. data.*)

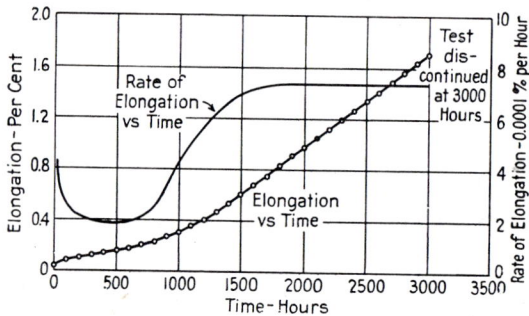

Fig. 82b. Abnormal dependence of creep and rate of creep on time. 18Cr–8Ni steel (AISI Type 304); 1300°F; 6,000 psi. (*U.S. Steel Corp. data.*)

illustrate here what may be observed. In an extreme case, negative creep, that is, contraction rather than elongation under tensile stress, may be observed. Thus McVetty[105] has reported an instance in which a test showed negative creep over a period of 2,500 hr. Such an effect is, of course, readily recognized. Far more difficult to recognize is the abnormal behavior shown in Fig. 82b. Such behavior is generally more readily detected by plotting the rate of creep as well as the creep against time, as shown, for without structural changes the rate should decrease to a minimum and then continuously accelerate until fracture occurs. This obviously did not occur in the test shown, and the inference to be drawn is that structural change occurred. In this case it is thought that carbide precipitation or the formation of sigma, or both, is the offending structural change. The behavior of the test depicted in Fig 82*b* contrasts with the normal behavior apparent in Fig. 82*a*, in which the rate of creep decreases to a minimum and then increases continuously to rupture.

Recrystallization may occur during creep test upon attaining the requisite critical deformation corresponding to the temperature, according to Greenwood and Orr,[106] and is evidenced by an increased rate of creep during this period. However, as Karnop and Sachs[108] have shown, the critical degree of strain required for recrystallization increases greatly with increasing temperature of plastic deformation. Thus this critical value should not be assumed to be identical with that determined for material deformed at atmospheric temperature. If a metal is plastically deformed and then tested in creep at a temperature at which it will recrystallize, the rate of creep is much greater than for an annealed material.[109]

It is possible, and in fact it is the rule rather than the exception, for structural changes to occur during test and not be evident in the creep-time curve, for very few metals are entirely free from these changes. Thus the spheroidization of carbide which occurs in all carbon steels during sojourn at elevated temperatures does not exert a recognizable effect on the creep curve.

Whether or not the structural changes are evident in the creep curve, they exert an influence on and complicate attempts at understanding the strength characteristics at elevated temperatures (a difficulty not generally encountered at ordinary temperatures), and it is therefore vital that creep testing be supplemented by either knowledge of or microstructural examination for changes. Figure 82*b* also illustrates a danger inherent in the extrapolation to long service on the basis of short-time tests. Thus, extrapolation, as we shall see later, is often effected on the basis of a plot of stress against the minimum or constant creep rate and the usual creep test is continued until the minimum creep rate is established. However, continued loading of the sample in Fig. 82*b* has suggested that the minimum rate reached early in the test is merely the result of structural change. There is no certain way of guarding against such errors, except to test materials whose structural changes and their effects are not well known for as long a time as possible, but not less than perhaps several thousand hours.

The characteristic form of the creep-time plot (Fig. 81), showing first a decreasing, then a constant, and finally an increasing rate, has generally been ascribed to the interplay of two opposing forces, a strengthening resulting from strain hardening and a weakening resulting from the influence of temperature in effecting recovery or recrystallization.[112] In the initial stage of decreasing creep rate, the effect of strain hardening is held to outweigh the softening, while during the constant-rate period (sometimes called the steady-state period) the opposing forces balance one another. Similarly, the final period of accelerating creep rate is held to result from a predominance of softening. Although this conception is superficially adequate, it is really not at all an explanation of the form of the creep curve, but is merely descriptive, making use of two generally ill-understood properties in a very qualitative way. No experimental evidence has been adduced in support of the concept. Tapsell[104] has pointed out that if temperature softening mitigates strain hardening during creep, then greater ductility should be expected in creep than in short-time tests, contrary to actuality. Similarly, softening can hardly predominate during the last stage of creep, when hardness tests reveal considerable strengthening, at least under some conditions.

It seems more likely that the characteristic form of the creep curve is merely a result of the normal stress-strain relation existing at the test temperature. In this connection, it should be borne in mind that the stress does not remain constant during a creep test such as that depicted in Fig. 81, and in fact changes quite appreciably for large deformations. The stress-strain relation of a metal may be, and under some circumstances certainly is, influenced by recovery and recrystallization, but the characteristic form of the creep curve can be explained qualitatively, as Zener and Hollomon[107, 110] have done, in the absence of such an effect. Zener and Hollomon revived an early concept of Ludwik[52] concerning the existence of a mechanical equation of state, which proposes that the flow stress depends only on the instantaneous values of strain, strain rate, and temperature　We shall examine this concept in greater detail in a subsequent section and find that it does not hold under all conditions, but it is of interest here in showing how the form of the creep curve may be derived qualitatively from the stress-strain relation, without the benefit of the influence of recovery and recrystallization (unless these are required for explaining the stress-strain curve). This qualitative derivation does not require that the mechanical equation of state concept be strictly valid.

Figure 83, after Hollomon,[107] illustrates schematically how the creep curve may be derived from nominal stress-strain (load-elongation) curves at different rates at constant temperature. Figure 83a shows these load elongation plots at different rates of strain, $\dot{\epsilon}_1$, $\dot{\epsilon}_2$, etc. Superimposed on these plots are horizontal lines L_1, L_2, etc., representing constant loads such as might be employed in ordinary creep tests. Each of these intersects each of the family of load-elongation curves at two points, and these intersections give two elongations under constant load for the specific strain rate. Then if the elongations are plotted against the corresponding strain rates, plots of the type shown in Fig. 83b are

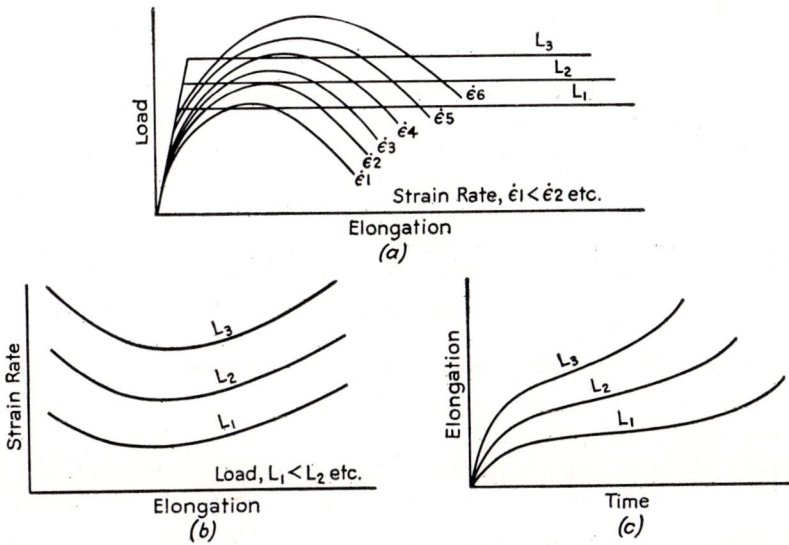

FIG. 83. Showing the derivation of creep behavior from tensile test data. (*Hollomon.*[107])

obtained from which in turn those in Fig. 83c may be derived by simple integration.*

Several inferences may be made from the schematic creep curves of Fig. 81. Thus the lower the stress (and also the lower the temperature, though not shown in Fig. 81), the longer the time before the minimum creep rate is attained, and the longer the period over which this rate remains substantially constant. Arguments as to whether there is any period of constant creep rate or only a point of inflection are largely academic; for practical purposes the rate may, in some cases at least, remain constant over an extended interval, as shown in Fig. 84.

* The derivation of Fig. 83b from Fig. 83c may be more readily apparent to some.

These 100,000-hr creep tests represent the longest on record and are therefore also of considerable interest in relation to extrapolation of short-time test results.   Tests by Cross and Lowther[115] lasting 20,000 hr have also shown a long interval of substantially constant creep rate.

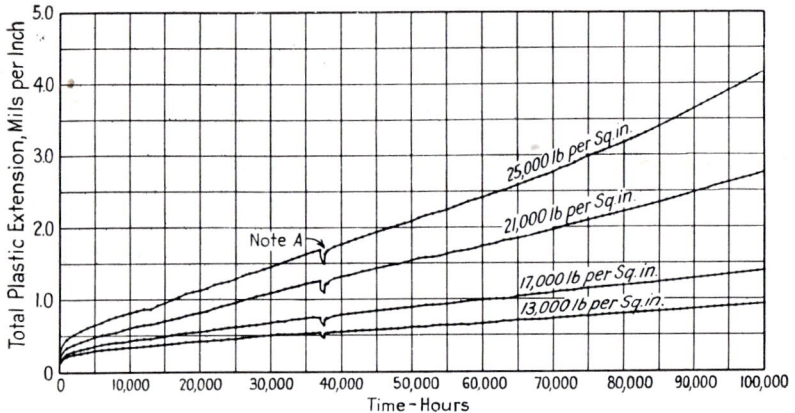

Fig. 84. Creep curves of 100,000 hr duration at 842°F.   Nickel-chromium-molybdenum steel (SAE 4330).   (*Robinson.*[111])   (Note *A*: After 37,000 hr, the loads were dropped to 1,000 psi for a period of 570 hr after which the furnace was shut down, moved to a different building, and started once more.   These curves show plastic recovery only.)

The Period of Decreasing Creep Rate (Primary Creep)

The period of decreasing creep rate has been attributed by Bailey and Roberts[113] to an initially uneven stress distribution, which tends to a uniform distribution with increasing deformation.   This view has been accepted by Gillett.[114]   Certainly, there can be no doubt that owing to the elastic anisotropy of metal crystals, and the constraints exercised by neighboring grains on one another, the stress is initially quite inhomogeneous and becomes less so with increasing plastic deformation. Furthermore, this readjustment is certainly associated with the decreasing creep rate which is characteristic of primary creep.   However, this association of phenomena implies an identity of the attainment of uniform stress distribution with the attainment of the minimum creep rate, an identity for which there is no evidence.   Since the most important cause of nonuniform stress distribution is the anisotropy and constraint of the grains, presumably primary creep should be nonexistent or greatly minimized in single crystals.   As described in the section on creep of single crystals, this does not appear to be true, although there are certain differences in characteristics, single crystals frequently showing an initial period of accelerating rate followed by a period of decreasing

rate. Too, although primary creep of polycrystalline metal is partly
or wholly recoverable as discussed below, single crystals do not show
this effect.

The primary creep of polycrystalline metals is partly or wholly recovered on removal of the load at the temperature of test (but not always
at lower temperature after cooling under load). We have already noted
this phenomenon in our discussion of Chalmers' study of microcreep in
tin.[19, 20] Other studies of creep recovery have been made by Tapsell
and Prosser,[116] Chevenard,[117] Bailey,[118] Johnson,[119] and Kê.[123] The nature of the effect may be illustrated by Fig. 85 which shows the recovery

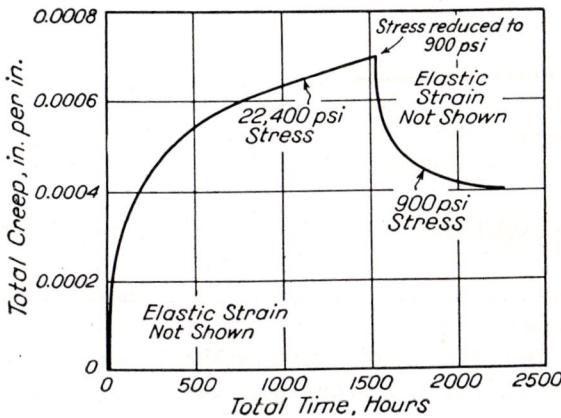

FIG. 85. Creep recovery for nickel-chromium-molybdenum steel at 840°F. (*Data of
Tapsell and Prosser*[116] *reported by Kanter.*[120])

in a nickel-chromium-molybdenum steel when the stress is reduced
after an initial period of creep at higher stress. The decelerating rate of
recovery is characteristic. Johnson[119] has shown an influence of the
stress level on the extent of recovery of primary creep; in his tests most
of the primary creep was recovered, but this was particularly true at low
stress levels.

The Minimum Creep Rate (Secondary Creep)

As we have already indicated, the concept of the minimum or constant
creep rate as the resultant of opposing forces of strain hardening and
annealing is hardly adequate to explain the period of constant creep
rate. In the same category is a suggestion by Clark and White[121] that
the period of minimum creep rate is characterized by continuous recrystallization. While this may occur in some instances, it seems unlikely

that it is a general behavior, for microstructural examination by the author of samples tested in creep to the period of minimum creep rate has generally failed to reveal any evidence of recrystallization.

Tapsell[104] has suggested that there is no really constant period of creep corresponding to the minimum rate, but only an inflection point. This suggestion is attractive, for it does away with the need for an explanation of the so-called second stage of creep, for this stage is then nonexistent. Constant creep rate over a considerable interval, as in Fig. 84, would, according to this view, be only apparent, not real. This view does not conflict with that expressed earlier in relation to Fig. 83, namely, that the shape of the creep-time plot is a resultant simply of the stress-strain–strain-rate relations, and the apparent constancy of creep rate is somewhat analogous to the flat portion at the maximum of the common load-elongation curve. In this respect, Tapsell[104] has also stated, but offered no experimental evidence, that creep is uniformly distributed along the specimen, that is, it is homogeneous until the point of inflection in the creep curve is attained, at which time local necking begins.

It is of interest to note, in passing, that if a period of constant creep rate exists, creep in this period might be considered to be of a viscous nature, since a viscous material by definition flows at a constant rate dependent upon the applied shear stress and temperature. However, the dependence of the rate of creep upon the stress and temperature, as we shall see later, is not that to be expected of a purely viscous substance.

The Accelerating Creep Rate (Tertiary Creep)

The accelerating rate of creep at the end of test is quite evidently associated with impending fracture of the specimen. The point at which fracture actually begins is a question of interest. If we accept the observation of Tapsell[104] that necking begins at the point of inflection in the creep-time plot, then fracture may be considered to commence at this point, in analogy to fracture in short-time tensile tests. However, further study is needed before this observation may be accepted as a generality. Kanter[120] has calculated the increase in creep rate which would be expected to result from the diminution of cross-sectional area accompanying creep and he has concluded that the observed increase in rate is much greater than can be accounted for by the reduction in area. This discrepancy would also appear to argue against a characterization of creep as viscous flow. A contributing factor, at least, in the discrepancy and one that makes the exact calculation and its interpretation uncertain is the stress concentration, as well as reduction in effective cross section resulting from the formation and propagation of cracks which quite commonly occur during the last stages of creep; this would be expected to result in faster creep rates than would be computed on the basis of the nominal section.

As Orowan[228] has pointed out, it is uncertain that Kanter's mathematics are generally valid. Orowan has furthermore noted an early experiment of Andrade[133] with lead in which the accelerating rate portion of the creep curve was observed to be absent when the load was reduced in proportion to the diminution in cross section, that is, when the stress, rather than the load, was maintained constant. Andrade's tests, however, were of relatively short duration—minutes rather than hours or days. It would appear that further tests with the stress maintained constant or alternatively more refined calculations are needed. Perhaps the character of the final stages of creep depends upon whether fracture is progressing transgranularly or intergranularly, as discussed later.

Since the accelerating creep rate is clearly associated with progressive failure, it is more properly considered under the general heading of fracture, which is treated later in this book (see Chap. V). It is of interest in the present consideration, however, to know when this stage of creep begins, so that precautions may be taken to avoid its occurrence during actual service. None of the several treatments of creep designed for extrapolation of short-time test data to long-time service behavior attempt to incorporate this portion of the creep-time curve.

Mathematical Expressions for the Creep-time Curve

Since the practical aim of creep testing is to acquire knowledge concerning the time dependence of creep during continued use under approximately constant stress and temperature, various attempts have been made to formulate mathematical expressions for the relations among the several variables, both as a means of analysis of data and as a means for prediction of long-time behavior. These attempts have been largely empirical in nature, except for several attempts in recent years to apply chemical reaction rate and dislocation theories to secondary creep. Although attempts at theoretical treatment are not to be disparaged, it must be pointed out that a successful theoretical treatment of secondary creep alone is, unfortunately, not all that is required for intelligent design for creep service, owing to the frequently appreciable magnitude of primary creep. Gillett[114] has written disparagingly of the mathematical attack on the creep problem, but a more moderate outlook seems justified. We shall defer our consideration of the theoretical treatments of secondary creep to a later section and instead shall commence with a consideration of the initial as well as later stages of creep.

If we consider the schematic creep-time curve, shown to cartesian coordinates in Fig. 86, it is evident by inspection that, under constant load and constant temperature, the total creep C at some time t beyond the beginning of constant-rate creep and short of the beginning of the period of accelerating creep is given by the sum of the intercept C_0 on the ordinate axis and the product of the minimum creep rate $\dot{C}_m$ and the time t. This may be expressed mathematically by the following relation:

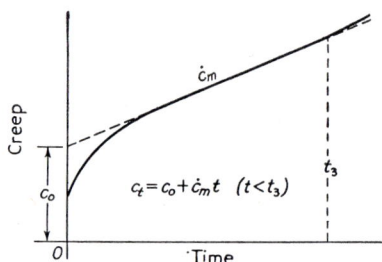

FIG. 86. Schematic creep curve showing how total creep at time t may be determined from the intercept C_0 and the minimum (or constant) creep rate $\dot{C}_m$ for times less than that at which the rate begins to accelerate.

$$C_t = C_0 + \dot{C}_m t \qquad (19)$$

This simple but important relation was probably first pointed out by McVetty[105, 122, 132] in a slightly different form.

An inspection of available creep-time plots suggested to McVetty that the constant creep rate (the minimum creep rate) is approached asymptotically. This is expressed by an exponential relation which may be written as follows:

$$\dot{C} - A = B e^{-\alpha t} \qquad (20)$$

in which $\dot{C}$ is the creep rate (the slope dC/dt of the creep curve) at time t and A, B, and α are parameters which remain constant during a test at constant stress and temperature. Integration of this differential equation yields the following expression for the total creep C:

$$C = C_0 + At - \frac{B}{\alpha} e^{-\alpha t} \qquad (21)$$

where the constant of integration C_0 represents the intercept of the creep-time curve on the strain ordinate. Since $e^{-\alpha t}$ approaches zero as t increases, the asymptote of Eq. (21) is

$$C = C_0 + At \qquad (22)$$

which is identical with Eq. (19) if we now recognize that the constant A is identical with the minimum creep rate $\dot{C}_m$.

The empirical relation, represented by Eq. (19), or its equivalent,

Eq. (22), may be used for extrapolation to times longer than those employed in the creep test. It is strictly accurate only within the range of essentially constant creep rate, which may generally be considered to last for an extended period in the ranges of stress, temperature, and deformation of practical interest, as illustrated in the data recorded in Fig. 84. Short of the beginning of essentially constant creep rate, extrapolation with Eq. (19) will yield strains which are too large, and beyond this period, the predicted strain will be too small. A prediction of larger strains than actual will result in conservative design and therefore is not of serious concern.* A prediction of too small strains, however, is quite serious, not only in itself, but because it portends fracture. Therefore it is to be emphasized that Eq. (19) should not be employed for extrapolation into the period of accelerating creep. This may be precluded by determining independently the relation between stress and the time for beginning of accelerated creep and employing this relation for extrapolation. In a subsequent section we shall consider this relation and how it may be employed together with Eq. (19) and other relations for intelligent design.

Several means of evaluating the constants of Eqs. (20) and (21) will be apparent to the reader, or have been illustrated by McVetty,[122] and will not be considered here, since we shall assume that Eq. (19) may be employed with sufficient accuracy for extrapolation. In the practical application of this latter equation for predicting behavior in the period beyond that of the laboratory creep test, it is necessary to evalute the effect of stress at constant temperature or of temperature at constant stress on the two constants C_0 and $\dot{C}_m$. Unless these relations are determined over at least some range of variation, there is danger that the extrapolation may lead to large errors, owing to factors inherent in the mathematics as well as to the occurrence of structural changes, such as those illustrated in Fig. 82.

Before proceeding to a consideration of the relation between stress and the strain intercept and between stress and minimum creep rate, it will be worth while to note briefly other methods of considering the creep-time curve.

Tapsell and Prosser[116] have observed a straight line to result from plotting creep on a linear axis and time on a logarithmic axis. This may be expressed by

$$C = a \log (1 + bt) \tag{23}$$

* It seems quite probable that most apparatus designed for long (10 to 20 years) service, will, during service, arrive in the period of constant creep rate, in which case this possibility is of academic concern.

where C is the total creep at time t and a and b are constants. Chevenard[117] has suggested the addition of a second term to Eq. (23) to express the constant-rate creep, thus separating the creep into declining rate and constant-rate portions. Thus

$$C = a \log (1 + bt) + \dot{C}_m t \tag{24}$$

where $\dot{C}_m$ is the minimum or constant creep rate.

The semilogarithmic relation does not always result in a straight line, as shown by various investigators,[129] and therefore is of limited value.

Weaver[125] has developed a relation, somewhat similar to that of McVetty, between the amount of creep and the asymptotic creep rate, but also includes terms designed to encompass the strain-hardening characteristics as well as those related to structural instability. Weaver's expression is represented by the following mathematical relation:

$$C = \dot{C}_m t + a \log t - a \log t_0 \tag{25}$$

where C is the total creep at time t and $\dot{C}_m$, a, and t_0 are material constants, of which $\dot{C}_m$ is the constant or minimum creep rate, a is a strain-hardening constant, and t_0 is a constant related to stability of microstructure; the expression $a \log t_0$ is considered to be zero for stable metals. Thus creep is conceived to be a summation of a viscous flow, represented by $\dot{C}_m t$, and a strain hardening, represented by $a \log t$, modified by a term related to structural stability.

The relation represented by Eq. (25), which will not be derived here, is based on an assumption that, with increasing time, the creep rate decreases in inverse proportion to time and approaches an asymptotic value. Weaver's effort to introduce the influence of microstructural instability is to be commended, but appears slightly overambitious for our present state of knowledge. Presumably, to evaluate the constants of Eq. (25) adequately would require quite extensive and lengthy testing. In fact, Weaver has reported that although the constant t_0 is a sensitive indicator of microstructural stability, it fails to predict the effect of spheroidization of carbide in steel. This was revealed by long-time creep tests which were analyzed to check the validity of Eq. (25) and which showed, according to Weaver, quite good agreement between formula and experiment up to 20,000 hr, but beyond this time the tested values became greater. Weaver attributed this difference to spheroidization. Why the effect of spheroidization does not become apparent before 20,000 hr is not clear, since it proceeds at a rate decreasing with the logarithm of the time, and it raises a question concerning the strict validity of the equation.

Inasmuch as the relation described in Eq. (25) as well as in previous ones is empirical, it may be argued that no advantage is to be gained, at least from the practical standpoint, in the introduction of additional terms beyond those which are essential, as in Eq. (19). From the theoretical standpoint of comprehending the underlying principles, however,

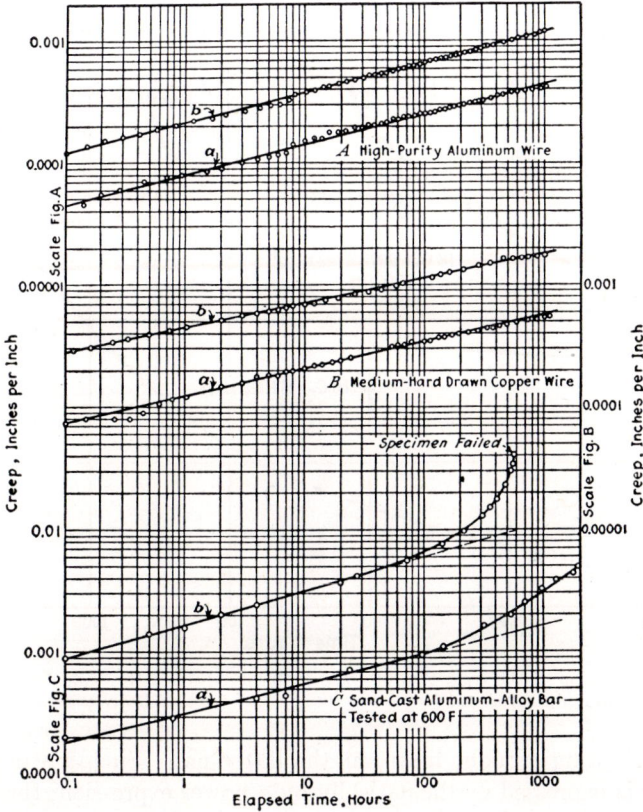

FIG. 87. Variation of the logarithm of creep with the logarithm of the time for several materials, stresses, and temperatures. *A*, high-purity aluminum tested at room temperature; (*a*) 10,000 psi; (*b*) 15,000 psi. *B*, medium-hard drawn copper wire tested at room temperature; (*a*) 25,000 psi; (*b*) 40,000 psi. *C*, sand-cast aluminum-alloy tested at 600°F; (*a*) 1,900 psi; (*b*) 3,400 psi. (*Sturm et al.*[126])

the additional terms which Weaver and others have introduced are desirable, provided that they may be properly evaluated.

Sturm, Dumont, and Howell[126] have described an empirical treatment of the creep-time curve which would appear to offer promise for extrapolation if generally valid. These investigators observed that plotting the logarithm of the creep against the logarithm of the time at constant load and temperature yielded a straight line during the initial periods of creep, although with impending failure departure from this relation was observed. Such linearity of the log-log plot had previously been observed for some but not all tests by Kanter and Spring.[128] Log-log plots of experimental data are illustrated in Figs. 87 and 88, the

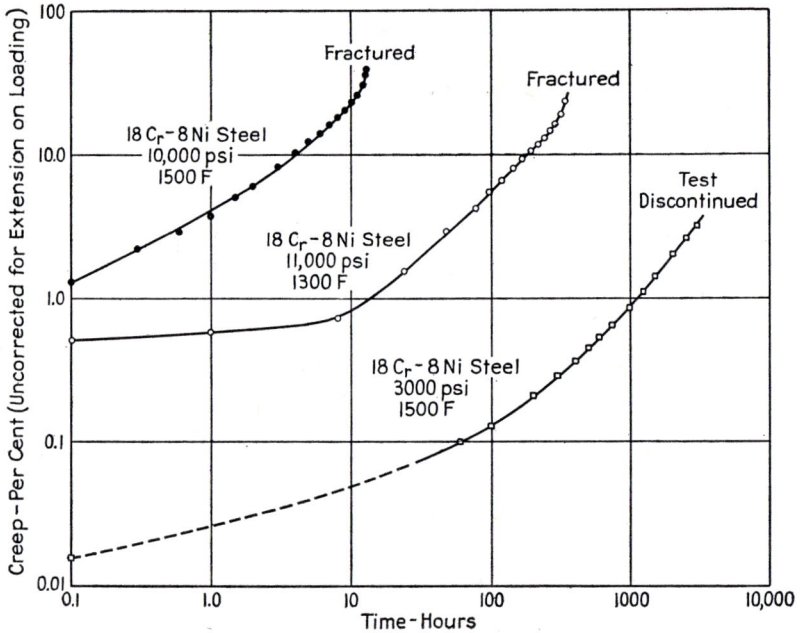

FIG. 88. Variation of the logarithm of creep with logarithm of the time for 18 Cr–8Ni steel at several temperatures and stresses. (*U.S. Steel Corp. of Del. Research Laboratory.*)

former showing straight lines but the latter not. Such a straight-line relation is expressed mathematically by a power expression; thus

$$C = C_1 t^K \qquad (26)$$

or alternatively

$$\log C - \log C_1 = K \log t \qquad (27)$$

where C is the creep at any time t and C_1 and K are material constants, of which K is the slope of the log-log plot and C_1 is the creep C at unit time. If a straight line is obtained, any departure appears to correspond with the beginning of the period of accelerating deformation on cartesian coordinates. This departure would limit the applicability of this method of analysis, just as with the McVetty analysis discussed earlier.

Sturm *et al.* corrected their creep plots, such as Fig. 87, by subtracting from the measured total deformation the so-called "initial instantaneous deformation" on loading. This quantity was determined graphically by extrapolation to the ordinate axis on cartesian coordinates or by an analytical technique, which may be derived from the relation expressed by Eqs. (26) or (27). It would seem, however, that since the instantaneous deformation as obtained by extrapolation includes, in general, both an elastic and a plastic strain, and since practical interest lies in the total plastic deformation, these should be differentiated and only the elastic strain deducted. In many cases this differential may not be important. The data shown in Fig. 88 have not been corrected for this instantaneous deformation, but such correction would not result in straight lines.

The constant K appears to be invariant over a wide range of stress at constant temperature, as revealed by the constancy of slope in the curves of Fig. 87.

In the practical application of the power relation to the prediction of long-time behavior, presuming that the data are represented by such a relation, the influence of stress on the height of the creep-time plot (Fig. 87), as measured for example by C_1, and on K, if this does not remain invariant, would be determined.

Soderberg[127] has proposed that the creep curves of the same material at different stresses are geometrically similar. According to this concept, the creep C may be expressed

$$C = ST \tag{28}$$

where S is a function only of the stress and T is a function only of the time. On the basis of data examined, Soderberg further proposes that the stress function S may be expressed as follows:

$$S = \frac{S_1}{E} \left(e^{\sigma/S_1} - 1 \right) \tag{29}$$

where σ is the applied stress, E is Young's modulus of elasticity, and S_1 is a material constant with the dimensions of stress. Soderberg does not propose an equation for the time function T, but suggests the use of a graphic form for this quantity determined from the creep-time curves and the stress function, Eq. (29). By such a technique, calculations were made for comparison with experimentally determined creep-time curves. The comparison is afforded in Fig. 89, the experimental determinations being shown by the curves and the calculations by the circles lying near the curves. The agreement is close.

Although Soderberg observed close agreement between experiment and calculation, it seems doubtful that the suggested relation, Eq. (28), has wide applicability, as will be confirmed in the later discussion of attempts to develop generalized expressions for creep. It is also of interest to note that it is implicit in Eq. (28) that the strain will be influenced by sojourn at temperature under no stress,* an effect impossible to conceive as occurring in metals. Soderberg, in a subsequent paper,[131] has proposed a differential equation involving terms representing viscosity, strain hardening, and annealing.

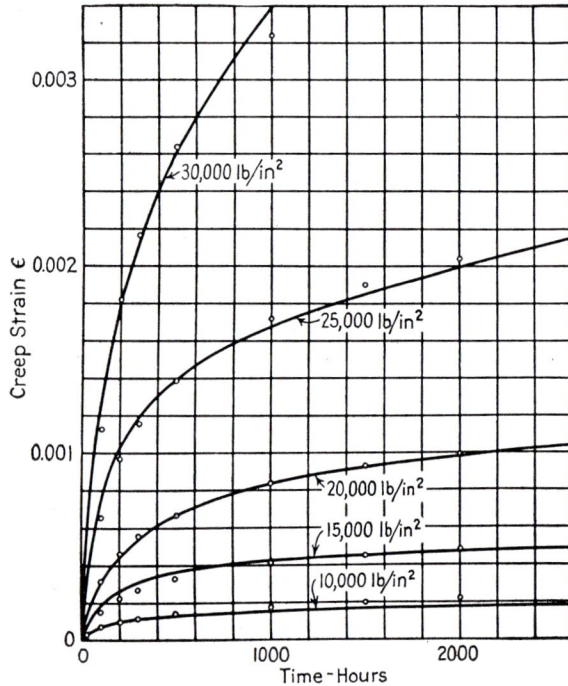

Fig. 89. Comparison of calculated (circles) and experimentally observed (solid lines) creep-time curves for 12 per cent chromium steel at 850°F. (*Soderberg.*[127])

Gentner[130] has classified creep-time curves, which do not show during the test period the inflection point corresponding to the beginning of accelerating creep rate, into three categories, depending upon whether the plot of creep against the logarithm of the time is (1) concave downward, (2) straight, or (3) convex downward. The first was termed

---

* This is additional to effects of structural change, that is, the strain will be influenced even in a pure metal showing no such changes.

parabolic, the second exponential, and the third hyperbolic in correspondence with the respective mathematical relations:

Parabolic: $C = at^m + b$ $(o < m < 1, a > o)$ (30)

Exponential: $C = a \log t + b$ $(a > o)$ (31)

Hyperbolic: $C = at^m + b$ $(m < o, a < o)$ (32)

where C is the creep at time t and a, m, and b are material constants.

Thus, Gentner considers that all creep-time curves cannot be represented by the same mathematical relation. Although this is probably correct for wide ranges of stress and temperature, and may explain why various investigators have observed different relations, it may be that one law will hold over the rather narrow range of rates of practical interest. Neither point can be answered by the data presented by Gentner to support his view inasmuch as the test times involved did not exceed 100 hr, which is far too short a time of test for adequate appraisal, at least in the range of practical interest.

Relation between Stress and Intercept of Constant Creep-rate Slope on Strain Ordinate

It will be recalled that in the McVetty analysis of the creep-time plot, a proposal was advanced that the extrapolation necessary to determine the total deformation at some time in excess of the test period, but short of the time for beginning of accelerating creep rate, could be obtained in terms of (1) the intercept on the strain ordinate of the tangent to the creep-time curve at the period corresponding to constant-rate creep and (2) the slope of this same line, that is, the creep rate. Accordingly it is desirable to explore the variation of this intercept and creep rate with stress.

McVetty[122] has reported a few data relating this intercept to stress, of which those in Fig. 90 may be considered illustrative. In this plot, the logarithm of the intercept C_0 is plotted against the stress at several temperatures for a

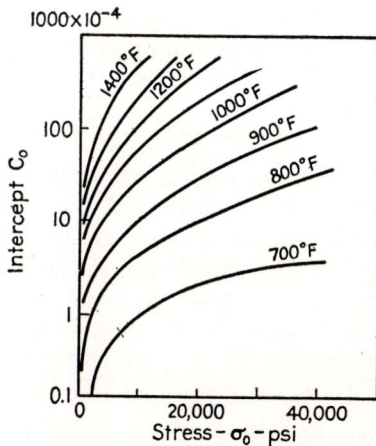

FIG. 90. Variation of logarithm of creep intercept C_0 with stress for a 12 per cent chromium steel at several temperatures. (*McVetty.*[122])

12 per cent chromium steel, such as that used for steam-turbine blades. The relation between the variables appears to be roughly exponential except at low stresses. In a subsequent paper, McVetty[132] has reported that at low stresses a hyperbolic sine relation, similar to that proposed for the relation between stress and minimum creep rate, discussed below, represents the relation between the variables. It was also reported that at relatively high temperature and stress, the intercept attains a maximum with increasing stress and then decreases. Such a variation cannot, of course, be represented by the hyperbolic sine relation.

The importance of the intercept deformation relative to the total is of decreasing importance with increasing stress, but at low stresses, such as those employed in design, this intercept deformation may represent a substantial portion of the whole; therefore its accurate determination is desirable.

Relation between Temperature and Intercept of Constant Creep-rate Slope on Strain Ordinate

McVetty[122] has also reported data showing the relation between temperature and intercept at constant stress. The plots relating these variables were quite similar in shape to those shown in Fig. 90 for the variation of intercept with stress at constant temperature.

Relation between Stress and Minimum Creep Rate

The variation of the minimum or constant creep rate with other variables has received more attention than any other single aspect of creep behavior. Many attempts have been made, both empirical and theoretical, to treat the relation of this rate to stress or/and temperature.

The influence of rate of deformation on the flow stress during short-time tension testing has already been discussed in an earlier section. It was shown there that Ludwik[52] had early proposed an exponential relation between these variables, that is, the stress on linear scale plots against the logarithm of the strain rate as a straight line; also that subsequent tests, perhaps first by Norton,[136] had shown that a power relation, in which the logarithm of the stress plots against the logarithm of the strain rate as a straight line, frequently represents the data quite well. Both of these relations have found frequent use for depicting the relation between stress and the minimum creep rate. In many cases, especially where the range of creep rates is not great, either relation may suit the data equally well, but in general the power relation has received wider acceptance.

Before examining the experimental data regarding the applicability of the two empirical relations noted in the preceding paragraph, let us consider an interpretation of the variation of creep rate with stress, which, though now generally discredited, has received considerable attention, especially in early studies of creep. This interpretation is that the constant creep rate of a material under constant load and temperature is a manifestation of viscous behavior. The similarity between the creep of metals at elevated temperatures and the flow of viscous fluids was recognized by the early investigators, of whom Andrade[133] was perhaps the first to report. Andrade's tests, however, were carried out for only short duration at relatively high stress.

A viscous material is one in which the rate of flow is proportional to the applied stress, or

$$\sigma = \theta R \tag{33}$$

where R is the rate of flow at stress σ and θ is the proportionality constant, or the viscosity. This relation is satisfied by a straight line when plotting stress against rate. Also, for a material to be truly viscous, the rate of flow should be constant as long as the stress and temperature remain constant. This is obviously not true of metals, as we have already noted, the rate first decelerating, then remaining essentially constant, and finally accelerating.* Exceptions, in which creep does appear to be of viscous nature, have been observed by Chalmers[19] for single crystals of tin at very low stresses, as noted earlier, and by Hanffstengel and Hannemann[109] and by Moore and Betty,[134] similarly at low stresses.

Although evidently inapplicable to the entire creep-time curve in the general case, many investigators have endeavored to treat the constant-rate, or steady-state, portion of the creep curves as viscous. These attempts, however, were all unsuccessful except over very limited ranges of flow rates and will not be reviewed here. The nonviscous nature of creep is evident in the experimental data shown in Fig. 91; the relation between creep rate and stress is distinctly not linear. As we shall see below, Kanter[120] has found that creep "viscosity" decreases exponentially with increasing stress, and therefore describes the flow as quasi-viscous.

The exponential (semilog) and power (log-log) empirical relations

---

* Although this description applies to constant-load creep tests, correction to constant stress would not alter the general characteristics. However, we have earlier noted that some few data have indicated that the period of accelerating creep may be absent if the stress is maintained constant.

which have been most commonly used for reporting the dependency of the minimum creep rate on the stress, as noted earlier, have been applied to several sets of data, with the results recorded in Figs. 92 and 93. These same data have been plotted linearly in Fig. 91. It is to be noted that either the exponential or power relation represents the experimental data quite well over a wide range of minimum creep rates, but that there is a definite superiority in these cases for the power func-

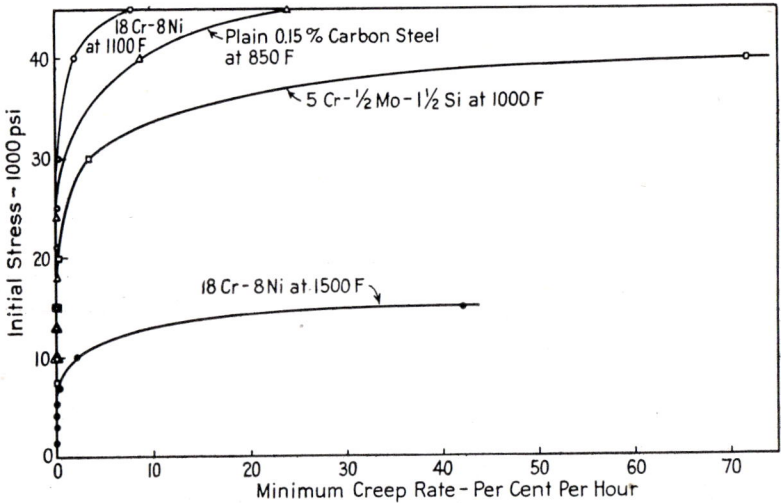

Fig. 91. Variation of minimum creep rate with stress for several materials; cartesian coordinates. Compare with other methods of plotting in Figs. 92 and 93. (*U.S. Steel Corp. data.*)

tion. In some other instances reported in the literature,[120] a superiority has been claimed for the exponential relation, but as stated earlier the power relation has received wider use.*

Mathematically the exponential and power functions may be represented by Eqs. (34) and (35), respectively. Thus

$$\sigma = \sigma_1 \log \frac{\dot{C}_m}{C_1} \tag{34}$$

where $\dot{C}_m$ is the minimum creep rate corresponding to stress σ, while σ_1 and C_1 are constants, and

$$\dot{C}_m = a(\sigma)^n \tag{35}$$

* The power relation was employed for the charts of the ASTM-ASME compilation of available creep data.[137]

where $\dot{C}_m$ is the minimum creep rate corresponding to stress σ and a and n are constants.

It will be noted that neither relation has any real physical significance,

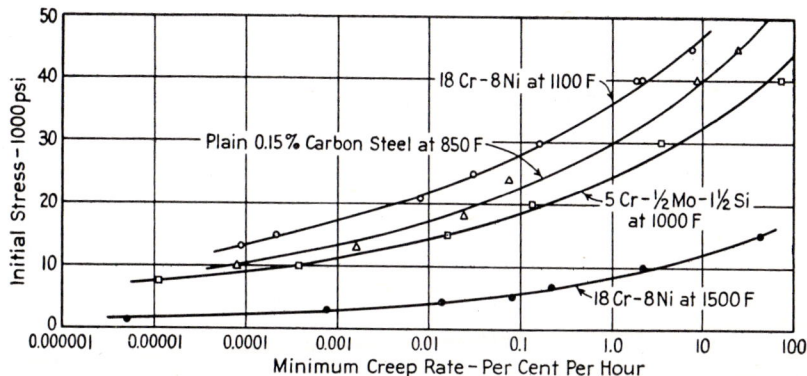

FIG. 92. Variation of the logarithm of the minimum creep rate with stress (plotted linearly) for several materials.   Compare with other methods of plotting in Figs. 91 and 93.   (*U.S. Steel Corp. data.*)

since neither can represent the zero rate corresponding to zero stress. One modification of the exponential function which has been proposed

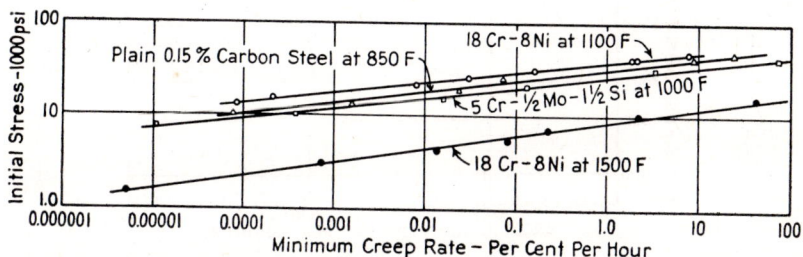

FIG. 93. Variation of the logarithm of the minimum creep rate with the logarithm of the stress for several materials.   Compare with other methods of plotting in Figs. 91 and 92. (*U.S. Steel Corp. data.*)

by Soderberg[135] to satisfy the requirement of zero rate at zero stress is worthy of note:

$$\sigma = \sigma_1 \log\left(1 + \frac{\dot{C}_m}{\dot{C}_1}\right) \tag{36}$$

where the significance of the various terms is the same as in Eq. (34).

It may also be pointed out that in the extrapolation of experimental data to slower rates, a faster rate is indicated by the semilog plot than by

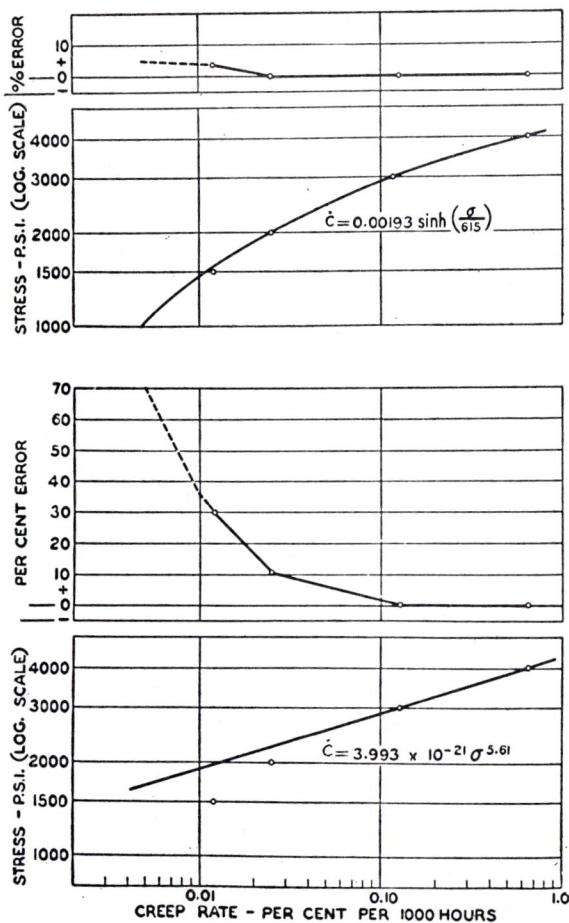

FIG. 94. Comparison of the errors resulting from extrapolation by power and hyperbolic sine functions to slower creep rates, assuming that only the test data at 3,000 and 4,000 psi are known. (*McVetty.*[140])

the log-log plot for the same stress.   The semilog plot therefore yields the more conservative extrapolation.

Nadai,[138, 139] on the basis both of test data and theoretical considerations, has suggested that the relation between stress and minimum creep rate is best expressed by the hyperbolic sine function.   Thus

$$\dot{C}_m = V_0 \sinh\left(\frac{\sigma}{\sigma_0}\right) \tag{37}$$

where $\dot{C}_m$ is the minimum creep rate corresponding to stress σ and V_0 and σ_0 are constants which depend upon the material and the temperature.

According to Nadai and later to McVetty and Nadai,[140, 141] available test data at low stress and low rates deviate systematically from the straight line of the much used log-log plot of the power function. Two features of the hyperbolic sine law are noteworthy: (1) at large stresses, the function reduces to the Ludwik logarithmic, or exponential, law*; (2) a power function defines the tangent to the hyperbolic sine curve, and under certain conditions is a close approximation to it.

The determination of the constants of the hyperbolic sine function, Eq. (37), offers some difficulties, but Nadai and McVetty[140, 141] have published charts which make this task easier.

Nadai and McVetty have reported that numerous tests of the hyperbolic sine creep law have shown it to be superior to the power-function law for extrapolation to low creep rates. Figure 94 is illustrative of these results. In this case, the two higher stress determinations were employed for calculating the curves corresponding to the hyperbolic sine and power functions, and the extrapolation of these curves was compared with test data at lower stresses. The superiority of the hyperbolic sine law in this case is evident. It may be pointed out that in some cases of practical interest the deviation from the power law at low stress seems to become apparent at rates of about 0.00001 per cent per hour.

Although additional test data, particularly at very low creep rates, are needed to test further the validity of the proposed hyperbolic sine relation, it seems clear on the basis of data reported by Nadai and McVetty that this relation offers the most accurate means of extrapolating test data to the lower creep rates which are of interest in certain commercial applications.

Relation between Temperature and Minimum Creep Rate

Although creep tests are generally made at a series of constant loads at constant temperature, and accordingly interest centers on the relation between stress and creep rate at constant temperature, this convention is purely arbitrary, and at least one method of interpretation of creep data considers temperature and rate as the variables and maintains the stress constant.

Kanter[120, 142] has provided this kind of treatment of the creep problem in terms of departure from ideal viscous flow. As has already been

---

* Since $\sinh x = \frac{1}{2}(e^x - e^{-x})$ and e^{-x} approaches zero at large values of x.

noted, there is some basis for believing that creep at small stresses is of viscous nature, but at high stresses this is clearly not true. This departure from pure viscous behavior is treated in terms of a variable viscosity and such flow is said to be quasi-viscous. Kanter chooses to express pure viscous flow at constant temperature by

$$\dot{C}_m = \phi_T \sigma \tag{38}$$

where $\dot{C}_m$ and σ are again the minimum creep rate and stress and ϕ_T is a proportionality constant for temperature T and is the reciprocal of the viscosity. This constant is termed "flowability." To extend the

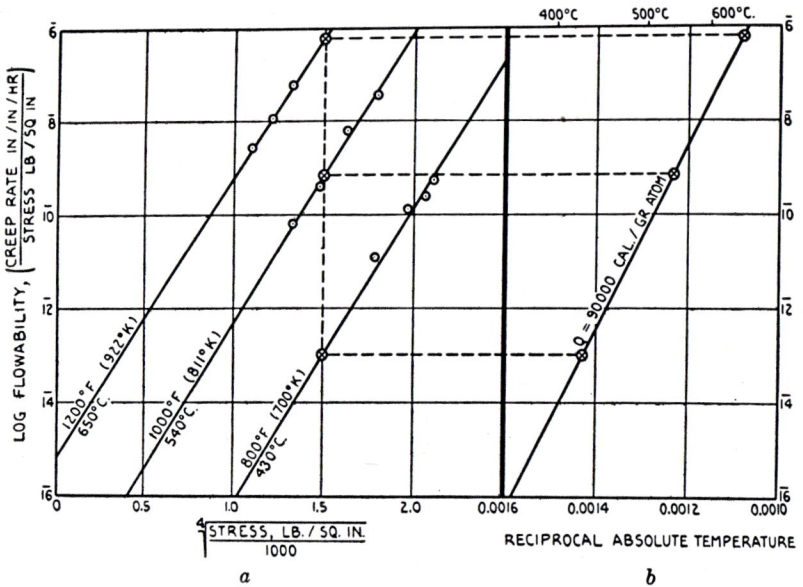

FIG. 95. Variation of the logarithm of the "flowability" of a 0.17 per cent carbon steel with the fourth root of the stress and with the reciprocal of the absolute temperature. (*Kanter*.[142])

applicability of Eq. (38) to higher stresses, the flowability is considered to be dependent on the stress. Plotting of flowability, which is equivalent to $\dot{C}_m/\sigma$, by Eq. (38), against the stress showed that the stress dependency, however, was not simple. The temperature coefficient of the flowability constant ϕ_T may be determined from the intersection at a common stress of such plots for different temperatures. Such a procedure is illustrated in Fig. 95. The fourth root of the stress was employed in this plot because it yielded a straight line for these data. When the logarithm of the flowability is plotted against the reciprocal of the absolute temperature at constant stress (Fig. 95b), a straight line is obtained. This is represented mathematically by

$$\ln \frac{\phi_T}{\phi_0} = -\frac{Q}{RT} \tag{39}$$

where ϕ_0 is the flowability constant at absolute zero temperature, Q is an energy quantity, R is the gas constant, and T is the absolute temperature. Kanter chooses to write the expression in this form because of a similarity to various chemical and physical processes which have been so treated, for example, diffusion.

Kanter also shows several plots of the logarithm of the minimum creep rate, at constant stress, against the reciprocal of the absolute temperature which are also straight lines and are held to be analogous to the plot in Fig. 95b. The energy value [Q in Eq. (39)] in either case is on the order of 90,000 cal/gram atom. This energy is similar in magnitude to the latent heats of evaporation and self-diffusion in iron.* Kanter then proceeds to draw an analogy between creep and diffusion, based on the similarities in the activation energies and also in part on the experimental observation, discussed in another section, of the rotation of grains during creep, and devises a self-diffusion theory of creep during the minimum or constant rate portion.

The value of Kanter's stimulating theoretical treatment of the creep problem is not clear and remains to be shown. It is similar in some respects to a treatment later proposed by Kauzmann[146] and others, discussed below, patterned after the chemical reaction-rate theory of Eyring. Aside from the theoretical aspect of the problem, the method of plotting the logarithm of the minimum creep rate against the reciprocal of the absolute temperature to obtain a straight line may have some value for interpreting creep data.[143]

The Velocity-modified Temperature for Flow

In an earlier section, attention was directed to the qualitative similarity in the effects of increasing strain rate and decreasing temperature on the flow curve and to the quantitative relation between these two variables developed by Zener and Hollomon.[102] MacGregor and Fisher [144, 145] have since developed a somewhat similar, but more rigorous expression, in terms of a parameter T_m, termed the "velocity-modified temperature."

---

* The most reliable value for the activation energy of self-diffusion in alpha iron is 77,200 cal/gram atom.[230]

Stress in Thousands of psi

100
80
60
40
20
0

$\dot{\delta} = 0.5$ Sec^{-1}
$\dot{\delta} = 2\times10^{-2}$ Sec^{-1}
$\dot{\delta} = 8.5\times10^{-4}$ Sec^{-1}
$\dot{\delta} = 34\times10^{-5}$ Sec^{-1}
$\dot{\delta} = 9.5\times10^{-7}$ Sec^{-1}

20°C
200°C
400°C
600°C

MILD STEEL
$\dot{\delta} = 100\times10^{-5}$ Sec^{-1}
k = 0.018

0 100 200 300 400 500 600 700 800 900 1000

T_m in °K

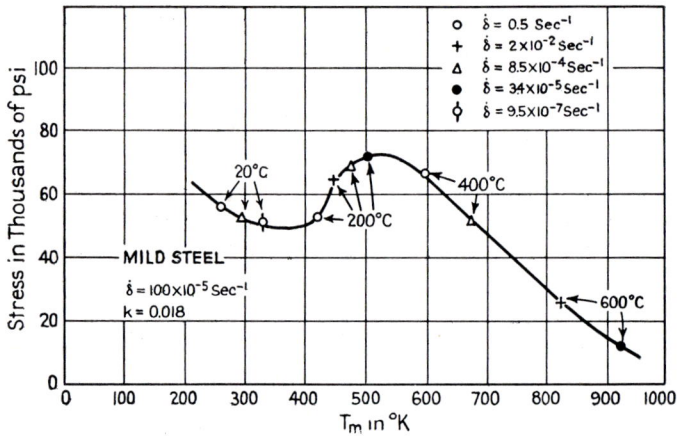

FIG. 96. Variation of the stress at a strain of 0.1 with the velocity-modified temperature for tension tests of mild steel. (*Data of Manjoine[147]; MacGregor and Fisher.[144]*)

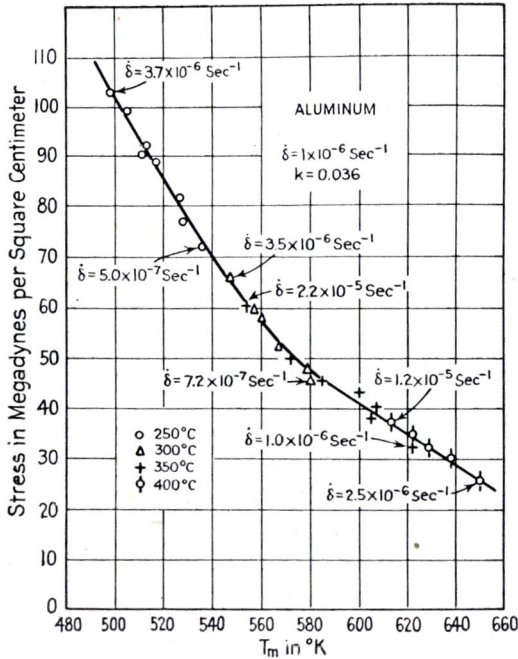

Stress in Megadynes per Square Centimeter

110
100
90
80
70
60
50
40
30
20
10
0

$\dot{\delta} = 3.7\times10^{-6}$ Sec^{-1}

ALUMINUM

$\dot{\delta} = 1\times10^{-6}$ Sec^{-1}
k = 0.036

$\dot{\delta} = 3.5\times10^{-6}$ Sec^{-1}
$\dot{\delta} = 5.0\times10^{-7}$ Sec^{-1}
$\dot{\delta} = 2.2\times10^{-5}$ Sec^{-1}
$\dot{\delta} = 7.2\times10^{-7}$ Sec^{-1}
$\dot{\delta} = 1.2\times10^{-5}$ Sec^{-1}

o 250°C
Δ 300°C
+ 350°C
♦ 400°C

$\dot{\delta} = 1.0\times10^{-6}$ Sec^{-1}
$\dot{\delta} = 2.5\times10^{-6}$ Sec^{-1}

480 500 520 540 560 580 600 620 640 660

T_m in °K

FIG. 97. Variation of the velocity-modified temperature with stress for secondary creep of aluminum. (*Data of Dushman et al.[148]; MacGregor and Fisher.[144]*)

The derivation of the velocity-modified temperature, which was based on the Kauzmann[146] expression for the dependence of creep rate (during the constant rate period) on stress and temperature, discussed later, will not be considered here. MacGregor and Fisher proposed that in general the flow stress is a function of the strain and the velocity modified temperature of flow:

$$\sigma = f(T_m, \delta) \qquad (40)$$

where σ is the flow stress, δ is the true strain, and T_m is the parameter velocity modified temperature of flow and has the form:

$$T_m = T\left(1 - K \ln \frac{\dot{\delta}}{\dot{\delta}_0}\right) \qquad (41)$$

where T is the absolute temperature, $\dot{\delta}$ is the strain rate, and k and $\dot{\delta}_0$ are constants. MacGregor and Fisher have checked the validity of the derived expression for various data at constant strain, with excellent agreement, as typified by the results shown in Figs. 96 and 97. It is particularly noteworthy that the relation holds for either tension tests or creep tests and over a wide range of temperatures.

Generalized Expressions for Constant-rate Creep

About a decade ago, Eyring and his associates advanced a theory for rate processes, based on statistical mechanical considerations and involving the concept of "activated" complexes or units, which has been successfully applied to a wide variety of chemical and physical rate processes. The theory is completely described in a book by Glasstone, Laidler, and Eyring[149] and the specific application to shear of liquids has been described by Eyring.[150] The applicability of the theory to creep of solids metals was pointed out by Condon[151] and subsequently considered in detail by Kauzmann[146] and by Dushman *et al.*[148] and Nowick and Machlin.[152]

According to the theory, creep results by a shear process involving units of flow, of generally undefined nature,* which pass one another, that is, undergo shear, only when they possess considerably greater energy than the average unit or are in the "activated" state. The energy requirement may be considered as that which is needed to surmount a potential energy barrier between equilibrium positions. On the basis of statistical mechanical considerations, a certain number of units will possess the required energy, that is, exist as activated

* In at least some fluids, these units are believed to be single molecules, while in solids many investigators consider the units to be dislocations.

units, able to surmount the barrier merely on the basis of the thermal energy resulting from the thermal vibration of the atoms. However, when the metal is not subjected to an external stress as many such units will move in one direction as in another and the net shear will be zero.

With the imposition of an external shear stress, it is considered that the potential barrier for flow in the direction of the applied stress is lowered in proportion to the magnitude of the stress, while the potential barrier for shear in the opposite direction is correspondingly increased, so that a net shear results.

On the basis of the considerations briefly outlined above, a complex expression relating the creep rate during the constant, or steady-state, period and the stress, strain, and temperature was derived. This may be expressed as follows:

$$\dot{\gamma} = \frac{2\lambda}{L} \frac{kT}{h} e^{\Delta S*/R} e^{-\Delta H*/RT} \sinh\left(\frac{qAl\tau}{kT}\right) \tag{42}$$

where $\dot{\gamma}$ is the constant shear creep rate corresponding to the shear stress τ at absolute temperature T, λ is the average motion of the flow unit per jump, L is the average distance between layers of flow units, k is the Boltzmann constant, h is Planck's constant, $\Delta S*$ and $\Delta H*$ the entropy and heat of activation, and R is the gas constant. The term qAl takes into account the idea that the force on a flow unit is not identical with the external shear stress; in this term, q is a stress concentration factor, A is the projected area of the unit of flow in the shear plane, and l is the distance through which the shear stress acts in moving the flow unit from the normal to the activated state.

The appearance of the stress in the hyperbolic sine function adds weight to the Nadai proposal mentioned earlier. Furthermore, the complex expression may be reduced by certain procedures and assumptions and at constant temperature becomes essentially identical with the exponential or logarithmic relation [Eq. (34)] previously developed empirically.

The application of the general rate theory concepts to constant rate creep represents a highly theoretical consideration of the problem, which cannot be considered here in detail. It should be stated, however, that, except that it provides some technical basis for the previously deduced empirical hyperbolic sine and exponential laws relating creep rate and stress at constant temperature, provided its tenets are proper, it would appear to be of limited practical value, both because of the many terms which must be evaluated experimentally and because it applies only to the constant-rate period of creep, which as stated earlier is only a portion of the total creep. Too, the structural changes which occur in most metals during creep service are not considered.

Nowick and Machlin[152] have derived on the basis of dislocation theory and rate-processes theory an expression for the constant-rate creep of metals which is similar to that developed by Kauzmann,[146] but one in which the heat and entropy of activation and the lowering of the potential barrier are expressed in terms of physical constants of the material. The concept of dislocations will be considered in a subsequent section.

The Mechanical Equation of State

Hollomon and associates[107, 110, 153] have considered the possibilities, contained in an early proposal of Ludwik,[52] of the existence of a so-called "mechanical equation of state," analogous to the familiar gas equation of state. The existence of a mechanical equation of state would mean that the flow stress depends only on the instantaneous strain, strain rate, and temperature, not on their past history. Such an equation, if valid, involves far-reaching possibilities. Of special interest among these is the possibility that the creep rate corresponding to a particular stress, strain, and temperature may be obtained much more readily than in the conventional test by quickly straining to the desired limit, at the temperature of interest or even at atmospheric temperature, and then establishing the stress and temperature of interest, whereupon the creep rate may be determined. Thus the very long test periods commonly required for accurate evaluation of creep behavior may be appreciably diminished. Moreover, as illustrated in Fig. 83, discussed earlier, creep-test data may be derived from tension tests, and vice versa.

The range of validity of a mechanical equation of state yet remains to be established, although data already reported cast considerable doubt that it will be very widely applicable. As Hollomon *et al.* carefully point out, the equation of state cannot be expected to be valid whenever structural changes such as phase transformations and recrystallization occur. Strictly speaking, this would appear to exclude the vast majority of metals, and especially so at elevated temperatures. However, the influence of the changes on the flow properties may in some cases be sufficiently slight so that the concept of a mechanical equation of state may be of some practical utility.

Hollomon *et al.* suggest that the flow stress, strain, strain rate, and temperature are related in the following way:

$$\sigma = CG^T \left(\frac{\dot{\delta}}{\dot{\delta}_0}\right)^{DT} \delta^{(E - FT \ln \dot{\delta}/\dot{\delta}_0)} \tag{43}$$

where σ is the flow stress, δ the corresponding true strain, $\dot{\delta}$ the strain rate, T the temperature, and C, D, E, F, G, and $\dot{\delta}_0$ are constants independent of the variables. Equation (43) may be rewritten

$$\ln \sigma = \ln (C\delta^E) + T \ln \left[G \left(\frac{\dot{\delta}}{\dot{\delta}_0}\right)^{D - F \ln \delta} \right] \tag{43a}$$

from which it is evident that the logarithm of the flow stress should vary linearly with the temperature when the strain and strain rate are held constant.

Some data in support of the validity of the mechanical equation of state concept have been presented by Hollomon, though these are not extensive. Of particular interest are those reproduced in Fig. 98, which indicate the inherent possibilities relative to creep behavior. It should be pointed out, however, that the material in this case was quite stable structurally, having been tempered (after an initial quench) at a temperature 175°F above the test temperature prior to test. Fisher and MacGregor[154] have reported data in support of the validity of the mechanical equation of state in steel undergoing tempering as determined by true stress-strain tension tests.

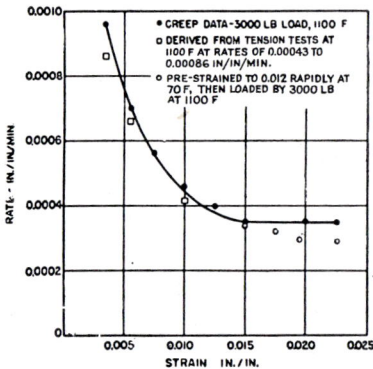

FIG. 98. Results of tests designed to test the validity of a mechanical equation of state; heat-treated steel. (*Hollomon and Lubahn.*[153])

On the other hand, Orowan[228] has shown in tests of copper deformed in steps alternately at room temperature and at the temperature of liquid nitrogen that the flow stress at any particular strain may be greatly influenced by the temperature of prior strain, that is, by the strain history; this is contrary to the teachings of the mechanical equation of state. This invalidity of the concept was confirmed by Dorn, Goldberg, and Tietz[231] who interestingly found that prestraining at a high temperature had greater effect on flow stress at a low temperature than for the reverse case of prestraining at a low and testing at a high temperature. The effects are illustrated by Figs. 99 and 100; in the former, samples were strained various amounts at 194°K, then the temperature was lowered to 78°K, and straining completed; in Fig. 100, the reverse experiments were performed.

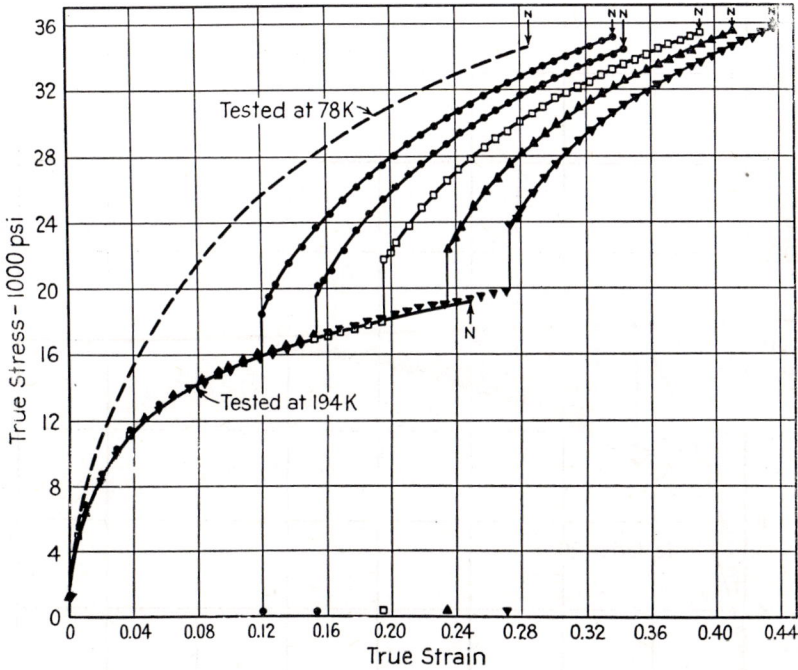

FIG. 99. Effect of prestraining at 194°K on true stress-strain curve at 78°K for 2S-O aluminum. *N* denotes beginning of necking. (*Dorn et al.*[231])

Relaxation

A special aspect of the problem of the creep of metals is that of relaxation which relates to the decrease in stress at an essentially constant deflection owing to creep strain. In effect, elastic strain is exchanged for plastic or creep strain, and consequently the stress is diminished. Relaxation is of considerable practical importance in such applications as bolting, in which it results in loosening of the bolts.

Hitherto, little success has rewarded the efforts of investigators to correlate relaxation behavior with the results of constant-load creep tests, and consequently a type of testing known as "relaxation testing," simulating the actual problem involved, has come into wide use for such applications.

Relaxation tests are generally made by simply straining a sample at

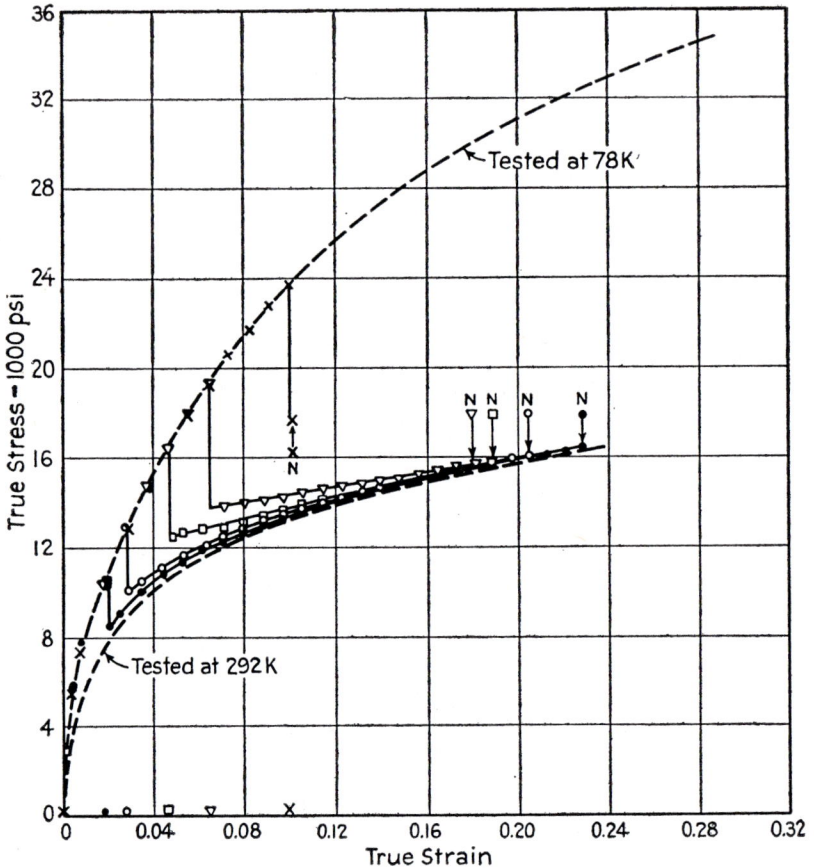

Fɪɢ. 100. Effect of prestraining at 78°K on true-stress–true-strain curve at 292°K for 2S-O aluminum. *N* denotes beginning of necking. (*Dorn et al.*[231])

the temperature of interest to some specific strain and corresponding stress, "locking" at this strain, and then observing the decrease in stress with time. As creep occurs, the elastic strain corresponding to the initial stress is replaced by plastic strain with resulting decrease in stress.* Several relaxation curves obtained in this way are reproduced in Fig. 101. The rate of decrease in stress is most rapid initially and soon levels off. This is a consequence both of the decreasing

---

* Since there are generally other elastically strained members in a relaxation stand, the creep strain replaces not only the elastic strain in the specimen but also in the other members. Advantage is frequently taken of this in commercial applications.

stress and of the fact that even at constant stress the creep rate decelerates with time.

Some investigators have studied relaxation phenomena by a series of "downstep" load creep tests. These are conducted like the conventional constant-load creep tests except that when the extension reaches a preselected value, the load is decreased by a small increment and creep permitted to proceed until the limiting strain again is attained, whereupon the load is again decreased, etc. The increments can be made quite small by automatic apparatus such as that described by Boyd.[155]

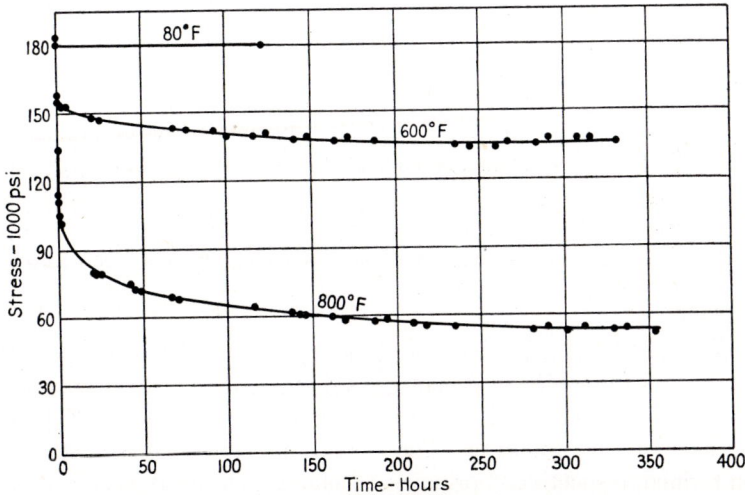

FIG. 101. Relaxation of the precipitation-hardenable alloy stainless W at several temperatures. (*U.S. Steel Corp. data.*)

Many treatments of the relaxation problem have been attempted with particular attention to the use of constant-load creep-test data. From the practical standpoint, at least, one of the most interesting, but yet not entirely adequate, approaches is that suggested by Robinson[156, 157]. Robinson experimentally observed that if a specimen is tested by the decremental loading technique so that some specific strain is not exceeded, a plot of the logarithm of the stress against the logarithm of the creep rate yielded a straight line similar to but with a different slope than that observed for constant-stress tests with individual specimens for each test*; that is, the stress and creep rate

* The step-down test generally, but not always, yields faster creep rates at higher stresses, and slower creep rates at lower stresses, than the conventional constant load test.

are related by a power function. Using this relation and the condition that the total extension remains constant, Robinson developed an expression relating the time with the initial and remanent stresses. It is not clear, however, that this treatment adequately considers the initial period of so-called "primary" creep. In this respect, it is of interest to note that when bolts which have relaxed during service are retightened, they almost always relax less readily than initially.

Nadai[139] has provided a treatment of relaxation similar to that of Robinson except that the hyperbolic sine function (discussed earlier) rather than the power function relation between stress and creep rate is employed. Davis[158] explored this question even further, attempting to predict the shape of the relaxation curve from creep-test data, but without success. Davis pointed out that recovery associated with the decrease in stress must be at least partly responsible for the experimental observation that the creep rate during the later stages of a relaxation test is less than the constant creep rate of the conventional constant-load creep test.

It should be apparent that relaxation phenomena are quite complex and that no adequate treatment of the problem has yet been afforded.

Summary

The curve of creep versus time, in a constant-load tensile creep test, characteristically shows a period of decreasing creep rate, then a period of substantially constant rate, and finally a period of accelerating creep rate leading to fracture. The creep in these three stages is often termed, respectively, primary, secondary, and tertiary. The characteristic form of the creep curve has been generally attributed to the interaction of two forces, a strengthening as a result of strain hardening and a weakening as a result of recovery or recrystallization. In the secondary stage of constant creep rate, these forces are considered to be exactly balanced. However, few pertinent experimental data are available to support this point of view.

The period of accelerating creep rate is associated with impending fracture, but the exact point at which the fracture crack first appears is uncertain. Some investigators consider fracture to begin simultaneously with the beginning of tertiary creep. In this connection, the type of fracture, transgranular or intergranular, has probably not been adequately considered. Some data suggest that the period of tertiary creep is absent if the stress, rather than the load, is maintained constant.

Various mathematical expressions for representing the creep curve have been suggested, but none of these are entirely adequate. From the practical standpoint of predicting long-time behavior, that is, of extrapolating beyond the laboratory test interval, a method of analysis first proposed by McVetty seems adequate. This method is based on the constant-rate portion (secondary creep) of the creep-time plot and the intersection of this slope on the creep axis. The total creep at any time is then given by the sum of this intercept and the product of the time and the creep rate. The analysis is limited to times less than the beginning of tertiary creep, which must be determined by an independent extrapolation.

The McVetty type of analysis is facilitated by the existence of a relatively simple relation—a power function—between stress and the rate of secondary creep. This relation seems to fit the available data somewhat better than does an exponential function which has been suggested. A hyperbolic sine function has also been suggested for the relation, and a few data indicate that it may be superior to the power function for extrapolation to small creep rates.

Several attempts have been made to develop general mathematical expressions for creep, relating creep, creep rate, stress, and temperature, but these do not appear entirely adequate. The most promising treatment has resulted from the application of concepts employed by Eyring for a wide variety of chemical and physical rate processes.

CHAPTER V

THE FRACTURE OF METALS

The end result of stressing a metal, whether it flows plastically or not, is fracture. In the preceding chapters we have considered in some detail the subject of the flow of metals. We now propose to consider the subject of fracture, about which, it may be said at the outset, considerably less is known than in the case of flow.

As we did in our consideration of flow, we shall consider the behavior of metals at elevated temperatures as merely a particular aspect of the general problem. Similarly we shall begin with the simplest case, that is, with the behavior of single crystals.

THE FRACTURE OF SINGLE CRYSTALS

The Crystallographic Nature of Fracture

In our consideration of the flow of single crystals, we noted that slip occurs on specific crystallographic planes which depend on the type of crystal lattice. Moreover, flow begins when the maximum shear stress resolved into this plane attains a certain critical value characteristic of the material.

The fracture of single crystals is also crystallographic in character, occurring on specific lattice planes which may or may not be identical with the slip plane. There appear to be two kinds of fracture in single crystals, a shearing type and a cleavage type.[8] The shearing type occurs along the slip plane at a critical value of the resolved shear stress. In effect, slip does not cease after proceeding so far, but, rather, glide of the two portions of the crystal continues and causes complete separation. Shearing fracture is common in single crystals of tin, magnesium, zinc, and cadmium, and is characterized by a rough surface resulting from small steps from one slip plane to another parallel one, in contrast to the smooth surface of the cleavage type of fracture. Whether shearing or cleavage fracture occurs depends, at least in some cases, on the crystal orientation, as discussed below. Shearing fracture has not been as extensively studied as cleavage fracture.

Cleavage fracture occurs on certain crystallographic planes, characteristic of the metal and its lattice, when the normal stress acting

132

on this plane attains a critical value (Fig. 102). It may occur with or without prior plastic flow. Its occurrence is obviously abetted by increasing the ratio of normal to shear stress, as by notching. Whether shearing or cleavage fracture will occur must obviously depend on which attains its critical value earlier, thus depending on orientation. Similarly, as we shall discuss in greater detail later, whether plastic flow or cleavage occurs depends on whether the critical shear stress for slip is attained before the critical normal stress for cleavage. The cleavage plane and the critical normal stress for cleavage fracture of several of the common metal crystals are compiled in Table V. Attention is directed to the data for zinc containing 0.03 per cent cadmium, which shows the normal stress for cleavage on two different planes, with quite different critical stress. Thus, it may be considered that every plane of a lattice has a corresponding critical normal stress for cleavage; the critical stress can, in general, not be determined experimentally for more

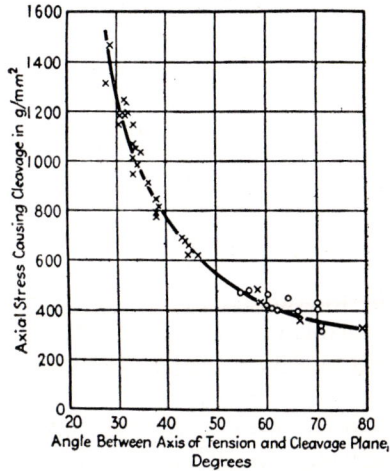

FIG. 102. Variation of the cleavage stress with orientation of single crystals of bismuth at 20°C (*O*) and −80°C (*X*). (*Georgieff and Schmid.*[159])

TABLE V. CLEAVAGE PLANE AND CRITICAL NORMAL STRESS FOR CLEAVAGE OF SEVERAL METAL CRYSTALS*

Metal	Temperature, °C	Plane	Critical normal stress, kg/mm²
Zn (0.03% Cd)	−80	(0001)	0.19
Zn (0.03% Cd)	−185	(0001)	0.19
Zn (0.03% Cd)	−185	(10$\bar{1}$0)	1.80
Zn (0.13% Cd)	−185	(0001)	0.30
Zn (0.53% Cd)	−185	(0001)	1.20
Sb.................................	+20	(111)	0.66
Bi.................................	+20	(111)	0.32
Bi.................................	−80	(111)	0.32
α-Fe...............................	−100	(100)	26
α-Fe...............................	−185	(100)	27.5

* Data from Barrett[10] and Seigle and Brick.[161]

than one or two of these, inasmuch as before the normal stress attains its critical value on the plane under consideration, it will have exceeded this value for one of lower critical stress.

Effect of Plastic Deformation on the Fracture Stress

Inasmuch as a variable amount of plastic deformation may occur before fracture, it is of interest to inquire what effect this prior deformation may exert. Like most other aspects of fracture, this question has not been studied adequately, in part owing to the experimental difficulties. It should be evident that flow and fracture cannot be varied at will, and accordingly certain stratagems, such as changing the velocity of loading or the temperature, must be employed and inferences drawn from such tests in order to find the influence of flow on the fracture strength. The conclusion to be drawn from the few data available on single crystals is that the magnitude of the effect is probably not very great. Results of Fahrenhorst and Schmid[160] for zinc crystals at −185°C indicate a slight decrease in the normal stress for cleavage with increasing prior deformation. Further test data are needed. The influence of flow on fracture of polycrystalline metal has been more extensively studied, and we shall again consider this question when we discuss polycrystalline metals.

Effect of Temperature on the Fracture Stress

The critical normal stress for cleavage appears to be virtually unaffected by temperature, as may be noted from several of the data in Table V for atmospheric and lower temperatures. Apparently no studies of this kind have been made at elevated temperatures. Since the flow stress increases with decreasing temperature, and if the fracture stress remains unchanged as indicated in Table V (or, at least, does not increase so rapidly as the flow stress), it is to be expected that the critical stress for cleavage will be attained relatively earlier with decreasing temperature, with consequent increased brittleness, or decreased ductility. This is confirmed for the hexagonal metals, zinc, cadmium, and magnesium (Fig. 103),

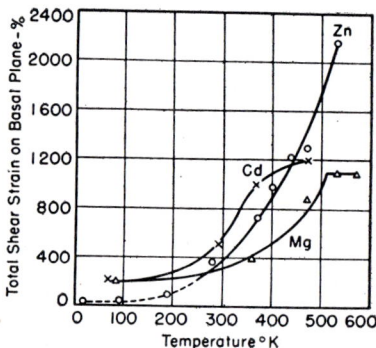

FIG. 103. Variation of total shear strain along basal plane with temperature for single crystals of the hexagonal metals zinc, cadmium, and magnesium tested in tension. (*Seigle and Brick.*[161])

from data compiled from different sources by Seigle and Brick,[161] and for alpha iron by Barrett, Ansel, and Mehl,[162] but not for aluminum.[8] Aluminum is apparently the only face-centered cubic metal which has been tested as single crystals at low temperatures, but other such metals may be expected similarly to retain ductility to low temperatures; such behavior has been found for polycrystalline metal. That aluminum crystals retain ductility to low temperatures must mean that the flow and cleavage fracture stresses vary proportionately with temperature, that the cleavage strength is sufficiently greater at atmospheric temperature so that it remains greater at low temperatures in spite of a disproportionate variation, that fracture is not of the cleavage type, but of the shearing type, or that the simple concept employed is inadequate. Certainly more investigation is required.

Effect of Composition

The few data in Table V illustrating the influence of addition of cadmium to zinc show that this alloying increases the cleavage stress.

The Effect of Repeated Stressing—Fatigue

When subjected to repeated applications of load, metals fail at considerably lower stress than when subjected to sustained loading or to continuously increasing stress. Fracture under repeated stressing is generally termed "fatigue," and tests of this characteristic are termed "fatigue" or "endurance" tests. The number of repetitions of stress which may be supported by a metal depends upon the stress magnitude, as would be expected; this is illustrated schematically

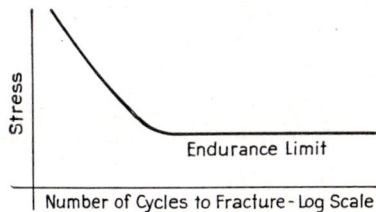

Fig. 104. Variation of number of cycles to fracture with stress; schematic.

in Fig. 104. With decreasing stress, the number of cycles to fracture increases, the stress approaching an "endurance limit" below which for practical purposes fracture does not occur.*

Gough[163] has provided a comprehensive review of the experimental investigations of single crystals under repeated stresses. While the outstanding characteristic of fatigue fracture of polycrystalline metal is the apparent lack of plastic distortion, tests of single crystals have

* At elevated temperatures, and even at atmospheric temperature for some metals, a "true" endurance limit is not reached; the curve relating stress to number of cycles to failure slopes continuously even at millions of repetitions of the stress cycle.

related fatigue failure to the slip process. Slip markings have been observed on the surface of single-crystal fatigue specimens, and Gough has stated that in its very early stages the fatigue crack coincides with the trace of the operative slip plane. However, as the fatigue crack progresses in face-centered cubic metals it departs from this course in an irregular manner and follows what Gough describes as the "path of least resistance to the external applied forces." This is probably determined by the normal stress, in contrast to the initiation of the crack, which is determined by the shear stress (since this latter determines the slip process). In close-packed hexagonal zinc, on the other hand, a fatigue crack was observed variously to lie parallel to traces of the basal slip plane as well as the twin plane. In body-centered cubic iron which, it will be recalled, may slip simultaneously on three slip systems, Gough observed again that the fatigue crack originated on a plane of maximum resolved shear stress, but progressed in a noncrystallographic direction apparently of maximum shear stress (not resolved).

Why metals fracture under repeated loading at stresses far less than ordinarily required is ill understood.

THE FRACTURE OF POLYCRYSTALLINE METALS

Although tests on single crystals under simple states of stress have seemed to show that fracture, of the cleavage type, occurs on reaching a critical value of the maximum normal stress, extensive tests of polycrystalline metals under various complex states of stress have shown that fracture cannot be generally described so simply. A great deal of experimental, as well as theoretical, work has been performed in recent years, and although this work has advanced our understanding of the problems, our degree of ignorance is still great. Exhaustive reviews of this subject have recently been presented by Hollomon,[100] and by Gensamer *et al.*[167]

In spite of its limited applicability, the concept of fracture occurring on attainment of a critical value of the normal stress has been successfully employed in aiding our understanding of the processes of flow and fracture. As an example, a diagram such as that shown in Fig. 105 has been widely employed to show qualitatively the variation of the temperature of embrittlement of iron with the type of test.[99] In this sketch is shown the variation with temperature of the critical normal stress to produce fracture and of the critical shear stress to produce plastic flow.* The variation of normal stress for fracture is much less

* As we noted in an earlier section, a more accurate criterion of flow is the shear-strain energy, or octahedral shear stress, but the maximum shear stress may be considered sufficiently accurate for most purposes.

than the variation of the shear stress for flow. With increasing stress either flow or fracture will occur, depending upon whether the critical shear stress or the critical normal stress is reached first. The ratio of the greatest shear stress to the greatest normal stress varies with the type of test, being 1 for torsion, 2 for tension, and greater than 2 for notch tests, depending upon the sharpness of the notch. With decreasing temperature, brittleness will occur in tension when the critical normal stress for fracture becomes less than twice the critical shear stress for flow; in torsion this does not occur until the ratio becomes less than 1. Thus toughness is retained to a lower temperature in

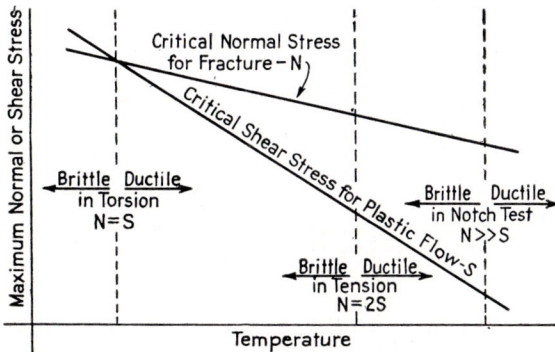

Fig. 105. Variation of critical shear stress for flow and of critical normal stress for fracture with temperature; schematic.

torsion than in tension, while similarly, toughness is retained to a lower temperature in tension than in a notch test. Although Fig. 105 explains qualitatively why iron remains tough to a lower temperature in tension than in a notch test, it fails quantitatively because the normal stress for fracture probably depends upon the state of stress, as we shall see later.

An analysis of the type illustrated by Fig. 105 may tell whether fracture or flow will occur, but it fails to reveal the extent of flow should it occur. This aspect of the problem has generally been considered in terms of a viewpoint advanced many years ago by Ludwik.[52] According to this concept, the fracture stress varies, like the flow stress, with the deformation, as well as with other variables, such as strain rate and temperature. The fracture stress is believed to increase less rapidly than the flow stress with increasing deformation, other factors remaining constant, and the fracture- and flow-stress curves intersect at the point of actual fracture, as indicated schematically in Fig. 106. It should be emphasized that the fracture-stress curve is purely hypothetical, since only the single point of actual fracture is experimentally measured.

Ludwik assumed that fracture generally occurs when the maximum normal stress reaches a certain critical value, independent of the other stresses. Then, since the flow curve is raised by notching or by transverse tensile stresses, that is, its position depends upon the other stresses, reduced ductility is effected in such cases because the fracture strength curve is intersected at lower strains (Fig. 106). This was Ludwik's theory of notch brittleness. It should be noted that this concept explains a decrease in strain at fracture, but not a change in type of fracture from "fibrous" to "cleavage" as commonly encountered in notch-bend or notch-impact tests. Also casting some doubt on the theory is the well-known fact that a notched tensile specimen fractures at a tensile normal stress (based on the reduced cross section) considerably greater than in an unnotched specimen, even though at very small strains. This would require that the fracture curve of Fig. 106 should rise to very high values at very small strains.

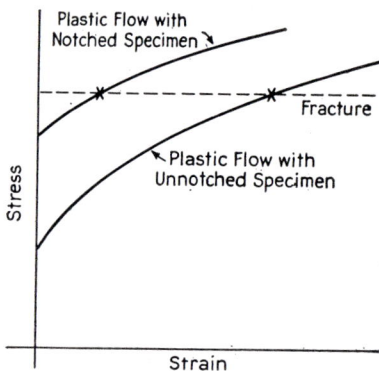

FIG. 106. Variation of flow and fracture stresses with strain according to Ludwik;[52] schematic.

Kuntze[174, 175] accepted Ludwik's view and attempted to determine experimentally the fracture versus strain curve of Fig. 106, but as discussed in a later section on the effect of deformation, Kuntze's assumptions and techniques are not now generally accepted.

Criterion of Fracture—The Effect of the State of Stress

The criterion of fracture of polycrystalline metals has not been established beyond question, owing primarily to the lack of suitable experimental data, particularly for multiaxial states of stress. The experimental difficulties in the study of fractures are great. The fracture stress at which a tensile test terminates, for example, is that corresponding to the deformation at which fracture occurs and is dependent upon this deformation. Not only does deformation usually precede fracture, but this deformation results in preferred orientations with resultant anisotropy of properties. These effects, and others which have often been ignored, render exceedingly difficult an evaluation of the influence of multiaxial stresses on fracture. To avoid the difficulty introduced by such effects, experimenters have attempted to restrict the deformation by employing metals with limited ductility, or have employed low test temperatures to induce brittleness.

Tests of cast iron in biaxial tension by Maier[168] have indicated that fracture occurs when the maximum normal stress attains a critical value. Other data, however, such as that of Jelinek *et al.*[62] on magnesium tubes, appears to favor a maximum shear-stress criterion of fracture.

Attempts to study fracture under triaxial states of stress have largely employed notched specimens, but the evaluation of the results of such tests has been subject to considerable controversy. McAdam *et al.*[169–171, 176] as well as Sachs *et al.*[172, 173] have made notched-bar tension tests. McAdam has interpreted his results to invalidate the maximum normal stress law for fracture because the fracture strength increases with increasing triaxiality. Sachs *et al.* in similar tests have also reported an influence of triaxiality on fracture.

The stress distribution in notched bars is quite nonuniform, with gradients dependent upon the sharpness of the notch. Furthermore, this stress distribution is profoundly changed by even slight deformation. Average stresses as well as certain assumptions of questionable validity must be employed in interpreting the results of such tests. It has also been pointed out that the stress at the base of a notch is not triaxial but biaxial (since there can be no stress normal to a free surface), and accordingly, depending on whether fracture originates at the center or the surface of the specimen, it may or may not be the result of triaxial stress. Because of such difficulties, Gensamer *et al.*[167] have concluded that the influence of triaxial tensile stress on fracture cannot be studied by means of notched-bar tests.

Orowan[199] has suggested that all fractures should not be considered identical and has offered convincing arguments that the same criterion of fracture cannot govern the ductile type of fracture, such as in a necked tension-test specimen, as governs brittle fracture, such as occurs in glass. This latter type of fracture which Orowan considers to occur in notch-brittle samples is characterized by a high velocity of propagation, approaching that of the speed of sound in the metal, while the ductile type of fracture is characterized by further plastic flow after the crack has originated and while it is progressing, as strikingly shown by the void which develops in a necked tension specimen (Fig. 118). Orowan accepts the normal stress criterion when fracture is brittle, but considers that ductile fracture is too complex for analysis. In this latter case, since plastic deformation must precede and also occur concurrently with fracture, the shear stress is evidently of importance as well as some unknown factor governing the actual crack formation.

The Effect of Temperature

Certain metals, especially some types of ferritic steels, become brittle at subatmospheric temperature, that is, fracture with little or no plastic flow. Davidenkow and Wittman[165] and Hollomon and Zener,[166] as well as others, have employed this characteristic in attempting to obtain the influence of temperature as well as plastic strain on the fracture strength. This latter aspect will be discussed later. Much of the early work on the effect of temperature on fracture yielded conflicting results and should be repeated. The more recent and careful work of Hollomon and Zener however seems to indicate an increase of fracture stress with decreasing temperature in polycrystalline steels, in conflict with the generally accepted nondependency for single crystals. The rate of increase of fracture stress was less than for flow. An indirect method was employed, and it would seem desirable to check the conclusion by direct tests at various temperatures below the "critical" temperature for brittleness, so that plastic strain is avoided. McAdam et al.[176] have also concluded from results of notched-bar tests, discussed in the preceding section, that the breaking stress for constant prior deformation of ferritic steels increases continuously with decreasing temperature in the range from atmospheric temperature to about $-200°C$.

In view of the somewhat conflicting data, it is desirable to carry out further experimentation.

The Effect of Deformation

Since metals often deform plastically before fracturing it is of considerable interest to determine what influence deformation exerts on the fracture strength. Like all other aspects of fracture there is a dearth of reliable experimental data concerning this question. Moreover, the data which do exist have necessarily had to be obtained by somewhat indirect means, since in general the plastic deformation of a material before fracture cannot be changed except by changing the state of stress, the temperature, or velocity of testing.

Kuntze[174, 175] early attempted to determine the effect of deformation by tension-testing bars, which had been notched after different amounts and kinds of cold working. It is generally accepted now, however, that Kuntze's results are either incorrect or, misleading owing to improper analysis and techniques. McAdam *et al.*[169-171, 176] have made many similar tests in recent years and have concluded that the technical cohesion limit increases continuously with plastic deformation; the results have been the subject of some controversy, however, in respect to interpretation. The technical cohesion limit is defined by McAdam *et al.* as the technically determined resistance to fracture under a specific stress system.

Studies of unnotched specimens have been less subject to question, although brittle fracture in these instances has generally been induced by lowering the test temperature. Illustrative of the results of such tests are those of Hollomon and Zener,[177] reproduced in Fig. 107, for pearlitic steel deformed at room temperature and then fractured at −190°C with "practically no further deformation." A continuous increase of fracture stress with deformation is to be noted. It is presumed that the curve for fracture stress at room temperature (Fig. 106) would be

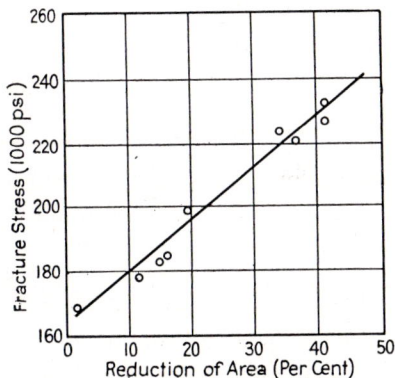

FIG. 107. Variation of fracture stress with prior deformation for pearlitic steel tested at −190°C. (*Hollomon and Zener.*[177])

of similar form but displaced to lower stress. However, other tests with tempered martensite microstructure showed no increase in fracture stress with prior deformation.

Studies in which samples prestrained by compression or by torsion are tested to fracture in tension have revealed some interesting effects, in part attributable to anisotropy developed during test. This anisotropy may be expected to play a double role owing to its effect on ductility as well as flow or fracture strength. Swift,[178] for example, has shown that if torsional straining is continued beyond a certain point, the subsequent fracture in tension test occurs on helical 45-deg planes rather than with the usual cup and cone. Körber *et al.*[179] showed that increasing prior compression continuously decreased the fracture stress in subsequent tension test.

Effect of Strain Rate

Although it might be expected that the fracture strength would increase with increasing strain rate at ordinary temperatures, this point seems not yet to have been investigated with any degree of thoroughness that yields quantitative results even for simple tension. Hollomon and Zener[177] have considered the problem and on the basis of indirect experiments concluded that the fracture stress varies with the strain rate in a manner similar to the variation of flow stress, but less rapidly.

At elevated temperatures, as we shall see later, the fracture stress decreases with decreasing average strain rate, but inasmuch as the mechanism of fracture changes and the strain prior to fracture also decreases, the evaluation of the strain-rate effect is uncertain.

Effect of Composition and Structure

Both composition and structure, and especially the latter, may be expected to affect the fracture stress markedly, although again, there have apparently been no direct investigations in this field. Some indirect evidence regarding the effect is available, especially for steels, in terms of the ductility at fracture, and this has been exhaustively considered by Hollomon[100] and will not be considered here. The relation between ductility and the fracture strength corresponding to the strain at fracture according to the Ludwik concept is apparent in Fig. 106.

Effect of Repeated Stressing—Fatigue

As was pointed out in our earlier consideration of the fracture of single crystals, repeated stressing results in fracture at a stress considerably below that in a static test; for example, the endurance limit often is approximately one-half of the static tensile strength or roughly equivalent to the plastic yield limit. The mechanism of fatigue fracture is not well understood. Presumably it is related to plastic flow, but this occurs so locally or is on such a small scale that it is often impossible to detect. Gough's work,[163] with single crystals, discussed earlier, has been especially valuable in shedding light on this subject.

Gough and Pollard[180] have investigated the influence of combined stresses (tension and torsion) and have concluded that the fatigue fracture of cast iron was determined by the maximum normal stress but that soft steel or a heat-treated steel obeyed a maximum shear or shear-strain energy law. Maier[181] observed that tubes under internal pressure obeyed the maximum normal stress criterion for fatigue failure, as have Morikawa and Griffis.[182]

FRACTURE AT ELEVATED TEMPERATURES

The end result of creep at elevated temperatures, if permitted to continue, is fracture, or as it is more commonly called rupture (Fig. 81). Consequently, the fracture of metals in creep is of great practical interest. In fact, in design for service at elevated temperatures, the relation between time for rupture and the applied stress and temperature is of equal or greater interest than is the relation between amount of creep and these variables. This matter is treated in somewhat greater detail in Chap. XII in regard to design, but a brief consideration is in order at this time.

In applying a metal to service involving creep, two limitations, dependent upon the application, must be considered. These are (1) that the metal will not creep more than some limiting amount and (2) that the metal will not fracture. Both of these are material characteristics. Although, in general, as the creep rate is lower, the time for rupture is increased, these two quantities are not uniquely interrelated, that is, knowing the variation of one does not reveal the other; both must be determined. This has not been generally recognized until recent years, and even yet considerable confusion exists, both in the published literature and among engineers who conduct creep tests or apply the data to design.

Fracture in the Short-time Elevated-temperature Tensile Test

The tensile strength decreases continuously with increasing temperature, except when unusual microstructural changes occur, and its magnitude becomes increasingly dependent upon the rate of straining. These effects are illustrated by the data in Fig. 108. Another quite interesting and important effect, probably first noted by Rosenhain,[187-189] is that fracture occurs in a different manner at high temperatures than at low temperatures. Instead of necking down (for a ductile metal), the specimen fractures rather abruptly even though considerable plastic strain may have occurred. Microexamination, moreover, reveals that the path of fracture is intergranular, that is, along the grain boundaries, rather than transgranular, that is, through the grains, as at ordinary temperatures.

This change in type of fracture with temperature was the basis of the so-called "equicohesive-temperature" concept, already discussed in some detail, which postulated that above some temperature (of equicohesion) the grain-boundary material is weaker than the material within the grain and fracture occurs at the grain boundaries, while below this temperature the grain boundary is stronger and consequently fracture occurs through the grains.

The type of fracture is dependent not only upon the temperature but also upon the strain rate. The two effects are of opposite sign, that is, intergranular fracture is more likely to occur with increasing temperature but with decreasing strain rate. The type of fracture

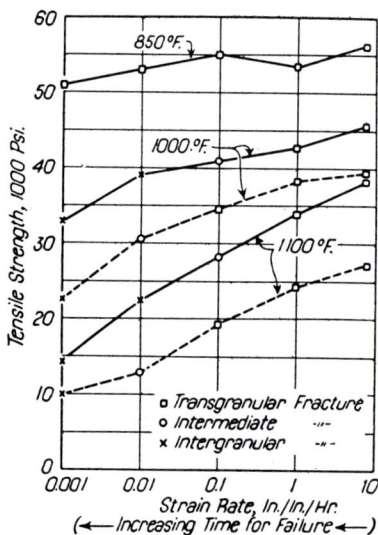

FIG. 108. Influence of strain rate on tensile strength of pearlitic (—) and spheroidized (- - - -) carbon-molybdenum steel at 850, 1000, and 1100°F; controlled strain-rate tests. (*Miller, Smith, and Kehl.*[101])

observed in the tests reported in Fig. 108 is indicated by an appropriate symbol, while photographs of the tensile-test fractures of two series of tests with decreasing strain rate are shown in Fig. 109. Thus, at constant temperature, transgranular or intergranular fracture may occur dependent upon the strain rate, while at constant strain rate the type of fracture depends upon the temperature. This question of fracture type will be further examined in consideration of creep-rupture-test fractures.

The Creep-rupture Test

Fracture data for metals used in service at elevated temperatures are obtained by continuing the ordinary creep test to fracture (rupture). Frequently, higher stresses than in the usual creep test are employed in order to obtain fracture in shorter time. By relating the

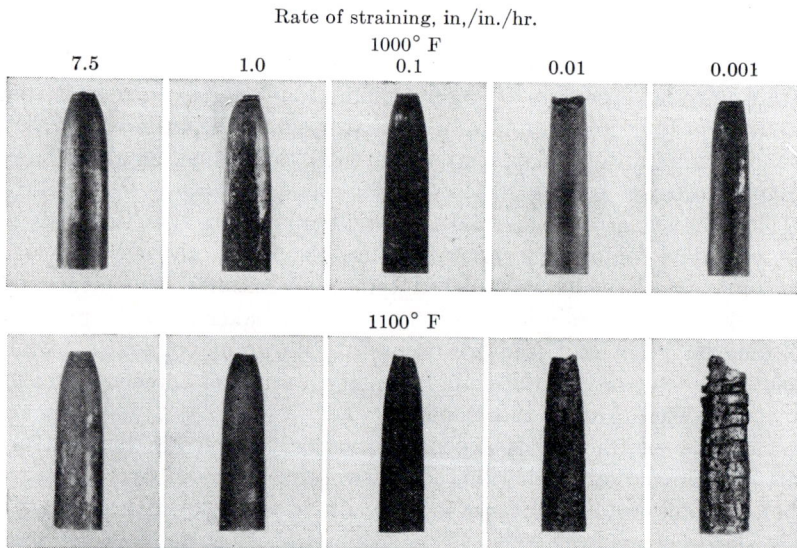

FIG. 109. Specimens of spheroidized C-Mo steel after fracture at various strain rates at 1000 and 1100°F in controlled strain-rate tension tests; X1. (*Miller, Smith, and Kehl.*[101])

applied stress to the time for rupture, the required design information may be had. Such tests have generally been termed "stress-rupture" tests, apparently because the conventional plot employed for representing the data is one of stress versus rupture time. Stress rupture is an obviously poor choice of terms, and since the test is simply a creep test continued to rupture, the terms "creep-rupture" or "creep to rupture" are being increasingly employed to describe such testing.

Although creep-rupture testing has become of great interest in recent years, beginning with the work of White *et al.*,[183, 184] the first investigators of creep actually made such tests.[185, 186] Generally, the loga-

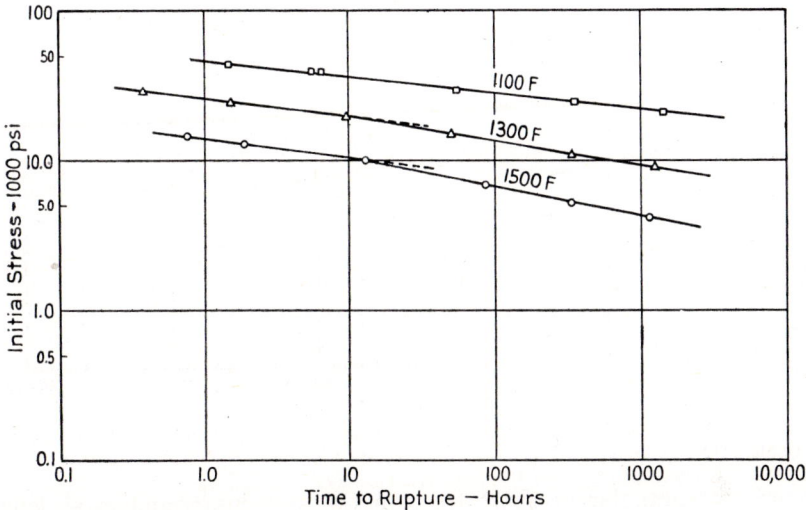

Fig. 110. Variation of time to rupture with initial stress for 18 Cr–8 Ni stainless steel at 1100, 1300, and 1500°F. Compare with Fig. 111 in which average true stress at fracture is plotted. (*U.S. Steel Corp. data.*)

rithm of the initial stress is plotted against the logarithm of the time for rupture at a constant temperature to yield one or two straight lines, as in Fig. 110. The linear relation thus established is represented mathematically by a power function:

$$t_r = a(\sigma)^n \tag{44}$$

where t_r is the time to rupture under the initially applied stress σ and a and n are material constants. The linear relation established by the logarithmic plotting is convenient for extrapolation to rupture times longer than can be conveniently employed in laboratory tests. A semilogarithmic plot, represented mathematically by an exponential function, has also been proposed, and although suiting some data fairly well seems not to be very widely used. It is to be emphasized that the stress plotted in Fig. 110 is that initially applied. As a consequence of and in proportion to the deformation which occurs, however, the true stress increases throughout the test.* If the true stress at fracture is calculated from the reduction in area measured after test and plotted against the time for rupture, the curves of Fig. 111 are obtained for the same test data shown in Fig. 110.

It will be noted in Fig. 110 that an abrupt change in slope occurs in the double logarithmic plots of stress versus time for rupture. This change in slope is quite generally observed, but after it has once occurred, there is apparently no reason on the basis of test results reported in the literature to expect another break. The break in the plot is generally considered to coincide with a change in type of fracture

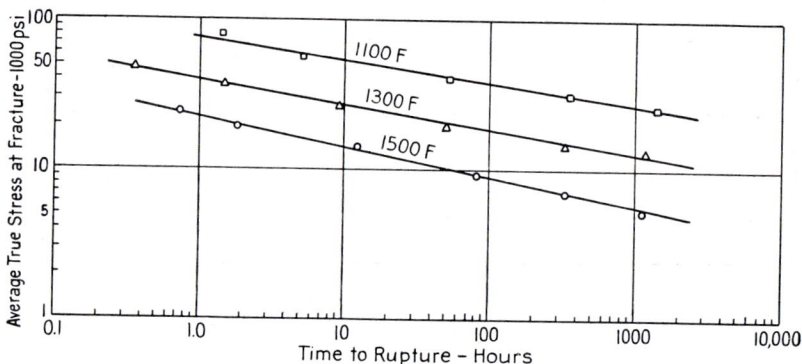

FIG. 111. Variation of time to rupture with average true stress at rupture for 18 Cr–8 Ni stainless steel at 1100, 1300, and 1500°F (compare Fig. 110). (*U.S. Steel Corp. data.*)

from transgranular at short fracture times to intergranular at long fracture times. The transition is not abrupt, and mixed fractures are encountered at intermediate rates   This is an effect of strain rate analogous to that in the conventional tensile test. In the author's experience, however, there appear to be exceptions to this generality and further investigational effort is desirable.

Intergranular Fracture

The change in character of the fracture with increasing time for rupture in the creep-rupture test, that is, with decreasing strain rate, is shown for an austenitic steel in Fig. 112. The similarity of the long-time fractures, at least, with those of the carbon-steel tensile tests of Fig. 109 is apparent.

Intergranular fracture is characterized by several readily recognized

---

* As discussed earlier, if necking occurs the stress is no longer uniaxial and the "true" stress calculated on the basis of the minimum cross section is in error.

features both in macro and micro appearance. As illustrated in Figs. 109 and 112, intergranular fracture is abrupt, that is, not preceded by necking (with cup and cone). The extension prior to fracture, however, is not a characteristic; although frequently less, it can be greater than for transgranular fracture. Frequently intergranular fracture is characterized by profuse surface cracking near the fracture, as in Fig. 112. These indicate that intergranular cracking commences at the surface.

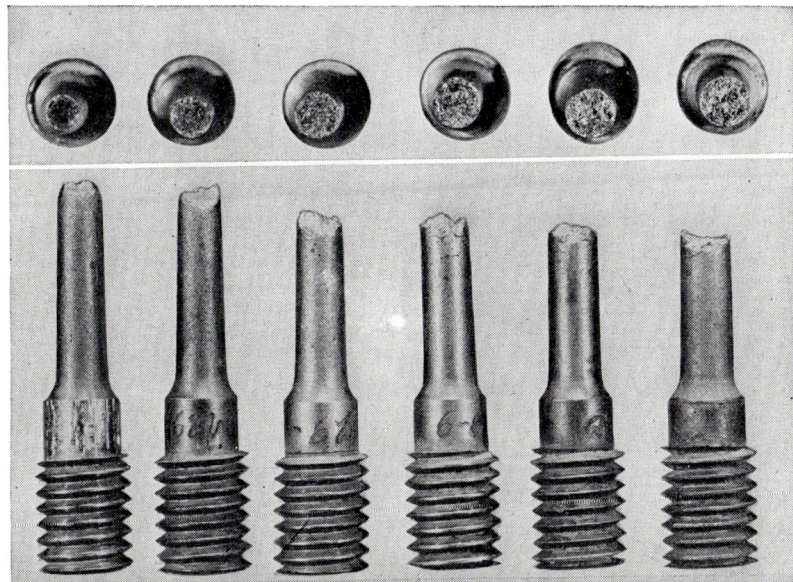

Stress, 1,000 psi	50.0	45.0	40.0	30.0	25.0	21.0
Hr to fracture	Instant.	1.45	6.33	55.0	357.0	1,446.0

FIG. 112. Change in appearance of fracture with time for rupture of annealed 18 Cr–8 Ni steel (AISI Type 304) at 1100°F; ×2.

Microscopic examination of etched sections through the fracture readily reveals the intergranular nature of fracture, as illustrated in Fig. 113 for a series of fractures ranging from transgranular to intergranular. Not only does the fracture clearly follow the grain boundaries in an intergranular fracture, both at the fracture surface and at the cracks remote from the surface if these are present, but the grains are equiaxed even though considerable deformation may have occurred, in contrast to the severely elongated grains of the transgranular fracture. A typical intergranular fracture has many intergranular cracks within the sample and away from the fracture surface. These are

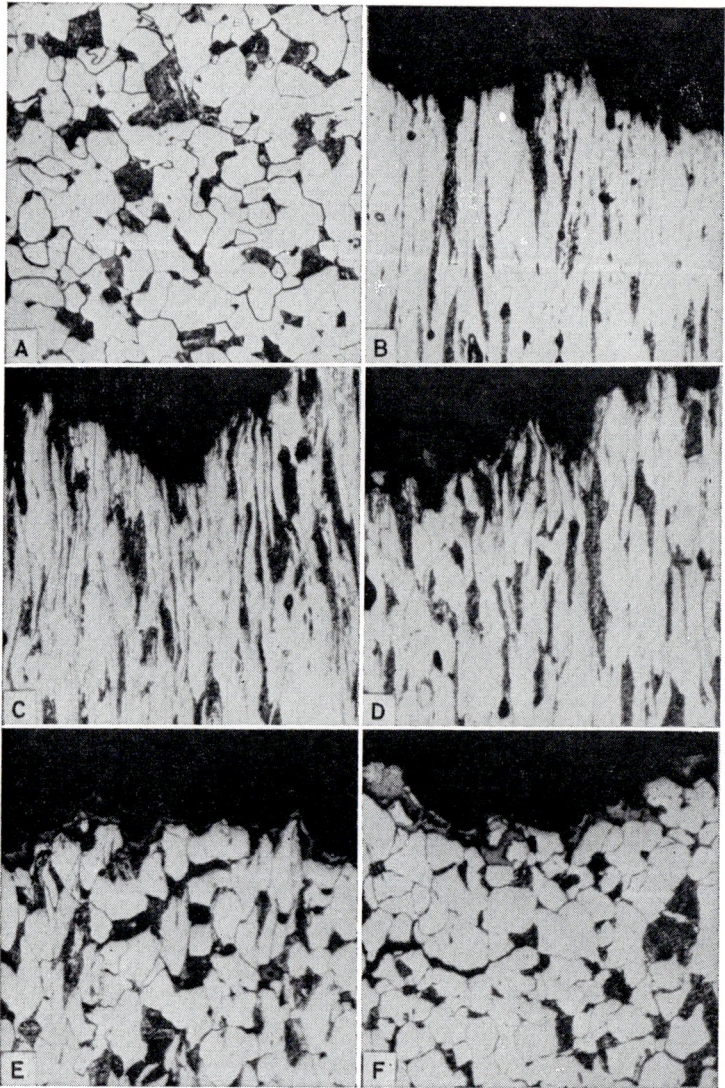

FIG. 113. Longitudinal section through fracture of controlled strain-rate tensile specimens of pearlitic C-Mo steel at 1000°F; ×250.   (*Miller, Smith, and Kehl.*[101])

A. Original microstructure	133 VPN
B. 7.5 in./in./hr	215 VPN
C. 1.0 in./in./hr	215 VPN
D. 0.1 in./in./hr	215 VPN
E. 0.01 in./in./hr	201 VPN
F. 0.001 in./in./hr	160 VPN

normal to the applied stress, that is, parallel to the fracture surface, and sometimes are covered with an oxide scale as though joined to the surface in some other section than that examined.

Effect of Atmosphere on Change in Slope of the Stress versus Rupture-time Plot

Since, as noted in the preceding section, intergranular fracture apparently begins at the surface of the specimen, it is not unreasonable to expect an effect of the surrounding atmosphere, provided that it is not inert. This, in fact, appears to be true, although considerable additional study is in order. This subject has recently been reviewed by Bleakney.[190]

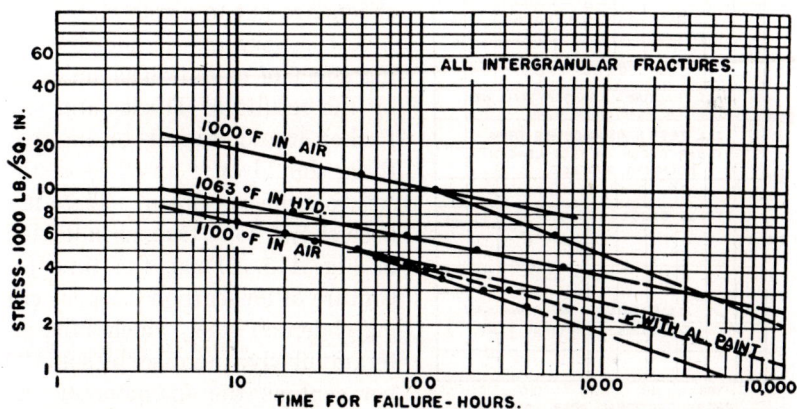

Fig. 114. Effect of atmosphere or protective coating on the variation of time for failure with stress for ingot iron. (*Thielemann and Parker.*[193])

Jenkins *et al.*[191, 192] have tested carbon steels and ingot iron in vacuum and observed that intercrystalline cracking occurs at high temperature and slow strain rate. Apparently no comparison tests in air were made. Thielemann and Parker,[193] have made tests of ingot iron in air, in hydrogen, and with the specimen coated with an aluminum paint (which confers some protection to scaling), with results recorded in Fig. 114. The samples tested in hydrogen did not display the change in slope in the log stress versus log rupture-time curve observed in the tests conducted in air. Aluminum painting resulted in an intermediate slope. The authors reported, however, that intergranular cracking and fracture developed independent of the atmosphere or of the change in slope. Further tests of a mild steel in air and in oxygen showed that the latter atmosphere yielded a sharper break in the stress versus rupture-time plot. These results led Thielemann and Parker to conclude that intergranular cracking is an inherent characteristic of fracture at elevated temperatures and slow strain rates, that this cracking precedes intergranular oxidation, and that the effect of intergranular oxidation is to hasten fracture with the resultant change in slope of the stress versus rupture-time plot. Further tests of this nature are greatly to be desired.

In relation to the influence of the atmosphere on the creep-rupture test, it is interesting to note that certain compositions seem to possess greater resistance to intergranular fracture. The high-chromium ferritic steels are particularly outstanding in this regard, while the austenitic steels have just the opposite characteristic. The nature of the effects are not understood.

A corollary of the life-shortening effect of oxidation as indicated by the results of Thielemann and Parker would appear to be that there should exist an effect of the size of the specimen. This has been shown to be true, as indicated in Fig. 115. Thus, the time for rupture of low-carbon 0.5 per cent molybdenum steel, which fails intergranularly, increases by some 20 per cent as the diameter of the specimen is increased from 0.25 to 0.50 in. In contrast, the fracture time of the higher chromium, higher silicon steel, which fractures transgranularly under the test conditions, is unaffected by the specimen size within the limits examined. Further tests of other materials should be made to see whether this effect is generally observed.

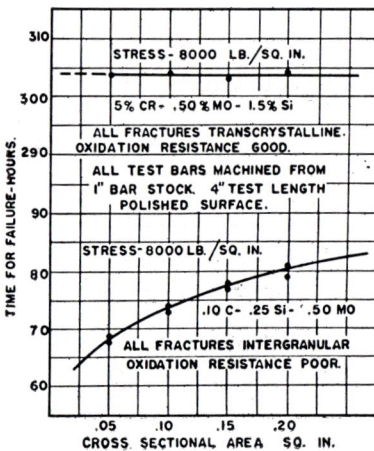

FIG. 115. Effect of specimen size on time for rupture of Cr-Mo-Si and Mo steels at 1200°F. (*Thielemann and Parker*.[193])

Creep-rupture tests by Agnew, Hawkins, and Solberg[194] in steam appeared to show longer life than in air, although the data appeared somewhat erratic and showed considerable scatter, attributable at least in part to mechanical difficulties in testing.

The Variation of Elongation and Reduction in Area with Rupture Time

With increasing time for rupture (decreasing strain rate) in either the conventional tensile test with continuously increasing load or the

constant-load creep-rupture test, there is a general tendency, but with
not infrequent exceptions, for the elongation and reduction in area to
decrease. This change in ductility, however, is of very irregular nature, as apparent in Fig. 116, which charts the percentage elongation
as a function of the time for rupture in creep-rupture tests of an austenitic stainless steel at several temperatures. Obviously these data
cannot be extrapolated to long times with any degree of confidence,
though such an extrapolation is greatly to be desired.

The author has discovered an apparently original empirical method,
which has proved in numerous tests with available data to be quite

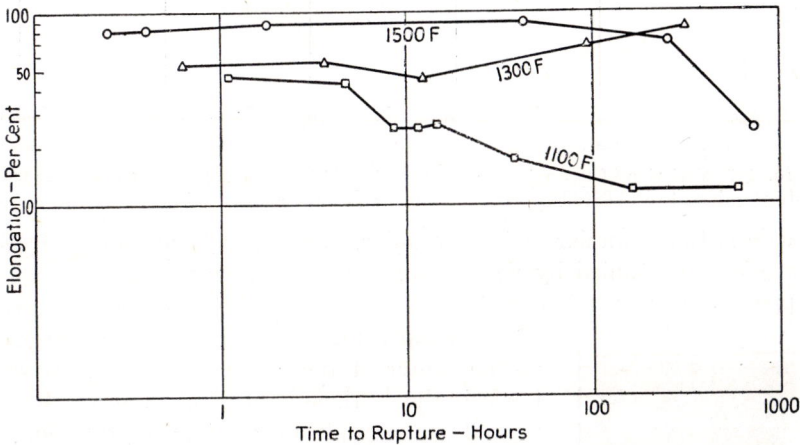

FIG. 116. Variation of elongation at rupture with time to rupture for 18 Cr–8 Ni–Mo
stainless steel (AISI Type 316) at 1100, 1300, and 1500°F. (*U.S. Steel Corp. data.*)

suitable for the prediction of the elongation for intervals of time exceeding the usual test period. The basis of this method was the discovery that if the percentage of elongation at fracture is divided by
the time for fracture to give what might be termed an average creep
rate and the logarithm of this rate is plotted as dependent upon the
logarithm of the initially applied stress, a linear relation is obtained
analogous to that when the minimum creep rate is employed. Having
this convenient relation, which may be extrapolated with confidence,
it is a simple matter to calculate the elongation corresponding to any
applied stress. This is obtained by multiplying the *average* creep rate
at this stress by the time to fracture at this stress. Data illustrating
the linear relation between the logarithm of the applied stress and the
average creep rate are shown in Fig. 117 for the same data shown in
Fig. 116. A similar relation was observed for reduction of area at
fracture.

The Beginning and Progress of Fracture in Creep to Rupture

The final period of accelerating creep rate (Fig. 81) quite evidently leads to fracture. Fracture is presumed to be progressive whether the

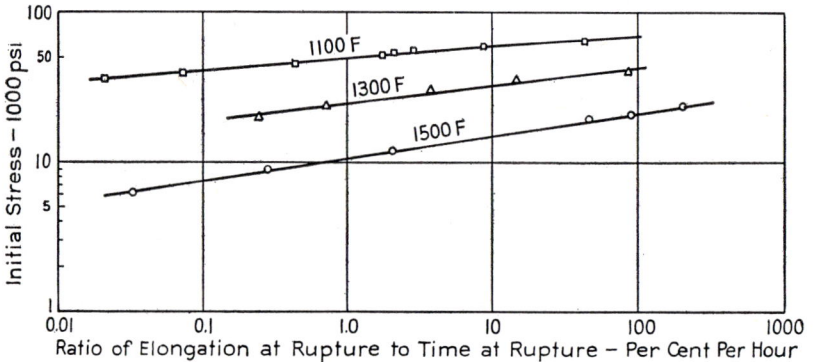

Fig. 117. Variation of "average" creep rate with initially applied stress for 18 Cr–8 Ni–Mo stainless steel (AISI Type 316) at 1100, 1300, and 1500°F. (*U.S. Steel Corp. data.*)

mode is transgranular or intergranular. Since the transgranular fracture is accompanied by necking and generally shows a cup and cone appearance, it may be presumed that as in ductile fracture at atmospheric temperature, the fracture crack begins at the center of the specimen and progresses toward the surface. At first the crack is normal to the applied stress forming the "cup," but then veers off at 45 deg. Figure 118 shows a crack in a copper tensile-test specimen on which straining was discontinued after necking had begun but just before fracture. Presumably a similar observation would be made on discontinuing a creep-rupture test in which fracture was preceded by necking.

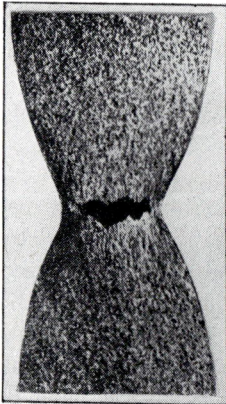

Fig. 118. Longitudinal section through copper tensile test specimen in which straining was discontinued just prior to fracture. (*Gensamer.*[99])

Although it has been generally assumed that fracture in the cup of the fracture (Fig. 118) is of the cleavage type governed by the normal stress and that in the cone part is of shear type, experimental studies of Parker *et al.*[196] appear to show that fracture is of the shear type across the entire section, at least in steel at ordinary temperatures. This conclusion was based on microscopic observation of etch pits developed in the grains of the specimen at the fracture, which showed fracture parallel to the slip planes, not to the cleavage planes. An experimental analysis of the state of stress in a necked specimen tended to confirm this conclusion by revealing that the shear stress is a maximum at the specimen center.

Fracture of the intergranular type which shows little or no necking apparently starts at the surface and progresses inward. This may be illustrated by the photomicrographs of Fig. 119 which show the progressive increase in depth of cracks migrating inward from the surface. Specimens were strained at a rate which would result in an intergranular fracture and discontinued after successively greater strain. Although the illustration is for a slow tensile test, there is no reason to believe that fracture in the creep-rupture test would be in any way different.

The point at which the fracture crack begins is of interest, but very few data are available. Tapsell[104] considers that local contraction of a tensile creep-rupture-test specimen coincides with the point of inflection of the creep curve. Although not stated, it is presumed that this observation is meant to apply only to the necking type of fracture, since presumbaly no local contracting occurs in the purely intergranular fracture. As pointed out earlier, Kanter[120] has attempted to show that the acceleration of creep rate in the final stage of creep is greater than should be expected as a result of the diminishing cross-sectional area. This presumably must be associated with progressing failure. Microscopic study of creep-rupture-test specimens strained to different fractional life intervals should prove illuminating, but this seems not to have been attempted.

McAdam *et al.*[197] consider that in many cases the period of accelerating creep begins when the rate of strain hardening decreases below a certain value. These authors reported the occurrence of microscopic intergranular cracks in certain cases. The cracks were observed to form early in the final stage of creep and to increase in number with increase in the temperature and with decrease in the creep rate.

An interesting insight into the problem of fracture at elevated temperatures is afforded by the experiments of Miller, Smith, and Kehl[101] summarized in Fig. 120 and Table VI. In this case, a 0.5 per cent molybdenum steel was tested in tension at one rate to the maximum load and then at another to fracture. In one case, the specimen was strained to maximum load at a rate, 0.01 in./in./hr, which if continued would have caused intergranular fracture; the strain rate was then changed to one, 1.0 in./in./hr, which had been found to produce transgranular failure if employed from the outset. Necking occurred, and fracture was transgranular. The test was also made in the reverse fashion: a specimen was strained to maximum load at a rate, 1.0 in./in./hr, which would result in transgranular failure, and then the strain

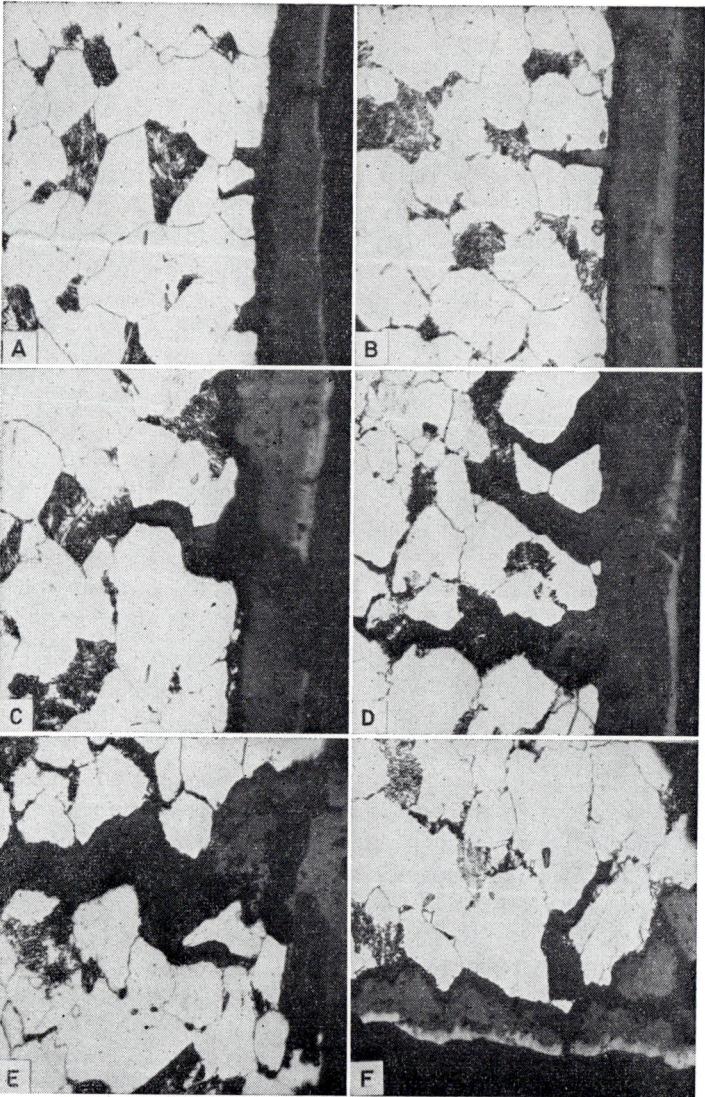

Fig. 119. Mechanism of intergranular failure in pearlitic C-Mo steel strained at 0.01 in./in./hr at 1100°F. (*Miller, Smith, and Kehl.*[101]) Micrographs taken on longitudinal sections parallel to axis of specimens; (*a*) to (*e*) show migration of cracks inward from surface of specimen; (*f*) shows final fracture. Tests stopped and successive specimens examined after the following:

A. 12.0 per cent extension in 14.5 hr
B. 17.0 per cent extension in 19.5 hr
C. 22.5 per cent extension in 25.0 hr
D. 27.5 per cent extension in 30.5 hr
E. 30.0 per cent extension in 37.0 hr
F. 30.0 per cent extension in 37.0 hr

rate was changed to 0.01 in./in./hr, producing intergranular fracture. The nominal stress-strain curves obtained in the two cases are shown in Fig. 120; the decrease in nominal stress at the maximum was a result of the time interval consumed in changing gears to effect the change in

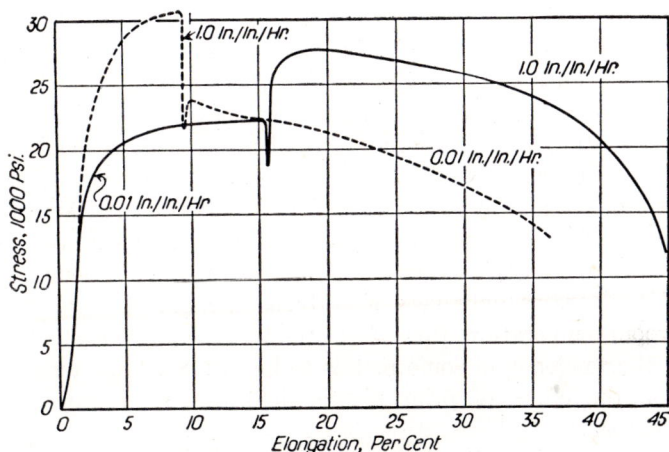

FIG. 120. Effect of change of strain rate on tensile properties of carbon-molybdenum steel at 1100°F. (*Miller, Smith, and Kehl.*[101])

rate. These experiments showed that the strain rate employed to the maximum load exerted a minor influence on the subsequent behavior, this being dependent primarily upon the strain rate from the maximum load to fracture.

TABLE VI. TWO-RATE TESTS ON A PEARLITIC 0.5 PER CENT MO STEEL AT 1100°F

Type of test	Strain rate, in./in./hr	% elong.	% red. in area	Type of fracture
Two-rate................	0.01–1.0	41	75	Transgranular
Two-rate................	1.0–0.01	43	43	Intergranular
Single-rate.............	1.0	56.5	80.5	Transgranular
Single-rate.............	0.01	35	42.5	Intergranular

Summary

Fracture occurs on specific crystallographic planes which depend on the metal and the type of crystal lattice, and which may or may not be identical with the slip planes. In single crystals, fracture may occur either by a cleavage or in some cases by shearing off along the slip planes. The former type of fracture occurs on attaining a critical value of the normal stress acting on the cleavage plane, while the shearing type of fracture occurs at a critical value of the resolved shear stress.

Fracture of polycrystalline metal is not as simple as for single crystals, and no universally accepted criterion is available for predicting fracture under complex states of stress. The maximum normal-stress criterion has been widely employed for qualitative explanations of the effects of variables, but owing largely to the experimental difficulties involved in studying fracture, few quantitative data are available.

The fracture stress may be expected to be influenced by variables such as temperature, prior plastic deformation, rate of straining, chemical composition, and structure, but the specific effects are not very well known in most instances. The fracture stress is generally considered to increase only very slightly as the temperature is lowered below room temperature; this affords the basis for a qualitative explanation of the tendency of some metals to be brittle at low temperatures. Data on the effect of prior plastic deformation appears somewhat contradictory.

Under repeated applications of stress, metals are observed to fracture at stresses far below those encountered on static loading. The mechanism of this fatigue type of fracture is not well understood.

Fracture at elevated temperatures may be either transgranular or intergranular. The latter type is more apt to occur the higher the temperature and the lower the strain rate. The time for rupture (fracture) in a creep-rupture test varies with the initially applied stress according to a power function. An exponential law, also suggested for this variation, does not appear to suit the available data so well. In the log-log plotting of the power relation, two straight lines are frequently observed. The initial slope is associated with transgranular fracture, the final slope with intergranular fracture. The change in slope is absent in a nonoxidizing atmosphere, and is more marked the more oxidizing the atmosphere.

The elongation and reduction in area in the creep-rupture test vary rather erratically with time for rupture, but the ratio of either of these quantities to the time for rupture varies as a power function with the initially applied stress. This observation furnishes the basis for the prediction of ductility for times beyond those which can be studied in laboratory tests.

CHAPTER VI

THEORIES OF FLOW AND FRACTURE

Metallographic Characteristics of Flow and Fracture

We have already discussed and illustrated several metallographic characteristics of the flow and fracture of metals. These include the slip lines, twin markings, and deformation bands associated with flow and the transgranular and intergranular types of fracture. In the present section we shall consider certain features which appear to be unique with creep and in addition we shall consider briefly what has been learned from X-ray diffraction examination. Since this latter technique of examination has not yet been considered, it will be best to consider it first. For a comprehensive review of X-ray diffraction techniques for studying metals, see Barrett.[10]

Upon exposure of an annealed single-crystal or large-grained specimen of metal to a beam of X-rays, the resulting diffraction effects will be recorded on an appropriately placed film as distinct sharp spots whose size and shape depend upon the geometry of the beam and on the camera. As the number of grains irradiated by the X-ray beam increases, the number of the spots increases. (This behavior may be used for grain-size estimation.) When the X-rays are monochromatic, the spots tend to group into concentric rings. Upon cold working even a slight amount, the sharp spots of the annealed material become blurred and show a radial lengthening termed "radial asterism" (when the X-rays are of a range of wave lengths) as well as a broadening. With fine-grained material (and monochromatic radiation) the individual spots tend to lose their individual identity on cold working and merge with neighboring spots to form continuous or nearly continuous rings. This characteristic change is a sensitive indicator of cold work. On recrystallization annealing, the individual spots again become apparent.

The radial asterism and broadening of individual diffraction spots may be conceived as originating in a bending of the planes of the crystal lattice and resulting in a corresponding distortion of the diffracted beam, much as a bent mirror would reflect a beam of light. Or the asterism may be attributed, in some cases at least, to an actual range in orientation of small crystallites of varying orientation resulting from fragmentation of the original grains.

Wood and Tapsell[198] have employed X-ray diffraction examination, with particular reference to the effects described above, to reveal an interesting difference between relatively fast and slow creep deformation. Straining a specimen of annealed aluminum to an extension of 0.9 per cent at 570°F in an ordinary tensile test, that is, relatively rapidly, and then cooling to atmospheric temperature resulted in a characteristic cold-worked appearance to the X-ray diffraction pattern, similar to Fig. 121a. However, when a similar specimen was extended the same extent in 50 min. by creep under constant load at the same temperature and then cooled, the diffraction spots appeared still relatively sharp as in the original sample, or similar to Fig. 121b. Reheating the first sample to 570°F and holding for a time equal to that employed in the creep sample did not result in any appreciable change. Clearly, there is indicated that there is a difference in the mode of deformation in the two instances.

Microscopic examination has also revealed characteristic differences between creep deformation and that effected at a relatively rapid rate. We have already noted one outstanding difference, namely, that under a slow rate of deformation at high temperatures, the grains at the fracture may be equiaxed even though the specimen may have had a total strain of 50 per cent or more; this contrasts with the severely elongated grains of the fast-rate and low-temperature deformation (Fig. 113). This effect is most remarkable. Evidently, to maintain its equiaxed shape, each grain must be continuously in a state of flux at its boundaries, giving to and receiving from surrounding grains. It would appear that careful microscopic examination of this process, apparently not yet done, would provide valuable insight into the nature of the effect.

A related and equally striking feature of creep, noted by Rosenhain and Humphrey,[33] Hanson and Wheeler,[11] and Moore *et al.*,[34] is that flow seems to occur principally at the grain boundaries. This is evident as a rotation of the grains during creep, as indicated in Fig. 122, which represents the appearance after creep of an originally microtomed surface of a lead alloy containing 2 per cent tin. The grain structure of this unetched specimen has been revealed owing to a relative displacement normal to the surface as well as to a rotation of the grain, as shown by the fact that the originally straight scratches, although remaining straight within a grain, now vary in direction from one grain to another. Apparently a spatial rotation has occurred. No slip lines

(a) Deformed at room temperature.

(b) Deformed in creep at 1100°F.

FIG. 121. Back reflection have x-ray diffraction patterns obtained from 18 Cr–8 Ni stainless steel after approximately 0.5 per cent plastic strain in a tension test at room temperature and in a 3,000-hr creep test at 1100°F. Chromium monochromatic radiation.

are observed, although a similar strain effected at a relatively rapid rate readily results in such markings. In fact, it is difficult to rationalize the appearance shown in Fig. 122 with the slip process; rather it has been likened to grains swimming in their own boundaries.

The apparent rotation of grains is undoubtedly associated with the previously mentioned observation of the occurrence of equiaxed grains at the fracture of samples which have been strained more than 50 per cent. Moreover, the mechanism of creep whereby grain rotation occurs is clearly a complex one with either or both severe deformation near the grain boundaries and interchange of atoms from one grain to another, that is, of migration of grain boundaries, since in general the individual grains are so interlocked as to preclude rotation.

Fig. 122. Microtomed surface of a lead sample tested in creep, showing rotation of grains. (*Moore et al.*[34])

Aside from the numerous observations of creep-rupture fractures, the most extensive study of creep by means of the microscope is that of Hanson and Wheeler[11] who tested annealed aluminum sheet with different grain sizes, including single crystals, at different strain rates and temperatures. One face of each specimen was polished prior to test and examined afterward. On slow deformation at elevated temperatures no slip markings were noted, but the grain boundaries became prominent; this was termed "slipless" flow. Microscopic examination suggested a uniform strain within the grains and a complex strain at and near the boundaries. In contrast, single crystals showed profuse slip markings at creep rates which produced no sign of slip in the aggregate specimens. However, if straining was sufficiently slow, even single crystals showed no slip markings. Furthermore, in samples of large and small grains, the former showed slip markings and the latter did not under certain strain rates. Hanson and Wheeler suggest that the absence of apparent slip does not necessarily mean viscous flow, but may mean only that the markings are so close together as to be irresolvable.

Hanson and Wheeler observed intercrystalline fracture in polycrystalline aluminum; this was associated with an apparent density decrease during creep, as would be anticipated owing to the intergranular voids. Single crystals, however, tended to fail by shear along the slip planes, and no decrease in density was noted. An interesting observation was that the slipping during the final stage of creep preceding fracture appeared to be confined to comparatively few of the slip markings, these assuming a very prominent appearance and frequently branching.

Some investigators have explained the commonly observed equiaxed grains at creep fracture as arising by a mechanism of creep involving continuous recrystallization. Although microscopic examinations which might confirm this are not plentiful, such studies only occasionally show recrystallization, at least, in the accepted sense of the term— visible new grains. When recrystallization occurs during creep, it seems to be associated with abnormally high creep rates while the process is proceeding, according to scattered reports in the literature. This subject is also considered in another section.

The scarcity of reports of microscopic examination attempting to follow creep deformation and the relative ignorance existing on this subject would indicate that this useful tool could be profitably employed to a greater degree.

Theories of Fracture: Crack Theory and Thermodynamic Theory

The actual strength of metals, as of all solids, is considerably less than that suggested by theoretical calculation. This is true of either the flow or fracture strength, which are of essentially the same magnitude relative to the theoretical strength. The most important problem in any theory of flow or fracture is therefore to obtain an understanding of this apparent weakness.

The theoretical strength to be expected of a metal may be calculated in several ways based on a consideration of surface energies, the attractive and repulsive forces between atoms, and by other means.[199-201] Such calculations give strengths 100 to 10,000 times greater than those experimentally observed. Since, historically, the subject of fracture received theoretical treatment earlier than flow, fracture will be considered first.

The theoretical calculations of strength all deal with the case in which all the atoms across the plane of separation are displaced simultaneously, that is, the process of fracture (or flow) is homogeneous. This has led many investigators to suggest the presence of cracks or other discontinuities on a microscopic scale which would result in stress concentrations, which in turn would reduce the apparent strength.

Griffith[202, 203] pointed out the possible influence of imperfections such as cracks and developed a theory which has met with some success in explaining the observed weakness as well as the marked effect of specimen size in brittle materials. For example, Griffith found glass fibers 0.003 mm in diameter to be 20 times as strong as fibers 1 mm in diameter. In brittle materials these imperfections may be considered to be surface cracks, but this cannot be true for ductile materials where fracture begins in the interior of the sample (Fig. 118). Griffith assumed that small cracks gave rise to stress concentration and he developed a relation between the size of these cracks (which determines the stress concentration), the surface energy, and the observed strength. With this relation and the assumption of the normal-stress criterion of fracture, Griffith calculated that the observed strength of glass corresponds to cracks of length 1 to 2 microns. Griffith also performed several experiments which supported his theory. By testing freshly drawn fibers of superheated glass, Griffith observed strength up to 20 times the normal strength, or of the same fibers after "aging." If the fibers were touched, the high strength disappeared immediately. Aging or touching was considered to allow flaws to form. Orowan[199] has also cited other supporting evidence obtained in tests of mica using grips narrower than the test sheet to avoid the edge cracks; these showed strengths about 10 times greater than usual.

Joffe[204] found that by testing under water the fracture stress of rock salt could be raised from about 0.5 kg/sq mm to from 30 to 160 kg/sq mm or nearly equal to that theoretically calculated, 200 kg/sq mm. The continuous dissolving of the crystal in the water so that the surface was constantly fresh and free of surface cracks was considered responsible for the increase in strength.

Griffith's theory was not found applicable to ductile fracture, that is, fracture preceded by plastic deformation; application of the concept for this case in fact led to unreasonably large cracks, 1 to 2 cm in size.

In recent years, though recognizing the difficulties in applying the microcrack theory to metals, Zener and Hollomon[102] have tried to interpret certain fracture phenomena in metals in terms of microcracks assumed to be present. In particular, a qualitative explanation for the effect of kind and degree of straining was advanced on the basis of the reorientation of the microdefects with deformation. In still further work, Fisher and Hollomon[205] have attempted a quantitative application of the microcrack theory to metals, with apparently moderate success for some data.

Another approach to the problem of fracture is what might be termed the thermodynamic approach. First advanced by Born[208] and Furth, [206, 207] the process of fracture is likened to that of melting. Assuming the maximum normal-stress criterion of fracture, as did Griffith, and no plastic deformation, Furth has developed a relation between breaking strength and the energy of melting which yields values of strength in fair agreement with those observed experimentally. Saibel[209, 210] has more recently formulated a thermodynamic theory of fracture, assuming a relation between fracture and the latent heat and volume change of melting. The criterion of fracture was that of a critical strain energy per unit volume. Saibel's calculations indicated that if no plastic deformation occurs prior to fracture the breaking strength would correspond to that calculated from theoretical calculations. If plastic deformation occurs, the fracture stress is reduced to the magnitude experimentally observed; Saibel's calculations were in fair agreement with experimental observation. Consequently, it was concluded that plastic flow precedes all fractures. Whether such theory may correctly embrace the influence of metallurgical structure, by which means the strength of certain metals can be varied widely, is not known. It is also not clear that the thermodynamic approach is capable of explaining the surface effects noted by Griffith and by Joffe, which have already been discussed.

The principal lack retarding the development of a sound theory of fracture is the scarcity of adequate experimental data, and it is questionable how far theoretical considerations may profitably proceed in this subject until such data are available.

A theory of fracture in creep-rupture tests has recently been proposed and should be mentioned. This theory advanced by Machlin and Nowick[211] involves the application of the general reaction rate theory, developed by Eyring *et al.*,[149, 150] to the creep-rupture test. The basic principles of this theory have been discussed in an earlier section on generalized expressions for creep, and will not be repeated at this time. Machlin and Nowick assume that creep to rupture is a rate process governed by the maximum shear stress but do not speculate as to the nature of the unit process or physical mechanism which is involved.

An expression relating the time to rupture in its dependency on the applied stress and temperature, as well as certain material constants, was derived as follows:

$$\log t_r = \frac{A + BT - D\sigma}{T} \tag{45}$$

where t_r is the time to rupture, T the absolute temperature, σ the applied stress, A and B are material constants, and D is defined as

$$\log D = E + FT$$

where E and F are material constants. The evaluation of the numerous material constants requires that many tests be made. The authors suggest that tests of four different stresses at each of three or four different temperatures are required for this purpose, and further suggest the desirability of a number of duplicate tests for greater reliability. Machlin and Nowick estimate the precision of the creep to rupture data available to them as ±25 per cent; this appears somewhat less than would be encountered generally. Satisfactory agreement between experiment and theory was observed for the available data. The authors report also that a given material may have three different sets of constants, depending on the temperature and stress and the occurrence of microstructural changes during test. This would appear to be a severe limitation to the practical application of the derived expression.

One important consequence of Eq. (45), developed from the reaction rate theory, is that the applied stress is related to the time to rupture at a constant temperature in a semilogarithmic rather than in a double logarithmic relation as commonly employed. As we have already seen, however, the latter rather than the former method of plotting appears to represent many data accurately suggesting skepticism of the treatment. It should be borne in mind that the creep-rupture test is of quite complex nature with varying stress as well as deformation rate throughout the test, and it would be rather surprising that a simple expression, in terms, for example, of the initially applied stress, such as that derived by Machlin and Nowick, be generally applicable.

Theories of Flow

As we have already seen, plastic flow may occur by slipping or by twinning at ordinary temperatures and possibly by other modes at elevated temperatures. The twinning mode of deformation has received little theoretical consideration, in part because it plays a somewhat secondary role in the deformation of many of the commercially important metals. Accordingly we shall ignore twinning in our consideration of plastic flow, but without doubt, an adequate treatment of twinning will necessarily involve concepts developed for understanding plastic flow.

As with fracture, the most outstanding characteristic of flow is that it occurs at such relatively low stresses. Although on a macroscopic scale, slip appears to occur across a grain in a manner analogous to the motion of playing cards past one another, the theoretical shearing stress required for such a macroshear is many times that experimentally observed. Accordingly, theoretical investigators have postulated various mechanisms involving defects with resultant stress concentration, much in the manner of those postulated to explain the low fracture stresses experimentally observed (see preceding section). Another, perhaps less evident, fault of the deck of cards analogy is that it does not account for strain hardening, for if one plane of atoms simply slid past another, like cards, the periodicity of the crystal lattice would not be disturbed, and slip should not cease, that is, strain hardening should not occur, as long as the applied stress does not decrease. Quite evidently then, the basis of plastic flow and strain hardening must be sought on a microscopic or atomic scale. None of the several theories of plastic flow which have been advanced seem entirely adequate, and they will not be considered in all their details. This subject has recently been thoroughly reviewed by Seitz and Read.[36] It should also be recalled that certain theories of the creep of metals have already been considered in the section on Creep. These were of somewhat limited nature and will not be again discussed here.

Smekal and Zwicky Theories. To account for the plastic yielding of metals at the relatively low stresses experimentally observed, Smekal[212] suggested that real crystals, as contrasted with ideal crystals, contain flaws. These flaws were considered to be sites at which the regular arrangement of the crystalline lattice was disturbed. Upon application of an external stress, these sites acted to concentrate the stress resulting in flow at much lower stress than that theoretically calculated for an ideal crystal. This concept is thus quite similar to that of Griffith for fracture, discussed earlier. Smekal considered the submicroscopic crystalline faults to be of somewhat regular nature and to be a natural consequence of the growth process by which the crystal formed. Slip was considered to be a process of "self-diffusion" of the atoms in the region of stress concentration, that is, occurring in an inhomogenous manner on an atomic scale, in some manner which is not entirely clear. As indicated by the analogy to diffusion, it would be expected that temperature should play some role, though perhaps of secondary nature, in determining the yield value.

Although it is generally accepted that real crystals are not perfect, and in fact, various sorts of experimental evidence show this, the exact nature of at least certain kinds of these defects is not known. It would therefore appear that Smekal's theory can at best provide nothing more than a qualitative explanation of the problem.

Zwicky[213] has proposed a somewhat different picture of the lattice defects. In contrast to other views. Zwicky postulated that it is not the ideal, or perfectly ordered, lattice that possesses minimum energy, but rather that this energy, owing to certain physical reasons, will be found in a crystal containing regular deviations of a mosaic nature, giving rise to crystalline mosaic pattern. Thus at regular intervals of perhaps several hundred atom distances there is assumed to exist planes of atoms which form what might be considered a secondary lattice and which represent planes of weakness along which shear movement may occur at relatively low applied stress. Much controversy has developed as to whether such mosaic patterns occur in crystals, but the evidence cannot be considered here.

Becker-Orowan Theory. Becker[214] proposed that as a result of the thermal vibration of the atoms of a crystal at temperatures above absolute zero the energy in any small unit of volume undergoes statistical variations which superimpose upon and modify an externally applied stress. Accordingly, with a given external stress, the local fluctuations will result at certain sites in sufficiently great shearing stress, that is, the critical shearing stress, to effect slip in these small regions. A sufficient number of these local deformations results somehow, in a manner which is not clear, in a macroscopic shear or slip.

On the basis of the Boltzmann probability theorem, Becker derived an expression relating the velocity of deformation to the applied shear stress, the temperature, and certain material constants. Thus the probability that a small volume V will have an increase in energy E needed to effect plastic flow is given by the Boltzmann expression:

$$\text{Probability} = c_1 e^{-E/kT} \qquad (46)$$

where k is the Boltzmann constant, T the absolute temperature, and c_1 is a constant. If τ is the external applied shear stress and τ_0 is the critical shear stress for flow, the additional stress required to be contributed by thermal motion is $(\tau_0 - \tau)$ and in terms of this stress and the shear modulus of elasticity G

$$E = \frac{V(\tau_0 - \tau)^2}{2G} \tag{47}$$

Assuming that the rate of deformation R is proportional to the probability, we may then, by substitution of Eq. (47) in Eq. (46), write

$$R = Ce^{-(V(\tau_0-\tau)^2/2GkT)} \tag{48}$$

where C is a proportionality constant.

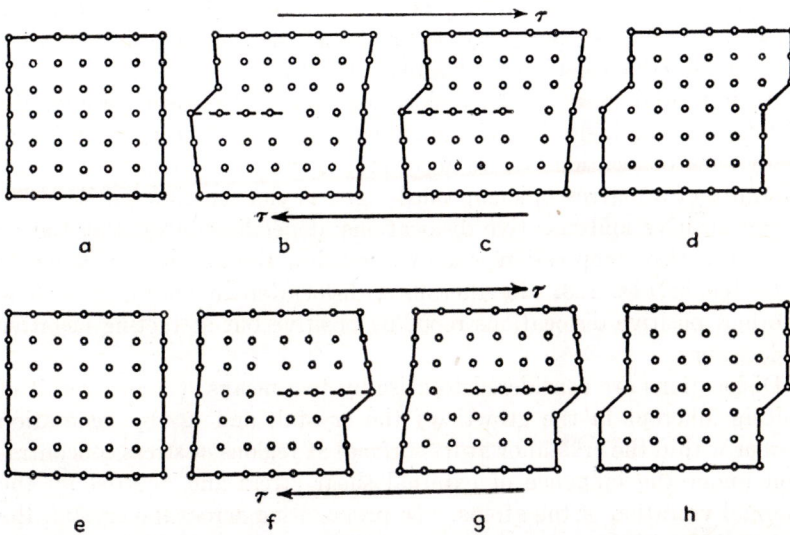

FIG. 123. Motion of positive (*a*, *b*, *c*, and *d*) and negative (*e*, *f*, *g*, and *h*) dislocations in a two-dimensional lattice, effecting a lattice displacement of 1-atom distance. (*Taylor*.[218])

Orowan has extended this relation by introducing the stress concentrating effect of lattice defects. Thus the applied shear stress τ is modified to $q\tau$ where q is a stress concentration factor, assumed to be a constant.

Some few experimental data have been obtained from which values for the several material constants in the expression have been estimated, while other investigators, assuming that the ratio of V and G in Eq. (48) does not vary with temperature, have derived an expression for the variation of the critical shearing stress for plastic flow with temperature. These applications of the Becker-Orowan theory, however, appear to have only qualitative value at present.

Dislocation Theory. A theory for plastic flow which has received much attention and wide acceptance in recent years is that which involves the concept of dislocations. This theory is an outgrowth of work by Orowan,[216] Polanyi,[217] and Taylor,[218] but many other investigators have made valuable contributions. The dislocation from which the theory takes its name is a type of lattice defect best described by illustration (Fig. 123). As is apparent in this two-dimensional sketch, the dislocation is a local deviation from the regular arrangement of a perfect lattice, there being one more atom on one side of the plane of the dislocation than on the other. This gives rise to local distortion with resulting increase in elastic strain energy; consequently with an external applied shear stress, flow may occur at a stress considerably below the theoretical value calculated for a perfect lattice.

As indicated in Fig. 123, dislocations may propagate through the lattice effecting a shear of single lattice distance. The propagation of many such dislocations would according to the theory result in the appearance of a macroscopic slip marking. Taylor has differentiated between positive and negative dislocations, depending on whether the region of lattice compression is above or below the dislocation plane, as indicated in Fig. 123. Furthermore, dislocations exert forces on one another, positive dislocations repelling positive but attracting negative dislocations.

Dislocations are considered to arise by two means: (1) as a result of factors inherent in the growth of the crystal, and (2) by generation (either within the crystal or at its surface) at regions of stress concentration under the influence of external shear stress and abetted by the thermal vibration of the atoms. In propagating across the crystal, the dislocations either pass entirely out of the crystal, thus effecting plastic shear, or become obstructed at certain sites. These latter may be lattice defects of one kind or another, including the force fields of other dislocations, or grain boundaries if the sample is polycrystalline. Such obstructions are considered to be the cause of strain hardening. Various investigators have attempted to calculate the magnitude of the force fields surrounding a dislocation with appropriate assumptions concerning such unknown quantities as the dimensions of the dislocation.

Although dislocation theory is widely accepted as accounting for plastic flow, it permits few predictions which may be used to test its validity and therefore would appear to be principally of qualitative value at present. In fact, to a fault, the theory seems to be so elastic as being capable of explaining any mechanical characteristic, provided the proper assumptions are made as to the exact nature of the dislocations.

CHAPTER VII

TESTS AND TEST EQUIPMENT

The nature of plasticity and strength having been considered in the preceding chapters, it is now appropriate to treat methods of testing for these characteristics and the types of apparatus employed in such tests. The more common tests, such as tension, creep and creep to rupture, relaxation, and fatigue, will be considered, as well as several less common ones, such as hardness, modulus of elasticity, notch impact, and torsion. In general, the equipment for any one of these tests is not unique; in a few cases, commercial apparatus is available, but many laboratories have designed and constructed their own apparatus, or adapted it from apparatus of commercial manufacture. No attempt will be made to present an exhaustive survey, particularly from the historical standpoint, of all the individual types of apparatus, since this would yield a voluminous result of questionable value, and most types differ in relatively minor details. For this reason, as well as because of familiarity, the apparatus with which the author has had direct experience will generally be that most completely described.

The Hot Hardness Test

The hardness test is a tool which is widely used by metallurgists and engineers, both in research investigations and in control of commercial processes. Although it by no means provides all the information which is desired for most of these purposes, its relative simplicity, the readiness with which the test may be made, the smallness of sample required, and its nondestructive nature offer distinct advantages. The hardness test provides a reasonably good measure of the ultimate tensile strength in any specific type of alloy (Fig. 124). As such, it is a wonderful control test as well as a sorting tool in experimental studies of specific alloy systems (Fig. 127).

The hardness test has not been widely used at elevated temperatures, and has in fact been deprecated by some writers. However, it would appear that the hardness test should be relatively as valuable a tool at elevated temperatures in relation to the short-time tensile test as it is at atmospheric temperature. Of course, the short-time tensile test is of somewhat limited value at elevated temperatures, and this coupled with the experimental difficulty of testing at elevated temperatures provides a natural limitation to the widespread use of the hot hardness test. Aside from its value in providing an approximation of the short-time hot strength of structurally stable alloys, the hot hardness test should be especially valuable in studying, at temperature, the progress of phase changes, such as in allotropic transformations or precipitation hardening,

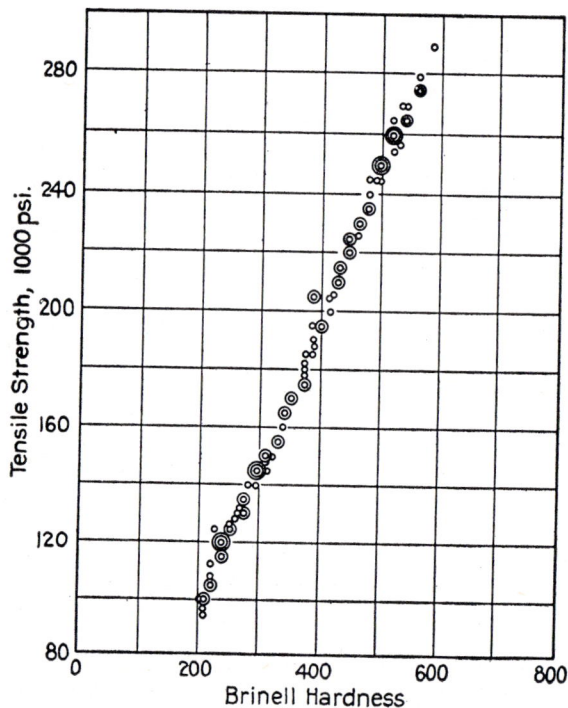

FIG. 124. Relation between tensile strength and hardness of quenched and tempered samples of some 15 different hardenable alloy steels at atmospheric temperature. (*Janitzky and Baeyertz.*[232])

which in many instances can be only imperfectly followed by atmospheric examination of samples in which the phase change has been interrupted and, it is hoped, suppressed by rapid quenching.

Because the hot hardness test is so little used, no standard test equipment or procedures have developed. Actual tests have ranged from the extremely crude, in which the specimen is removed from a heating furnace and tested with an unheated indenter in one of the common testers employed at atmospheric temperature, to refined ones in which the specimen and indenter are both heated and the test conducted in a protective atmosphere. Brinell,[233] who was among the first to attempt hot hardness tests employed the former procedure. With the passing years, greater and greater refinement has been effected.

As indicated in the preceding chapters, the strength of metals at elevated temperatures is greatly dependent upon the rate at which they are strained. Accordingly, the duration of the application of load is an important variable which must be controlled if consistent results are to be obtained. It will be recalled that the time of loading must be controlled even at room temperature when testing the hardness of the softer metals, such as lead. In terms of the duration of loading, hot hardness tests which have been made may be grouped into two broad categories, dynamic and static. Dynamic hardness testing involves loading of essentially impact nature, while the static test involves loading durations at least of the order of seconds.

The Dynamic Hot Hardness Test

The dynamic hardness test has been extensively employed in Germany, but has received little attention in this country. Fetz[234] has reviewed the field and described the types of dynamic test apparatus employed. In this type of test, a hard indenter, identical or similar to those employed in the conventional static test, is rapidly impressed into the test sample by some such means as a hammer blow or falling weight; the hardness number is determined from the relation between load and depth of penetration or from the rebound of the indenter. The test sample is heated to temperature and removed to the unheated apparatus for testing. The short time required for the test is considered to preclude the errors ordinarily inherent in such procedure. The dynamic hardness depends upon the elastic characteristics of the material, since the indenter rebounds from the test surface. In this respect, the dynamic hardness test is not measuring exactly the same characteristics of the metal as is measured in the static test.

Because of variations in test conditions, it is difficult or impossible to compare the results of different dynamic hardness tests or to compare dynamic hardness with static hardness. The proponents of the dynamic test claim certain advantages for it. In particular, it is claimed that owing to its dynamic nature it simulates the conditions involved in many commercial hot-forming operations, such as forging and rolling, more closely than does the static test. From the standpoint of the relative rates of deformation of the two tests, this is certainly true, and perhaps the dynamic test is of value in studying such operations. However, it should be borne in mind that commercial forming operations are complex in nature, one of the principal characteristics of interest being that of ductility (embrittlement), about which the hardness test provides little or no information. Accordingly the alleged relation between dynamic hardness and commercial hot-forming operations should be viewed with caution. In recent years, several investigations relating to formability have been reported; these involve hot twist tests or other tests involving consideration of ductility.

The Static Hot Hardness Test

The more widely used and more generally useful static hot hardness test has been made in a variety of ways with a variety of test equipment. The first refinement of Brinell's early tests, in which only the specimen was heated, was to heat both the specimen and indenter. With such refinement, however, came difficulties such as softening and deformation of the ordinary steel-ball indenter as well as scaling. This necessitated frequent replacement of the test ball. To preclude deformation of the indenter ball, sintered tungsten carbide balls have been employed; presumably a diamond ball could also be used. Scaling is detrimental from two standpoints: (1) the indenter is progressively reduced in dimensions as the scale is formed and broken off; (2) the scaling of the test specimen results in a hardness determination that is not characteristic of the metal itself. Thus a controlled atmosphere, preferably of inert nature, is required for best results. A reducing atmosphere might be suitable in some cases, but not in others, such as steel, in which a loss of carbon from the metal surface might result in as great, or greater, error than results from scaling.

Several types of apparatus suitable for accurately measuring hardness at elevated temperatures have been described in the literature. Bishop and Cohen[235] have described a furnace and testing arrangement which is fitted into a standard Rockwell hardness tester. The apparatus, which is sketched in Fig. 125, provides for the heating of both test sample and indenter (standard diamond Brale) in a purified nitrogen atmosphere. Standard Rockwell C readings are directly obtained without having to cool the specimen to atmospheric temperature for measuring, since the Rockwell measurement is based on the difference in depth of penetration of the standard indenter when a minor and then a major load is applied. Bishop and Cohen employed this apparatus primarily for obtaining the hardness of high-speed steel as dependent upon temperature and time of tempering and for evaluating the structural changes encountered in its heat-treatment.

A somewhat similar type of apparatus, but based on the Vickers hardness tester and employing a vacuum, has been described by Bens.[236] Details of this apparatus are shown in Fig. 126. The Vickers type of

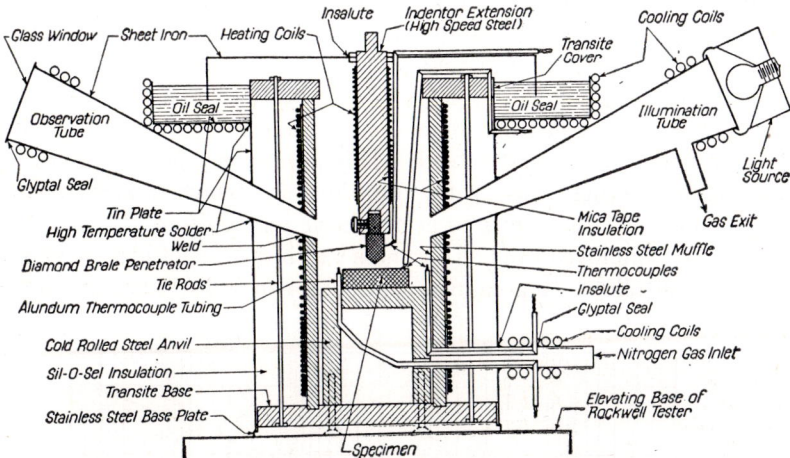

FIG. 125. Apparatus which when fitted into the standard Rockwell hardness tester may be used in measuring Rockwell hardness at elevated temperatures. (*Bishop and Cohen.*[235])

indenter, namely, a square base diamond pyramid, is employed. This type of hardness test has the great advantage that the hardness number is independent of the load employed. This is a desirable feature in any

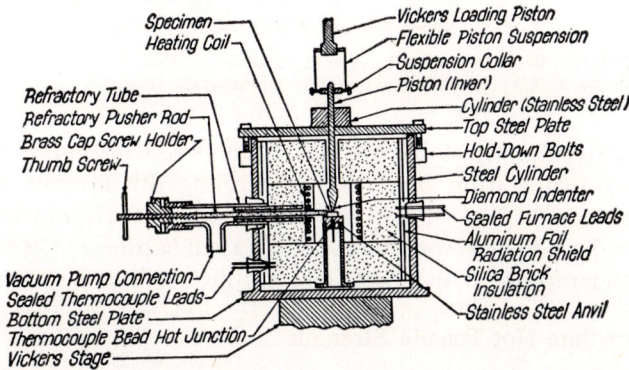

FIG. 126. Hot hardness tester employing a vacuum and based on the standard Vickers tester. (*Bens.*[236])

event, but is especially so where a wide range of temperature, with consequent wide variation in hardness, is being investigated. The test apparatus suffers one disadvantage; since the hardness is calculated from the projected area of the indentation, the specimen must be cooled to atmospheric temperature to measure the size of the impression.

Another type of apparatus, being developed by the author, involves the square-base diamond pyramid but employs an inert atmosphere of purified helium or argon. Although accurate hardness determinations are obtained by measuring the indentation after cooling to atmospheric temperature, an approximation of the hardness is obtained immediately at temperature by measuring the motion of the loading ram, that is, the depth of penetration, under load. This approximation will serve to guide further testing, such as the duration of a tempering treatment, without intermediate cooling to atmospheric temperature.

Bens[236] has employed the hot hardness test in studies of high-strength heat-resistant alloys (superalloys) and has concluded that in alloys

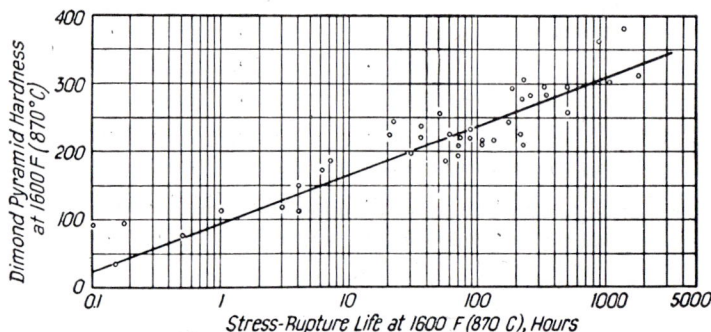

Fig. 127. Relation between diamond pyramid hardness at 1600°F and hours to rupture at 1600°F under 20,000 psi for some chromium-base alloys. (*Bens.*[236])

which are structurally stable the hot hardness test is a useful measure of elevated-temperature strength. Illustrating this are the data for various chromium-base alloys, reproduced in Fig. 127, which show a well-defined relation between diamond pyramid hardness at 1600°F and the time for rupture at this same temperature under a common stress.

The Short-time Hot Tensile Strength

The ordinary tensile test is the means most commonly employed for evaluating the load-carrying ability of a metal. The results of a tensile test are best expressed in terms of the stress-strain curve, shown schematically in Fig. 128. This curve is characteristic of most metals and alloys except mild steel, which shows an abrupt onset of plasticity, often accompanied by a decrease in load (Fig. 129) in contrast to the gradual onset of plastic flow illustrated in Fig. 128. The initial plastic flow, or yielding, of mild steel is inhomogeneous in nature, that is, the strain is not uniform along the gauge length; this can often be seen in strain markings, often called Lüders' lines, on the surface of the specimen.

Several features of the stress-strain curve are of interest and should be defined.

Elastic Limit: The maximum stress which may be supported without a permanent deformation upon release of the stress.

Proportional Limit: The maximum stress which may be supported without deviation from linear relation between stress and strain (Hooke's law).

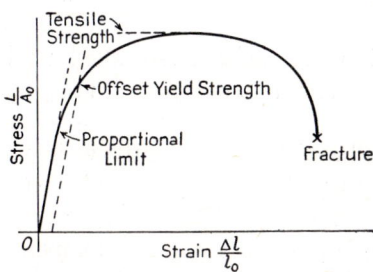

FIG. 128. Schematic stress-strain curve characteristic of metals in which the onset of plastic flow is gradual.

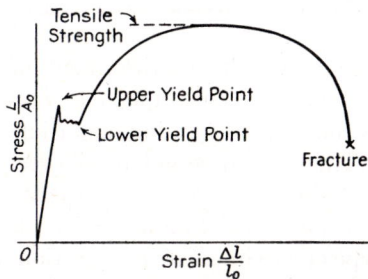

FIG. 129. Schematic stress-strain curve for mild steel in which plastic flow begins abruptly.

Modulus of Elasticity (Tensile): The ratio of unit stress to unit strain below the proportional limit.

Yield Strength: The stress at which a specified permanent deformation is attained. This is frequently determined by the offset method, illustrated in Fig. 128, a line being drawn parallel to the elastic portion of the stress-strain curve, but offset 0.1, 0.2, etc., per cent; the intersection of this line with the stress-strain curve gives the yield strength corresponding to the arbitrarily selected offset.

Yield Point: The stress at which, as in mild steel for which the term is generally reserved, there is an increase in strain without an increase in stress(or with a decrease in stress, Fig. 129).

Tensile Strength: The stress obtained by dividing the maximum load encountered during test by the original cross-sectional area.

Per Cent Elongation at Fracture: The ratio, multiplied by 100, of the increase in gauge length measured after fracture to the initial gauge length.

Per Cent Reduction in Area at Fracture: The ratio, multiplied by 100, of the decrease in cross-sectional area to the original cross-sectional area.

Tensile tests made at elevated temperatures yield stress-strain curves which are generally quite similar to those encountered at atmospheric temperature.* However, as we have noted in preceding sections, the effect of the rate of straining becomes more marked and strict attention must be paid to control of this variable. The short-time hot tensile test is of distinctly limited value in so far as predicting long-time strength, but like the hot hardness test it provides an approximation and serves as a sorting tool in studies of this kind. In addition, however, the short-time hot tensile test is of value in revealing ranges of temperature in which embrittlement of one kind or another, so-called "hot shortness," for example, may occur, and therefore is of interest in respect to commercial forming operations.

The short-time hot tensile test is employed to a sufficiently wide extent that the American Society for Testing Materials has established a Recommended Practice[237] for conducting the test. This prescribes the type of specimen, its preparation, the uniformity and control of temperature, and the procedure employed in making the test, as well as other pertinent details.

Many types of hot tensile-testing equipment are used, most of which have been of original design. Commercially built apparatus has now become available. Nearly all types, whether of commercial manufacture or not, make use of standard tensile-testing equipment and simply provide a heating furnace to surround the test specimen and a means of measuring the extension. This latter need is the most difficult one to fulfill, especially if interest lies in the initial stages of deformation, that is, in proportional limit and yield strength.

The Heating Furnace. The heating furnace may be of several types. At relatively low temperatures, a liquid bath is sometimes effectively employed. In general, however, an electric resistance-wound furnace is used throughout the entire temperature range of interest. Generally, the specimen is entirely enclosed within the furnace along with portions of the pull rods, but some tests are made with a specimen which passes entirely through the furnace, gripping being effected outside the furnace;

---

* The abrupt yield point of mild steel disappears above the "blue brittle" temperature range, about 500°F.

in this latter case it is common to employ a reduced section at a constant-temperature zone within the furnace. The bar-type specimen is more often entirely enclosed within the furnace, since it can be readily gripped therein with threaded adaptors, while sheet-type specimens, which are more difficultly gripped, often extend through the furnace and have a reduced section near the central portion of the furnace. Specimens suitable for such tests are sketched in Fig. 130.

Since the heat losses are not uniform along the specimen (and pull rods), it is necessary to design the furnace to compensate for these non-

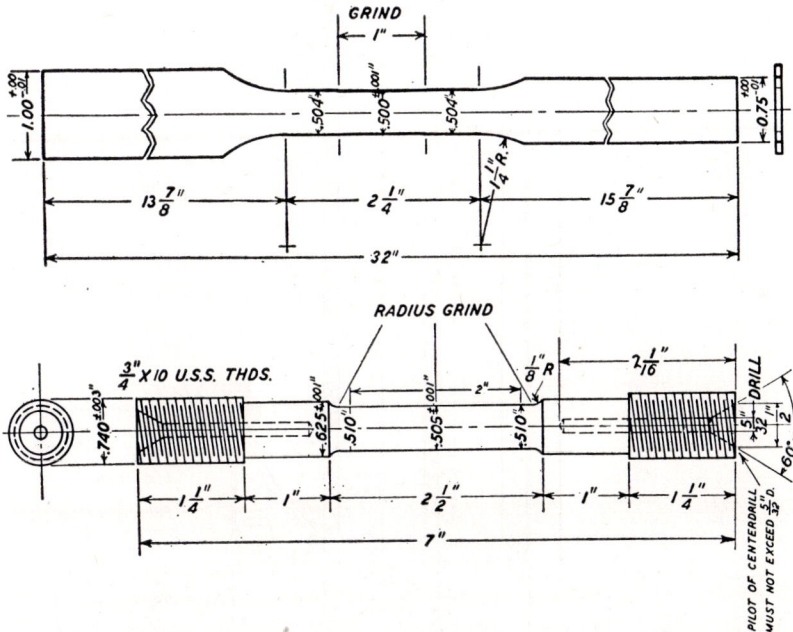

FIG. 130. Short-time hot-tensile-test specimens for sheet and bar stock used at U.S. Steel Corp. of Del. Research Laboratory.

uniform losses. This is accomplished by proportioning or spacing the winding in accordance with the heat losses or by providing separate windings, individually controlled, or both. Generally a combination of the two means is most efficacious. A sketch showing a furnace having three separate windings, one at the center and one at each end, is given in Fig. 131. The current through each is adjusted by means of external resistances. Over-all control of temperature is effected by a thermocouple located in the central windings which actuates a commercial temperature controller. Measurement of the specimen temperature is made

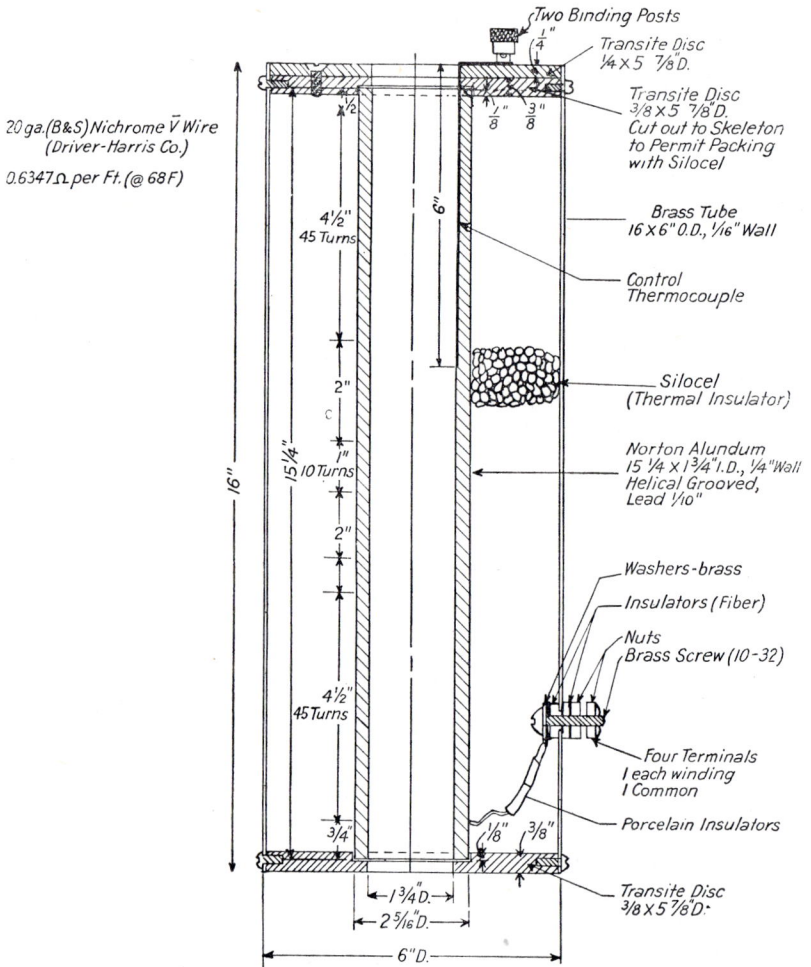

FIG. 131. Hot tensile furnace used at U.S. Steel Corp. of Del. Research Laboratory.

with three thermocouples attached to the specimen at its center and at the two ends of the gauge length.

High-temperature Extensometer. Various types of extension-measuring devices are employed. Except for techniques which involve sighting with a telescope through a window in the furnace,* the extension occurring within the gauge length is transferred by some mechanical means

* Such a scheme is employed in creep testing by the author and will be described in some detail in a following section.

to the outside of the furnace where it may be measured by any one of several standard techniques.

Tapsell[238] has described a type of extensometer employed in the National Physical Laboratory (of England). This apparatus, shown in

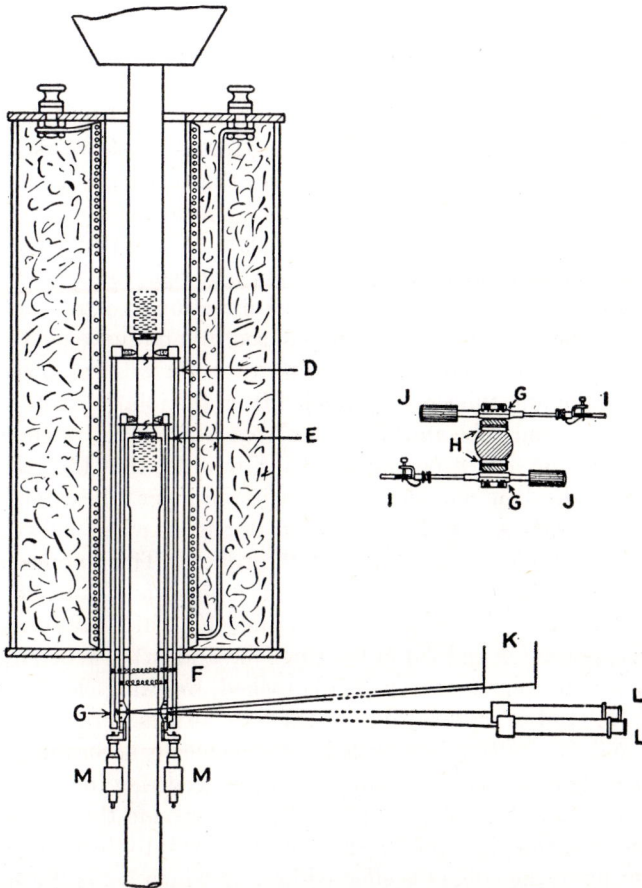

Fig. 132. Extensometer employed at the National Physical Laboratory (England) for short-time hot-tensile tests. (*Tapsell.*[238])

Fig. 132, employs the mirror extensometer principle of Martens. The extension occurring in the gauge length is transferred by extension arms *D* and *E* to the outside of the furnace. These extension arms are attached to the specimen with pointed screws and are held in place inside the furnace by tying with heat-resistant wire and at the outside by the springs F. The relative motion of the two extension arms is transmitted through steel shank G and roller H resting on the pull rod to mirrors I, which are counterbalanced by the holders J. The mirrors tilt with extension of the specimen, and the magnitude of this tilt and thus the extension is determined by observing the relative displacements on the scale K by sighting through telescopes L. Micrometers M attached to the inner extension arms are provided for measuring extensions beyond the range of the mirrors. The sensitivity of this type of mirror extensometer is very high, being in the order of 0.000002 in./in.

In the short-time hot-tensile-testing apparatus employed in the U.S. Steel Corp. of Del. Research Laboratory, the extension is transferred from the specimen to outside the furnace by means of concentric tubes (Fig. 133).* To the test specimen (1) collars (2) are attached by pivot points (3). These collars have joint pins (4) at right angles to the pivot points. Thus the collar can rock in one direction and the tube in the other. A tube (5) is passed over the pull rod (6) and suspended from the joint pins of the lower collar. A second tube (7) is telescoped concentrically over the first tube and suspended from the joint pins of the upper collar. The second tube and the collar from which it is suspended must be larger than the first tube and its collar, in order that the telescoping may be effected. The outside end of the first or inner tube extends below that of the outer tube; and an extensometer is attached between rings (5a and 7a) provided on the ends of the tubes. This extensometer is attached to the rings as shown in Fig. 134; it consists of top and bottom yokes (8 and 9) each provided with ball pins (10) which are screwed into V-shaped grooves (5b and 7b) in the rings (5a and 7a). When extension of the specimen occurs, a lever (11) is rocked, breaking electric contact at (12). An electric motor drives one of the contacts to remake the contact (12) and this motion is recorded autographically according to standard procedures as a measure of the extension occurring in the specimen.

To ensure that the collars are attached to provide the proper gauge length and that the pivot points are exactly normal to the specimen axis, the mounting of the collars is effected in a jig which holds the specimen and collars in proper relation to one another. Although a circular-section test specimen has been shown in describing the extension-measuring device, the same technique is employed for sheet specimens, the only essential difference being that the collars have a slit rather than a circular hole. The sheet specimen is gripped outside the furnace rather than inside, but has a reduced section at the hot zone. Figure 135 shows the

---

* U.S. Patent 2,301,872 to Q. M. Henderson.

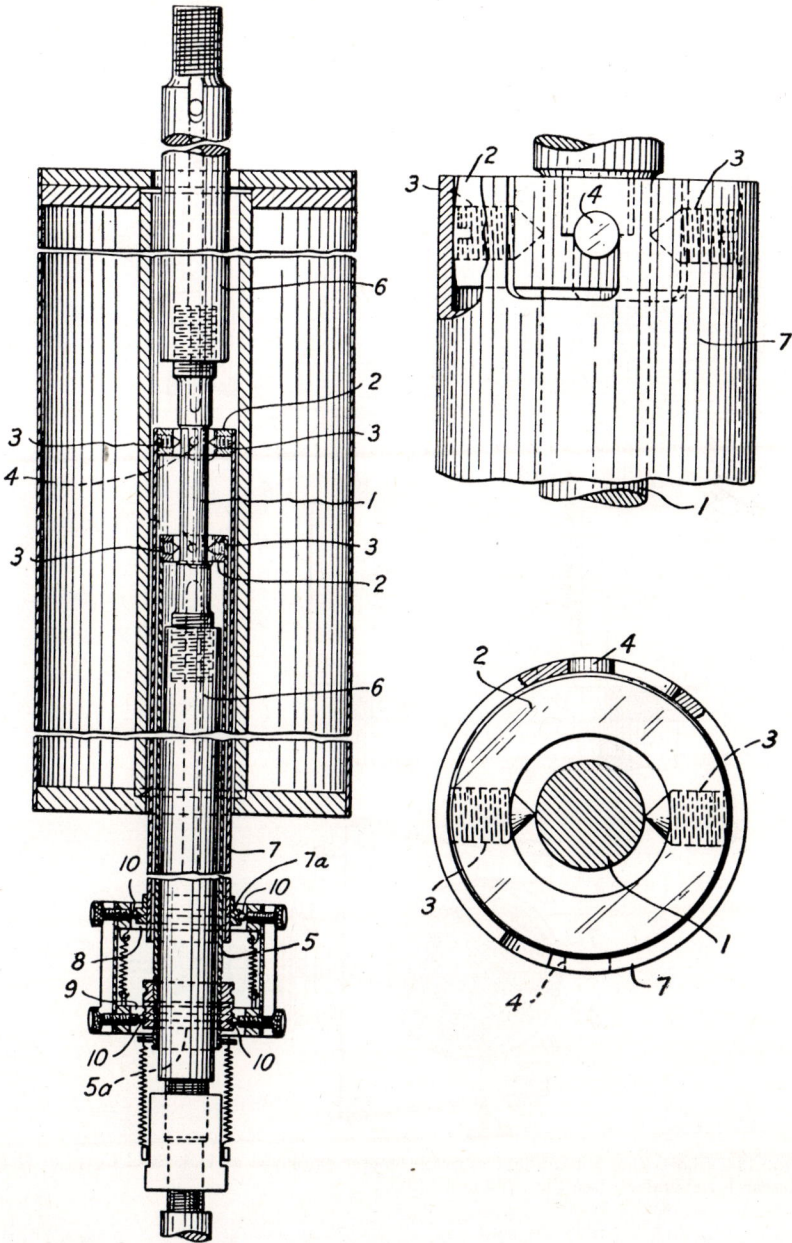

FIG. 133. Short-time hot-tensile-test extensometer employed at U.S. Steel Corp. of Del.
Research Laboratory (see also Figs. 134 and 135).

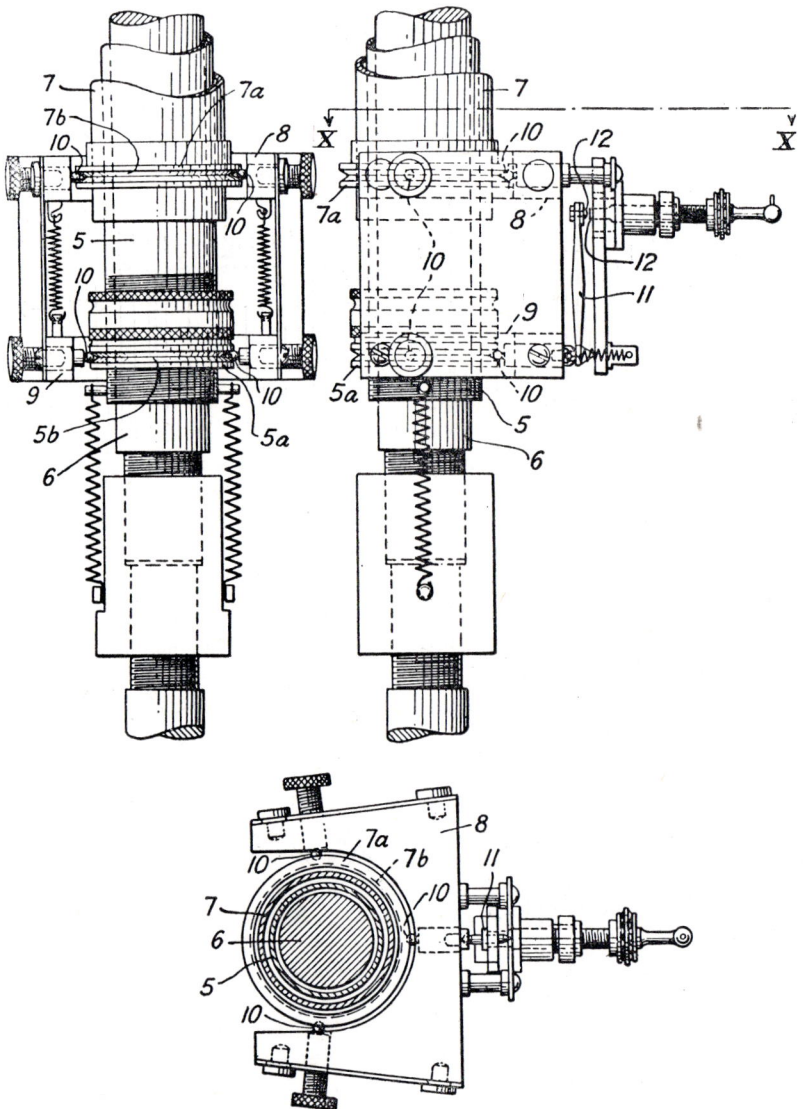

FIG. 134. Short-time hot-tensile-test extensometer employed at U.S. Steel Corp. of Del. Research Laboratory (see Figs. 133 and 135).

method of attaching the collars and of mounting the assembly for test of a bar specimen.

A photograph providing a general view of the short-time hot tensile testing equipment is reproduced in Fig. 136, while Fig. 137 provides a close-up of the furnace and extensometer during test of a sheet specimen.

Special Types of Short-time Hot-tensile-testing Equipment. In the foregoing section, consideration has been given to what might be termed essentially standard hot-tensile-testing equipment in which the specimen is stressed in a standard testing machine but is enclosed in a furnace.

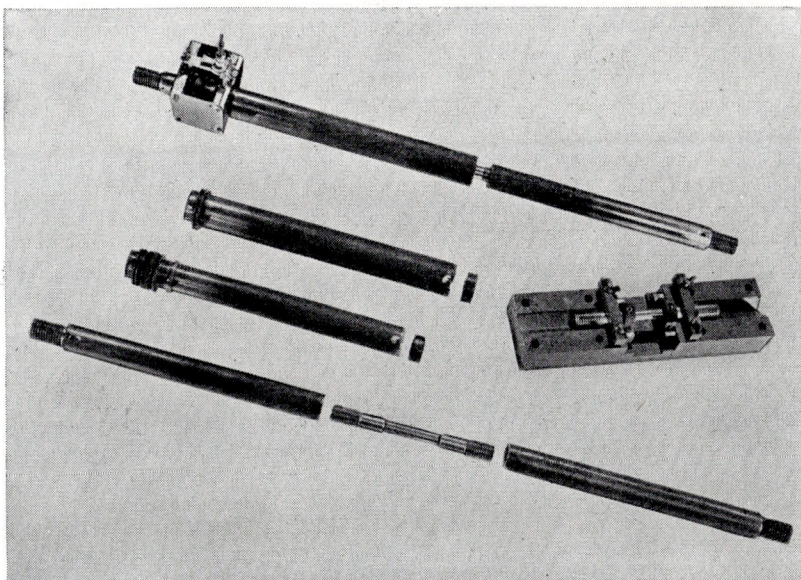

Fig. 135. Mounting of the short-time hot-tensile-test specimens. (*U.S. Steel Corp. of Del. Research Laboratory.*)

We shall now consider briefly several types of apparatus that have been devised for special purposes.

Manjoine and Nadai[239] have described a machine for making high-speed tension tests at elevated temperatures. The apparatus is shown in Fig. 138. The specimen c heated by an induction furnace e is attached through a force-measuring bar a to an upper head k and is threaded at its lower end into an anvil d, through which the force is applied; this is accomplished by striking the anvil with hammers f pinned at i to a flywheel g. The hammers are tripped by the trigger h and rotated into striking position by means of spring j. The deflection of the force-measuring bar a under load changes the width of an optical slit l through the motion of the pin m. This changes the amount of light projected through the slit and absorbed by the photocell n to o, thus providing a measure of the force when properly calibrated. The strain is determined from the downward motion of the anvil, which cuts a light beam projected on a photoelectric cell r to s, mounted in coaxial tubes p and q. The outputs of the photoelectric cells are recorded as stress-strain curves on the screen of an oscillograph.

Fig. 136. General view of short-time hot-tensile-test apparatus for sheet specimen at U.S. Steel Corp. of Del. Research Laboratory.

At the U.S. Steel Corp. of Del. Research Laboratory an apparatus of rather simple design has been employed for making high-temperature tensile tests under various uniform rates of straining. With this apparatus, shown in Fig. 139, a specimen held at a constant temperature is elongated at a uniform rate by means of a motor-driven gear train. Interchangeable gears permit the use of a variety of strain rates: 1.0, 0.1, 0.01, and 0.001 in./in./hr. The stress is calculated from the elastic extension of a weighbar in series with the specimen, and the strain from the strain rate employed and the elapsed time. Observations of the weighbar extension and of the elapsed time are recorded photographically with an automatically actuated motion-picture camera.

Jenkins and Mellor[240] have described an apparatus employed at the National Physical Laboratory for making short-time hot tensile tests in vacuum. This apparatus, shown in Fig. 140, is designed to fit into a standard tensile-testing machine and has been employed for studies of the structural changes occurring at the surface of metals during

FIG. 137. Close-up view of hot-tensile-test apparatus at U.S. Steel Corp. of Del. Research Laboratory.

deformation at elevated temperatures; it may also be employed for studies of the effect of atmosphere on deformation. Similar apparatus has been designed for creep-rupture testing in vacuum. No extension-measuring device was used with the vacuum tests.

General Considerations in Hot Tensile Testing. As pointed out earlier the strength of metals becomes increasingly dependent upon the rate of deformation, as the temperature is increased. Accordingly it is essential that this rate be controlled if the results of a series of tests are to be comparative. Control of this rate is generally effected, for the sake of convenience, by controlling the rate of motion of the movable crosshead of the testing machine although this rate does not exactly correspond to the actual rate of deformation of the specimen, especially so in the elastic range of the test specimen. A value of crosshead speed quite commonly employed in the plastic range of the specimen in conventional hot tensile tests is in the order of 0.25 in/min.

In addition to controlling the rate of deformation during test, it is generally desirable to control the time of holding at temperature prior to test. Some time of holding is obviously necessary in order that the

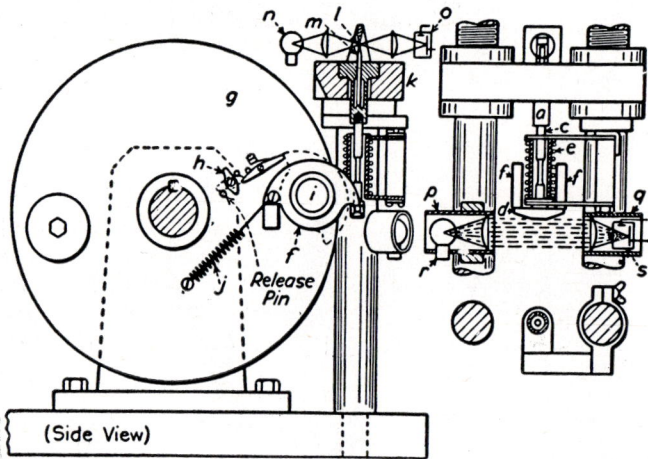

Fig. 138. Apparatus for high-speed tension tests. (*Manjoine and Nadai.*[239])

temperature control may be stabilized. But it should be borne in mind, as discussed in some detail in Chap. XI, that structural changes occur with time at elevated temperatures, independent of deformation of the specimen, and result in corresponding changes in strength. At relatively low temperatures these changes may be insignificant in magnitude, but at relatively high temperatures they may be of quite important magnitude. Consequently, for comparative results, the time of holding before test is generally maintained constant at one to two hours.

Creep and Creep-rupture Testing

The short-time tensile test which is commonly employed for evaluating the strength of metals for use at ordinary temperatures, for either short- or long-time service, has proved inadequate for evaluating the strength of metals under long-time service at elevated temperatures. This is a consequence of the continuing deformation of a metal at high temperatures when under stress,* that is, of creep, and contrasts with the essentially elastic or instantaneous deformation of most atmospheric

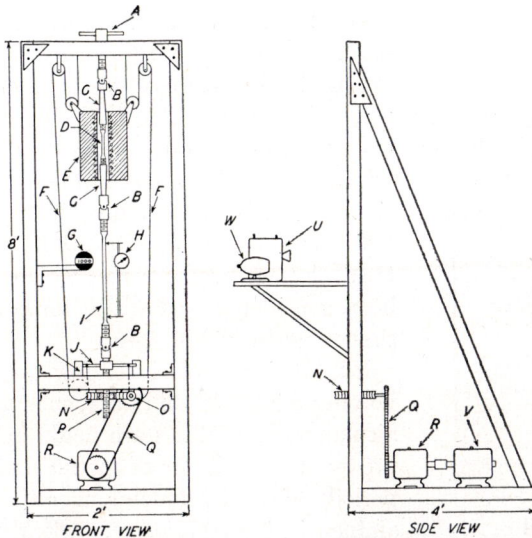

A—Adjustable top anchorage
B—Universal joint fittings to insure alignment of specimen (D) and weigh bar (I)
C—Specimen pull rods of chromium-nickel steel
D—Specimen
E—Electric furnace supported by cords (F)
F—Furnace support cords—lowering of furnace during test through cords by downward movement of torque arm (J)
G—Electric time clock
H—Olsen extensometer attached to weigh bar (I)
I—Calibrated weigh bar of chromium-nickel-molybdenum steel, austempered to obtain a yield strength of 150,000 psi
J—Torque arm to prevent weigh bar and specimen from turning when lead screw (P) is drawn downward by revolving worm wheel

K—Torque-arm pressure plates to provide a bearing surface for ends of torque arm
N—Internally-threaded worm wheel actuated by worm
O—Worm which actuates worm wheel
P—Lead screw
Q—Sprocket chain
R—Speed reducer, ratio 100 to 1
U—Single-exposure motion-picture camera—by suitable auxiliary equipment, camera will take a picture of extensometer dial (H) and time clock (G) at predetermined time intervals
V—Combination electric motor (1,725 rpm) and speed reducer (57.5 rpm), ratio 30 to 1
W—Camera spotlight, one mounted on either side of camera

Fig. 139. Apparatus for controlled strain-rate tension tests at elevated temperatures. (*U.S. Steel Corp. of Del. Research Laboratory.*)

temperature design. Thus design at elevated temperatures is a dynamic problem, and some form of creep test has come into almost universal use for determining the permissible working stresses of metals used at elevated temperatures. The creep test and the creep-rupture test will

* The stress applied to a metal at high temperatures may be chosen sufficiently slight so that, for practical purposes, no measureable creep occurs. It is, however, not economical to design at such a low stress.

be considered together since they differ only in that the latter is made at higher stress and the test continued to failure of the specimen.

Because many applications of metals at elevated temperatures involve an essentially constant stress, or have a superimposed varying stress, and because of the relative simplicity with which the test may be made, the vast majority of creep tests involve essentially the application of a constant load to a sample heated to the temperature of interest, and the periodic observation of the dimensional changes which result. Thus the primary measurements are of creep and time. In simple tension, which is most commonly used for creep tests, this results in the familiar elongation-time plot, or creep curve, which has already been considered, but which for convenience is shown again in Fig. 141.

Except for a relatively few applications involving relatively short life, such as in jet-type airplanes, creep tests are made in an effort to predict the behavior of metals under stress for periods of service much longer than can be examined in the laboratory. Clearly, for a contemplated service of 20 years it is physically, as well as economically, impossible to make a laboratory test of 20 year's duration. Thus, although the creep test is of relatively long duration compared to the hot tensile test, it is still a short-time test relative to most service. It is perhaps axiomatic that the longer the duration of the creep test relative to the contemplated service life, the more nearly may it properly evaluate the strength of the metal. Yet some compromise must be made in the interest of shortening the length of test; this has been largely a question for the individual testing laboratory. Actual test times range from 2 to 3 days up to several months or more. In the same category is the question of just what characteristics of the creep curve are of interest and how extrapolations are to be made. This question is inseparably bound up with

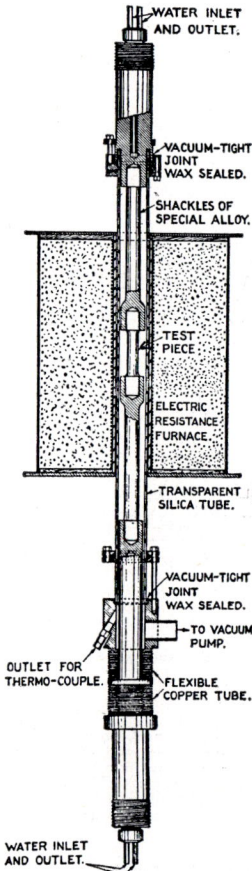

FIG. 140. Apparatus for short-time hot-tensile testing in vacuum. (*Jenkins and Mellor.*[240])

Labels on figure:
WATER INLET AND OUTLET.
VACUUM-TIGHT JOINT WAX SEALED.
SHACKLES OF SPECIAL ALLOY.
TEST PIECE.
ELECTRIC RESISTANCE FURNACE.
TRANSPARENT SILICA TUBE.
VACUUM-TIGHT JOINT WAX SEALED.
TO VACUUM PUMP.
OUTLET FOR THERMO-COUPLE.
FLEXIBLE COPPER TUBE.
WATER INLET AND OUTLET.

that of design, which is discussed in Chap. XII. Consideration will be given to most of the measures (usually quite arbitrary) of creep strength which have been proposed, as well as modifications of the creep-test procedure employed to obtain these measures.

Stress to Produce a Specific Minimum Creep Rate. The most commonly used measure of long-time strength at elevated temperatures in the United States is obtained from a plot of stress versus minimum creep rate* and expressed in terms of the stress to produce a specific rate, for example, the stress to produce a creep rate of 0.0001 or of 0.00001 per cent per hour.† Such a plot to logarithmic coordinates is shown in Fig. 142, the minimum creep rate and corresponding stress being obtained from a family of creep curves such as in Fig. 141.

Stress to Produce Rupture in a Specific Time. Another measure of long-time high-temperature strength widely employed in this country is obtained from a plot such as that in Fig. 143 of the logarithm of the stress versus the logarithm of the time for rupture. Thus the strength may be reported in terms of the stress to produce rupture in 1,000 hr, or 10,000 hr. This measure of strength is entirely different in nature from that defined above in terms of minimum creep rate, and should not be expected, as

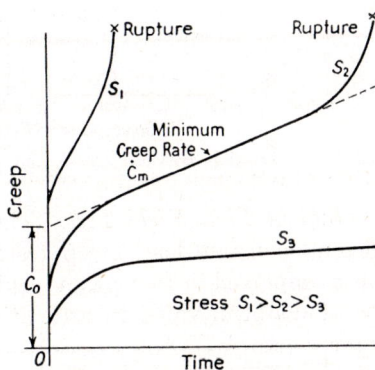

FIG. 141. Family of creep curves; schematic; cartesian coordinates.

many workers have thought it might, to be related to it in more than a very general way. Actually, as will be seen in Chap. XII on design, the strength of the metal defined in both ways is required for proper design for elevated-temperature service; the two strengths supplement one another. It is interesting to note that the creep-rupture test was among the first of the long-time tests studied.

The Sustained-load Tension Test. The so-called sustained-load tension test, proposed by Kanter,[246] is identical, except in method of analysis, with the standard constant-load creep test from which the stress to

---

* This is the rate corresponding to the so-called second stage of creep; it is also termed constant-rate stage.

† These are equivalent to the more common expressions 1 per cent per 10,000 hr or 1 per cent per 100,000 hr, which, however, are somewhat misleading in that the test is not run this long.

produce a specific minimum creep rate is determined, as described above. Instead of plotting stress versus minimum creep rate, Kanter plots this rate versus temperature; if the logarithm of the creep rate is plotted against the reciprocal of the absolute temperature, a straight line is obtained.

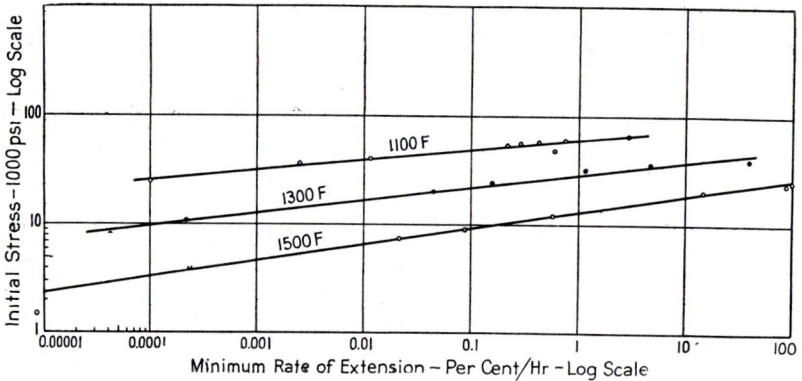

FIG. 142. Relation between stress and minimum creep rate; logarithmic coordinates. 18 Cr–8 Ni–Mo steel. (*Smith et al.*[247])

Hatfield Time Yield Test. The Hatfield time yield test[241] is one of several constant-load creep tests of quite short duration which have been employed in Europe and which most American engineers regard to be of doubtful value in estimating long-time strength. The Hatfield

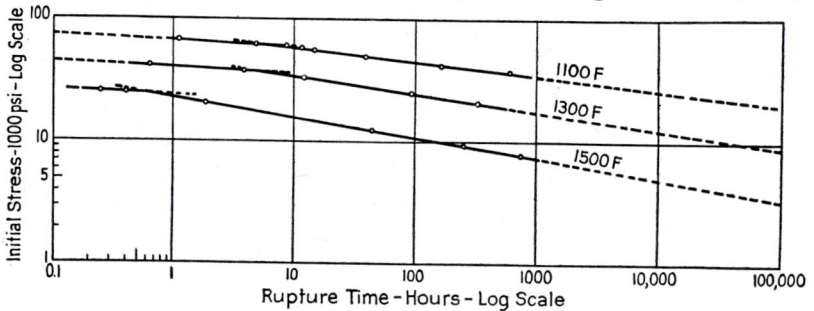

FIG. 143. Relation between stress and time for rupture; logarithmic coordinates. 18 Cr–8 Ni–Mo steel. (*Smith et al.*[247])

time yield stress is defined as the maximum stress which (1) will not produce a deformation exceeding 0.5 per cent in the first 24 hr and (2) which will at the same time result in an average rate of creep between the 24th and 72d hour which does not exceed 0.0001 per cent per hour. Thus the test requires only 72 hr. It is inconceivable that such an arbitrary index of strength can have any general value in estimating working stress for long-time service, since, as indicated in an earlier section, structural changes during the early part of a creep test may actually result in negative creep. It is, no doubt, of some value as an acceptance or control test of nominally identical material.

The German DIN (DVM) Test. The so-called DIN[242] creep test which has received general acceptance in Germany is a constant-load creep test of 45 hr duration. The creep strength is defined as the greatest stress which at the same time results in (1) an average creep rate not exceeding 0.001 per cent per hour and (2) a permanent creep not exceeding 0.2 per cent at the end of 45 hr. This test thus differs in only minor details from the Hatfield time yield test.

Relaxation-type Tests. Several types of creep tests employing a varying load have been and are employed, and although these will be considered under a subsequent section on Relaxation Testing, they will be mentioned here, since some investigators have considered this type of test of value for design of structures operating under constant load. This has not been clearly shown, however, and is not generally accepted.

One of the earliest of the relaxation-type tests was that proposed by Barr and Bardgett.[243] In this measurement, several tests all for 48 hr are made with different initial stresses, the specimen being fixed in a heavy frame in series with a weighbar, for measuring the stress. As the specimen creeps, the stress decreases. In effect the elastic extension is replaced by plastic extension, the total length remaining constant (except for the elastic contraction in the weighbar, the frame, etc., as a consequence of the decrease in stress). The decrease in stress in the 48-hr test is plotted against the initial stress on cartesian coordinates, and the intersection of this curve with the axis of initial stress yields the "limiting creep stress," or the stress which will result in no measurable decrease in stress, that is, relaxation, in 48 hr.

In the flow-rate test, or step-down relaxation test, proposed by Robinsin,[244] a specimen is loaded in tension at a constant temperature to a predetermined total strain. When this strain is reached, the stress is reduced slightly, and creep allowed to continue at this lower stress until the predetermined total strain is again reached, whereupon the stress is again reduced slightly. This is continued for a number of times and a plot prepared of the stress versus the corresponding creep rate. The flow-rate strength is defined in a manner similar to that employed for the constant-load creep test, and it is the stress to cause a creep rate of 0.0001 per cent per hour, or some other specific rate. In general, the creep strength is not the same in the two tests for corresponding creep rates.

Of entirely different nature is a test, proposed by Rohn,[245] in which temperature is the variable. The temperature of a specimen under constant load is gradually lowered until a level is reached at which the creep rate decreases to some arbitrarily selected value corresponding to no "measurable" extension. The creep strength is then defined in terms

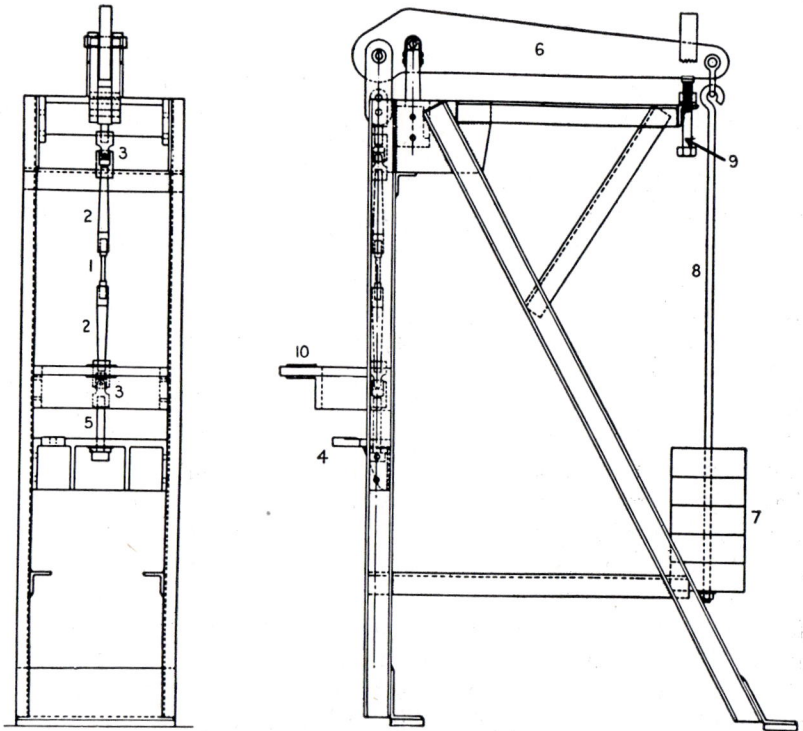

FIG. 144. Creep testing stand. (*U.S. Steel Corp. of Del. Research Laboratory.*)

of this temperature. It is not clear, however, how such a measure may be employed in design for service at elevated temperatures.

Apparatus for Making Creep and Creep-rupture Tests

For the most part, apparatus for making creep and creep-rupture tests in different laboratories is of essentially similar character, differences existing mainly in details of construction and in the extension-measuring devices. Most tests are made by heating the specimen in a resistance-wound electrically heated furnace and applying a constant dead-weight tensile load by means of a lever.

Tapsell[238] has described many of the types of apparatus employed prior to 1931, quite a few of which are still in existence. No attempt will be made here to describe all these various types of apparatus, but instead detailed consideration will be devoted to the apparatus in use at the U.S. Steel Corp. of Del. Research Laboratory; and then brief consideration will be given to a few of the types of equipment originating

Fig. 145. Measuring the creep strain. (*U.S. Steel Corp. of Del. Research Laboratory.*)

since the appearance of Tapsell's book. The equipment employed for making creep-rupture tests is quite similar to that employed for making creep tests. The latter equipment will be described first and then note will be made of the modifications which have been made to permit rupture tests. Attention will also be paid to some of the test procedures. This apparatus as well as the test procedures has been described in some detail in the literature.[247]

The Test Stand. The creep-test specimen is loaded by means of dead weights and a lever in the stand shown in Fig. 144. For clarity, the furnace for heating the specimen as well as the microscope used for measuring the extension are not shown; these may be seen in the photograph of Fig. 145 and will be described later. The stand is of welded construction and occupies a space approximately $20 \times 45 \times 80$ in.

With reference to Fig. 144, the specimen (1) mounted in pull rods (2) is threaded into a pair of universal joints (3) which serve to minimize nonaxial loading. The lower universal joint is attached to anchorage bracket (4) by a spherically seated bolt (5); the upper universal joint is connected to the short arm of the lever(6). This lever has an arm ratio of 9 to 1 and a sensitivity of several grams, which is negligible in terms

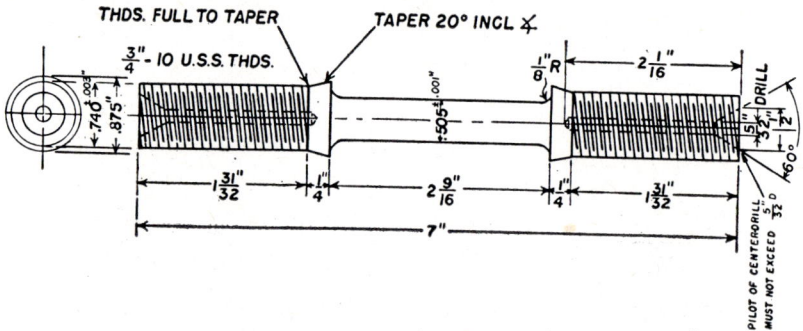

Fig. 146. Creep-test specimen. (*U.S. Steel Corp. of Del. Research Laboratory.*)

of stress. The loading weights (7) are carried on a weight hanger (8). Prior to loading the specimen, the lever is supported in position by a thrust bearing (9). To support the furnace around the test specimen, a special collar (not shown) is screwed onto the lower pull rod. The microscope for measuring extension is mounted, as shown in Fig. 154, on a special post attached to yoke (10).

The Creep-test Specimen and Mounting of Extension-measuring Units. The specimen employed for creep testing is shown in Fig. 146. The end holes are for thermocouples and the tapered shoulders for supporting the extension units. The extension of the specimen during test is determined directly by sighting through a hole in the furnace wall with a microscope upon reference marks engraved on polished platinum beads which are attached on units secured to the tapered shoulders of the test specimen, as shown in Fig. 147. The pure platinum beads are welded on the arms of the units *B*, which in effect refer the extension occurring between shoulders of the specimen to a central point for observation. The measured extension thus includes that occurring in the fillets, but by comparison with measurements after completion of test on the straight section, this was found to be small, introducing an error of less than 4 per cent.

The microscope used in making the extension measurement has a magnification of 100 diameters, and accordingly the platinum beads must be polished before engraving. Polishing is effected by mounting the specimen when it has been assembled to the state shown in *C* of

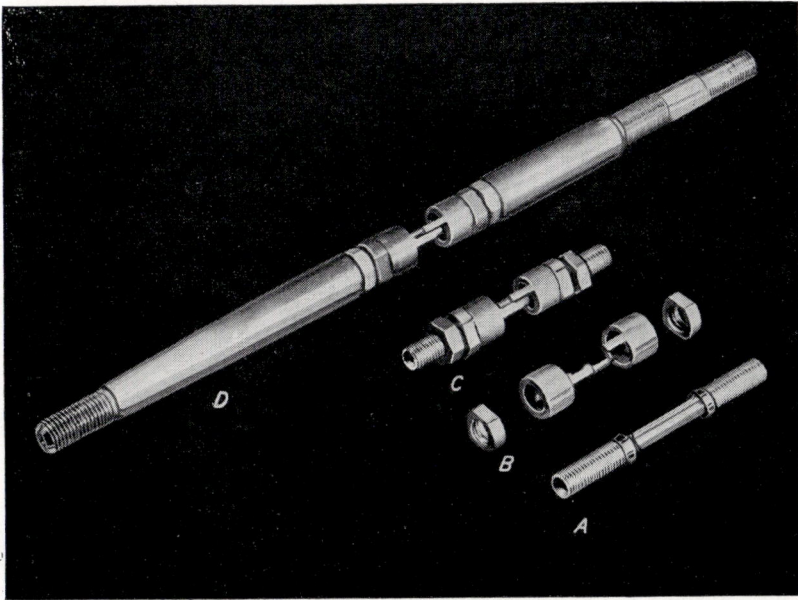

FIG. 147. Extension unit and test specimen assembly for creep test. (*U.S. Steel Corp. of Del. Research Laboratory.*)

Fig. 147 in a jig (Fig. 148) and employing standard metallographic polishing procedures; of course, the beads need not be as free of scratches as is desirable for microscopic examination.

Engraving of the platinum beads is done in the jig shown in Fig. 149. The specimen assembly is clamped in V blocks *K* and placed on the table *T* against the stop screw *A* which is initially backed off so that engraving is begun at the edge of the platinum farthest away from screw *A*. Table *T* is a moving block pivoted in the center to permit rotation of 60 deg in the plane of its base, and is initially placed in the position shown in the photograph. The engraving tool is a 60-deg conical diamond *D* whose horizontal position relative to the platinum surfaces *a* and b is adjusted by means of screw B. The engraving stroke is controlled by the screws E_1 and E_2, which limit the motion of the vertical frame F about point G. The frame W, pivoted at M, is counterbalanced to control the depth of engraving, and elevation is controlled by chain P over pulley C.

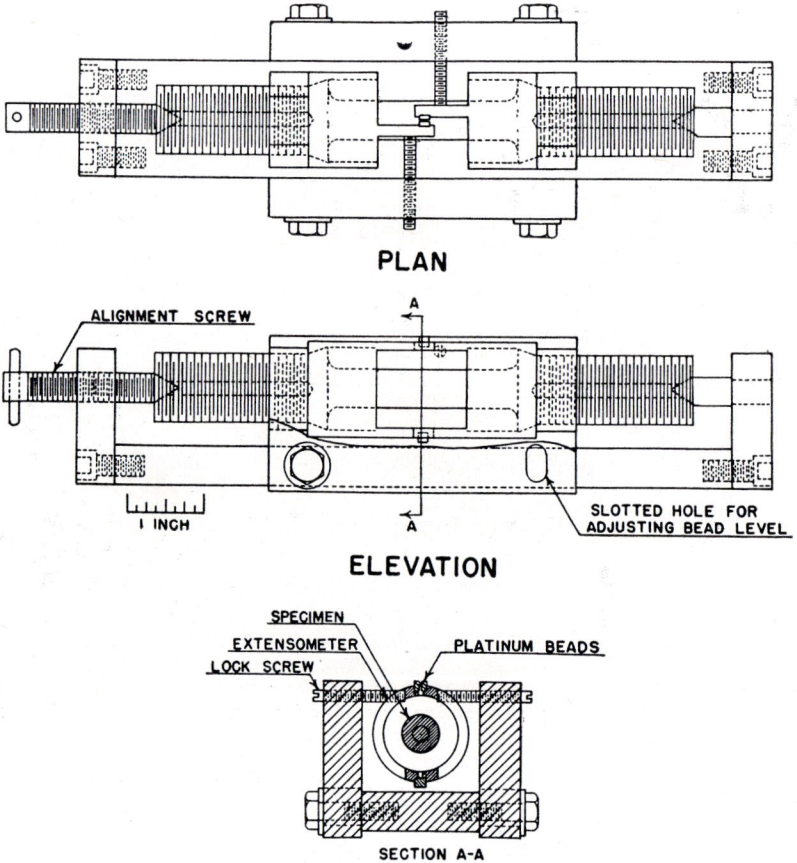

PLAN

ALIGNMENT SCREW

I INCH

SLOTTED HOLE FOR
ADJUSTING BEAD LEVEL

ELEVATION

SPECIMEN
EXTENSOMETER
LOCK SCREW
PLATINUM BEADS

SECTION A-A

FIG. 148. Jig for polishing extensometer units after mounting on creep-test specimen (*U.S. Steel Corp. of Del. Research Laboratory.*)

With frame F forward against stop E_1, the diamond is lowered by pulley C until the chain is slack, and then handle H is pushed slowly toward stop E_2. The diamond is then raised, screw A turned to advance the assembly into position for the next engraving, and the process repeated until the whole of the platinum surface is engraved in this one direction. The table T is then rotated against stop J and a second series of lines engraved. The appearance of an engraved surface is shown in Fig. 150.

After engraving, the specimen is mounted and aligned in the pull rods, D of Fig. 147. Alignment is effected by mounting one end of the complete assembly in a lathe chuck; if on rotation, the other end runs out of line, the assembly is readjusted.

Fig. 149. Jig for engraving reference marks on platinum surfaces of creep extensometer units. (*U.S. Steel Corp. of Del. Research Laboratory.*)

The Heating Furnace and Control of Temperature. Temperature must be closely controlled during the creep test both because the creep rate changes rapidly with temperature and because the magnitude of the creep observed in periodic measurements is of the same order as the thermal length change resulting from a slight temperature change.

The creep furnace employed is shown in Fig. 151. It consists of heating elements of nichrome or kanthal wire wound on an Alundum tube enclosed in a casing of chromium-plated seamless tubing. Plating with chromium minimizes heat loss by radiation. The ends of the furnace, one of which is removable, are insulating Transite disks, and the space between the heating units and the casing is filled with Sil-O-Cel No. 3 for thermal insulation. A sleeve of nickel inside the Alundum tube and held centrally by means of top and bottom Alundum spacers promotes temperature uniformity over the gauge length of the specimen.

A conical nichrome tube is fitted through a window in the casing into

FIG. 150. Engraved platinum reference units for creep measurements; ×50. (*U.S. Steel Corp. of Del. Research Laboratory.*)

the inside of the furnace; through this opening a microscope is sighted on the engraved platinum beads to measure the extension. The window opening is closed against air currents by a circular glass disk held against asbestos packing by a threaded retaining washer.

Separate windings, connected in parallel, are wound on the top and bottom halves of the Alundum tube; the spacing of the turns is proportioned to the heat losses. The current through the two windings may be separately adjusted by external resistances to aid in obtaining temperature uniformity. The maximum power required is about 750 watts for temperatures up to 1500°F.

The temperature is controlled by a chromel-alumel thermocouple and a temperature controller of commercial manufacture. The hot junction

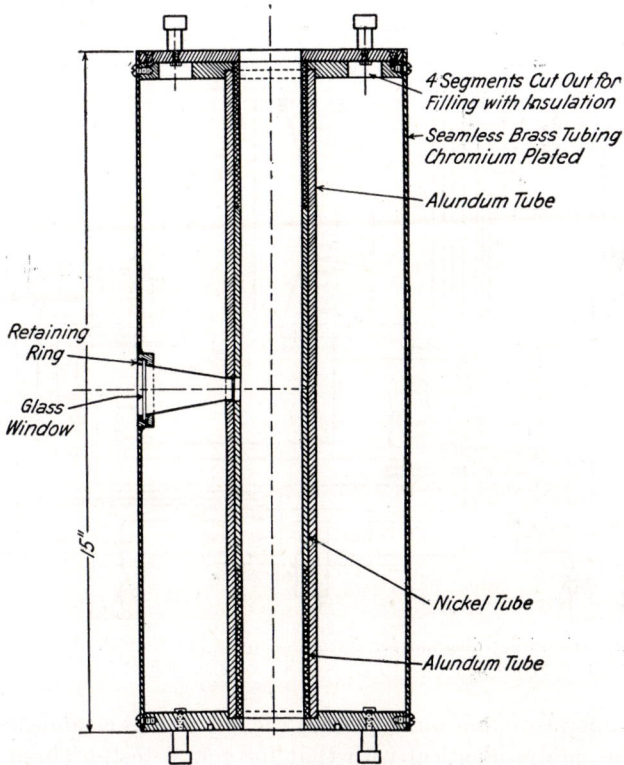

FIG. 151. Creep furnace. (*U.S. Steel Corp. of Del. Research Laboratory.*)

of the control couple is located in the windings. The controller actuates a relay which cuts in and out any two taps on the secondary of a tap transformer. The transformer has a 220-volt primary and the secondary stages are of 3 volts. A wiring diagram showing the various electric connections is given in Fig. 152. The common tap (4) of the transformer leads to the top (*T*) and bottom (*B*) furnace windings through fine adjustment rheostats. The two other transformer taps lead through 1-ohm variable rheostats to the relay which connects one or the other to the common lead (*C*) to the furnace. Thus the power input varies between two levels, which depend upon the furnace temperature desired. The higher voltage tap is selected and the rheostats so adjusted that the specimen temperature will be maintained approximately 25°F above the test temperature; on the lower voltage side, this adjustment is made so that the temperature will be maintained approximately 25°F below the test temperature. This limitation of heat input at the two levels is essential for close temperature control.

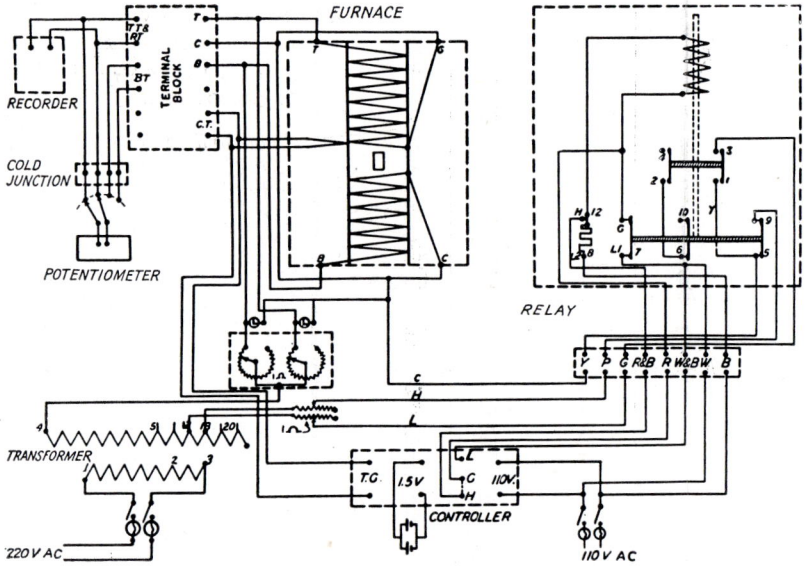

FIG. 152. Electric-wiring diagram for furnace-temperature control. (*U. S. Steel Corp. of Del. Research Laboratory.*)

The temperature uniformity within the hot zone is established with a dummy assembly, identical with that for actual test. Three thermocouples are spaced along the reduced section of the specimen and one each inserted through the pull rods into the shoulders of the specimen (Fig. 146). Having established by this means that the temperature uniformity and control is within satisfactory limits for the particular test temperature, only the two shoulder thermocouples are employed for measurement and adjustment of temperature during actual test. The temperature uniformity attained is within ±1°F for temperatures up to 1100°F and within ±2°F for up to 1500°F. The day-to-day variation in temperature is of the same order, except for unusual occurrences.

The Creep Microscope. The microscope employed for measuring creep has the optical system shown in Fig. 153 and is mounted as indicated in

Fig. 154. The essential feature of the microscope is a 2× relay lens, having a working distance sufficient to pick up the image of the reference marks on the platinum beads attached to the specimen; this image is presented to a high magnification objective of necessarily short focal

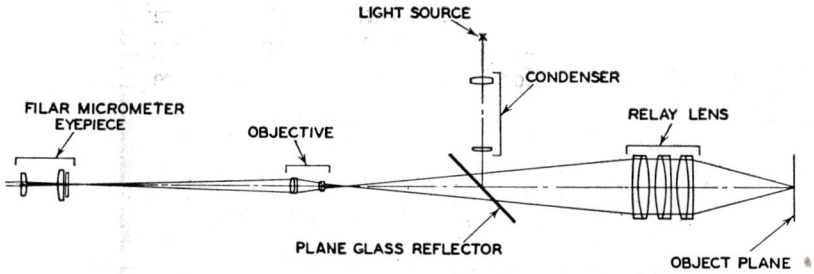

FIG. 153. Optical system of creep microscope. (*U.S. Steel Corp. of Del. Research Laboratory.*)

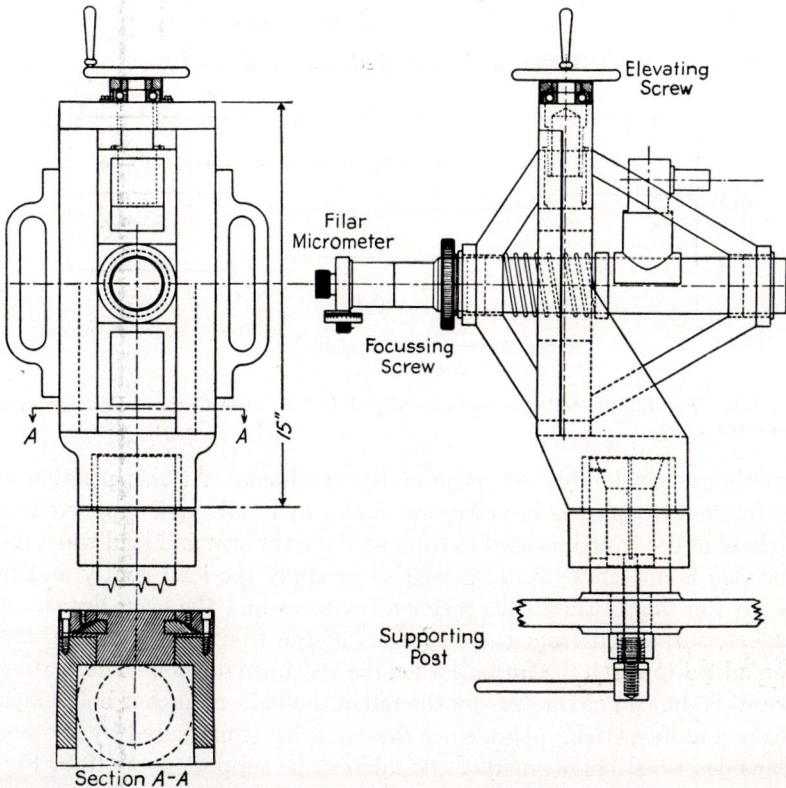

FIG. 154. Creep microscope mounting. (*U.S. Steel Corp. of Del. Research Laboratory.*)

length. The periodic displacement between selected reference marks is determined with a 10× filar-micrometer eyepiece. The least reading of the microscope is approximately 0.00004 in. The microscope mount is moved from stand to stand on the mobile support shown in Fig. 145.

Creep-rupture Tests. The test stand employed for creep-rupture tests is identical with that for creep tests except for several minor modifications. The thrust bearing (9 of Fig. 144) for supporting the lever has been removed to allow for greater lever movement as required by the

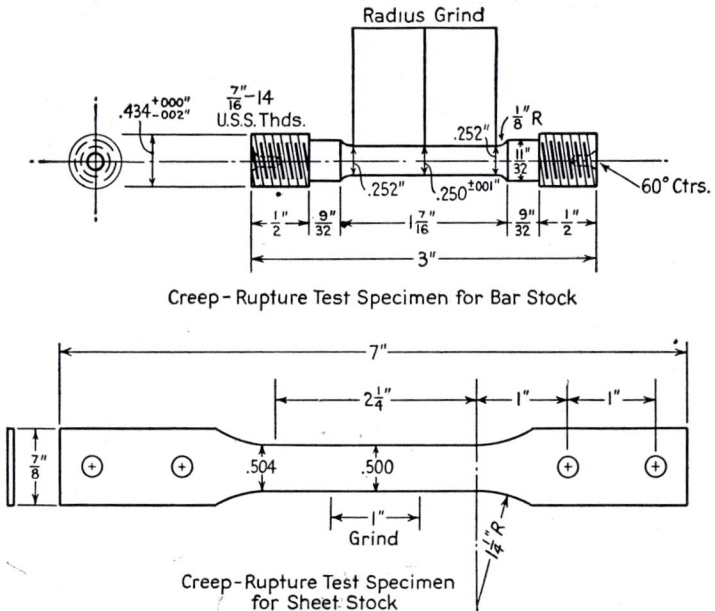

Creep – Rupture Test Specimen for Bar Stock

Creep-Rupture Test Specimen
for Sheet Stock

FIG. 155. Creep-rupture-test specimens employed in U.S. Steel Corp. of Del. Research Laboratory.

sometimes considerable extension of the specimen. At this position in the frame a trough has been formed, and a hydraulic jack supported on the base of the trough is used to support the lever arm and load when the specimen is not under load, as well as to apply the load gently and to absorb the shock when the specimen fractures and the lever drops. A bracket, suspended from the two sides of the front of the frame, has been added to catch the furnace when the specimen breaks. The heating current is shut off at fracture by the fall of the bottom anchor bolt which breaks a knife switch. Also, since the extension is measured by another means described below, neither the microscope support post (10 of Fig. 144) nor the window in the heating furnace is required.

Two types of test specimens are employed for creep-rupture tests, one for bar stock, the other for sheet; these are shown in Fig. 155. The sheet-type specimen is gripped inside the furnace with grips shown in Fig. 156.

The extension occurring in a creep-rupture test is generally of much greater magnitude than that in the conventional creep test. In the former, extensions of 100 per cent are not uncommon, while in the latter, the extension usually does not exceed 1 to 2 per cent and is often less. Accordingly the high sensitivity of the creep microscope is not needed in creep-rupture tests and in fact would be disadvantageous

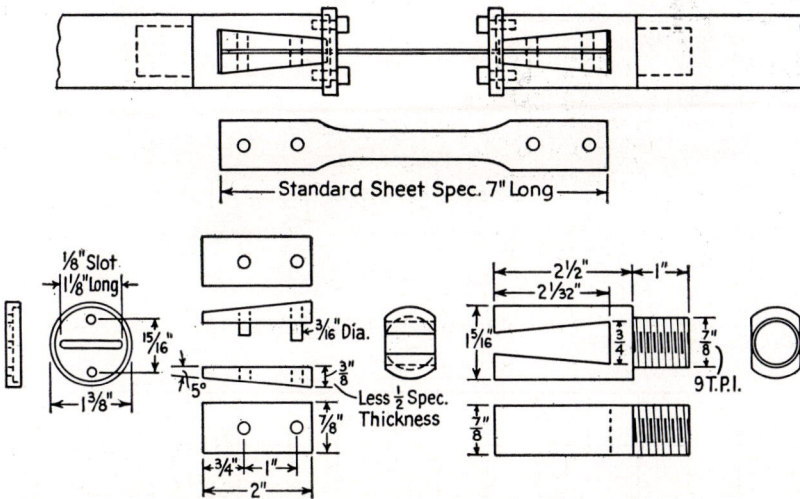

Fig. 156. Grips for creep-rupture tests of sheet. (*U.S. Steel Corp. of Del. Research Laboratory.*)

in many instances. For measuring these extensions, it is quite satisfactory to use the motion of the loading lever which drops as the specimen extends. By running a fine metal chain from the lever to draw a pen along a drum rotating at constant speed an autographic elongation-time curve of sufficient sensitivity and accuracy may be obtained. A photograph of such a strain-time recorder is shown in Fig. 157, and an actual test record is reproduced in Fig. 158. This means of measuring extension is not as crude as might first appear. This has been shown by comparison with data obtained by direct observation with the creep microscope.[247] The extension occurring on application of load is in error when measured this way owing to the elastic deflection in the test stand, but since the load remains constant during test and since the

FIG. 157. Autographic strain-time recorder for creep-rupture tests. (*U.S. Steel Corp. of Del. Research Laboratory.*)

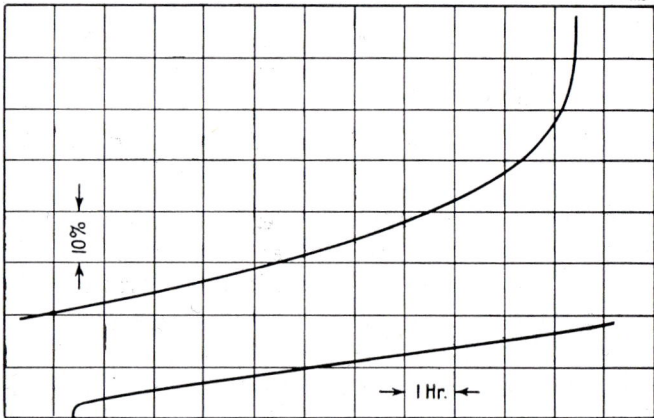

FIG. 158. Autographic strain-time record of a creep-rupture test, obtained with the apparatus shown in Fig. 157.

specimen is of reduced section, the only strain occurring during test is the plastic strain or creep of the test specimen. The initial deflection in the test stand is proportional to the load, and by suitable correction for this deflection a reasonably good measure of total extension may be obtained. A small error may be introduced in some cases owing to creep in the threads if they are not screwed entirely into the adapters or pull rods.

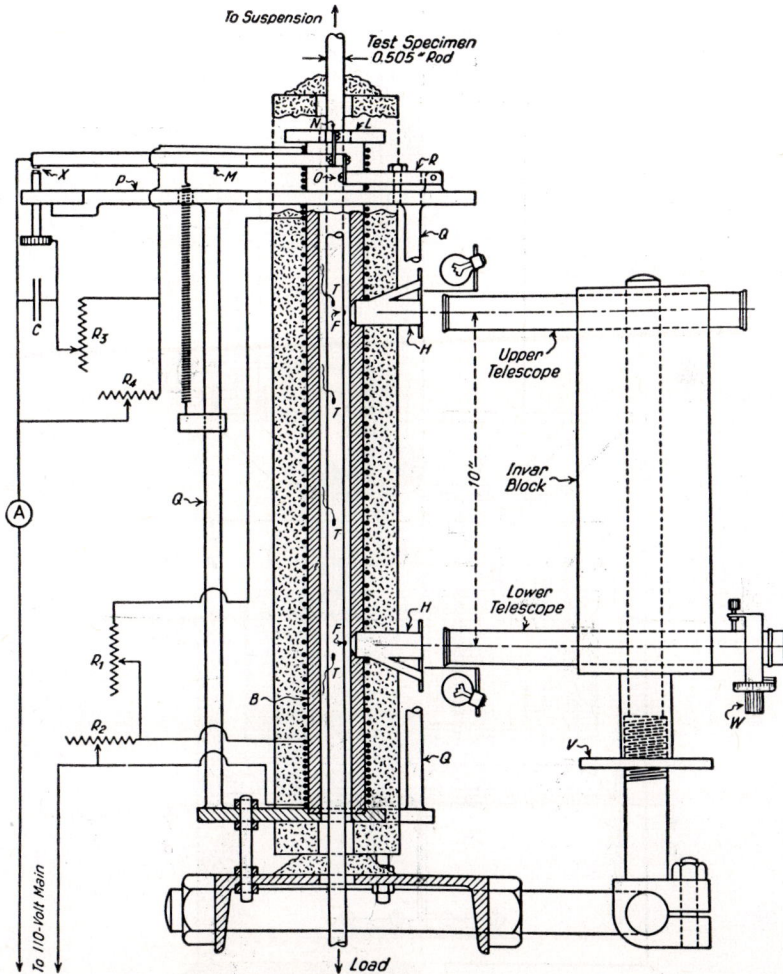

FIG. 159. Creep-testing apparatus showing methods of controlling temperature and of measuring extension. (*Norton and Fellows.*[248])

Other Creep and Creep-rupture-test Apparatus. Norton and Fellows[248] have described the temperature-controlling and extension-measuring apparatus shown in Fig. 159. The test specimen which has a 10-in. gauge length and extends to the outside of the furnace is enclosed within a heavy tube of austenitic stainless steel *B*. This tube is wound with mica tape for electric insulation and then with the heating coil, this latter being in three sections. Control of temperature is effected automatically by the thermal expansion and contraction of the tube B.

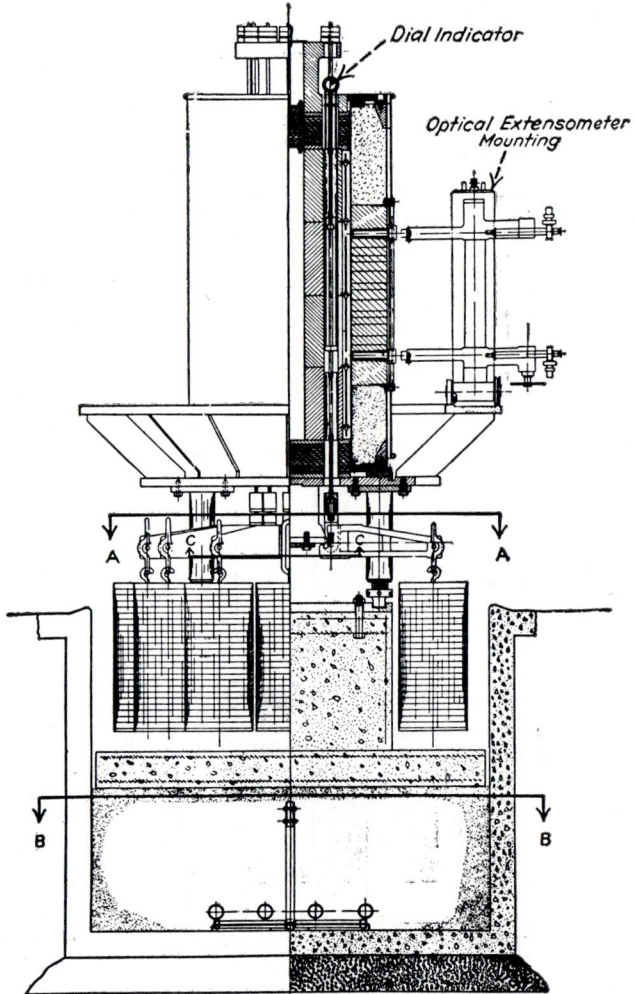

FIG. 160. Multispecimen creep-testing apparatus. (*McVetty.*[249])

The bottom of this tube being fixed, the expansion resulting from heating raises the casting L joined to the top of the tube; through strips N, this motion raises the forked lever M which is fixed at one end by strip O to yoke R. This yoke is in turn fixed to the platform P which is joined to the base of the furnace by three invar rods Q. The heating current is altered by the contacts at X at the end of the lever M. Closing the contact increases the current by approximately 10 per cent. The specimen temperature is determined with three thermocouples T welded to the specimen as indicated.

The extension occurring in the specimen is determined by sighting through an opening in the furnace on two short lengths of platinum wire F welded to the specimen at the gauge points. Each wire has a fine scratch as reference mark. The two telescopes with $100\times$ magnification are rigidly joined by an invar block. A fixed crosshair in the upper telescope is sighted on the upper reference mark, and the extension determined by adjusting, with micrometer screw W, the crosshair in the lower telescope to coincide with the lower reference mark. The sensitivity of measurement is 4 parts per million.

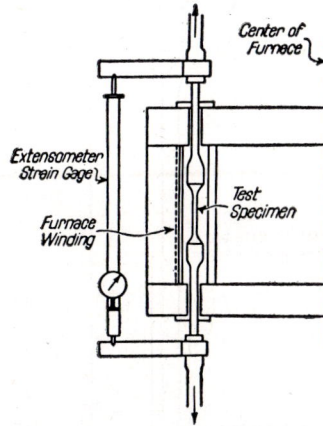

McVetty[249] has described a unique type of creep-testing equipment designed to test simultaneously within the same furnace some 12 to 60 tests. The apparatus, shown in section in Fig. 160, consists of a cylindrical furnace, multiple compartments for test

Fig. 161. Multispecimen creep-rupture apparatus in cross section showing extensometer. (*Thielemann.*[251])

specimens, radial levers and weights, and a micrometer microscope which rides on a track around the furnace and is sighted through windows upon reference marks on the specimen. An alternative method of measuring extension employs comparison rods extending from both ends of the gauge length to the top of the furnace, the difference in displacement being determined with a dial gauge. The furnace itself consists of a large cylindrical mass of heat-resistant metal containing 12 vertical holes at 30 deg apart in which the test specimens are supported. In each of the holes one specimen of 20-in. gauge length or several specimens of shorter gauge length may be tested. The windows through which the microscope is sighted may be adjusted vertically to correspond with the gauge lengths employed.

Thielemann and Parker[250] have described a 12-specimen creep-rupture apparatus. A section through the furnace[251] (Fig. 161) shows the location of the test specimen and also the means employed for measuring the creep extension.

Fellows *et al.*[252] measure creep extension by sighting with a microscope through a window in the heating furnace upon reference marks (Fig. 162) on a wire moving within a tube, both of an alloy of platinum and 10 per cent rhodium and spot-welded to the specimen at the ends of the gauge length.

Manjoine[253] has recently described two types of creep-rupture machines, which have since been put into commercial manufacture. One is of the conventional lever-loaded type, the other a screw-driven machine in which the specimen is loaded through a stiff spring in series with it. The load is maintained constant by maintaining the spring at fixed deflection by means of a motor-driven jack. This is effected automatically by electric contact controls. The motion of the jack required to maintain the spring at constant deflection is magnified and recorded autographically with the time, resulting in a curve of elongation versus time.

Some investigators have made creep tests in torsion, in bending, or under combined stresses in contrast to the most commonly employed tension test, and it will be worth while to note a few of these briefly. Many of these have been on lead or other relatively soft metals and alloys at atmospheric or near-atmospheric temperatures where the experimental problems are vastly simpler than at elevated temperatures. Elaborate apparatus can be devised and the whole enclosed in a constant-temperature room in which the technician himself can work. Thus, McCullough[254] and Tapsell and Johnson[255] have studied the creep of lead beams subjected to bending at atmospheric temperature and Marin and Zwissler[256] have performed similar studies with aluminum. Bending creep tests at elevated temperatures have been made by Davis[257] with the apparatus shown in the schematic sketch of Fig. 163. The deflection of the beam is measured with a dial gauge as shown.

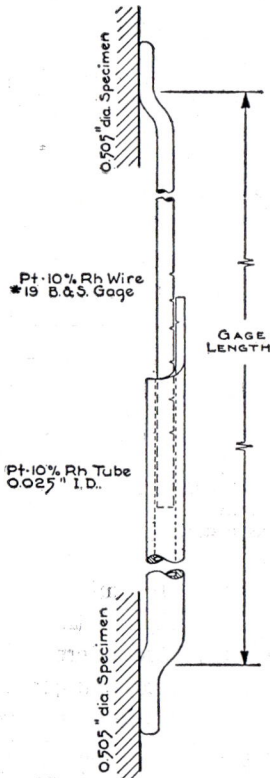

FIG. 162. Schematic representation of creep-test extensometer. (*Fellows et al.*[252])

Everett[258] has made torsional creep tests. Thin-walled tubular specimens were employed. The torsional creep occurring in the specimen was transferred outside the hot zone by mechanical means and then measured by optical means.

Several studies of creep in tubes subjected to internal pressure have been reported. Illustrative of these are experiments on lead cable sheathing at near-atmospheric temperatures by Phelps *et al.*[259] and on steel at elevated temperatures by Norton.[260] In both of these investigations a gas was used to provide the pressure. Norton's specimen had dimensions approximately 30 in. in length, 4 in. outside diameter, and ⅜-in. wall thickness. The tube was closed by welded-on hemi-

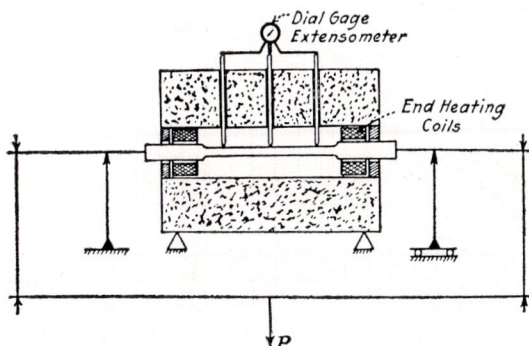

FIG. 163. Sketch of apparatus for making creep tests in bending. (*Davis.*[257])

spherical ends and the whole enclosed within a resistance-heated furnace. The diametral and axial length changes were determined by sighting through the furnace wall with a telescope.

General Considerations. As pointed out in the discussion of hot tensile testing, microstructural changes occur during heating at elevated temperatures whether or not the metal is under stress. Since these can be marked in some cases, resulting in significant changes in mechanical properties, it is desirable to fix at least the pretest holding time. The author has employed a holding time of approximately 20 hr, or overnight, before test. This allows ample time for stabilization and control of the temperature.

Since most laboratories which conduct creep tests employ at least minor variations in procedures, time of holding prior to test, method of application of load, and methods of controlling temperature and measuring extension, a survey made by the Joint Research Committee on the Effect of Temperature on the Properties of Metals[261] is of considerable interest. In this survey, samples of the same 0.35 per cent carbon steel, identically heat-treated, were tested in seven different laboratories at the same temperature and stress, and the results reported for comparison. The creep curves obtained by the several laboratories are shown in Fig. 164, and the agreement is fairly good.

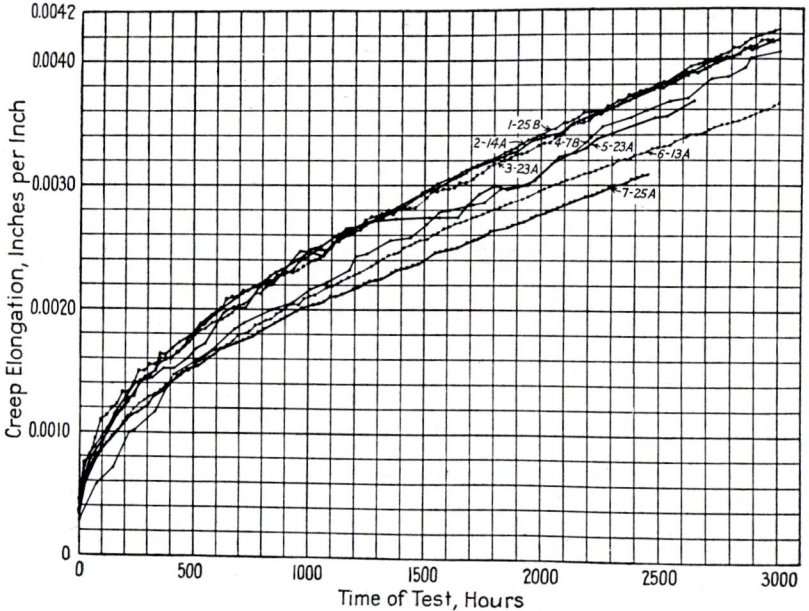

FIG. 164. Reproducibility of creep data. Elongation-time curves obtained by seven different laboratories, identified by numbers on curves, for the same 0.35 per cent carbon steel identically heat-treated, under 7,500 psi at 850°F (see reference 261).

Relaxation Testing

We have already noted in the preceding section several tests of the relaxation type, namely, the Barr-Bardgett test, the so-called flow-rate or step-down relaxation test, and the Rohn test. Relaxation is, of course, a decrease in stress as a consequence of creep, in a rigidly fixed member such as a bolt, the original elastic strain being in effect exchanged for plastic strain with time, resulting in a decrease of stress. Thus bolts which originally are drawn up tight may be found loosened after service at high temperatures. Although relaxation is a result of creep, there is apparently yet no means of accurately correlating relaxation with creep data obtained in the conventional constant-load creep test. Accordingly, most tests for resistance to relaxation attempt to simulate the actual conditions of a bolt or other member subject to essentially fixed deflection and thus relaxation of stress.

Boyd[262] has described the relaxation apparatus shown in Fig. 165 which automatically maintains a constant length of the specimen by decreasing the load. The change of distance between gauge points *AB* (20 in.) is transferred by four steel rods to a dial gauge outside the furnace. This gauge has a contact which is made at a preselected position of the pointer, that is, of the elongation, and through a relay starts a motor. This motor drives a screw which releases the springs by which the specimen is loaded. This decrease in stress returns the specimen to its original length. The sensitivity of the apparatus corresponds to a change in stress of about 10 psi. A newer version of this type of apparatus has been described by Nadai and Boyd.[266]

Mochel[263] has described a type of relaxation test (Fig. 166) in which a specimen of 10-in. gauge length is stressed in a test block of the same composition as the test specimen but with many times the cross-sectional area. The specimen is stressed at atmospheric temperature by tightening the nuts (the degree of tightening being determined with an extensometer), the assembly placed in a furnace for a test interval at the temperature of interest, cooled, and the permanent deformation between gauge marks determined after removal of the load. Different specimens are employed for different initial stresses and different time intervals at constant stress. This type of test has the virtue of rather closely duplicating actual service conditions.

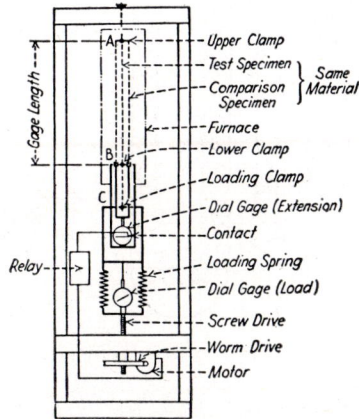

FIG. 165. Relaxation apparatus which automatically maintains the test specimen at constant length. (*Boyd.*[262])

Since the process of relaxation is one of exchanging elastic deformation for plastic, so that a strain which is initially elastic becomes partly elastic and partly plastic, it is evident that the degree of relaxation is a function of the total elasticity in the test assembly.* Kanter[264] has considered this question in some detail. Although Boyd's apparatus is concerned only with the test specimen itself and Mochel's test block assembly has a minimum of extraelasticity, many test assemblies have additional elastic members in the test train. Such a test setup is illus-

---

* In service, advantage is frequently taken of this fact by designing for additional elasticity in the part subject to relaxation.

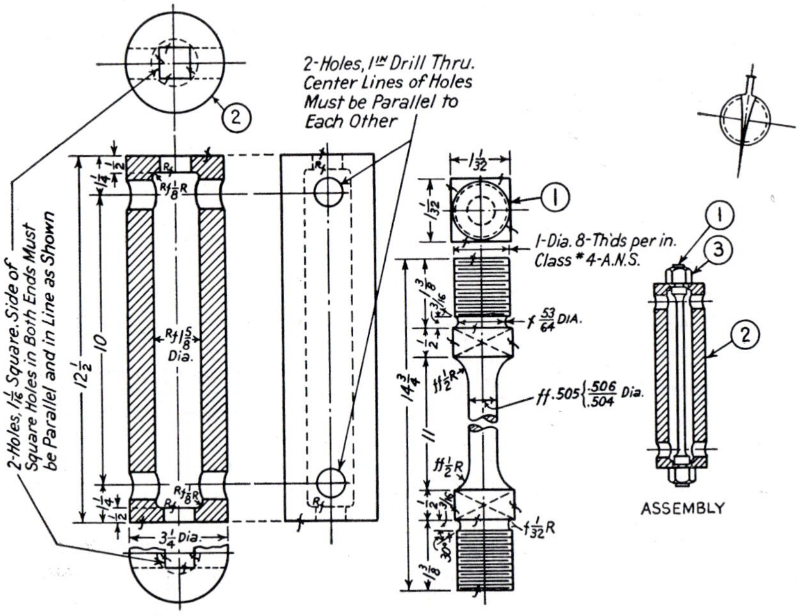

Fig. 166. Relaxation-test specimen and assembly. (*Mochel.*[263])

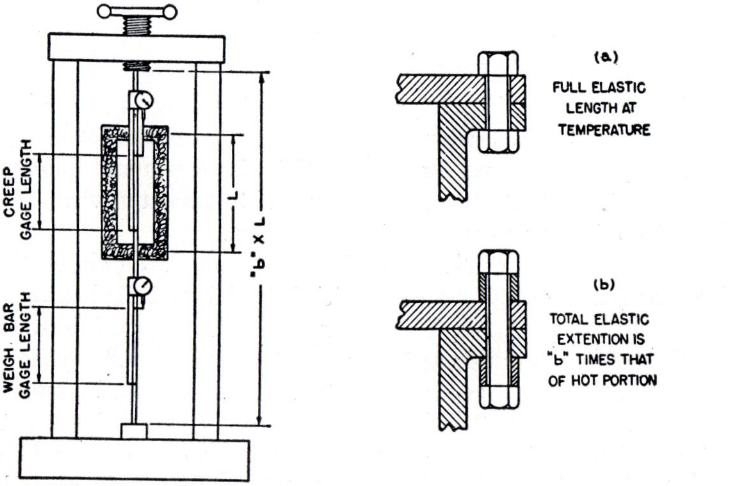

Fig. 167. Sketch of relaxation-test apparatus and also (*a*) and (*b*) of "elastic" bolts. (*Robinson.*[263])

trated diagrammatically in Fig. 167, in which a weighbar in series with the test specimen but at atmospheric temperature is used to measure the stress in the system at any time.

Fatigue Testing

In structural parts subject to dynamic stressing, that is, changing, cycling, or alternating stress as contrasted with essentially constant stress, the fatigue or endurance strength of a metal is of considerable interest; often it is the sole interest. As noted in Chap. V on fracture, the stress which a metal may withstand for many repetitions is considerably less than that which may be supported for only a single loading. Moreover, dynamic behavior cannot be predicted, except in a very general and approximate way, from the static properties. Consequently, fatigue testing is an important aspect of the problem of the evaluation of metals for use under stress. The vast majority of all failures of machine parts in service are of fatigue nature.

The fatigue test is most commonly made with specimens stressed by bending with completely reversed cycles, that is, opposite surfaces alternate between tension and compression. With round specimens, a rotating beam, either simple or of the cantilever type, is generally employed, and most commercially available apparatus has been of this type. In determining an endurance strength in this type of test, a series of specimens is tested, each at a different stress, to fracture, or to a sufficiently large number of reversals without fracture so that the endurance limit may be considered to have been attained. A plot of the stress (S) against the logarithm of the number of reversals (N) generally yields two approximately straight lines which merge with one another, one inclined to the N axis, the other parallel with it (Fig. 168, room-temperature curve). The level of stress corresponding to the horizontal portion of the S-N plot is termed the endurance limit and it represents a stress below which, for completely reversed stressing, a metal test specimen may be cycled indefinitely. The number of reversals required to establish the endurance limit is on the order of 10,000,000 for many metals. However, for at least some nonferrous metals and for all metals at a sufficiently high temperature, a definite endurance limit seems to be lacking, the S-N curve continuing to slope downward (Fig. 168).

Since millions of reversals of stress are required to establish an endurance limit, or the S-N curve, fatigue-testing machines have been devised with very high speeds of cycling, many of the order of 10,000 per min, since it has been established that up to this limit the effect of speed on the number of cycles to failure is not significant, at least at ambient temperature. Above this limit, a slight effect of speed has been found to exist.

Since in bending, the maximum stress, tensile or compressive, occurs in the outermost fibers of the sample, it is not unreasonable to anticipate that the character of the specimen surface is quite important. Not only is the nature of the metal structure* itself important, but also the mechanical nature of the surface (machine-tool marks, scratches, pits). These latter act as stress concentrators and may result in materially lower endurance limit. Accordingly most laboratory fatigue tests are

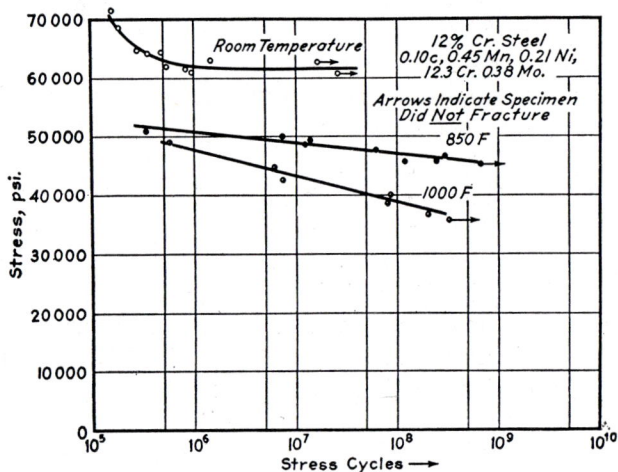

Fig. 168. Variation of number of cycles to failure with stress for 12 Cr steel at room temperature, 850 and 1000°F. (*Welch and Wilson.*[268])

made with carefully prepared specimens free from such defects. This ideal surface contrasts sharply with that existing in actual service parts, and recognizing the importance of natural stress-concentrating defects, some effort has been devoted in laboratory tests to the evaluation of such effects by testing samples with artificial notches. The importance of such effects may be appreciated from the fact that the nominal endurance limit may be halved by the presence of a sharp notch.

Another type of fatigue test, and one which seems to be increasing in

---

* Thus surface decarburization of a steel specimen during heat-treatment may result in significantly lowered endurance strength. Or the surface may be carburized or nitrided to make it more resistant. In this same category may be placed such a commercially important process as shot peening of the surface to induce desirable compressive stresses, which in effect raise the endurance limit.

popularity, is that in which the specimen is stressed in axial tension and compression. The limits of stressing may be equal in tension and compression, all in tension, or any other combination of interest. In this type of test, the stress is, of course, uniform across the specimen, and therefore presumably less influenced by the surface than is the bend type of test. On the other hand, there exists the very difficult problem of avoiding nonaxial loading.

Much discussion has arisen in recent years regarding the value of laboratory fatigue tests in predicting behavior in service. This is a consequence not only of the difference between actual surfaces and carefully prepared ones but also of the complex stress states existing in service assemblies, which result from stress concentration at changes in cross sections, combined bending, torsion and tension stressing, etc. Because of the difficulty of relating laboratory test data to service, there has come into use a great amount of testing of actual parts, subassemblies, or even of finished assemblies. Although it cannot be denied that the application of laboratory test data to service is difficult and that the procedure of testing actual parts is needed, it seems probable that with increasing knowledge of the behavior of metals in fatigue it will some day be possible to relate the two.

An important aspect of the fatigue problem which has not yet been considered is that of the influence of corrosion. It should be evident that corrosion may play a very important role especially in bending fatigue where the stress is greatest at the surface, which is consequently the origin of the fatigue crack. Corrosion may act in either or both of two ways: (1) to form a discontinuity in the surface at which the fatigue crack may nucleate, or (2) to accelerate the rate of propagation of the crack across the specimen once it has started. Data assembled by Moore[267] have shown that the endurance limit of various steels may be reduced by 10 to 80 per cent when the test is made in a stream of fresh water. Generally, corrosion fatigue tests reveal no leveling off of the *S-N* curve. The types of corroding media are innumerable and only a few data have been obtained in spite of the manifest importance of corrosion on fatigue. Fatigue tests in air at elevated temperatures should be classed as corrosion fatigue because of the scaling which occurs.

Comparatively few fatigue tests have been made at elevated temperatures, and opinions are contradictory even as to whether or not fatigue is of importance, since it has been claimed by some workers that the fatigue strength is greater than the creep strength and that the latter property is therefore the determinant factor in design. Although this conclusion may be justified in some cases it is certainly not generally true because fatigue fractures have been observed and reported in parts operating at elevated temperatures. Clearly more data are required to judge properly the importance of fatigue at elevated temperatures. In recent years, there has been a revival of interest in the subject, growing out of experience during the Second World War with gas turbines in superchargers and similar equipment. Toolin and Mochel[284] have reported the results of fatigue tests of many "gas-turbine" alloys.

Fatigue at elevated temperatures is more complicated in nature than fatigue at ordinary temperatures. Fatigue fracture at ordinary temperatures is characterized by the absence of apparent deformation;

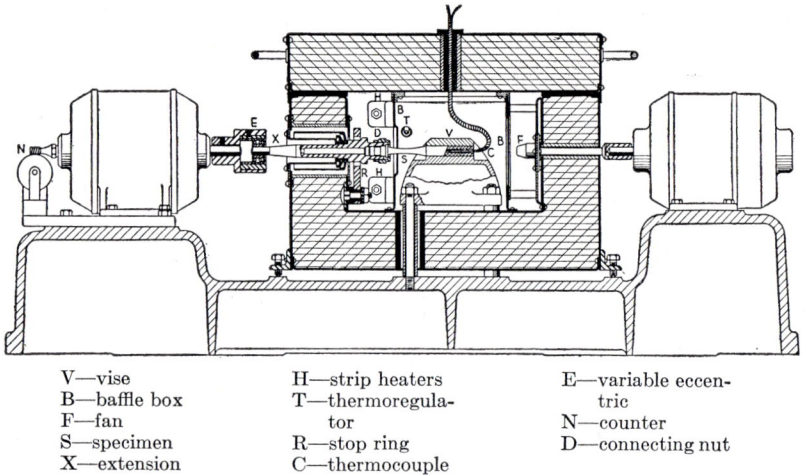

V—vise	H—strip heaters	E—variable eccen-
B—baffle box	T—thermoregula-	tric
F—fan	tor	N—counter
S—specimen	R—stop ring	D—connecting nut
X—extension	C—thermocouple	

Fig. 169. High-temperature fatigue machine of a fixed cantilever-beam type. (*Howell and Howarth.*[269])

the fractured surface, moreover, frequently shows characteristic conchoidal markings distributed about the point of beginning of fracture. Fatigue fracture at an elevated temperature may show the characteristics of ordinary temperatures, but in other instances may apparently be preceded or accompanied by creep, as may occur when the cycling stress is not completely reversed. This possibility would arise in a part such as the blades of a turbine which may be subjected to essentially steady centrifugal stress with superimposed vibratory stress. Possibly a new term such as "creep fatigue" should be coined to describe such combination failures.

Apparatus employed for fatigue tests at elevated temperatures has been generally adapted from apparatus employed at ordinary temperatures; several types of commercial apparatus expressly for hot fatigue tests either of the axial or bending type are now available. One type will be described to illustrate the nature of the problems involved. This apparatus, shown in section in Fig. 169, has been described by Howell and Howarth.[269] The specimen S, stressed as a fixed cantilever beam, is entirely within the furnace. One end is rigidly gripped by a vise V, while the other end is joined by a connecting nut D to an extension X which extends outside the furnace, where it is revolved in a circle by a variable eccentric E at a speed of 3,600 rpm. The furnace is heated by electric strip heaters H on the front and rear walls of the furnace; air heated by these elements is circulated by means of a fan F into a baffle box B which surrounds the specimen. The stop ring R through which the specimen assembly passes acts as an automatic shutoff when the specimen fails. The stress on the test specimen is calculated from a load-deflection calibration experimentally obtained at the temperature of interest on one of the series of specimens by means of a loading spring and feeler gauge.

Other hot fatigue apparatus has been described by Moore and Alleman,[270] Welch and Wilson,[268] Kinney,[271] Hempel and Krug,[272] and Toolin and Mochel.[284]

Moduli of Elasticity

In some applications of metals at elevated temperatures, the elastic strains corresponding to the applied stresses are of appreciable magnitude relative to the total strains which are permissible. The elastic moduli are the proportionality constants which relate stress to strain and from which, if the stress is known, the strain may be calculated. For materials which are isotropic, that is, free of directionality of properties, two moduli are of interest, namely, that relating tensile or compressive stress to tensile or compressive strain, commonly termed Young's modulus, and that relating torsional or shear stress to torsional strain, and generally termed the shear modulus.

The moduli of elasticity at elevated temperatures may be experimentally determined in a number of ways (but depend to an increasing degree with increasing temperature on the rate of straining). Thus, Young's modulus may be determined from the elastic portion of the stress-strain curve in a hot tensile test, provided purely axial loading is employed. Similarly, the shear modulus may be obtained from a torsion test at the temperature of interest. A novel apparatus by means of which both the tension and shear moduli may be determined simultaneously has been designed by Everett and Miklowitz.[273] A diagrammatic sketch of this apparatus is shown in Fig. 170. By stressing a specimen simultaneously in bending and in torsion as indicated and observing the resulting angular deflections of the mirrors attached to the ends of the gauge length, the moduli are readily obtained.

Young's modulus may also be determined from vibration studies. Roberts and Nortcliffe[274] have described an apparatus for making such determinations at elevated temperatures and have presented some results obtained with it.

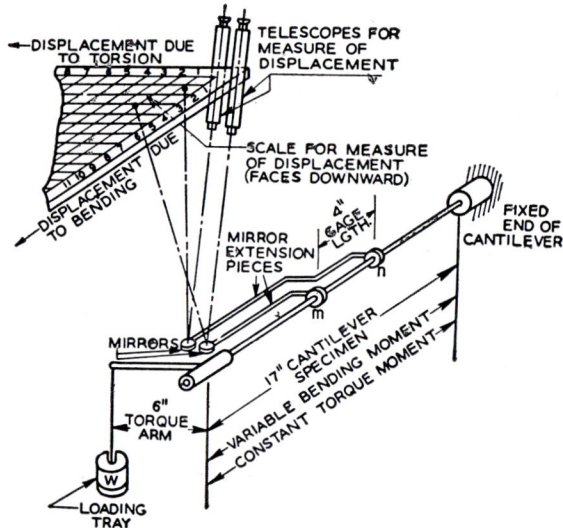

Fig. 170. Apparatus for simultaneously measuring torsion and tension moduli of elasticity at elevated temperatures; furnace not shown.   (*Everett and Miklowitz.*[273])

Miscellaneous Mechanical Tests at Elevated Temperatures

Several investigators, among the first of whom was Sauveur,[275] have made torsion (twist) tests at elevated temperatures. These have generally been of relatively short duration, although some long-time tests have been reported.[276]   In recent years some interest has developed in the hot twist test at relatively fast rates of deformation as a means of evaluating hot workability, that is, the ease of shaping metals by plastic deformation at elevated temperatures. Ihrig[277] as well as Clark and Russ[278] have described apparatus designed for such tests and presented experimental results for a number of steels.

Compression tests are not commonly made at elevated temperatures. Flanigan *et al.*,[279] however, have recently described an apparatus employed for making such tests on sheet specimens.   Using an oil bath as the heating medium, the short-time compressive properties of several aluminum alloys were determined at temperatures up to 300°F.

Notch-impact tests at elevated temperatures are generally made by heating the test specimen in a separate chamber—a hot oil bath or electric muffle furnace—and quickly transferring the specimen with heated tongs to the testing fixture where it is immediately broken. This procedure is analogous to that employed in making the now quite common subatmospheric temperature notch-impact test. Characteristic of the results obtained in such tests are those reported by Quick[280] and by Kinney *et al.*[281] Bend tests at elevated temperatures may be made in a similar way,[282] but since the time consumed in the test is relatively long, the specimen temperature may be expected to drop to some extent.

The ability of a material to damp out vibrations, generally termed the "damping capacity" or "internal friction," is of interest in service which involves fluctuating stresses. Such stresses may be quite important under conditions of resonance or near-resonance, that is, when the frequency of fluctuations corresponds to the natural frequency of the structural element. Schabtach and Fehr[283] have described an apparatus of the tuning-fork type which is suitable for measuring the damping of materials at temperatures up to 1400°F. The damping is determined by the free-vibration-decay method at frequencies from several hundred to several thousand cycles per second and at maximum bending stresses up to 40,000 psi. The vibration is determined with a resistance-type electric strain gauge mounted on the tuning fork whose output is measured with an oscillograph. Since damping depends upon the stress and upon the frequency, data should be obtained under conditions closely simulating those in the contemplated service.

CHAPTER VIII

EFFECT OF CHEMICAL COMPOSITION ON CREEP

The interrelation of stress, strain, temperature, creep rate, and time for rupture has been considered in the preceding chapters. It is now of interest to consider specific experimental studies directed at determining the effects of material variables which account for the differences in behavior of different materials. It will develop that the creep properties of metals are "structure sensitive" and accordingly are affected by many variables, the principal ones of which are chemical composition, manufacturing practice, heat-treatment, and grain size; some of these are, of course, interrelated. Some attention will also be given to reviewing specific experimental studies of the effects of varying temperature and stress and to creep under different states of stress.

Experimental investigations devoted primarily to the study of the effect of chemical composition upon creep behavior have not been many, and the correlation of scattered results of various investigations is not an easy task. Too, various criteria of creep strength have and are being used, and since these are generally quite arbitrary, no simple relations among them exist; this adds further to the difficulties of correlating the work of different investigations. Accordingly, except for individual studies of rather complete nature in themselves, only data reported in terms of the stress to produce a rate of extension equivalent to 1 per cent per 10,000 hr, the stress to produce rupture in 1,000 hr, or similar criteria can generally be considered. These methods of reporting data are those now most commonly used, at least in the United States. This will mean, however, omitting some early work, but this will not be serious inasmuch as many of the early data were obtained under conditions now recognized as inadequate.

There are three ways in which chemical composition influences strength: (1) by solid-solution strengthening, such as results from the addition of zinc to copper to form the solid solution of alpha brass; (2) by the formation of a new phase or constituent, such as the carbide of annealed steel; and (3) precipitation hardening, such as occurs in duralumin. All three methods have been employed for increasing the high-temperature strength of metals, though a critically dispersed precipitate is unquestionably the most effective means. However, the dearth of data available on the influence of individual elements, alone or in combination, and a similar dearth for the influence of heat-treatment, discussed in a subsequent section, indicates that many advances in this field are yet to be made.

The field considered in this section naturally divides itself into two groups, ferrous and nonferrous materials, and these will be considered in turn. In addition there has come into existence, largely since the beginning of the Second World War, a field of so-called "superalloys" which cannot clearly be classed either as ferrous or nonferrous and is therefore treated separately.

The Influence of Alloying Elements in Ferrous Alloys

In all ferrous alloys, certain elements are always present in some degree—carbon, manganese, phosphorus, sulfur, silicon—either to play some particular role or as inadvertent impurities. Besides these, a number of other elements—chromium, nickel, molybdenum, tungsten, columbium, titanium, and others—are added purposely for one reason or another. In no instance are the data on the effects of the elements on creep all that could be desired; in many cases, they are both so meager and so poor that no more than tentative inferences can be drawn as to the role played by specific elements. The space devoted to a particular element reflects the availability of data, not the relative importance. The use of certain elements in steels for bolting applications will not be considered at length, since this is largely a matter of hardenability and resistance to tempering.

Carbon. Increase of carbon in normalized or in annealed plain or low alloy steel invariably results in greater strength as determined in the conventional short-time tensile test either at room or at elevated temperatures. However, no such generalization can be made in regard to the effect of carbon on creep behavior, partly because the influence of carbon appears to depend upon the actual temperature of interest, partly because its influence is not great, and partly because in many investigations, the effect of carbon has been hidden by insufficient control of other test variables.

The early work of Lea,[285] Tapsell and Clenshaw,[286] Pomp and Dahmen,[287] and of Cournot and Sasagawa[288] on the influence of carbon on the creep strength of carbon steel has been reviewed by Tapsell[289] and summarized in Fig. 171. The data shown represent different criteria of "creep limit" and therefore the absolute values are of little interest; attention is therefore directed rather to the variation of creep limit with carbon.

It is also to be pointed out that of the data summarized in Fig. 171, only those of Tapsell and Clenshaw represent long-time tests. Figure 171 shows that at 570 and 750°F both the long-time data of Tapsell and Clenshaw and the short-time data of the other investigators indicate an increase in strength with increasing carbon; at the higher temperatures 930 and 1110°F the effect of carbon is diminished or almost nonexistent, particularly in the long-time tests.

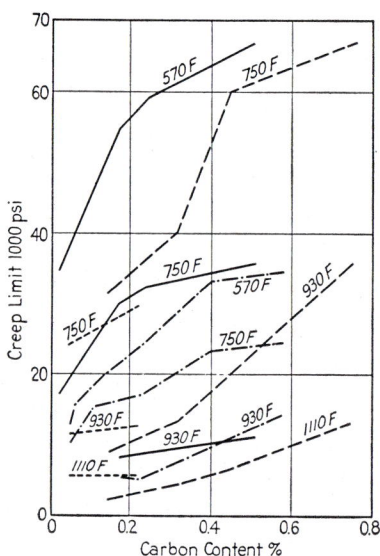

FIG. 171. The effect of carbon content on the creep strength of steel, as summarized by Tapsell.[289]

Lea[285]— — —
Tapsell and Clenshaw[286]———
Pomp and Dahmen[287]— · — · —
Cournot and Sasagawa[288]– – – –

Norton[290] reported an increase of some 10 per cent in strength of carbon steel in long-time tests at 1000°F when the carbon was increased from 0.2 to 0.4 per cent. Similarly other investigators have reported either no effect or a slight increase, but it is difficult to appraise the value of much of this early work, because of failure to report all the variables now recognized to be of importance.

More recently, White, Clark, and Wilson[291] investigated the effect of carbon in a series of two annealed plain carbon and two annealed silicon-chromium-molybdenum steels in 1,000-hr creep tests at 800, 1000, and 1200°F and made a special effort to control all other variables. In each case the low-carbon steel had about 0.10 per cent carbon, while the higher had about 0.45 per cent carbon. At all temperatures, the creep strength of the plain carbon steels was higher in the higher carbon steel, but in the alloy steels the reverse was true. However, these data, which are summarized in Table VII, are probably too meager to permit generalization.

Cross and Lowther[297] report an increase of creep strength with increase of carbon in 500-hr creep tests of 0.35 to 0.60 per cent carbon steels at 850°F, although there was considerable scatter in the data.

Jenkins et al.[292] have studied the effect of carbon on the creep of steel, reporting that in the range 1020 to 1200°F carbon up to 1.2 per cent exerts "no pronounced strengthening action." Below this temperature range, carbon is effective in increasing strength, while above this range low- and high-carbon steel are of essentially equal strength.

Austin, St. John, and Lindsay,[293] studying laboratory-prepared heats in which the amounts of other elements was maintained quite low, found that at 800°F, an increase of carbon up to 0.9 per cent continuously decreased the creep rate in comparative tests, but that at 1000°F, the effect of carbon was inappreciable, and in fact the resistance to creep

TABLE VII. INFLUENCE OF CARBON ON THE CREEP STRENGTH OF PLAIN AND SI-CR-MO STEEL*

Steel	% carbon	Temp., °F	Stress (psi) to produce creep rate of 0.1%/ 1,000 hr
Plain-carbon.....................	0.15	800	17,200
	0.43	800	18,500
	0.15	1000	3,300
	0.43	1000	5,500
	0.15	1200	540
	0.43	1200	860
¾ Si-1¼ Cr-½ Mo..............	0.07	800	29,000
	0.48	800	24,500
	0.07	1000	22,500
	0.48	1000	8,200
	0.07	1200	3,950
	0.48	1200	3,200

* Data from White, Clark, and Wilson.[291]

was little more than that of plain ferrite. These tests were upstep tests, that is, tests in which the same specimens were tested in turn at a series of successively higher stresses, and accordingly, as pointed out elsewhere, there is some question as to the relation between the rates so obtained and those which would be obtained in tests at a single constant stress. However, the tests are comparative, and probably represent one of the most careful investigations which has been conducted on the effect of carbon in plain or low alloy steels. Results of Glen[422] on low-molybdenum and low-chromium–molybdenum steels have indicated that the effect of carbon on creep strength depends on the temperature, stress, and strain at which it is measured.

The effect of carbon on the creep behavior of the intermediate alloys 2 Cr–Mo, 5 Cr–Mo, and 12 Cr–Mo does not appear to have received any attention.   However, the influence of carbon in the austenitic stainless grades has been examined by Cross[352] and at the U.S. Steel Corp. of Del. Research Laboratory.[296]   Cross[352] has reported creep data, summarized in Table VIII, for two portions of a split heat differing principally in carbon, in both the cast and rolled conditions.   It is quite apparent that the increase in carbon from 0.07 to 0.12 per cent has ef-

TABLE VIII.   INFLUENCE OF CARBON ON THE CREEP OF 18 PER CENT CHROMIUM-8 PER CENT NICKEL STEEL*

Steel	C	Mn	Si	Cr	Ni	N
Low-carbon...................	0.067	0.50	0.65	18.21	9.56	0.056
High-carbon...................	0.125	0.47	0.58	18.50	9.67	0.035

Carbon	Rolled or cast	Heat-treat.	Test temp., °F	Stress, 1,000 psi, to produce	
				Min. creep rate 1% 10,000 hr	1% total def. in 10,000 hr
0.067	Rolled	A.C. 2000°F	1000	<17.3	<17.3
0.125	Rolled	A.C. 2000°F	1000	>21.8	<17.3
0.067	Rolled	W.Q. 2000°F	1000	20.0	17.5
0.125	Rolled	W.Q. 2000°F	1000	25.0	20.2
0.067	Rolled	W.Q. 2000°F	1100	14.0	13.6
0.125	Rolled	W.Q. 2000°F	1100	17.3	<17.3
0.067	Rolled	W.Q. 2000°F	1200	8.2	7.1
0.125	Rolled	W.Q. 2000°F	1200	10.5	10.0
0.067	Cast	W.Q. 2000°F	1000	>17.3	14.5
0.125	Cast	W.Q. 2000°F	1000	22.5	<19.6
0.125	Cast	W.Q. 2000°F	1100	17.0†	†
0.067	Cast	W.Q. 2000°F	1200	8.5	8.5
0.125	Cast	W.Q. 2000°F	1200	9.3	9.0

* Data from Cross.[352]
† Fractured before total deformation of 1 per cent.

fectively increased the creep strength of this steel for these test conditions.   This finding is substantiated by the results[296] in Table IX, carbon exerting a profound strengthening effect.   In the plain and molybdenum types of 18 per cent chromium–8 per cent nickel steel, the effect is directly apparent, the low-carbon variety having a creep strength of only slightly more than one-half the high-carbon variety in either case.   The difference is believed to be largely attributable to carbon in spite of some variation in the other elements because the data published by various investigators for the standard varieties show good agreement in spite of normal variation of composition. The data on the columbium and titanium grades are included to show an apparently pronounced effect of the ratio of either of these elements to carbon, the creep strength being greater, the lower this ratio for the titanium grade, and quite similar for the two similar columbium steels.

TABLE IX. INFLUENCE OF CARBON ON CREEP OF 18 CR–8 NI TYPE STEELS*

Type	Composition								
	C	Mn	Si	Ni	Cr	Mo	Cb	Ti	Ti/C or Cb/C
18–8 (0.08 max. C)	0.055	0.28	0.43	10.12	18.40				
18–8 (ultralow C)	0.028	0.61	0.55	10.35	19.30				
18–8 Mo (0.10 max. C)	0.07	1.55	0.34	12.48	17.62	2.57			
18–8 Mo (ultralow C)	0.022	1.47	0.34	10.68	17.56	2.00			
18–8 Cb (Cb/C = 12)	0.07	1.51	0.32	11.12	18.10		0.82		11.7
18–8 Cb (Cb/C = 11)	0.06	1.23	0.58	10.93	17.90		0.64		10.6
18–8 Ti (Ti/C = 9)	0.05	0.52	0.39	10.90	17.50			0.44	8.8
18–8 Ti (Ti/C = 4)	0.085	0.48	0.61	11.29	18.50			0.33	3.9

Type	Heat-treat.,°F	Creep strength		
		Stress (1,000 psi) to produce min. creep rate of 0.0001%/hr		
		1100°F	1300°F	1500°F
18–8 (0.055C)	1900, quench	13.0	5.2	2.1
18–8 (0.028C)	1900, quench	8.1	3.4	1.5
18–8 Mo (0.07C)	2000, quench	26.0	9.7	3.2
18–8 Mo (0.022C)	2000, quench	13.5	4.2	1.5
18–8 Cb (Cb/C = 12)	1950, quench	27.0	8.0	1.8
18–8 Cb (Cb/C = 11)	1950, quench	26.5	7.5	1.5
18–8 Ti (Ti/C = 9)	1950, quench	16.5	4.6	0.85
18–8 Ti (Ti/C = 4)	1950, quench	21.0	7.8	2.7

* Data from U.S. Steel Corp.

Molybdenum. Molybdenum is unquestionably the most effective element generally employed to improve the creep strength of steel, both low-alloy ferritic and high-alloy austenitic steel, and is extensively used in commercial practice for this purpose.

Jenkins *et al.*[298] and Bailey[299] have found an improvement in the creep strength of steel by the addition of up to 1 per cent molybdenum. Similarly the data of various commercial manufacturers reported in trade publications show molybdenum to be an effective creep strengthener.

Aside from the engineering data reported for commercial alloys, the most comprehensive work on the influence of molybdenum on creep is that of Miller, Benz, and Unverzagt.[294] These investigators studied the effect of molybdenum on the creep strength (stress to produce a creep rate of 0.0001 per cent per hour) of several standard and modified commercial grades of steel. The variation of other factors was kept to a minimum; carbon varied from 0.13 to 0.21, manganese from 0.33 to 0.86, and silicon from 0.01 to 0.16 per cent. The results, summarized in Fig. 172, show a profound effect of molybdenum in either a normalized, or normalized and tempered condition.

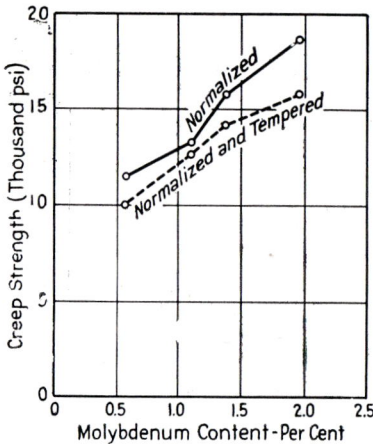

FIG. 172. Effect of molybdenum on the creep strength, stress to produce minimum creep rate of 0.0001 per cent per hour, of steel containing about 0.15 per cent carbon at 1000°F. (*Miller, Benz, and Unverzagt.*[294])

Holtmann[309] has considered the influence of molybdenum (and also vanadium) at various carbon contents in quenched and tempered steels. However, it is generally believed that this initial condition, although strong at the outset, is the most unstable and results in inferior strength in long-time service at moderately elevated temperatures. Accordingly, it is not applied in the United States except for service in bolting applications where the operating temperature is ordinarily sufficiently low so that advantage can be taken of martensitic strengthening.

Austin *et al.*[293] in comparative upstep creep tests, have shown that considerable strengthening results at 800°F from the addition of molybdenum to commercially pure iron. These results are summarized in Fig. 173. Additional, though less comprehensive, tests at 1000°F showed that molybdenum is also an effective strengthening agent at this temperature.

Plain low-molybdenum steel has scaling resistance roughly the same as plain carbon steel, and accordingly cannot be used for long service above about 1000°F. To provide adequate resistance to oxidizing or other corrosive environment, chromium is universally added, and commercial manufacturers supply a series of alloys containing up to 25 per cent or more chromium. As discussed later, chromium seems to exert little influence on creep strength, and all the creep-resistant alloys with chromium up to 12 per cent contain molybdenum to confer strengthening. The few data that are available for these commercial alloys indicate that the creep strength depends upon the molybdenum content in a manner similar to that in the plain molybdenum steel.

Hildorf, Clark, and White[351] have examined the influence of molybdenum up to 2 per cent on the creep-rupture strength at 1200°F of steels containing either 5 or 7 per cent chromium and 1 or 1.5 per cent silicon,

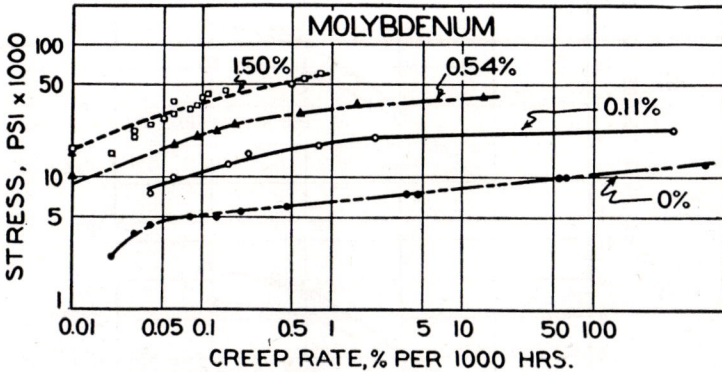

Fig. 173. Effect of molybdenum on the relation between stress and creep rate of commercially pure iron at 800°F. (*Austin et al.*[293])

with results summarized in Fig. 174. The steels containing 1.5 and 2.0 per cent molybdenum were made in an induction furnace, while the other heats were melted in commercial electric-arc furnaces. The alloys were mostly normalized at 1750°F and drawn at 1500°F, but a few were annealed at 1550°F. All alloys had a Brinell hardness at atmospheric temperature of 160 to 200. The beneficial influence of molybdenum in these alloys is apparent in Fig. 174. The variation in chromium from 5 to 7 per cent with constant silicon did not effect any significant change in the rupture strength of steels containing more than 1 per cent molybdenum, and effected only a very slight improvement of the 0.5 per cent molybdenum steel. The change from 1 to 1.5 per cent silicon was slightly detrimental at the higher molybdenum levels.

The effect of molybdenum carries over into the field of the austenitic steels, and of the several modified 18 per cent chromium–8 per cent nickel steels, that containing 2 to 3 per cent molybdenum (AISI Type 316) has the greatest strength, especially in the higher range of temperatures (see Table IX). Also, many of the so-called superalloys developed in recent years for exceptionally high strength at high tempera-

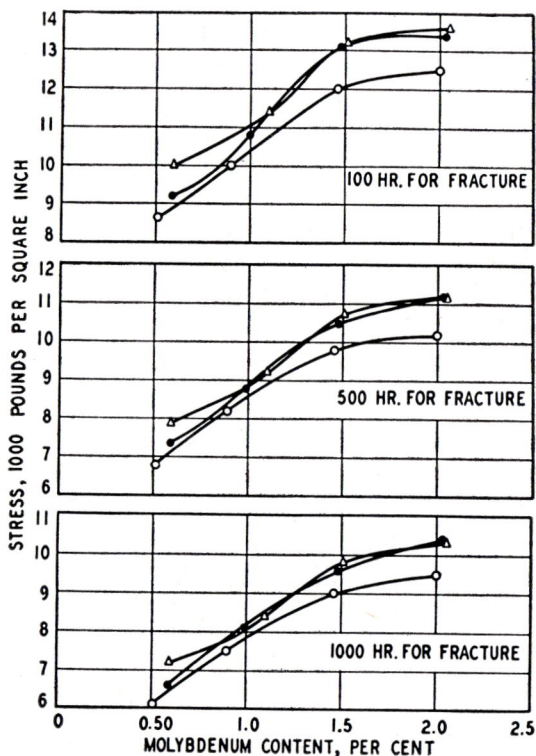

FIG. 174. Effect of molybdenum on the stress to rupture in 100, 500, and 1,000 hr of three steels containing 5 to 7 per cent chromium and 1 to 1.5 per cent silicon at 1200°F. (*Hildorf et al.*[351]) Nominal analysis: ● 5 Cr, 1 Si, 0.1 C; ○ 5 Cr, 1.5 Si, 0.1 C; △ 7 Cr, 1 Si, 0.1 C.

tures for gas-turbine and similar applications have effectively employed molybdenum as a strengthening agent.

Chromium. As mentioned in the preceding section, chromium is added to steels used at high temperatures primarily for improving oxidation and corrosion resistance. Its effect on creep strength has been studied by several investigators.

Austin *et al.*[293] have studied the effect of chromium on the creep strength of commercially pure ferrite at 800°F with results as shown in Fig. 175. Comparison with Fig. 173 for molybdenum shows that as a strengthener chromium is slightly the inferior at low percentages and appreciably inferior at high percentages. The few data obtained at 1000°F were inconsistent in trend. As pointed out earlier, too great reliance should not be placed on these data, since they were obtained in upstep tests, wherein the behavior at any step may have been influenced by the prior history.

The effect of chromium as found by Austin *et al.* does not seem to carry over into the commercial molybdenum alloys, which indicates that the effects of alloying elements on creep behavior are not additive. Clark and White[295] report the data in Fig. 176 which, particularly at 1000°F, shows a curious reversal in the effect of chromium. No details of the experiments are given, and it is impossible to appraise the value

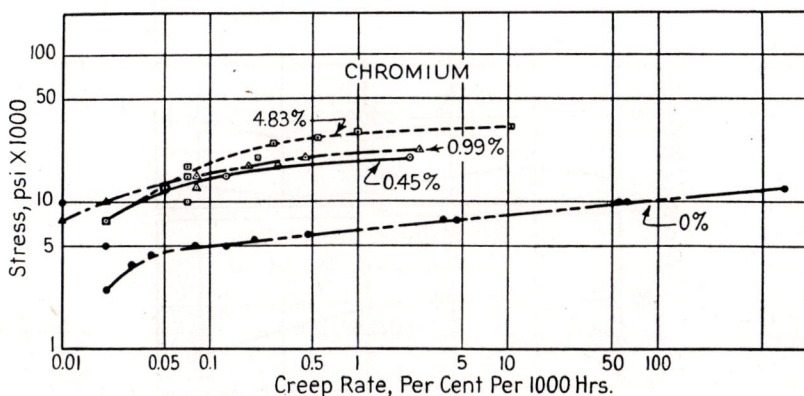

FIG. 175. Effect of chromium on the relation between stress and creep rate of commercially pure iron at 800°F. (*Austin et al.*[293])

of the data. Bailey[299] found 1 per cent chromium to reduce in some cases and to increase in others the creep strength of 0.5 per cent molybdenum steel though not much in either case. Miller, Benz, and Unverzagt[294] studied the effect on creep strength of change of chromium in similarly heat-treated chromium-molybdenum or chromium-molybdenum-silicon steels. The creep strength (Fig. 177) is virtually unchanged as the chromium is increased to 2 per cent, but more chromium has a slight weakening effect, except in the 0.5 per cent molybdenum–1.5 per cent silicon alloys in which chromium exerts no influence. Figure 177 also shows that an increase in molybdenum is effective in increasing the strength of iron-chromium alloys in roughly the same degree as in plain iron-molybdenum steels. The limited data available on various commercial alloys indicate that this effect is maintained up to at least 12 per cent chromium. The commercial straight chromium ferritic grades 12 Cr, 17 Cr, and 27 Cr are of inferior creep strength, and the latter two, in particular, are seldom employed when creep resistance is of any great consequence.

Manganese and Copper. Austin et al.[293] show an increase in strength to result from adding manganese to commercially pure ferrite at 800°F (Fig. 178).

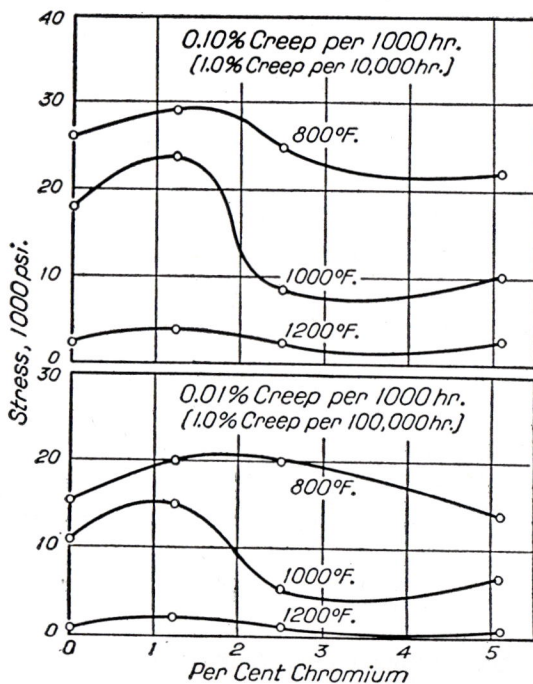

FIG. 176. Effect of chromium on the creep strength of steel containing 0.5 per cent molybdenum and 0.1 to 0.2 per cent carbon at 800, 1000, and 1200°F. (*Clark and White.*[295])

Other data have been reported by Clark and White[295] for 0.25 per cent molybdenum steel, shown in Fig. 179. The occurrence of a sharp maximum at 1.25 per cent manganese is unexpected and should be checked. No details about the heat-treatment or other variables are available, and the data accordingly cannot be appraised. It should be pointed out that manganese is not added to any commercial high-temperature steel expressly for improving creep strength, and this is indicative of at best only a minor influence of this element.

Glen[419] has made comparative creep-rate tests of experimental induction-furnace steels containing 0.1 per cent carbon and different amounts

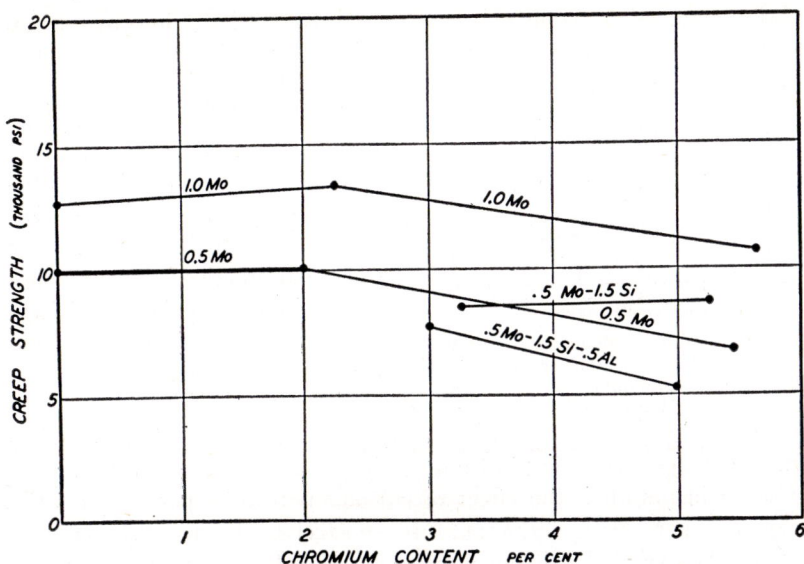

FIG. 177. Effect of chromium on the creep strength, stress to produce a minimum creep rate of 0.0001 per cent per hour, of several steels containing small amounts of molybdenum, silicon, and aluminum at 1000°F. (*Miller et al.*[294])

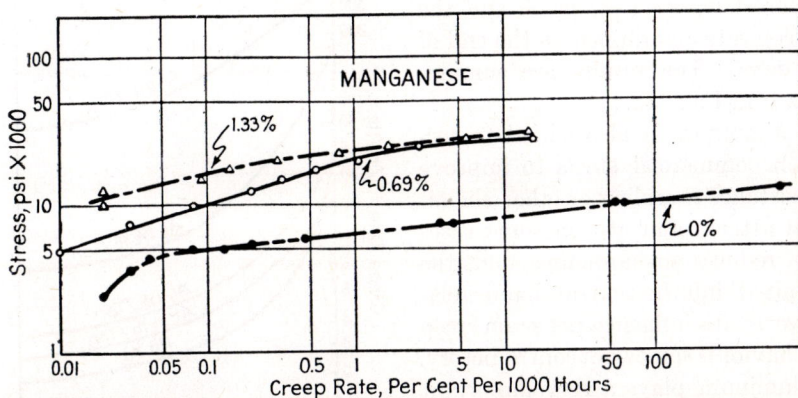

FIG. 178. Effect of manganese on the relation between stress and creep rate of commercially pure iron at 800°F. (*Austin et al.*[293])

of manganese at several different aluminum levels. All steels were tested under 18,000 psi at 840°F for 5 days, and had similar grain size and microstructure. Figure 180 shows the relation observed between the creep rate at the end of this period and the manganese content. Increasing manganese results in decreasing creep rate. A similar effect of manganese was also noted for a silicon level of 0.15 per cent.

Like manganese, copper is not added to steel to improve creep strength, and in lack of reported data, it can only be surmised that it is ineffective.

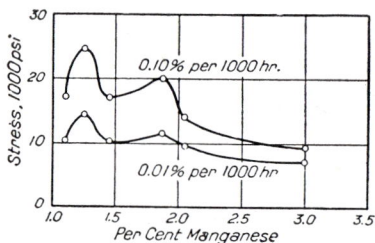

FIG. 179. Effect of manganese on the stress to produce indicated creep rate at 900°F of steel containing 0.25 per cent molybdenum and 0.15 per cent carbon. (*Clark and White.*[295])

Silicon and Aluminum. The studies of Austin *et al.*[293] (Fig. 181) indicate silicon to play a less powerful role than manganese (Fig. 178) and this seems to be borne out by commercial practice. Newell[306] has indicated that the only value of silicon in commercial alloys, aside from deoxidation, is for scaling resistance. Silicon is added in amounts up to 1.5 per cent to several of the chromium-molybdenum series, but only to improve scaling resistance.

Glen[419] has studied the effect of silicon up to 0.16 per cent on the creep of experimental induction-furnace steel containing 0.1 per cent carbon at several levels of aluminum deoxidation addition. Comparative tests under 18,000 psi at 840°F with similar grain size and microstructure were made and the creep rate determined at the end of 5 days. The results are summarized in Fig. 182.

Aluminum is also added to certain commercial steels to improve resistance to scaling or other chemical attack, and also in some cases to reduce air-hardening, but the limited information at hand relative to its influence per se on creep behavior is somewhat contradictory. Aluminum plays a very important role also through its effect on grain size.

Glen[419] has reported an abrupt increase in creep rate (Fig. 193) with increasing aluminum deoxidation of carbon steels of similar grain size and microstructure.

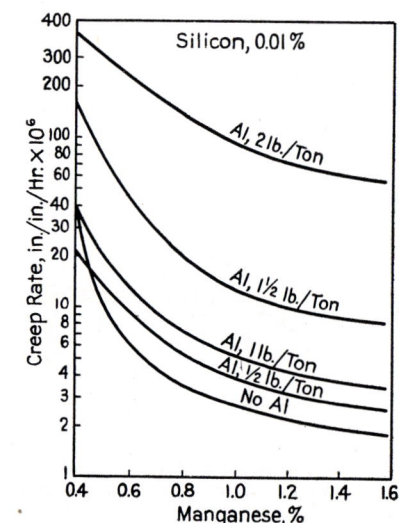

FIG. 180. Effect of manganese on creep rate of steel containing 0.1 per cent carbon, 0.01 per cent silicon, and deoxidized with different amounts of aluminum. 18,000 psi at 840°F for 5 days. (*Glen.*[419])

Nickel and Cobalt. Neither nickel nor cobalt are added to any low alloy steel with the aim of improving creep strength, and their ineffectiveness in this regard is indicated by the data of Austin *et al.*[293] (Figs. 183 and 184). However, nickel is an important ingredient, with chromium, of the austenitic stainless steels, but there are no data to

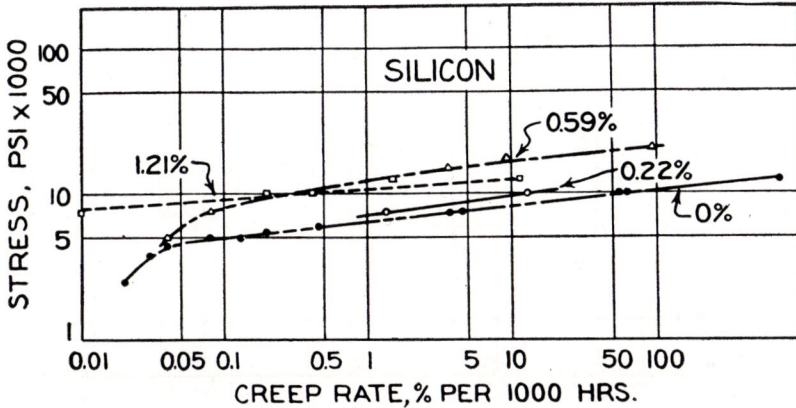

FIG. 181. Effect of silicon on the relation between stress and creep rate of commercially pure iron at 800°F. (*Austin et al.*[293])

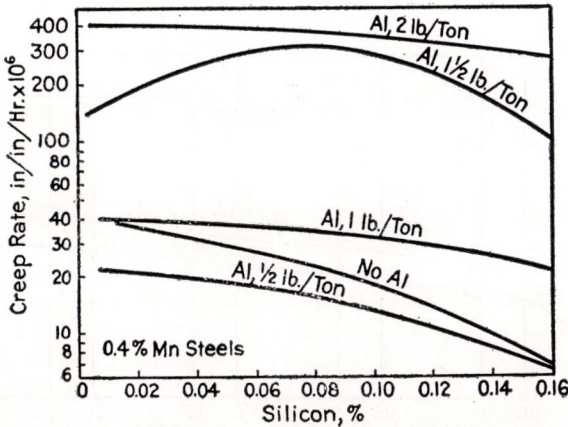

FIG. 182. Effect of silicon on the creep rate at the end of 5 days at 840°F under 18,000 psi of steel containing 0.1 per cent carbon for several levels of aluminum addition. (*Glenn.*[419])

evaluate its specific effect on creep behavior; cobalt plays an important role in many of the superalloys.

Tungsten, Vanadium, Titanium, and Columbium. These four elements act similarly to molybdenum in increasing the creep strength of steel, at least under certain conditions. However, none of these elements is commercially used for this purpose in low alloy steels, though in the superalloys they play a quite important role.

The data on the effect of tungsten are quite sparse, but Bullens[300] has concluded that tungsten is not more than one-half as effective as molybdenum in increasing the creep strength of carbon steel. This fact combined with the relative cost of tungsten explains its limited use.

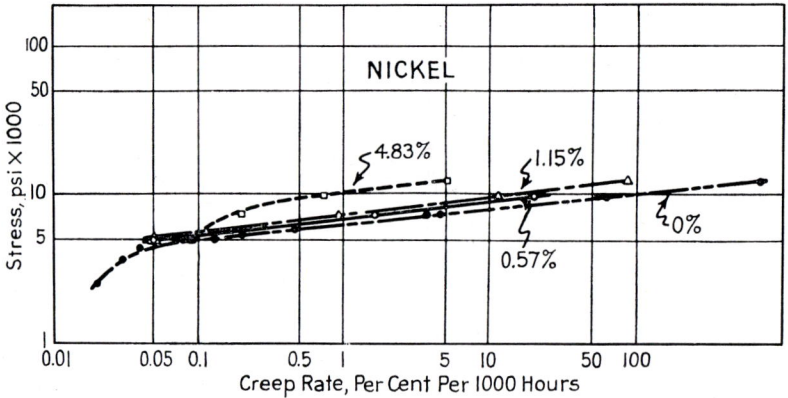

FIG. 183. Effect of nickel on the relation between stress and creep rate of commercially pure iron at 800°F. (*Austin et al.*[293])

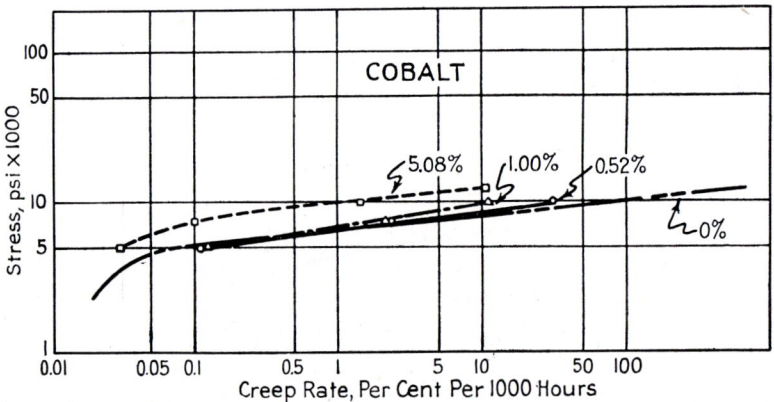

FIG. 184. Effect of cobalt on the relation between stress and creep rate of commercially pure iron at 800°F. (*Austin et al.*[293])

With regard to the influence of vanadium, Bailey[299] has shown in comparative tests that the addition of up to 0.4 per cent vanadium to steel containing 0.5 per cent molybdenum improved its creep resistance at about 1000°F. Similarly, Cross and Lowther[297] report that a normalized 0.2 per cent vanadium steel extended only about one-tenth as fast in a 500-hr test at 850°F as an annealed carbon steel of similar fine grain size. Robinson[420] has reported that the addition of up to 0.3 per cent vanadium improves the creep strength of steels containing up to 1 per cent molybdenum.

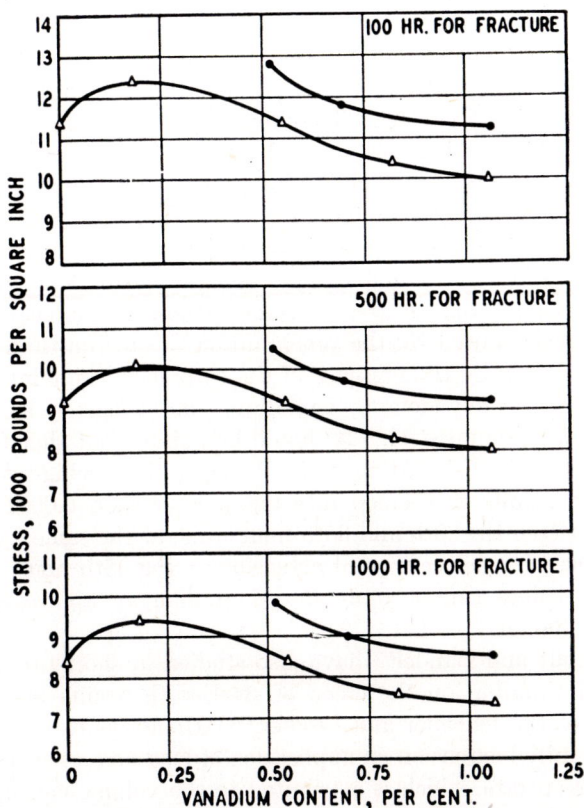

FIG. 185. Effect of vanadium on the stress to rupture in 100, 500, and 1,000 hr of two steels containing 5 to 7 per cent chromium and 1 per cent molybdenum and 1 per cent silicon at 1200°F. (*Hildorf et al.*[351]) Nominal analyses: ● 5 Cr, 1 Mo, 1 Si, 0.1 C; △ 7 Cr, 1 Mo, 1 Si, 0.1 C.

Hildorf, Clark, and White[351] have tested the influence of up to 1 per cent vanadium on the creep-rupture strength at 1200°F of steels containing either 5 or 7 per cent chromium and 1 per cent each of silicon and molybdenum. The steels were all normalized at 1750°F and drawn at 1500°F and had a room-temperature Brinell hardness of from 150 to 190. The results are summarized in Fig. 185. The rupture strength for each of the time intervals is increased by the first addition of vanadium and is then decreased with further addition. The 5 per cent chromium level appears to be superior to the 7 per cent level.

Titanium is not added to commercial steels expressly to improve the creep strength, but rather to tie up the carbon, as in enameling sheet steel, in the 5 per cent chromium steels or in the austenitic chromium-nickel steel. However, in recent years there has been increased interest in the use of titanium for improvement in creep strength.

Bardenheuer and Fischer[301] have studied the influence of titanium on the creep strength of steel. They report that titanium improved the strength at 930°F of low-carbon steel initially quenched from 2200°F and tempered at 1100°F. The improvement was related to the ratio of titanium to carbon, being greatest when this was in the range of 6 to 9. Since the amount of titanium necessary to combine with the carbon is 4 to 1 for the titanium carbide TiC, the existence of an optimum in the range 6 to 9, that is, greater than 4, is taken to indicate that the strengthening is caused by the precipitation of an iron-titanium compound rather than by the presence of the carbide. These investigators also report that molybdenum, vanadium, and tungsten increase the creep limit of titanium steel. It should be pointed out that these conclusions are based on short-time tests, the creep limit being taken as the stress which results in a creep rate not greater than 0.0001 per cent per hour between the 25th and 35th hour while at the same time giving not more than 0.2 per cent total extension at the 45th hour. Accordingly, such values cannot represent more than an approximation of long-time behavior.

Houdremont and Bandel[302] have also studied in short-time tests the influence of titanium on the creep of steel, with results in agreement with those of Bardenheuer and Fischer.[301] Houdremont and Bandel[302] report high initial extension on application of load and a low, sometimes negative, creep rate, which is attributed to the volume contraction accompanying the precipitation of iron titanide. In a few long-time creep tests, titanium proved to be beneficial, in qualitative substantiation of the short-time tests.

Data obtained in the U.S. Steel Corp. of Del. Research Laboratory[296] have confirmed the work of the German investigators, both as to high initial extension and low creep rate. The results are summarized in Table X.

The creep strength of this steel, 25,000 psi for a rate of 0.0001 per cent per hour (equivalent to 1 per cent per 10,000 hr) at 850°F is almost identical with that of 0.5 per cent molybdenum steel and exceeds the

15,000 psi strength of carbon steel at this temperature. However, the extension on application of load is inordinately large.

As mentioned earlier, titanium is added to the 5 per cent chromium–0.5 per cent molybdenum steels to tie up the carbon and effectively to reduce the tendency to air-hardening, and thus to increase the ease of welding. Its effect on creep strength is not great. Comstock[310] has reported that its strength is best if the ratio of titanium to carbon is not greater than 5 to 6. Similarly titanium is added to austenitic 18 per cent chromium–8 per cent nickel steel to tie up carbon (so-called stabilizing) and its effect on creep strength is again apparently not great, though the data are limited.

TABLE X. RESULTS OF CREEP TESTS AT 850°F ON LOW-CARBON–HIGH-TITANIUM STEEL*†

Steel	0.05 C	0.45 Mn	0.013 P	0.025 S	0.07 Si	0.13 Al	0.41 Ti

Stress 1,000 psi	Elong. on app. of load, %	Rate of ext. at 2,000 hr, %/hr	Contract on release of load, %	Stress for creep rate of 0.0001 %/hr, 1,000 psi
25.0	5.4	0.000102	0.135	
20.0	2.56	0.000057	0.104	25.0
15.0	1.22	Tested for only 150 hr	0.083	

* Data from U.S. Steel Corp.
† Air-cooled from 1550°F; 5-6 ASTM grain size; 82 Vickers hardness.

Comstock and Clark[307] have studied the effect of up to 2 per cent titanium on the high-temperature properties of 17 per cent chromium steel. They report that 0.25 per cent titanium exerted almost no influence on creep strength at 1100°F but materially reduced the customary loss in ductility of this steel on sojourn at high temperatures. Two higher titanium steels, 1 and 2 per cent, had inferior creep resistance.

Wever and Peter[303] have investigated the influence of columbium on the creep strength of steel. They find from short-time tests (but with a few long-time confirmatory tests) that columbium rather markedly improves the creep strength of steel if the columbium is maintained in solution by quenching and then caused to precipitate in a dispersed state in the range of 950 to 1300°F. The effectiveness is attributed to an iron columbide since only after the requisite amount of columbium to combine with the carbon had been added was its effectiveness fully attained. In this respect, columbium appears to act similarly to titanium. The authors report that columbium is also effective when other elements are present, provided that there is more than enough columbium to combine with the carbon.

Parker[308] has reported creep-rupture tests of an alloy containing 3 per cent columbium, balance iron, quenched from 2000°F, and then tempered at 1200°F. The stress for rupture in 1,000 hr at 1100°F was about 25,000 psi, which appreciably exceeds the 5,000 psi strength of ordinary 0.15 per cent carbon steel.

Columbium has in recent years been a favorite addition to many of the superalloys. Columbium is used in the 5 per cent chromium-molybdenum and austenitic 18 per cent chromium–8 per cent nickel steels for tying up with carbon. In the latter grade, the addition of this element, primarily for stabilizing, is beneficial to the creep strength, particularly below 1200°F; this may be the result of precipitation phenomena.

Phosphorus. Cross and Krause[304] have shown in 1,000-hr comparative tests that the addition of 0.2 per cent phosphorus to a 0.1 per cent carbon–1 per cent chromium steel resulted in a creep rate at 850°F which was approximately the same as when the addition was 0.2 per cent molybdenum. At 950°F a 0.1 per cent carbon–1 per cent chromium–0.5 per cent phosphorus steel stretched about the same amount as a steel in which 0.5 per cent molybdenum replaced the phosphorus. The 0.2 per cent phosphorus alloy was reported tough in notch-impact test after creep test, while the 0.5 per cent phosphorus alloy was brittle. Newell and Olzak[305] have similarly reported phosphorus to be beneficial in 5 per cent chromium–0.5 per cent molybdenum steel.

Data obtained at the U.S. Steel Corp. of Del. Research Laboratory show the quantitative effect of phosphorus in 0.5 and 1 per cent molybdenum steel (see Table XI).

The after-creep-test notch-impact strengths of the high-phosphorus steels were somewhat lower than for the low-phosphorus steels, but yet satisfactory.

High-chromium–High-nickel Austenitic Steels. The austenitic chromium-nickel-iron alloys which were developed primarily for corrosion resistance have proved also to possess superior scaling and creep resistance. In fact, the strongest of the common ferritic alloys is only some 40 to 50 per cent as strong at 1000°F as any of the 18 per cent–8 per cent nickel steels. These alloys do not ordinarily undergo the transformation to ferrite and therefore the same advantage cannot be taken of this transformation for controlling grain size, or for changing the strength by changing the structure as is possible in the ferritic grades. Therefore, these grades are ordinarily used in an annealed or stabilized condition.

Of the various 18 per cent chromium–8 per cent nickel alloys, that containing molybdenum has the best creep strength, except at relatively low temperatures, perhaps 1100°F, at which temperature the columbium grade seems to be superior. Of the other two common wrought austenitic grades, 25 per cent chromium–12 per cent nickel and 25 per cent chromium–20 per cent nickel, the former is quite similar in strength to the plain 18 per cent chromium–8 per cent nickel, while the latter tends to be somewhat superior.

General Considerations Concerning the Improvement of Creep Strength of Ferrous Alloys. It has become apparent in the preceding review that for the most part our knowledge about the influence of various elements on the creep strength of steel is meager. Data on carbon-free

TABLE XI. INFLUENCE OF PHOSPHORUS ON CREEP STRENGTH OF MOLYBDENUM STEEL AT 1000°F*†

Steel	C	Mn	P	S	Si	Mo	Stress for creep rate of 0.0001 %/hr, 1,000 psi
0.5 Mo low P	0.14	0.49	0.006	0.023	0.14	0.53	11.3
0.5 Mo high P	0.15	0.40	0.091	0.030	0.12	0.50	14.8
1 Mo low P	0.17	0.42	0.015	0.013	0.17	0.96	13.6
1 Mo high P	0.15	0.43	0.091	0.029	0.15	1.04	16.7

* Data from U.S. Steel Corp.
† All steels were air-cooled after 0.5 hr at 1650°F, and were of similar hardness, 140–150 Brinell, and microstructure. The two high-phosphorus steels were of experimental 20-lb induction furnace heats, silicon deoxidized.

iron, such as those of Austin *et al.*,[293] represent a valuable and logical first step, but commercial alloys contain carbon, which introduces a second constituent into the microstructure of nearly all ferrous alloys.

There appear to be available only two general studies of the influence of chemical composition on creep strength, both of which have short-comings: (1) that of Grün[311] based on short-time tests, and (2) that of Austin, St. John, and Lindsay,[293] already described in some detail, based on upstep tests. Parker[308] has considered the general problem of the development of high-temperature alloys, but has presented few data.

Grün[311] studied in short-time tests at 750 and 930°F a series of annealed experimental alloys containing about 0.1 per cent carbon and up to some 2 per cent of various other elements either alone or in combination. At 750°F the order of increasing effectiveness of 0.5 per cent of each of the elements on the short-time creep strength was as follows:

nickel, cobalt, manganese, titanium, silicon, chromium, copper, tungsten, molybdenum, and vanadium. The relative strength of the weakest was 10, that of the strongest 18. At 930°F the order of effectiveness was slightly different: nickel, silicon, tungsten, cobalt, manganese, chromium, copper, titanium, vanadium, and molybdenum. Here the relative strengths ranged from 3 to 11. Also of interest is Grün's finding from tests of several alloys containing several different elements that the individual effects of the elements in such instances may be expected to be additive, at least qualitatively. This possibility should be further checked. It is interesting to compare the data of Austin *et al.*,[293] summarized in Fig. 186, with those of Grün, particularly since the former alloys contained essentially no carbon. The elements which these latter investigators studied align themselves in roughly the same order as that determined by Grün, with nickel and cobalt exerting the least and molybdenum the greatest influence.

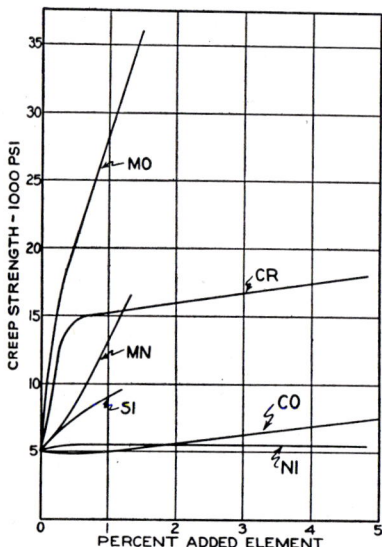

Fig. 186. Effect of different elements on the creep strength, stress to produce creep rate of 0.0001 per cent per hour, of commercially pure iron at 800°F. (*Austin et al.*[293])

Inspection of these data does not readily provide any clue as to the characteristics common to those elements most effective in increasing the creep strength. The occurrence of the relatively strong carbide-forming elements molybdenum, vanadium, and titanium among those most effective is of interest, but tungsten, a similarly strong carbide former, is among the most ineffective. Perhaps the tungsten data should be rechecked. It is also of interest to note that silicon, one of the most effective hardeners of ferrite at atmospheric temperature according to Bain[312] is one of the most ineffective at elevated temperatures.

Many investigators, perhaps the first of whom were Houdremont and Ehmcke,[315] have postulated a relation between recrystallization behavior and creep strength, and although this subject is treated in more detail in another section, it is of interest to examine here the limited data available regarding the influence of alloying elements on the recrystallization of iron, since these data provide a clue as to the relative effectiveness of the elements in increasing high-temperature strength. Austin, Luini, and Lindsay[313] have determined the softening or recrystallization temperature for the same alloys tested in creep (see preceding pages) by Austin et al.[293] These results (Fig. 187) showed that molybdenum was the most effective element in increasing the temperature of recrystallization and nickel and cobalt the most ineffective, an excellent

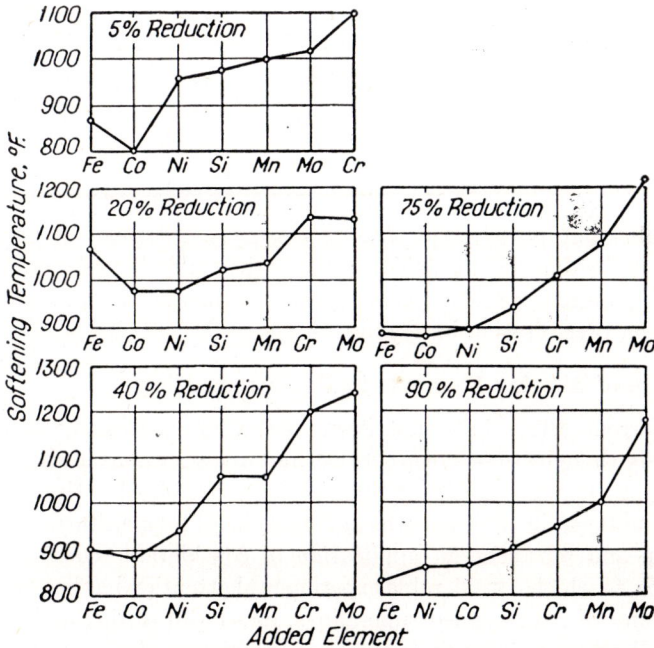

FIG. 187. Relative effects of 0.5 per cent (approximately) of the various elements in solid solution in iron on raising the softening temperature after cold rolling 5, 20, 40, 75, and 90 per cent reduction in thickness. Softening temperature has been defined as that temperature of annealing for a period of 1 hr at which the hardness of the alloy lies midway between that of the rolled and fully annealed alloy. (*Austin et al.*[313])

correlation with the creep studies (Fig. 186). Only chromium and manganese are out of order, being interchanged in the two instances. Earlier study by Tammann[314] had shown roughly the same results in respect to recrystallization, but also showed tungsten to be one of the most effective elements in raising the recrystallization temperature of iron. This is, then, additional reason for reexamining the influence of tungsten on creep strength in order to check the results of Grün.[311]

Thus, with the possible exception of tungsten, it appears that the elements most effective in increasing the creep strength of steel are those of strong carbide-forming tendency, and at the same time effective in increasing the recrystallization temperature.

Parker[308] has pointed out that the most effective method of increasing strength at ordinary temperatures by change of chemical composition is to form a critically dispersed precipitate and, furthermore, that a number of elements such as tungsten, molybdenum, columbium, tantalum, and titanium form intermetallic compounds with iron and can be distributed in a desirable state of dispersion by suitable heat-treatment. Creep tests on several such alloys supported his arguments by showing quite good strength. As yet this means of improving creep strength is not commonly used in commercial alloys, probably for a variety of reasons, perhaps chief of which is that such alloys lack other desirable characteristics such as scaling resistance. However, Parker's results should spur investigators to develop alloys which are not only precipitation-hardenable but possess the other necessary attributes. A great deal remains to be done in this field. Some of the superalloys for gas-turbine and other similar applications are given treatments which are described as causing precipitation hardening.

Influence of Alloying Elements in Nonferrous Alloys

Nonferrous alloys have not been used very extensively in what is ordinarily thought to be creep service, and investigations of the influence of alloying elements are fewer than in the ferrous field. However, lead alloys employed in cable sheaths at atmospheric temperature are subject to creep and represent an application of considerable commercial importance, to which considerable experimental attention has been directed. Too, many of the so-called superalloys, developed during and since the Second World War, contain one of the nonferrous metals as a major component and are of increasing commercial interest.

Lead and Lead Alloys. Archbutt[316] was one of the first to study the important problem of creep of lead cable sheathing, conducting creep-rupture tests on annealed and unannealed material. The annealed material was found to be appreciably stronger than the unannealed.

Since Archbutt's early studies of this very important problem, many investigations have been conducted, the most comprehensive of which have probably been those of Moore *et al.*[317-321] Working for the most part with specimens prepared from flattened cable sheath, these experimenters have studied by means of creep-rate and creep-rupture tests many aspects of the cable-sheathing problems, both theoretical and practical. Extrapolation of their data gave a range in stress to produce rupture in 100,000 hr at room temperature from about 100 psi for "common" lead to 900 psi for a lead-calcium-magnesium-tin alloy, although the extrapolation is subject to some uncertainty.

Phillips[322] reported that many of the elements which increase the tensile strength of lead decrease the resistance to creep under low loads. Among the specific elements tested, Phillips found that copper improved creep strength markedly; antimony lowered the creep strength except in a precipitation-hardened condition; tin lowered creep resistance, except in the heat-treated condition; tellurium lowered creep strength at low loads either when cold-rolled or when annealed.

Greenwood *et al.*[323–325] have also reported that tellurium adversely affects the creep strength. These investigators have studied many aspects of the creep of lead, and have shown that small amounts of impurities, for example 0.01 per cent of silver, exert a profound influence on the creep strength.

Bassett and Snyder[326] have also shown the marked influence of composition on the creep strength of lead, though, like many others, not conducting a systematic investigation of this problem.

Gohn, Arnold, and Bouton[327] have made creep tests on a number of commercial lead cable sleeves and on a number of lead alloys prepared experimentally and extruded as tape. The commercial sleeves represented six different compositions: (1) chemical lead with 0.9 per cent antimony; (2) secondary lead with 0.7 per cent antimony; (3) secondary lead with 3 per cent tin; (4) detinned lead; (5) secondary lead; (6) chemical lead. Chemical lead sleeves proved to be more creep-resistant than lead-antimony or lead-tin sleeves at low stresses, but not at high stresses; the secondary lead and detinned lead were inferior to chemical lead sleeves. The experimental lead tapes included high-purity fire-refined lead and chemical lead and mixtures of these with up to 0.07 per cent tellurium, 1.0 per cent antimony, and 0.5 per cent calcium. The high-purity lead, containing lesser amounts of minor impurities than chemical lead, was inferior to chemical lead at all stresses. The chemical lead tape was likewise superior to all the lead alloys except those containing the higher percentages of calcium.

Smith and Howe[328] have reported the results of creep tests on a number of lead alloys, with results summarized in Fig. 188. At low stress, the copper-bearing alloy is superior to the antimonial leads, except that one containing 6 per cent antimony. At 210°F the antimonial alloy is quite weak.

Zinc and Zinc Alloys. Zinc flows under constant stress at atmospheric temperature, and zinc-alloy die castings are not suggested for uses involving continuous stress at temperatures above 210°F.[330]   Very few data on the creep of zinc and zinc alloys have been reported in the literature.

Ruzicka[329] has made comparison creep tests at 85°F on eight different rolled zinc alloys used for weather stripping, with results summarized in Table XII.   These tests indicate that creep is quite sensitive to many conditions.   For example, the difference between alloys 404 and 403 is probably attributable to a different prior rolling history, since the as-rolled condition is an uncertain one.   Such differences make it impossible to evaluate the influence of individual elements in these tests.

Kelton and Grissinger[330] have reported limited data on creep of zinc, though primary interest was in testing techniques and evaluation of data.

TABLE XII.   COMPARATIVE CREEP TESTS AT 85°F ON SEVERAL ROLLED ZINC ALLOYS*

Alloy No.	Composition, zinc plus indicated % of added element					Stress, 1,000 psi, to cause 1% creep per day	
	Cu	Mg	Cd	Pb	Fe	In rolling direction	Across rolling direction
154	1.1	0.0057	0.0046	0.09	0.012	18.0	22.4
153	1.0	0.0036	0.0043	0.09	0.011	15.8	22.5
404	1.0	†	0.0049	0.084	0.015	12.1	14.2
403	1.1	†	0.0047	0.077	0.012	7.6	9.9
637	...	†	0.13	0.28	0.021	7.2	8.0
281	...	†	0.09	0.80	0.017	7.0	7.3
341	...	†	0.11	0.15	0.017	6.2	6.7
10	...	†	0.12	0.24	0.011	4.7	5.0

* Data from Ruzicka.[329]
† Less than 0.0005%.

The authors report that the ASTM zinc alloys 23 and 25 containing 3.5 to 4.3 per cent aluminum and, respectively, 0.10 per cent maximum and 0.75 to 1.25 per cent copper are essentially equal in strength, but that alloy 21 containing 2.5 to 3.5 per cent copper is somewhat stronger (though subject to undesirable dimensional change on aging).   No values were reported for this latter alloy.

Tin and Tin Alloys.   Tin, like lead and zinc, creeps at room temperature.   Little investigational work has been done on the creep of tin and its alloys, except for that of Hanson and Sandford.[331,336].

Hanson and Sandford[331] conducted a rather extensive investigation of the creep of tin (99.99 per cent pure) and of tin containing up to 3.5 per cent silver, up to 5 per cent bismuth, up to 10 per cent antimony, or up to 33 per cent cadmium, as well as of several lead-tin solders.   Creep-rupture tests were made on rolled material at atmospheric temperature out to nearly 2 years duration.   Silver greatly improved the creep resistance.   Bismuth-tin alloys were more creep-resistant than pure tin at stresses greater than 300 psi, but inferior at lower stresses.   Antimony up to 8.5 per cent improved creep resistance; the alloy containing 10 per cent antimony was slightly inferior to that containing 8.5 per cent of this element.   Cadmium-tin alloys up to 4 per cent cadmium were

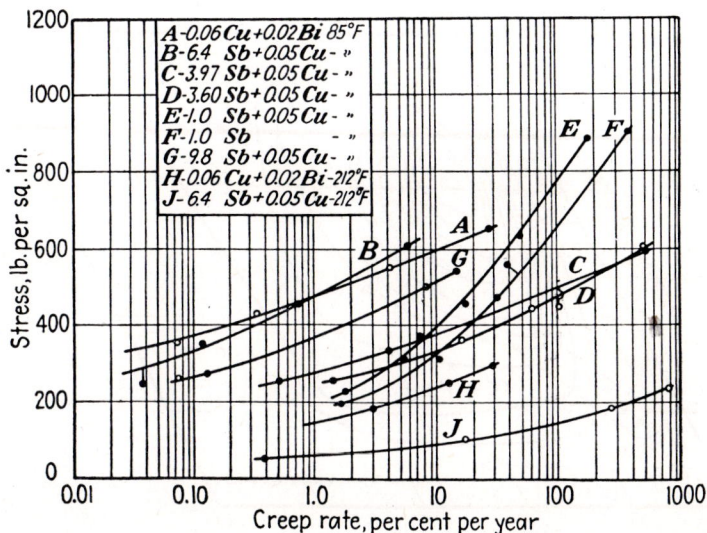

FIG. 188. Effect of several elements on the relation between stress and creep rate of lead at 85 or 212°F, as indicated.   (*Smith and Howe.*[328])

quite resistant to creep, but that containing 6 per cent was quite weak. In contrast to all the other materials, which were self-annealed for at least 1 month prior to test, the cadmium alloys up to 4 per cent had been quenched and tempered.   Therefore, the 6 per cent alloy may have appeared weak only because it was not heat-treated like the others of the series.   A lead-tin solder containing 40 per cent lead was found to be inferior in creep strength to a cadmium-tin alloy containing 33 per cent cadmium.

In a subsequent investigation, Hanson and Sandford[336] made creep-rupture tests on alloys of tin containing antimony and cadmium, shown by prior study to be the most beneficial elements.   The alloys contained from 2 to 7 per cent cadmium and from 3 to 9 per cent antimony. Several conditions of heat-treatment were studied. Heat-treatment resulted in marked improvement in strength, but even when not heat-treated, these alloys were much stronger than pure tin, as might be expected. For example, an alloy containing 7 per cent cadmium and 9 per cent antimony in the self-annealed condition required a stress of 1,950 psi to produce rupture in a year, while pure tin ruptured in a year at 250 psi. The results of test in the condition as annealed at 340°F, which was the condition most extensively studied, are shown in Fig. 189. Addition of antimony to cadmium-tin alloys apparently improves the

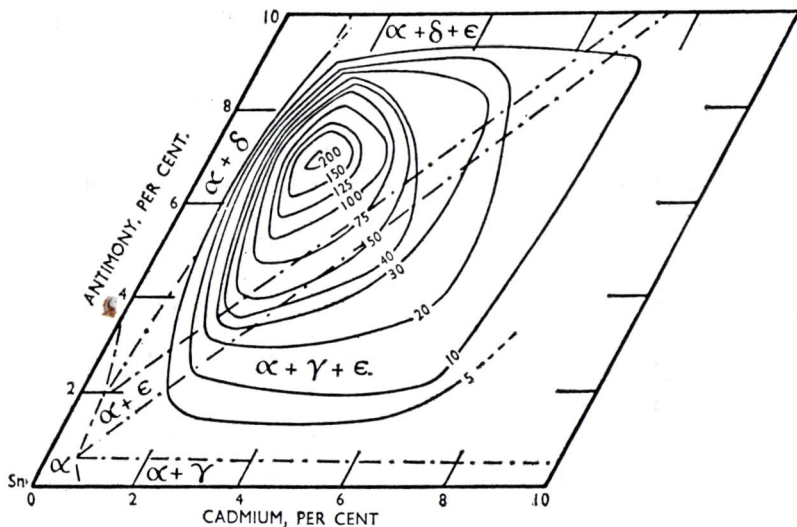

Fig. 189. Effect of antimony and cadmium on the creep rupture of tin at atmospheric temperature. The contours represent the number of days required for rupture under 5,500 psi, while the dashed lines represent the constitution diagram at atmospheric temperature. (*Hanson and Sandford.*[336])

creep strength up to an optimum, which occurs at 2 per cent cadmium and 7 per cent antimony.

The effects of addition of 1 and 2 per cent silver, 1 per cent copper, or 0.3 per cent nickel were also investigated by Hanson and Sandford[336] who found that the silver and copper alloys had similar strength, but that the nickel alloy was inferior to both.

Magnesium and Magnesium Alloys. Pure magnesium creeps at atmospheric temperature. In recent years, with the development of magnesium alloys to an important commercial position for many applications, interest has developed in their creep behavior. This is particularly true of alloys developed for use in lightweight aircraft engines and other stressed members operating at slightly elevated temperatures.

Leontis and Murphy[332] have reviewed the early literature on magnesium alloys containing cerium and report further experimental data on this important class of alloys which has come into use for certain engine parts in Germany, Great Britain, and the United States. Creep

TABLE XIII. CREEP BEHAVIOR OF MAGNESIUM ALLOYS†

Composition, Mg plus indicated % of added elements	Condition‡	Stress, 1,000 psi, to produce 0.1 % creep in 100 hr, °F				
		70	300	400	500	600
Cast:						
6 Ce	S	....	10.5			
6 Ce	A	....	14.2			
6 Ce–2 Mn	S	....	11.8	8.4	4.2	2.4
6 Ce–2 Mn	A	....	17.0			
10 Ce	S	....	12.7	9.2	4.0	1.7
10 Ce	A	....	18.5	10.4	4.4	2.3
10 Ce–2 Mn	S	....	12.8			
10 Ce–2 Mn	A	....	20.0	12.5	6.0	2.5
6 Al–3 Zn–0.18 Mn	S*	20.7	4.3			
Wrought:						
0.5 Ce–2 Mn	Forged	....	18.0			
2 Ce–2 Mn	Forged	....	21.0			
4 Ce–2 Mn	Forged	....	21.0			
1.5 Mn	Extruded	16.5	8.7			
8.5 Al–0.7 Zn–0.15 Mn	Forged, A*	22.0	2.8			

† Data from Leontis and Murphy.[332]
‡ S = stabilized = as cast plus 16 hr 600°F.
A = heat-treated and aged = 24 hr at 1070°F; aging not specified.
S* 500 to 730°F in 2 hr plus 16 hr at 730°F + 4 hr at 500°F.
A* two hours at 760°F plus 24 hr 350°F.

tests were continued to only 100 hr at which time the rate was still decreasing; an arbitrary creep limit, the stress to produce an extension of 0.1 per cent in 100 hr, was chosen. Such a limit is quite satisfactory for qualitative comparison, though the relation of such a limit to a limit defined in terms of a longer time is uncertain. The data of Leontis and Murphy are summarized in Table XIII. Increasing the amount of cerium increases the strength of magnesium, and the strength of a specific alloy can be enhanced by heat-treatment. The improvement in strength of magnesium-cerium alloys by the addition of 2 per cent manganese is not great. The comparison alloys of magnesium-aluminum-zinc-manganese and plain magnesium-manganese are quite weak in comparison to the cerium-containing alloys.

Moore and McDonald[333] have reported further data on the behavior of magnesium alloys in creep-rupture tests of 1,000 hr duration. These tests were made principally on commercial alloys to obtain engineering data and are not particularly suited to an evaluation of the influence of individual alloying elements. The magnesium-manganese alloy containing 1.5 per cent manganese was reported to have the best creep properties of the commercial alloys at temperatures up to 300°F.

Aluminum and Aluminum Alloys. Welter[334] showed in 1928 that pure aluminum would creep at atmospheric temperature under a constant load in the neighborhood of the elastic limit. The investigations of Welter and of other early investigators have been reviewed and summarized by Tapsell.[289] These data, which were reported in terms of "limit of viscosity," "useful strength," and "creep limit," are difficult to interpret in terms of present-day creep limits, but are useful for comparison. The few aluminum alloys tested, such as duralumin, proved to be stronger in creep than pure aluminum.

In recent years, and particularly with the development of jet-propelled airplanes, in which the skin of the rear two-thirds of the fuselage is heated to some 300 to 400°F,* considerable interest has developed in the creep properties of aluminum alloys at moderately elevated temperatures. In response to the need for such data, Flanigan, Tedsen, and Dorn[335] made creep-rupture tests on a number of commercial alloys at temperatures up to 375°F. The materials tested were of the precipitation-hardening type, subject to "overaging" during test, and since the composition of the several alloys did not vary in an orderly manner, the specific test results are not reported here. At the highest test temperature, the 24S alloy (4.5 per cent copper, 0.6 per cent manganese, 1.5 per cent magnesium) had the highest rupture strength, R301 alloy (4.5 per cent copper, 1.0 per cent silicon, 0.8 per cent manganese, 0.4 per cent magnesium) was somewhat weaker, and the 75S alloy (1.6 per cent copper, 5.6 per cent zinc, 0.2 per cent manganese, 2.5 per cent magnesium, 0.3 per cent chromium) was weakest. At 94°F, however, the 75S alloy was strongest.

Kennedy[349] has made 500- to 700-hr creep tests at 400 and 600°F on a

---

* At speeds near that of sound, about 750 miles an hour at atmospheric pressure, air friction is expected to raise skin temperature to nearly 500 F°.

number of commercial cast or wrought aluminum alloys used at elevated temperatures, but these data (owing to simultaneous variation of several variables) are not suited to an evaluation of the influence of composition.

Copper and Copper Alloys.   The creep behavior of copper alloys seems to have been the most extensively studied of the nonferrous alloys, and accordingly considerable data are available.   Such alloys find use at moderately elevated temperatures, particularly in the electrical industry.

Tapsell[289] has reviewed the early investigations in this field, which dealt largely with determinations of the limit of viscosity, or the stress below which creep would shortly cease altogether.   This limit was found to be quite low for pure copper.   Of particular interest in regard to the influence of chemical composition were the investigations of Brown,[337] who determined that between 400 and 600°F phosphor bronze was superior to gun metal which in turn was superior to 60 per cent copper–40

TABLE XIV. CREEP DATA ON SOME COPPER ALLOYS*

Alloy	Approximate temperature, °F, permitting creep of 1% in 10,000 hr		
	10,000 psi	3,000 psi	1,000 psi
Copper-zinc-tin (rolled naval bronze)....	340	400	540
Copper-zinc-lead (57.5, 39.5, 3) (extruded).	340	420	
Copper-tin (95.5-4) (phosphor bronze) ...	460	610	695
Copper-aluminum (91.5-7.5) (7.5 die-cast aluminum bronze).....................	560	840	

* Data from Kanter.[340]

per cent zinc brass; and of Cournot and Pagès[338] who observed in tests from 400 to 750°F a continuous decrease in creep limit with increase of the zinc content of brass; they found also that a leaded 60 per cent copper–40 per cent zinc brass was superior to a similar alloy not containing lead.

Bolton and Hehemann[339] and Bolton[350] have reported that, in comparative creep tests, an alloy containing 88 per cent copper–10 per cent tin–2 per cent zinc extended at a rate approximately twice as fast as an alloy containing 88 per cent copper–6 per cent tin–4 per cent zinc–2 per cent lead.   They do not attribute the difference to the lead, but believe that the presence of the greater amount of tin is detrimental owing to the occurrence of the "delta eutectoid."   At 500°F, the latter alloy required a stress of 10,000 psi to produce a creep rate of 0.1 per cent per 1,000 hr.   Insufficient tests were run on the other alloy to obtain the creep strength.

Kanter[340] has reported data, summarized in Table XIV, which shows copper-zinc alloys to be quite inferior to the copper-tin and copper-aluminum alloys, with the aluminum-bronze alloy showing greatest creep resistance. The role of the phosphorus in the phosphor bronze is not shown by these data.

Montgomery[356] has reported the superiority in creep of an 85 per cent copper–5 per cent tin–5 per cent zinc–5 per cent lead alloy over an 88 per cent copper–10 per cent tin–2 per cent zinc alloy.

Clark and White[341] have reported creep data, summarized in Table XV, for several commercial copper-zinc and copper-zinc-tin alloys. Although the composition differences among these alloys are not well suited to analysis in terms of the influence of individual elements, it is worth noting that (1) the addition of 1 per cent tin to either 70-30 or 60-40

TABLE XV. CREEP DATA FOR SEVERAL COMMERCIAL BRASS AND BRONZE ALLOYS*

Nominal composition, %				Stress, 1,000 psi, to produce 0.1% creep per 1,000 hr; temperature,°F			
Copper	Zinc	Tin	Condition	300	400	600	800
70	30		Cold-drawn 15%	....	18.0	0.9	
70	29	1	Cold-drawn 15%	....	19.0	2.0	0.2
85	15		Hot-rolled	....	12.0	2.6	
60	40		Hot-rolled	12.0	4.8		
77	22	1	Hot-rolled	....	13.0	2.5	
59	40	1	Hot-rolled	15.0	5.7		

* Data from Clark and White.[341]

brass does not greatly affect the creep strength; (2), the 60-40 level is appreciably weaker in creep than the 70-30 level, while the two alloys most rich in copper have an intermediate strength. This confirms the early work of Cournot and Pagès[338] on the influence of zinc.

Tapsell and Johnson[353] have reported the results of creep tests at 575 and 660°F of copper containing either 0.34 per cent arsenic or 0.31 per cent arsenic plus 0.07 per cent silver. The latter proved to be slightly more creep-resistant, but as several discussers pointed out, there is some question of whether adequate attention has been paid to possible variation in the amounts of other impurities.

Parker[344] has determined the creep-rupture strength of an oxygen-free high-conductivity copper at 390°F and of an oxygen-free copper containing 0.54 per cent silver at 480 and 390°F. In the condition as furnace-cooled from 1560°F, the stress required to fracture in 100 hr at 390°F was 20,000 psi for the alloy containing silver and only about 14,000 psi for the silver-free alloy. Some experiments on the influence of heat-treatment are described in the section on the influence of heat-treatment.

Parker and Ferguson[345] have reported the results of creep-rupture tests at 390°F on a number of commercial copper alloys. Although these data are not well suited for the evaluation of the influence of individual

TABLE XVI. COMPARATIVE CREEP-RUPTURE DATA AT 390°F FOR SEVERAL COMMERCIAL COPPER ALLOYS*

Alloy	Treatment	Stress to produce rupture in 1,000 hr at 390°F; 1,000 psi; extrapolated
Tough pitch copper.............	Annealed at 930°F	12
Tough pitch copper.............	Annealed at 570°F	11
Manganese-copper (0.1% Mn)...	?	21
Cadmium-copper (0.2–0.6% Cd).	?	25–28
Chromium-silicon-copper (0.9% Cr–0.09% Si).................	Annealed 1830°F, cold-drawn aged 850°F; cold-drawn	45
Phosphor-bronze (5% Sn–0.01% P)............................	Spring hard	50
Cobalt-beryllium-copper (2.59% Co–0.46% Be)...............	Water-quenched from 1650°F; cold-reduced 40%; aged 4 hr 930°F	100
Beryllium copper (2.25% Be)....	Water-quenched from 1560°F; half hard-drawn; aged 1.5 hr 570°F	160 (approx)

* Data from Parker and Ferguson.[345]

elements, they are of some interest and are therefore summarized in Table XVI.

Martin and Parker,[354] in further studies of the creep characteristics of copper, report that small amounts of impurities may play an important role. As one example, a total of 0.012 per cent soluble impurities increased the rupture life twentyfold. These authors state that the role played by these impurities seems to be related to the softening temperature on heating after cold working, but admit that the exact role is not clearly understood.

Burghoff, Blank, and Maddigan[346] have conducted a very extensive investigation of the creep characteristics of a number of copper alloys at elevated temperatures. Some of these results are summarized in Table XVII, while the results bearing more directly on the influence of grain size or cold working are reviewed in the appropriate section. Of the alloys listed in Table XVII, the 70-30 copper nickel is by far the best.

Nickel and Nickel Alloys. Tapsell[289] has summarized the early studies of the creep behavior of nickel and nickel alloys. As the data reported by these early investigators were in terms of limit of viscosity or limiting creep stress and therefore cannot be collated and as many of the studies

TABLE XVII. CREEP CHARACTERISTICS OF SEVERAL ANNEALED COPPER ALLOYS*

Alloy†	Grain size, mm	Stress, 1,000 psi, for creep rate of 0.01%/1,000 hr at		
		300°F	400°F	500°F
70-30 brass	0.085	16.0‡	7.7	2.0
Silicon bronze	0.100	.....	8.5	5.3
85-15 brass	0.060	8.0	6.2	
Naval brass	Annealed at 1000°F	10.5	1.9	0.25‡
Admiralty brass	0.055	.....	...	2.2
70-30 copper nickel	0.020	35.0‡	...	30.0‡

* Data from Burghoff, Blank and Maddigan.[346]
† 70-30 brass: 70.5 Cu, 0.01 Fe, <0.05 Pb, 29.5 Zn.
  Silicon bronze: 96.3 Cu, 2.8 Si, 0.06 Fe, 0.005 Pb, 0.80 Zn.
  85-15 brass: 84.8 Cu, 0.004 Fe, 0.002 Pb, 15.2 Zn.
  Naval brass: 60.0 Cu, 0.65 Sn, 0.015 Fe, <0.05 Pb, 39.4 Zn.
  Admiralty brass: 71.1 Cu, 0.92 Sn, 0.008 Fe, 0.015 Pb, 28.0 Zn.
  70-30 copper nickel: 69.1 Cu, 30.1 Ni, 0.80 Mn, 0.03 Fe, 0.005 Pb.
‡ By extrapolation

were not suited to evaluation in terms of influence of alloying elements, most of this work is not reviewed here.

Jenkins *et al.*[347] have obtained comparative creep data on alloys of nickel containing various amounts of chromium in the cast or rolled conditions. These are summarized in Table XVIII. Apparently the addition of up to 30 per cent chromium effectively improves the load-carrying ability of nickel in either the cast or rolled condition while a larger addition such as 40 per cent is detrimental. The addition of 0.5 per cent carbon to the chill-cast alloys improved their strength markedly, while the influence of carbon in the rolled alloys appears to have been erratic.

Jenkins *et al.*[347] have also studied the creep behavior of ternary nickel-chromium-iron alloys with results summarized in Table XIX. Carbon is observed to be undesirable except for the high-iron alloys. The influence of nickel, chromium, and iron cannot be differentiated owing to the simultaneous variation of these elements.

TABLE XVIII. COMPARATIVE CREEP-RUPTURE DATA AT 1200 AND 1475°F FOR SOME NICKEL-CHROMIUM ALLOYS*

Alloy				1200°F		1475°F	
Ni	Cr	C	Condition	Applied stress, tons/sq in.	Time to fract., days	Applied stress, tons/sq in.	Time to fract., days
Pure nickel	....	....	Rolled bar	..	....	0.8	17.5
90.0	10.0	....	Rolled bar	10	1	1.2	2
80.0	20.0	....	Rolled bar	10	7.5	2.0	8.75
70.0	30.0	....	Rolled bar	10	30	2.0	33.5
60.0	40.0	....	Rolled bar	10	5	2.0	4
88.7	10.1	0.32	Rolled bar	10	5.5		
77.4	21.5	0.26	Rolled bar	10	1–3		
69.5	29.0	0.39	Rolled bar	10	6		
90.0	10.0	....	Chill cast	..	....	1.2	1.33
80.0	20.0	....	Chill cast	..	....	2.0	5
70.0	30.0	....	Chill cast	..	....	2.0	115
60.0	40.0	....	Chill cast	..	....	2.0	21
90.0	9.5	0.5	Chill cast	..	....	4.0	1–2
80.0	19.5	0.5	Chill cast	..	....	5.0	4.5
70.0	29.5	0.5	Chill cast	..	....	5.0	5.5
70.0	29.5	0.5	Chill cast	..	....	4.0	10
60.0	39.5	0.5	Chill cast	..	....	5.0	7
60.0	39.5	0.5	Chill cast	..	....	4.0	25
90.0	10.0	....	Sand cast	..	....	1.8	68 not broken
80.0	20.0	....	Sand cast	..	....	3.2	5–6
70.0	30.0	....	Sand cast	..	....	3.2	24
60.0	40.0	....	Sand cast	..	....	3.2	40
Pure nickel	....	....	Cast	..	....	0.8	55

* Data from Jenkins *et al.*[347]

Betty, Macqueen, and Rolle[348] have made comparative relaxation tests of several commercial nickel alloys. In these tests, wire springs of the materials were compressed by a specific stress and held to the resulting length during a 7-day period at an elevated temperature. After test, the holding bolts were removed and the load required to compress the

TABLE XIX. COMPARATIVE CREEP-RUPTURE DATA AT 1200°F FOR SOME ROLLED NICKEL-CHROMIUM-IRON ALLOYS*

Nominal composition, %			With less than 0.05 % carbon; time for fracture, days		With 0.5 % carbon; time for fracture, days	
Ni	Cr	Fe	10 tons/ sq in.	7 tons/ sq in.	10 tons/ sq in.	7 tons/ sq in.
70	20	10	9.0	27.0	1.5	8.5
60	20	20	14.5	32.0	1.0	4.0
40	20	40	4.5–5.5	21–30	12.0	17.0
20	20	60	4–6	14–15	14.5	73.0
10	20	70	5.0	17.0	10.5	43.0
50	30	20	12.0	23.0	9.0	18.0
40	30	30	1.0	4.5	3.5	14.0
30	30	40	5.5	18.5	9.0	17.0
20	30	50	1.5	10.0	4.0	15.5

* Data from Jenkins et al.[347]

TABLE XX. RELAXATION OF NICKEL ALLOYS*

Indicated Maximum Fiber Stress to Produce Given Percentages of Relaxation in 7 Days, 1,000 psi

Temp., °F	Monel			K Monel			Z Nickel			Inconel		
	2%	4%	6%	2%	4%	6%	2%	4%	6%	2%	4%	6%
300	52.5	70.5	80.0									
400	43.0	57.5	65.5	73.0	90.0	100.5	83.0	108.0	....	72.0	91.0	100.0
450	16.0	32.5	48.0	53.0	81.0	96.0	78.0	107.0	....	68.0	86.5	93.0
500	4.0	7.5	11.0	21.5	43.0	58.0	70.0	95.5	104.0	61.0	81.0	91.5
550	....	....	....	9.0	18.0	27.0	30.0	80.0	100.0	55.0	77.0	88.0
600	....	....	....	3.5	7.0	11.0	16.0	50.0	71.0	44.0	68.0	83.0
650	....	....	....	....	....	....	8.0	20.0	30.5	31.0	55.0	74.0
700	....	....	....	....	....	....	....	....	....	....	4.5	27.0

Material	C	Mn	Fe	Si	Cu	Ni	Al	Cr	Treatment after coiling of springs formed of cold-drawn wire
Monel	0.18	0.94	1.24	0.10	28.5	69.0	....	....	650°F, 1 hr
K Monel	0.18	0.12	0.25	0.20	29.7	66.1	2.92	....	1000°F, 6 hr; 900°F, 16 hr
Z Nickel		0.05	0.14	0.14	0.03	98.6	....	....	900°F, 6 hr
Inconel	0.06	0.16	5.77	0.22	0.04	80.7	....	13.1	900°F, 1 hr

* Data from Betty, Macqueen, and Rolle.[348]

spring to the original loaded length measured.   The "load loss" resulting from creep during sojourn at temperature cannot be correlated with the usual type of constant-load creep test, as discussed in another section; but the relaxation is certainly a result of creep deformation.   The data obtained by Betty *et al.*[348] is summarized in terms of percentage of relaxation or load loss in Table XX, although they are not well suited to evaluation of the influence of composition.   It may be noted that Z nickel and K monel, both precipitation-hardenable, will withstand greater stress than inconel at the lower temperatures, although inconel is best at the higher temperatures.

Betty, Eiselstein, and Huston[355] have reported creep data for the commercial alloys monel and inconel. Monel essentially contains 70 per cent nickel and 30 per cent copper; inconel contains 80 per cent nickel, 14 per cent chromium, and 6 per cent iron.   Inconel had a creep strength at 1000°F of 7,000 psi to produce a creep rate of 0.01 per cent per 1,000 hr, while the monel, considerably weaker, had a strength of about 3,300 psi.

Chromium and Chromium Alloys.   Chromium-base alloys have not found any important use at elevated temperatures except in some experimental superalloys.

CHAPTER IX

EFFECT OF MELTING AND DEOXIDATION PRACTICES, HEAT-TREATMENT, AND GRAIN SIZE

EFFECT OF MELTING AND DEOXIDATION PRACTICES

The creep data reported in the literature for carbon steel (0.1 to 0.2 per cent carbon) show a great spread in the values. These data, taken from the ASME-ASTM compilation of available creep data,[357] are summarized in Fig. 190. The band in Fig. 190 has been drawn to exclude data obtained in tests of excessively short duration, or under other questionable conditions. Even so, the range in values is quite wide, and it appears that since these data are representative of no single melting or deoxidation practice, or of any specific heat-treatment, the range of values is attributable to differences in such practices. It will be seen in the following review of the literature that, excluding heat-treatment which is considered in a following section, the most important manufacturing variable is the deoxidation practice, which for carbon steel can vary within wide limits. Most alloy steels, particularly those of higher alloy content, are made to a much more standardized practice than is carbon steel, and therefore can be expected to show a correspondingly lesser range of variation in creep strength.

The range of strength of carbon steel at high temperatures has been recognized for a long time. In 1931, Kinzel[358] reported that silicon-killed steel had definitely greater creep strength than rimmed or semi-killed steel. Jenkins et al.[298] conducted comparative tests at 840°F on 13 carbon steels, of two carbon levels and of several manufacturing and deoxidation practices, and observed a wide variance in the creep rate. Clark and White[295] made an extensive comparison of nominally identical carbon steels, one made in the electric-arc furnace the other in an open-hearth furnace, and found the former to be the superior. Further tests on manganese-molybdenum-vanadium steel showed induction-furnace steel to be superior to electric-arc steel. These data are quite limited and do not permit broad generalization; they do indicate that melting practice is one of the important variables for consideration.

Gillett[359] has reviewed these data and has concluded in effect that because of discrepancies it is necessary to run creep tests on each heat of steel. More recent work has indicated that this is probably unnecessary if all variables are properly recognized and controlled.

White and Crocker[360] tested in creep a number of commercial molybdenum steels to which various amounts of aluminum had been added for deoxidation. Some of these results are summarized in Table XXVI, which indicates that the aluminum addition plays a role secondary to structure.

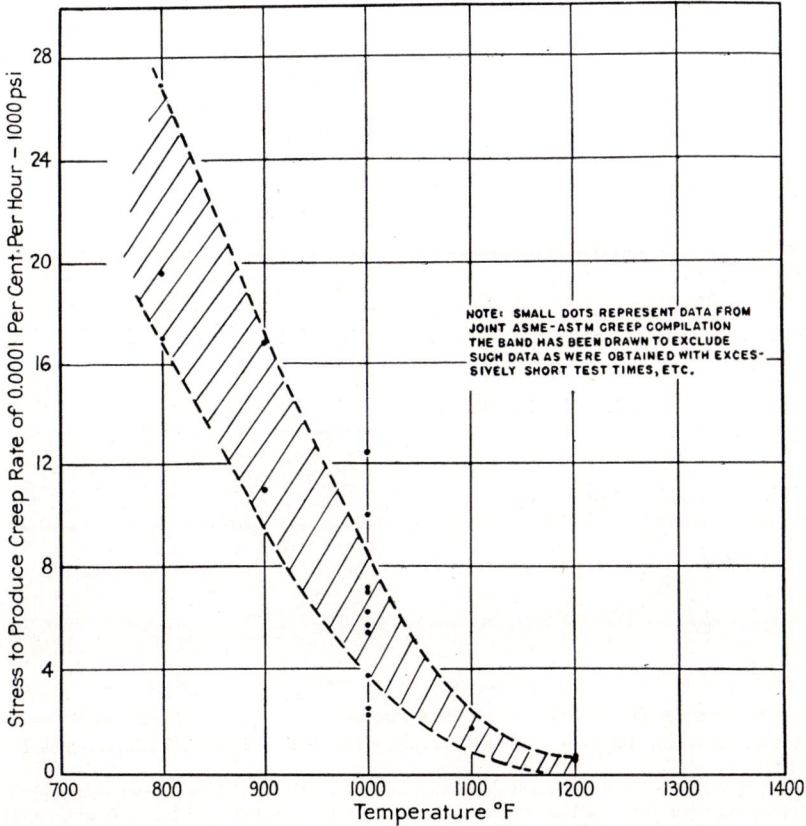

NOTE: SMALL DOTS REPRESENT DATA FROM JOINT ASME-ASTM CREEP COMPILATION THE BAND HAS BEEN DRAWN TO EXCLUDE SUCH DATA AS WERE OBTAINED WITH EXCESSIVELY SHORT TEST TIMES, ETC.

FIG. 190. Creep strength of 0.1 to 0.2 per cent carbon steel. (Compiled from the literature.[357])

In an effort to evaluate the influence of various manufacturing variables, the ASME-ASTM Joint Research Committee on the Effect of Temperature on the Properties of Metals has sponsored a program of research. The results of this investigation have been reported in a series of progress reports.[361-363] It is difficult to present any general summary of these studies because the tests were primarily comparative and constant conditions of stress were not maintained. However, the data in Table XXI, which have been taken from the second report,[362] illustrate the important influence exerted on the strength of carbon steel by deoxidation and, incidentally, the influence of heat-treatment. It is apparent that silicon-killed steel is superior to rimmed steel in all conditions of heat-treatment, and it is also superior to silicon-aluminum and

Steel deoxidized with 1.5 lb of aluminum per ton

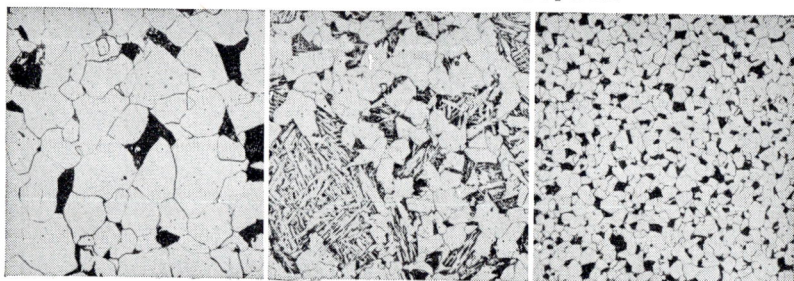

| Structure *A* | Structure *B* | Structure *C* |
| 2000°F, 30 min, furnace-cooled | 2000°F, 30 min, air-cooled | 1750°F, 5 min, air-cooled |

Steel deoxidized with 0.5 lb of aluminum fer ton

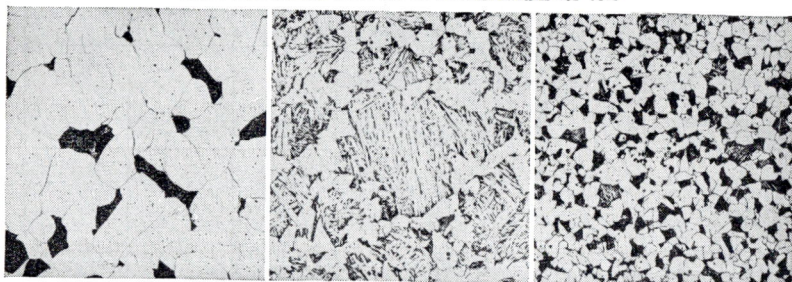

| Structure *D* | Structure *E* | Structure *F* |
| 1800°F, 90 min, furnace-cooled | 1800°F, 90 min, air-cooled | 1615°F, 5 min, air-cooled |

FIG. 191. Similar microstructures developed in differently deoxidized 0.5 per cent molybdenum–0.15 per cent carbon steels; nital etch; ×100. Structures *A* and *D* are coarse ferrite pearlite, *B* and *E* ferrite Widmanstätten, and *C* and *F* fine ferrite pearlite. Creep-test results are presented in Fig. 192. (*Miller.*[364])

aluminum-killed steels as fine-grained or as slow-cooled after coarsening. When air-cooled after coarsening, the silicon, silicon-aluminum, and aluminum-killed steels are nearly identical in strength. Of particular interest were comparative tests[361] at 850°F for two steels of similar grain size and similar chemical composition except that one had 0.025 and the other 0.050 per cent aluminum, in which the higher aluminum steel had a creep rate 5 times that of the lower aluminum steel.

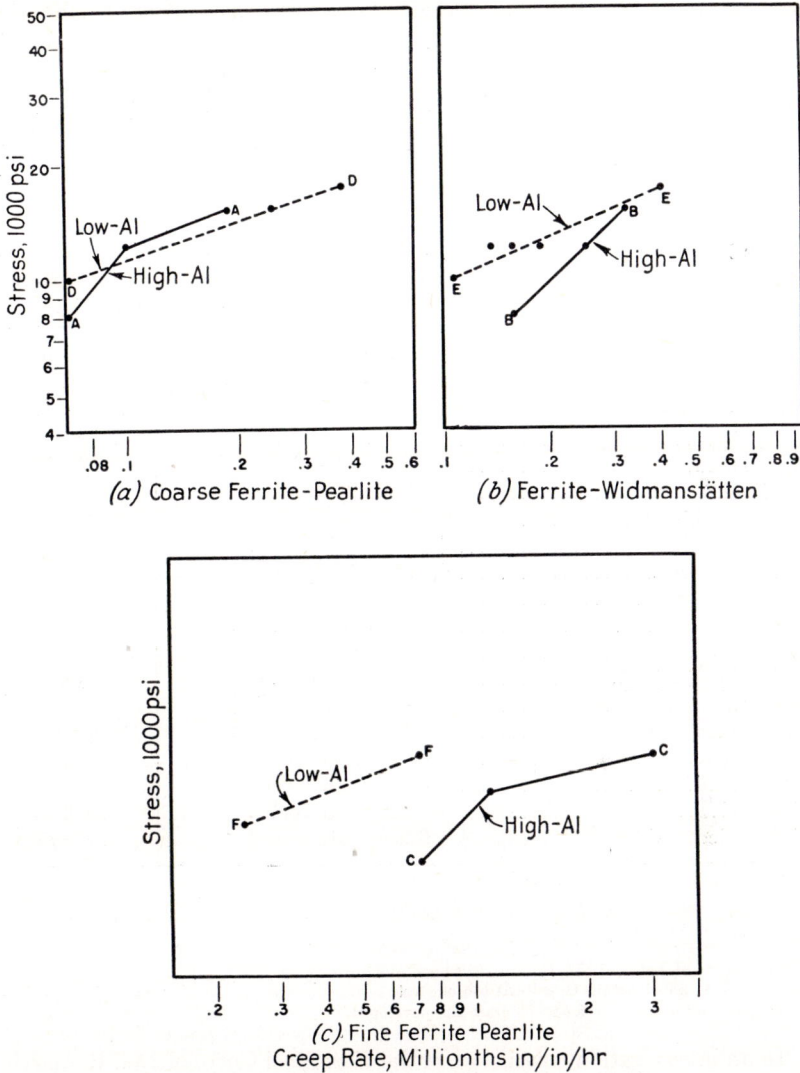

FIG. 192. Effect of amount of aluminum added for deoxidation on the relation between stress and creep rate of 0.5 per cent molybdenum–0.15 per cent carbon steels with the controlled microstructures shown in Fig. 191. (*Miller.*[364])

Miller[364] has reported the results of a carefully conducted cooperative investigation of the effect of deoxidation practice on the creep strength of molybdenum steel. Two steels of quite similar composition containing 0.5 per cent molybdenum, one deoxidized with 0.5 and the other with 1.5 lb of aluminum per ton of steel, showed that with similar microstructure the low-aluminum steel has superior creep resistance.   These results are summarized in Figs. 191 and 192, which show, respectively, the several microstructures examined and the relation between stress and creep rate for each of these microstructures.   It is to be noted that with the fine ferrite-pearlite structure the high-aluminum steel is much the inferior. The careful control of microstructure maintained in this investigation is in contrast to that of many investigations.

TABLE XXI. CREEP RATES OF SEVERAL CARBON STEELS OF DIFFERENT DEOXI-
DATION PRACTICE AND DIFFERENT HEAT-TREATMENT AT THE END OF 500-HR
COMPARATIVE CREEP TESTS AT 850°F UNDER A STRESS OF 15,000 PSI*

Steel†	Condition‡	Creep rate, %/hr
Si-Al killed, 2 lb Al	Coarse, slow-cooled	0.06
Si-Al killed, 2 lb Al	Fine, air-cooled	0.05
Al killed	Fine, air-cooled	0.04
Rimmed, skin	Fine, air-cooled	0.0045
Rimmed, skin	Coarse, air-cooled	0.0042
Rimmed, core	Fine, air-cooled	0.001
Rimmed, core	Coarse, air-cooled	0.0008
Al killed	Coarse, slow-cooled	0.00085
Si killed	Fine, air-cooled	0.00015
Si-Al killed, 1 lb Al	Fine, air-cooled	0.00015
Si killed	Coarse, slow-cooled	0.00009
Si-Al killed, 1 lb Al	Coarse, slow-cooled	0.00008
Al killed	Coarse, air-cooled	0.00006
Si-Al killed, 2 lb Al	Coarse, air-cooled	0.00006
Si Killed	Coarse, air-cooled	0.000045
Si-Al killed, 1 lb Al	Coarse, air-cooled	0.000035

* Data from Cross and Lowther[362]
† Steels: Rimmed: core 0.26% C; skin 0.16% C.
    Si killed: 0.14% C.
    Si-Al killed: 0.15% C; 1 lb Al/ton of steel.
    Si-Al killed: 0.15% C; 2 lb Al/ton of steel.
    Al killed: 0.15% C; 2 lb Al/ton of steel.
‡ Coarse and fine refer to austenite grain size developed.

In an investigation conducted at the U.S. Steel Corp. of Del. Research Laboratory, creep-rupture tests were made on 12 heats of carbon steel, listed in Table XXII, representative of all manufacturing and deoxidation practices employed commercially in the making of this grade of steel for use at elevated temperatures.   Heats A and B represent, at one extreme, steels essentially not deoxidized.   Capped steel is quite similar to rimmed steel except for the lack of a "rim" and "core" common to the latter.   The remaining steels represent different degrees and types of deoxidation. All steels were given a common heat-treatment, air-cooling after ½ hr at 1650°F, and tested in creep rupture out to rupture times of approximately 1,000 hr.

TABLE XXII. CREEP-RATE AND CREEP-RUPTURE STRENGTH OF CARBON STEEL AT 850°F. DESCRIPTION OF STEELS TESTED*

Code	Heat No.	Type	Chemical Analysis†								Main deoxidizers added,‡ lb/ton
			C	Mn	P	S	Si	Al	Al₂O₃	Ti	
A	9188	Capped open-hearth	0.07	0.45	0.006	0.020	0.005	.....	.....	.....	None
B	22432	Capped bessemer	0.08	0.38	0.079	0.037	0.005	.....	.....	.....	None
C	2261	Si-Ti killed open-hearth	0.19	0.47	0.009	0.028	0.18	0.005	0.002	0.002	10 FeSi, 6 FeCTi
D	7250	Si-Al-Ti killed open-hearth	0.16	0.48	0.008	0.022	0.20	0.004	0.002	0.003	10 FeSi, 4 FeCTi, 0.5 Al
E	2257	Si-Al killed open-hearth	0.15	0.47	0.011	0.023	0.19	0.007	0.003	0.001	10 FeSi, 1 Al
F	11019	Si-Al killed open-hearth	0.24	0.86	0.013	0.021	0.23	0.033	.....	.....	8.4 FeSi, 1.8 Al
G	25424	Si-Al killed open-hearth	0.16	0.51	0.013	0.020	0.16	0.035	0.006	.....	7 FeSi, 2 Al
H	10200	Si killed open-hearth	0.27	0.52	0.016	0.025	0.22	0.006	.....	.....	7.7 FeSi, 0.14 Coal
I	22770	Si-Al killed bessemer	0.14	0.54	0.074	0.022	0.18	0.025	.....	.....	6.8 FeSi, 3.4 Al
J	9934	Si-Al killed bessemer	0.13	0.48	0.087	0.029	0.21	0.047	.....	.....	10 FeSi, 3 Al
K	4345	Si-Al killed bessemer	0.15	0.46	0.088	0.018	0.22	0.024	0.005	.....	10 FeSi, 2.5 Al
L	22773	Al killed bessemer	0.18	0.51	0.077	0.022	0.03	0.066	.....	.....	3.4 Al

* Data from U. S. Steel Corp.
† The absence of a value indicates that no determination was made.
‡ FeSi refers to ferrosilicon; FeCTi refers to ferro-carbon-titanium; Al refers to aluminum.

The results of the tests are summarized in Table XXIII, and it is apparent that a very wide range in properties exists—from 12,000 to 22,000 psi in stress to cause rupture in 10,000 hr, and from 19,500 to 32,000 psi in stress to produce a creep rate of 0.1 per cent per hour. Although the primary aim of the investigation was to determine the range of properties to be expected in commercial carbon steel, the results indicate that by far the most important factor affecting the creep behavior in these tests is deoxidation practice. Excluding the capped steels, the weakest of the open-hearth steels tested, both in creep rate and in creep rupture, is steel G, deoxidized with the greatest amount of aluminum, and the strongest in both respects is steel H, deoxidized with silicon and no aluminum. (However, the comparison is clouded somewhat by the fact that steel H has a high-carbon content and a duplex grain size.) The next strongest open-hearth steel is E, deoxidized with silicon and 1 lb of aluminum per ton of steel, and this steel is also next to H in the series of

TABLE XXIII. CREEP-RATE AND CREEP-RUPTURE STRENGTH OF CARBON STEEL AT 850°F. SUMMARY OF TEST RESULTS*

Code	Type†	ASTM structural grain size	Vickers hardness	Stress, 1,000 psi, for rupture		Stress (1,000 psi) for minimum creep rate of 0.1%/hr
				1,000 hr	10,000 hr‡	
A	Cap. O.H.	5–7	88	18	15	19.5
B	Cap. Bess.	4–5, 6–8	117	21	18	22.5
C	Si-Ti O.H.	6–8	118	25.5	19.5	29
D	Si-Al-Ti O.H.	7–8	113	22.5	18	27
E	Si-Al O.H.	6–8	114	26	20	30.5
F	Si-Al O.H.	8–9	145	22	17	25
G	Si-Al O.H.	7–8	124	17.5	13.5	20
H	Si O.H.	3–4, 6–8	137	27	22	32
I	Si-Al Bess.	7–8	130	18	13	21
J	Si-Al Bess.	7–8	129	17.5	13	21
K	Si-Al Bess.	7–8	140	18.5	12	23
L	Al Bess.	7–9	129	17	12	20

* Data from U.S. Steel Corp.
† Cap. O.H. = capped open hearth; Al Bess. = aluminum-killed bessemer steel; etc.
‡ Extrapolated.
NOTE: All steels air-cooled after ½ hr at 1650°F.

increasing severity of deoxidation, as judged by the additions. The remaining open-hearth steels fall into an intermediate position. The four heavily deoxidized bessemer steels I through L, all of which had a quite large aluminum addition were equally weak, both in creep rate and creep rupture, and the influence of deoxidation cannot be judged, although it is presumed to be as important as in the open-hearth grade. The capped steels appear to be in a category of their own, having an intermediate to weak strength in spite of having had no deoxidizer addition.

A broad comparison of bessemer and open-hearth manufacturing processes cannot be made since only the extremes in deoxidation practice were employed in the former grade. However, comparison of steel G, the most severely deoxidized open-hearth steel, with bessemer steels I through L shows all to be of approximately the same strength, and indicates that whether one or the other process is used is relatively unimportant relative to the influence of deoxidation practice.

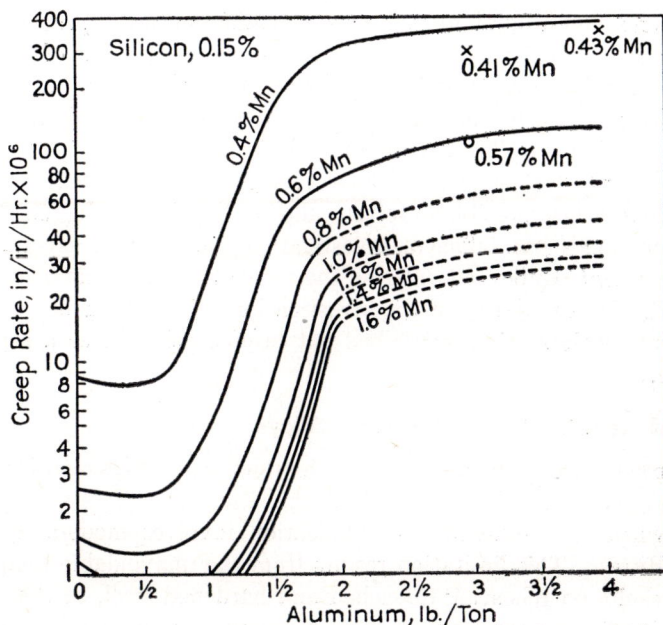

FIG. 193. Effect of amount of aluminum added for deoxidation on the creep rate at the end of 5 days at 840°F under 18,000 psi of steel containing 0.1 per cent carbon. (*Glen.*[419])

The excellent agreement observed among steels I, J, and K of quite similar manufacturing and deoxidation practice is noteworthy and indicates that the range in properties of carbon steel may be attributed to known and controllable variables.

A pronounced and abrupt increase in creep rate has been shown by Glen[419] to result (Fig. 193) from increasing the amount of aluminum added for deoxidation in experimental induction-furnace steels of similar grain size and microstructure containing 0.1 per cent carbon. This plot represents the creep rate observed at the end of 5 days' test under 18,000 psi at 840°F.

As mentioned earlier, the range in properties that may be expected in similarly heat-treated alloy steels is much less than in carbon steel. This may be attributed primarily to the fact that alloy steels are made more nearly in an identical manner. However, this subject has not been adequately studied.

Similarly, the influence of manufacturing variables has been little studied in the nonferrous field.

EFFECT OF HEAT TREATMENT (EXCLUSIVE OF GRAIN SIZE)

A given metal or alloy may show widely different creep properties depending upon how it has been heat-treated, for creep is one of the most structure-sensitive of properties. In steel, advantage can be taken of the allotropic transformation to produce a wide variety of structures; in most nonferrous alloys, such a possibility does not exist, but many systems offer the opportunity of developing precipitation reactions which are, of course, also possible in ferrous alloys. In neither the ferrous nor nonferrous fields has sufficient investigational effort been expended on heat-treatment studies, considering the gains which may confidently be expected. In a majority of the investigations of the influence of heat-treatment, grain-size variation has not been considered as a separate variable.

Effect of Heat-treatment of Ferrous Alloys

The pronounced increase in strength which can be effected by rapid quenching of carbon and alloy steels unfortunately suffers severe limitation when the contemplated application involves moderately high temperatures. This limitation results from the unavoidable tempering which results on reheating quenched and hardened steel, so that when the service temperature exceeds some minimum, depending on the steel, the tempered structure is less stable structurally and is likewise less strong than the pearlite structure resulting from normalizing or annealing. Accordingly, except for "bolting" applications, steels for use at high temperatures are not generally applied in a quenched and tempered condition.

In the use of steel for bolting, or holding together other members, the bolts, being for the most part externally placed, are often at a somewhat lower temperature than the main structure. Because of this, advantage can be taken of the increase in strength of the quenched and tempered structure martensite. An important aspect of this increased strength is that the ratio of yield to tensile strength is quite high in quenched and tempered steels. Resistance to softening during tempering is the attribute most desired in bolting steels, assuming that there is sufficient alloy content to permit initial through-hardening on quenching. Bain[312] has listed the strong carbide-forming elements such as vanadium, tungsten, and molybdenum as most effective in contributing to resistance to tempering.

The limiting temperature above which hardened and tempered steels cannot advantageously be employed depends to some extent on the specific steel, and in any event has not been adequately investigated. A conservative upper limit, though, may be taken as approximately 900°F. Kanter and Spring[365] compared normalized with quenched and tempered 0.35 per cent carbon steel and found the former to be more creep-resistant at 800 and 1000°F, although at 800°F the superiority was not of great moment. Annealed material was also tested at 800°F and proved to have about the same strength as the normalized. Pomp and Dahmen[287] reported 0.25 per cent carbon steel to have superior strength at 750°F when quenched and tempered than when annealed, but at 930°F the two structures showed about the same strength. The tests on which these results are based were of comparatively short duration as is true of so much German work, and are therefore in some question in regard to being representative of long-time service.

Kanter and Spring[373] tested a 6.5 per cent tungsten–6.5 per cent chromium steel containing 0.57 per cent carbon in the condition as annealed at 1675°F, having a room-temperature tensile strength of 125,000 psi, and as-quenched from 2050°F and drawn at 1300°F, having a room-temperature tensile strength of 164,000 psi, in creep at 1000, 1200, and 1400°F and found the annealed material to possess considerably greater creep resistance.

Cross and Johnson[382] reported creep tests at 1100 and 1200°F on two heats of 5 per cent chromium–0.5 per cent molybdenum steel in several conditions of heat-treatment. It was observed that the structures obtained on slow cooling from either 1550 or 2100°F were appreciably stronger in creep than the structures resulting on air-cooling. With either mode of cooling the structure resulting on cooling from 2100°F was the stronger, an effect which certainly is in part attributable to coarser grain size. The tests were not sufficiently extensive to yield numerical values of creep strength and accordingly cannot be given here.

Clark and White[295] state that, in general, the heat-treatment to be employed for high-temperature service should be that resulting in the greatest degree of structural stability. However, such a quantity is difficult to define, and in any event the arguments in support of such a point of view are to some extent controversial, a situation often existing when data are lacking. Certainly, a well-spheroidized steel should not be used in preference to a pearlitic one, if during the contemplated life the latter will not spheroidize to the same degree as the former when it begins its service.

Clark and White[295] have studied two 0.15 per cent carbon steels, one of open-hearth and the other of electric-furnace manufacture, heat-treated four different ways. These results are summarized in Table XXIV.

Of the four conditions, the hot-rolled material shows maximum creep strength, and the normalized and drawn (1 hr) is next highest. Of the two remaining conditions, the annealing treatment is better for the electric-furnace steel, but the spheroidizing treatment is the better for

TABLE XXIV. INFLUENCE OF HEAT-TREATMENT ON CREEP STRENGTH OF 0.15 PER CENT CARBON ELECTRIC AND OPEN-HEARTH STEEL AT 1000°F*

Designation	Heat-treatment	Stress, 1,000 psi for creep rate, %/1,000 hr		
		0.01	0.10	1.0
El.-A	Hot-rolled	7.0	12.8	15.8
El.-B	N 1725°F, D 1200°F†	4.9	9.9	12.1
El.-C	Annealed 1550°F	3.0	6.2	12.9
El.-D	N 1725°F, D 1200°F‡	2.7	5.8	8.2
O.H.-A	Hot-rolled	6.1	6.8	7.8
O.H.-B	N 1725°F, D 1200°F†	4.0	5.5	7.7
O.H.-C	Annealed 1550°F	2.4	4.5	6.2
O.H.-D	N 1725°F, D 1200°F‡	2.6	5.3	7.4

* Data from Clark and White.[295]
† Drawn 1 hr at 1200°F.
‡ Drawn 168 hr at 1200°F.
NOTE: Tests of 1,000 hr duration.

the open-hearth steel. This latter finding is rather unexpected and should be checked. It should also be recognized that the order of steels as observed in these tests will not necessarily be the same after years of service. All the structures will deteriorate in strength as spheroidization, and possibly graphitization, proceeds, and at presumably different rates.

Clark and White[295] also report a comparison (Table XXV) of the creep strengths of a silicon-chromium-molybdenum steel in the annealed and the normalized and drawn conditions.

These data show the normalized and drawn condition to be superior to the annealed in creep strength at 800 and 1000°F, but the reverse is true at 1200°F.

Grün,[311] on the basis of short-time tests at 750 and 930°F, has reported that the pearlite structure resulting during slow cooling has greatest creep strength for many steels, although molybdenum and vanadium steel are preferably air-cooled. Quenching generally causes inferior creep strength.

Wyman[366] examined the microstructure of several chromium-nickel-molybdenum bolting steels of similar composition but from different manufacturing sources and of different heat-treatment, which in "step-down" creep tests at 840°F (that is, each specimen is tested at a series of decreasing stresses) showed wide variation in results. Microscopic examination was reported to reveal that the difference in properties

TABLE XXV. INFLUENCE OF HEAT-TREATMENT ON CREEP STRENGTH OF SI-CR-MO STEEL AT 800, 1000, AND 1200°F IN 500-HR TESTS*

Steel	0.48 C	0.49 Mn	0.62 Si	1.20 Cr	0.52 Mo

Heat-treatment†	Test temp.,°F	1,000 psi stress for creep rate %/1,000 hr		
		0.01	0.1	1.0
ND	800	47.0	92.0	
Annealed................	800	19.0	27.0	38.0
ND	1000	7.8	23.0	68.0
Annealed................	1000	4.1	8.2	15.0
ND.................	1200	0.2	0.9	3.9
Annealed................	1200	1.0	2.2	4.8

* Data from Clark and White.[295]
† Normalized 1725°F; drawn 1180°F; annealing treatment not reported.

was primarily caused by banding, or dendritic segregation. If there were no banding, there existed practically no differences in creep strength which could be attributed to difference in heat-treatment. However, with severe banding, heat-treatment was found to be advantageous. Wyman's conclusion that the strength of banded steels can be improved by heat-treatment appears proper in that ferrite bands can logically be expected to exert a weakening effect, but his implied conclusion that heat-treatment is of minor importance in nonbanded steel is open to question in view of the results of other investigations.

Jenkins *et al.*[298] have conducted studies of the influence of heat-treatment, finding that spheroidization of cementite brings about decreased creep resistance. Steels containing 0.5 and 1.0 per cent molybdenum were found to be markedly affected by heat-treatment, as illustrated in

Fig. 194. Whether the strengths resulting from these various treatments will persist in the same order in long-time service is conjectural, but there can be no doubt that a wide range in properties exists in this steel, depending upon the heat-treatment. The finding that the oil-hardened and tempered condition was most resistant to creep is rather surprising, as is the difference between the oil and water-hardened conditions. Tests of a steel containing 0.4 per cent carbon on the other hand showed the air-cooled condition to be superior to oil quenching

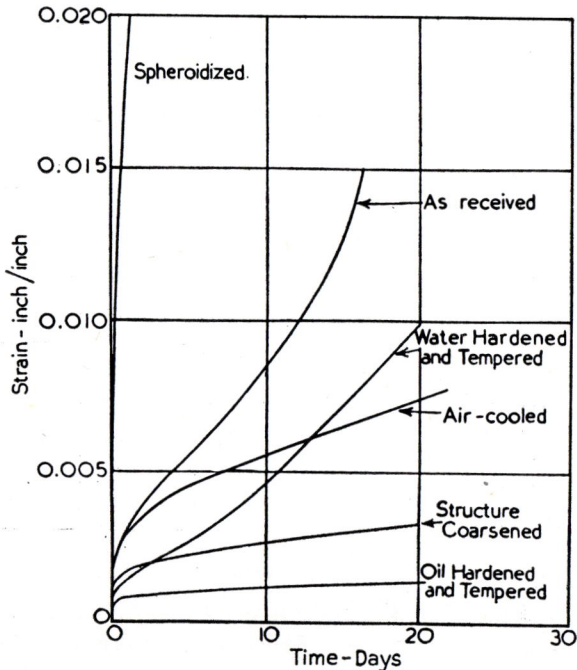

Fig. 194. Effect of heat-treatment on the creep curve of a steel containing 0.5 per cent molybdenum and 0.1 per cent carbon under 20,000 psi at 1020°F. (*Jenkins et al.*[298])

and tempering. Conflicting results of this nature, although very possibly real, always raise some question that an unusual and unrecognized condition may have existed in one or more of the tests. It is therefore desirable, although not always possible, to test several steels and several heat-treatments in order to establish whether there exists any unique features.

Miller *et al.*[367] conducted an extensive investigation of the influence of heat-treatment on the creep of molybdenum and chromium-molybdenum-silicon steel. Specimens of a 0.5 per cent molybdenum steel were tested in creep for 3,000 hr at 1100°F after normalizing at 1650°F and after six different tempering treatments subsequent to normalizing at 1650°F. The results, which are summarized in Fig. 195, showed that the most creep-resistant structure contains a fine shower precipitate of an iron-molybdenum-carbon compound, described in the section on microstructural changes. Of the seven heat-treatments investigated, maximum

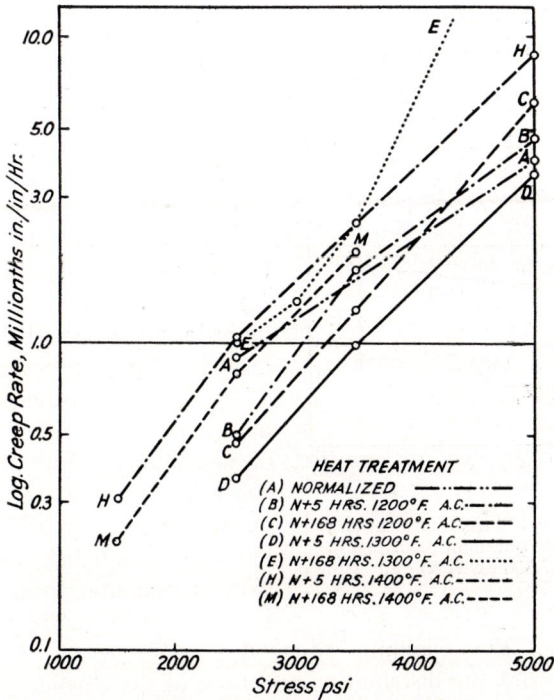

Fig. 195. Effect of heat-treatment on creep of steel containing 0.5 per cent molybdenum and 0.1 per cent carbon at 1100°F. (*Miller et al.*[367])

creep strength was observed in that obtained by normalizing and tempering 5 hr at 1300°F. Tempering a longer time at 1300°F resulted in inferior strength. The next best creep strength was observed in the structure formed by tempering at 1200°F for 168 hrs. It is noteworthy that the order of strength of many of the structures differs, depending upon the creep rate chosen for reference.

The investigation by Miller *et al.*[367] of the influence of heat-treatment on the creep strength of chromium-molybdenum-silicon steel was much less extensive. Only two initial conditions were studied: (1) heated $1\frac{1}{2}$ hr at 1750°F, air-cooled to 400°F, tempered 2 hr at 1375°F, furnace-cooled to 1000°F, and then air-cooled to room temperature; (2) heated $\frac{1}{2}$ hr at 1500°F and furnace-cooled at 50°F per hour to 570°F, and then air-cooled to room temperature. On testing at 1100°F, the annealed structure had only a very slightly slower creep rate than the normalized and tempered structure.

Weaver[368] considers, as did Wyman,[366] the effect of nonuniform microstructure such as banding and suggests that the effect on creep strength is proportional to the cross-sectional area occupied by bands. He further points out that the effect of banding can be masked by faster cooling, which results in transformation at lower temperature.

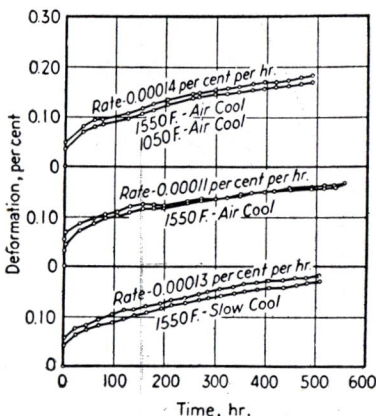

FIG. 196. Effect of heat-treatment on the creep of a steel containing 0.35 per cent carbon under 7,500 psi at 850°F. (*Cross and Lowther.*[361])

The investigations sponsored by the ASME-ASTM Joint Research Committee[361-363] mentioned in the section on the influence of manufacturing variables, have also furnished valuable information on the effect of heat-treatment. Unfortunately, it is quite difficult, at least so far as carbon and low alloy steels are concerned, to separate the influence of several variables which are quite likely to be changing simultaneously, namely, manufacturing and deoxidation practice, grain size, and microstructure. For example, when the grain size is changed, it is quite likely that the distribution and form of the carbide-ferrite aggregate will also be changed. This should be borne in mind in attempting to appraise experimental results.

Cross and Lowther[361] have attempted in comparative tests to distinguish among the variables. Figure 196 shows the results of comparative tests at constant austenite grain size of the influence of annealing, normalizing, and normalizing followed by tempering. All three structures proved to have nearly identical creep resistance in these tests at 850°F. In contrast, comparative tests of this same steel at 750°F in the condition as slow-cooled or air-cooled from 1550°F showed the latter to have about one-third the creep rate of the former. The same two conditions were tested at 950°F and proved to have nearly identical strength, as they did at 850°F.

Tests of relatively pure iron (0.003 per cent carbon) at 850°F by Cross and Lowther[362] showed that when slow-cooled this material had a creep rate 9 times that when air-cooled from the same austenitizing temperature. Contrary to Cross and Lowther's statement that no noticeable difference in structure could be observed, accompanying photomicrographs showed the slow-cooled sample to have a smaller ferrite grain size. Also, the cooling of the slow-cooled sample was unfortunately interrupted at 1560°F for 10 hr. Tests of pure iron to which had been added 0.5 per cent silicon showed results similar to those of the pure iron so far as the influence of cooling rate was concerned. In this case, however, the ferrite grain size appeared to be the same for both tests.

The data of Table XXI, discussed earlier in the section on the effect of manufacturing variables, provide a rather extensive comparison of the influence of cooling rate on creep resistance of carbon steel. The air-cooled condition provides superior creep strength; the effect is quite marked in the steel deoxidized with silicon and 2 lb of aluminum per ton of steel, but is of only slight magnitude in silicon-killed steel.

A subsequent report by Cross and Simmons[363] in this continuing investigation provides additional confirmation of the influence of cooling rate, and leads the authors to consider submicroscopic precipitation phenomena to play an important role in determining creep resistance of these steels. This hypothesis is admittedly quite speculative, and further tests will be necessary before it can be fully accepted. In steels, the form and distribution of the carbide is so radically changed when the rate of cooling is changed, with an attendant change in strength, that it is difficult to isolate the influence of any assumed submicroscopic precipitation process.

Miller, Benz, and Unverzagt[294] reported creep data at 1000°F for a number of low alloy steels up to and including the 5 per cent chromium-molybdenum series. Among these was a series of four molybdenum steels containing up to 2 per cent molybdenum which was examined in both the normalized and the normalized and tempered condition. In each composition, the creep strength of the normalized material was greater than that of the normalized and tempered material by some 10 to 20 per cent. Tests also showed 5 per cent chromium–0.5 per cent molybdenum steel to have a creep strength (stress for creep rate of 0.000001 in./in./hr, of 9,100 psi when furnace-cooled from 1600°F but only 6,600 psi when normalized from 1650°F and tempered at 1380°F.

Weaver[369, 370] has conducted extensive studies of the influence of spheroidization upon the creep strength of molybdenum steel. This investigation is of primary concern in regard to the deterioration in

TABLE XXVI.   INFLUENCE OF HEAT-TREATMENT ON CREEP STRENGTH
OF MOLYBDENUM STEEL AT 925°F*

Steel†	Heat-treatment	Microstructure	ASTM grain size	1,000 psi stress to produce creep rate of 0.00001%/hr
A	Hot-rolled	Widmanstätten	5–7	15.2
A	2 hr 1700°F; cool 50°F/hr to 1000°F; air-cooled	Pearlitic	3–6	12.1
A	1 hr 1800°F; water-quenched; 2 hr 1700°F, cool 50°F/hr to 1000°F; air-cooled	Pearlitic	3–6	11.2
A	1 hr 1800°F, water-quenched; 2 hr 1700°F, air-cooled	Widmanstätten	2–6	16.0
B	Hot-rolled; process-anneal 1300°F	Widmanstätten	4–6	16.7
B	1 hr 1650°F; air-cooled; 1 hr 1200°F; air-cooled	Pearlitic	7–8	12.0
C	1 hr 1650°F; air-cooled; 1 hr 1200°F; air-cooled	Widmanstätten	5–7	17.4
D	1 hr 1650°F; air-cooled; 1 hr 1200°F; air cooled	Pearlitic	7–8	14.5
E	3 hr 1950°F; furnace-cooled	Pearlitic	3–6	9.8

* Data from White and Crocker.[360]
† See the following table:

Steel	Type	C	Mn	Si	Mo	Al	Al₂O₃	Al added, lb/ton
A	Open-hearth	0.14	0.43	0.11	0.48	.....	.....	0.50
B	Open-hearth	0.16	0.45	0.14	0.58	0.043	0.010	2.25
C	Open-hearth	0.15	0.41	0.19	0.58	0.011	0.008	1.20
D	Open-hearth	0.17	0.52	0.16	0.54	0.045	0.010	1.80
E	Open-hearth	0.16	0.47	0.14	0.45	.....	.....	1.50

strength resulting from microstructural changes during service, and is accordingly discussed in Chap. XI, Changes during Service—Scaling and Microstructural Changes. As indicated there, prespheroidization of the carbide may result in a considerable decrease in strength.

White and Crocker[360] conducted an extensive investigation of the creep strength of 0.5 per cent molybdenum steel containing 0.1 to 0.2 per cent carbon. Unable to rationalize the creep behavior of normalized and drawn samples of six heats of this grade made by the electric-furnace or open-hearth methods with differing amounts of aluminum added for deoxidation, comparative creep tests were made of several of the heats

TABLE XXVII. INFLUENCE OF HEAT-TREATMENT ON CREEP OF 18 PER CENT CHROMIUM–8 PER CENT NICKEL STEEL AT 1000F*

Steel	C	Mn	Si	Cr	Ni	N
Low-carbon..........	0.067	0.50	0.65	18.21	9.56	0.056
High-carbon........	0.125	0.47	0.58	18.50	9.67	0.035

Carbon	Heat-treatment	1,000 psi stress to produce secondary creep rate of 0.0001%/hr	1,000 psi stress to produce total def. of 1% in 10,000 hr
0.067	Air-cooled, 2000°F	<17.3	<17.3
0.067	Water-quenched, 2000°F	20.0	17.5
0.125	Air-cooled, 2000°F	>21.8	<17.3
0.125	Water-quenched, 2000°F	25.0	20.2

* Data from Cross.[352]

in several different conditions of heat-treatments. These results are summarized in Table XXVI. As the authors point out, the superiority of the Widmanstätten structure over the pearlitic structure holds whether the grain size is coarse or fine, and in fact the influence of microstructure overshadows that of grain size, which in these tests appears to be of secondary importance.

Comstock[371] has reported data which, though incomplete, indicate that considerable improvement in strength of commercial 5 per cent chromium steel containing molybdenum and titanium can be effected by heat-treatment, depending upon the composition.

Cross[352] has reported creep data at 1000°F for two 18 per cent chromium–8 per cent nickel steels in both the air-cooled and water-quenched conditions. These tests, which are summarized in Table XXVII, indicate that the water-quenched condition yields somewhat superior creep strength.   Unfortunately, the tests of the air-cooled condition were not sufficiently extensive to provide specific values.

Austin and Samans[372] have reported that it is possible to strengthen fine-grained 18 per cent chromium–8 per cent nickel steel by partial precipitation of carbide before test.   However, the effect was not great, and since the same specimen was tested at several stresses, it is possible that erroneous indications may have been obtained.

TABLE XXVIII.   INFLUENCE OF HEAT-TREATMENT ON CREEP OF 18 CR–8 NI GRADES*

Steel†	Heat-treatment	Stress, 1,000 psi, to produce second stage creep rate of 0.0001%/hr		
		1100°F	1300°F	1500°F
18-8 Cb	1950°F, quench	26.5	7.5	1.5
	1950°F, quench; 1600°F, air-cooled	25.0	7.2	1.7
18-8 Ti	1900°F, air-cooled	16.6	4.3	0.5
	1950°F, quench	16.5	3.3	0.3

* Data from U.S. Steel Corp.
† See the following table:

Steel	C	Mn	Si	Ni	Cr	Cb	Ti
18-8 Cb	0.06	1.23	0.58	10.93	17.90	0.64	
18-8 Ti	0.05	0.52	0.39	10.90	17.50	. . . .	0.44

Results obtained at the U. S. Steel Corp. of Del. Research Laboratory, summarized in Table XXVIII, are of interest in regard to the influence of heat-treatment on the creep of various 18 per cent chromium–8 per cent nickel steels.   The differences in creep strength do not appear to be significant.

Effect of Heat-treatment of Nonferrous Alloys

Experimental studies of the influence of heat-treatment on the creep properties of nonferrous alloys are quite few and scattered.

Magnesium Alloys.   Leontis and Murphy[332] have shown that the creep strength of magnesium-cerium alloys can be improved by appropriate heat-treatment.   These data, summarized in Table XIII, indicate that the development of a precipitate phase in the matrix, and particularly the degree to which this precipitate is agglomerated, exerts an important effect on the creep strength.

Moore and McDonald[333] report creep data for many commercial magnesium alloys and also include some few data in regard to the influence of heat-treatment. Heat-treatment is shown to be of importance but was not systematically and separately investigated.

Tin Alloys. Hanson and Sandford[336] studied the creep behavior of alloys of tin containing from 2 to 7 per cent cadmium and from 3 to 9 per cent antimony. The alloys were cold-rolled to 0.1-in.-thick strip from ingots 0.5 in. thick and were tested in three conditions of heat-treatment: (1) self-annealed for at least 2 months after cold rolling; (2) heat-treated at 340°F for 2 days and cooled in the furnace; and (3) heat-treated at 340°F for 5 hr, then at 390°F for 1 day, and cooled in air. The effect of heat-treatment on these alloys was to produce a marked improvement in creep resistance. For example, an alloy containing 2 per cent cadmium and 9 per cent antimony fractured in 200 days under 1,400 psi when in the self-annealed condition, while material annealed at 340°F withstood 2,800 psi for 200 days. Microstructural examination showed a wide variation in grain size in these alloys and also the occurrence of the delta and epsilon phases. The larger grain size resulted in longer life. The best of the alloys in the condition annealed at 340°F was that containing 2 per cent cadmium and 7 per cent antimony; it required a stress of 5,200 psi for rupture in 200 days. The results of the tests in the condition as annealed at 340°F are shown in Fig. 189. The other two conditions were not tested so extensively. The self-annealed condition was inferior to the heat-treated. Annealing at 390°F resulted in a considerable improvement in strength in some instances, while in others little change resulted.

Copper Alloys. Jenkins *et al.*[342, 343] have studied the influence of heat-treatment in a precipitation-hardenable copper alloy containing 2.4 per cent nickel, 0.6 per cent silicon, and 0.4 per cent manganese. As the authors point out, there had been little or no data on the relation between precipitation hardening and creep behavior, although it has been generally assumed that a treatment producing maximum hardness will result in superior resistance to creep. Jenkins *et al.* prepared experimental ingots of the copper-nickel-silicon alloy, which were heated at 1650°F before rolling, cross-rolled to a total reduction of 75 per cent, and then reheated to 1650°F and quenched in cold water. Creep-rupture tests lasting to 3,000 hr were made at temperatures from 400 to 1100°F in the slowly cooled, rapidly cooled, and rapidly cooled plus precipitation-hardened conditions. Interpretation of the data is not easy since hardening occurred in some specimens at some temperatures, while other specimens at other temperatures may have softened owing to agglomeration of the precipitate. A general comparison of the results is given in Table XXIX for the three principal conditions: slowly cooled, quenched, and quenched and hardened. At 390°F, the fully hardened material is strongest both in short- and long-time tests, although the loss in strength with increased test time was marked. In short-time tests at 570 and 840°F, the fully hardened material was strongest, but in long-time tests it had become weakest, with the slowly cooled condition strongest and the water-quenched condition intermediate.

TABLE XXIX. INFLUENCE OF HEAT-TREATMENT ON CREEP BEHAVIOR OF A PRECIPITATION-HARDENABLE ALLOY OF COPPER CONTAINING 2.5 PER CENT NICKEL AND 0.6 PER CENT SILICON*

| Test temp., °F | Stress, tons/sq in., to bring about rupture in | | | | | |
| | 0.1 hr | | | 1,000 hr | | |
	Slowly cooled from 1650°F	Water-quenched from 1650°F	Fully hardened: water-quenched plus 2 hr at 930°F	Slowly cooled from 1650°F	Water-quenched from 1650°F	Fully hardened: water-quenched plus 2 hr at 930°F
392	14.5	15.8	35.5	14.0†	16.0†	22.0
572	12.7	15.6	25.0	8.8	7.2	6.6
842	8.4	10.3	12.2	3.55	2.3	1.85

* Data from Jenkins, Bucknall, and Jenkinson.[343]

† Specimen slowly loaded during previous 2 to 3 hr. Apparently this has resulted in strengthening by precipitation hardening, which is not possible to so great a degree on fast loading.

Parker[344] has conducted a few tests of the influence of heat-treatment on an oxygen-free high-conductivity copper and on an oxygen-free copper containing 0.054 per cent of silver. In creep-rupture tests of the silver-containing alloy at 480°F, the structure as furnace-cooled from 1560°F was somewhat stronger than that as water-quenched from the same temperature; in terms of the stress to produce fracture in 100 hr, the furnace-cooled condition showed about 21,000 psi, the water-quenched about 18,000 psi. Tests of the same two treatments at 390°F showed about 20,000 psi and 18,000 psi which are almost identical with the results at the higher temperature. This may be the result of a precipitation hardening, which was observed in a study of the recrystallization of this alloy. Tests at 390°F of the oxygen-free high-conductivity copper after cooling from 1560°F showed almost identical results in the furnace- or air-cooled conditions, but when water-quenched, this alloy suffered a marked loss in strength. The stress to produce rupture in 100 hr was about 15,000 psi for the furnace- or air-cooled condition, but only about 9,000 psi for the water-quenched condition, a decrease of over 40 per cent.

Martin and Parker[354] report in comparative creep-rupture tests of several commercial and high-purity coppers, either furnace-cooled or water-quenched from the annealing temperature, that the faster cooling rate resulted in shorter life and lower ductility. This difference ranged from 1,000 to 5,000 psi in the stress required for rupture in 100 hr at 390°F.

INFLUENCE OF GRAIN SIZE

The influence of grain size on the creep behavior of metals has probably received more attention than any other variable excepting stress and temperature. Unfortunately, however, much of this work is of questionable value owing to lack of knowledge of or inability to control other variables. Especially is this true of the ferritic steels, since creep behavior is so sensitive to the small differences in microstructure, other than grain size, that are developed in such steels by slight differences in cooling rate, deoxidation practice, chemical composition, and other variables. In addition, there has been considerable confusion as to whether interest should center on the austenitic or the ferritic grain size, or on the so-called "structural" grain size, that is, the proeutectoid ferrite–pearlite patches.

For a review and discussion of these various grain sizes of steel, the reader is referred to a paper by Vilella.[380] It is difficult to believe that any grain size other than that actually in the specimen at the time of test is of any direct significance. However, in the following discussion, all studies of the influence of grain size, however defined, will be reviewed.

Jeffries[374, 375] was apparently the first to study in any detail the influence of grain size on the strength of metals at elevated temperatures, although the occurrence of intercrystalline (grain boundary) failure, observed under certain conditions at high temperatures, had earlier been noted and described by Rosenhain et al.[376, 377] Jeffries extended to annealed metals the amorphorous theory, earlier developed by Beilby,[378] Bengough,[379] and Rosenhain and Ewen[376] to explain strain hardening of metals. According to the amorphous metal theory of strain hardening, films of amorphous metal are generated on the slip planes of a metal during plastic deformation, thereby causing strain hardening, since this material is assumed to be stronger than crystalline metal at strain-hardening temperatures. This theory is now not generally accepted. As applied to annealed metals, there was assumed to be a film of amorphous metal at the boundaries of the individual crystals which make up a polycrystalline metal. It was generally assumed, as Jeffries[375] pointed out, that amorphous metal was stronger than crystalline metal at relatively low temperatures, such as atmospheric temperature for the structural metals, while at relatively high temperatures, the amorphous metal was considered to be weaker than the crystalline. Jeffries reasoned that at some intermediate temperature the strength of the amorphous and crystalline phases must be identical and coined the expression "equicohesive temperature" to describe this state. Jeffries studied a wide variety of metals—tungsten, iron, gold, silver, platinum, and copper—and obtained data which he considered to support his concept of an equicohesive temperature, and further concluded that this temperature corresponded very nearly to the lowest recrystallization temperature. Jeffries also estimated that this temperature was approximately 0.35 to 0.45 of the absolute melting point.

Jeffries' concept of an equicohesive temperature, or more properly, a range of temperature, has been and still is the subject of much controversy and experimentation, and although perhaps an oversimplification in some respects, has been employed by many investigators to explain both the greater strength of coarse-grained metals in creep and the intercrystalline mode of failure encountered in metals at high temperatures.

Kanter and Spring[373] were among the first to note the influence of grain size in creep tests of relatively long duration. Among their results were data showing that austenitic 18 per cent chromium–8 per cent nickel steel had superior creep strength when quenched from 2100°F than when as-rolled. Microscopic examination revealed the former material to have coarser grain size. Of course, there is the possibility that residual cold work in the as-rolled material exerted a detrimental effect.

Clark and White[341] in 1932 reported the results of an extensive study of the interrelation of recrystallization, grain size, and creep characteristics and made a number of upstep loading creep tests of several brass and bronze alloys. They determined a "lowest" recrystallization temperature for the test materials by "severely" cold deforming and heating 100 hr at temperature, and then relating the resulting microstructure and hardness to the heating temperature. They reported that the slope of the log-log plot of stress against creep rate was steeper at temperatures above this lowest recrystallization temperature than at temperatures below this limit; but their tests appear to be too few to be conclusive as to whether there may not be a continuous change with no discontinuity at their lowest recrystallization temperature. The authors hypothesize that at temperatures above the "lowest" recrystallization temperature continuous flow occurs at any stress, while at temperatures below this level, stresses of a definite magnitude, depending upon the temperature and possibly related to a carefully determined proportional limit, are needed.

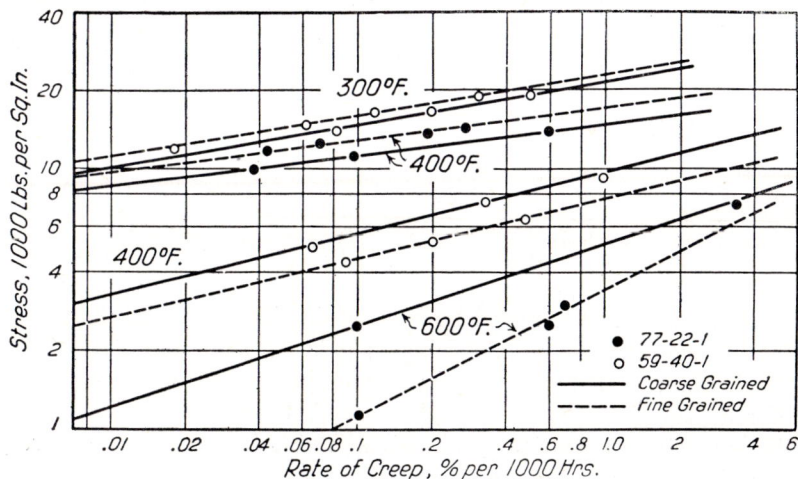

Nominal composition	Grain size, mm	Lowest recryst. temp., °F
77 Cu, 22 Zn, 1 Sn	0.020	500–600
77 Cu, 22 Zn, 1 Sn	0.045	500–600
59 Cu, 40 Zn, 1 Sn	0.025	300–400
59 Cu, 40 Zn, 1 Sn	0.045	300–400

Fig. 197. Effect of grain size on the creep of two brass alloys at several temperatures. (*Clark and White.*[341])

Their tests of the influence of grain size, summarized in Fig. 197, show that above the lowest recrystallization temperature the coarse-grained materials have superior creep strength while the fine-grained materials are stronger at lower temperatures. Thus support is adduced for the concept of an equicohesive temperature. However, as the authors recognize, this temperature relates to a particular strain rate and presumably to other conditions. Whether the concept of an equicohesive temperature has any fundamental significance or is merely descriptive in a very rough sense has yet to be shown.

Further work, reported in 1934 by White and Clark,[381] centered on the influence of the carburized (McQuaid-Ehn) grain size, sometimes termed "inherent" grain size. Two steels were tested, one containing 0.50 per cent molydbenum, the other 0.25 per cent molybdenum and 1.25 per cent magnanese. The steels are described in Table XXX.

TABLE XXX. DESCRIPTION OF STEELS TESTED TO DETERMINE INFLUENCE OF McQUAID-EHN GRAIN SIZE ON CREEP CHARACTERISTICS*†

Designation	C	Mn	Si	Mo	Heat-treatment	Brinell hardness	Grain size
C-Mo (F)	0.16	0.49	0.30	0.49	Annealed 1550°F	131	8
C-Mo (C)	0.16	0.47	0.23	0.42	Annealed 1550°F	126	4–5
MM 9 (F)	0.15	1.28	0.29	0.28	N 1725°F, D 1200°F	152	7–8
MM 9 (C)	0.15	1.25	0.19	0.25	N 1725°F, D 1200°F	140	4–5

* Data from White and Clark.[381]
† See Figs. 198 and 199.

The authors do not reveal how the grain size was determined; presumably standard 8-hr carburizing tests at 1700°F were used. Also, though not revealed, the different grain sizes probably resulted from different deoxidation practice. Since, as discussed in an earlier section, differences in deoxidation practice can result in differences in creep strength, independent of grain-size differences, it is questionable whether differences in the results of these tests, summarized in Figs. 198 and 199, are solely a consequence of grain-size differences. The results appear to be somewhat inconsistent with the equicohesive concept unless it be assumed that the lowest recrystallization temperature of the manganese-molybdenum steel is below 800°F, an improbable event. Actually it appears somewhat improbable that any well-defined relation would exist between creep strength and a grain structure, such as the McQuaid-Ehn, which does not exist at the test temperature. Any such relation must exist only because the actual structure is inherited from the former structure.

Clark and White[295] treat this question again but offer no additional experimental data in support of the "equicohesive" temperature.

Cross and Johnson[382] studied the influence of heat-treatment on the creep at 1100 and 1200°F of 5 per cent chromium–0.5 per cent molybdenum steel and observed better creep strength in this steel when annealed or normalized at 2100°F than when similarly heat-treated at 1550°F, an effect attributable in part, although probably not entirely, to the coarser grain size resulting from heating at 2100°F.

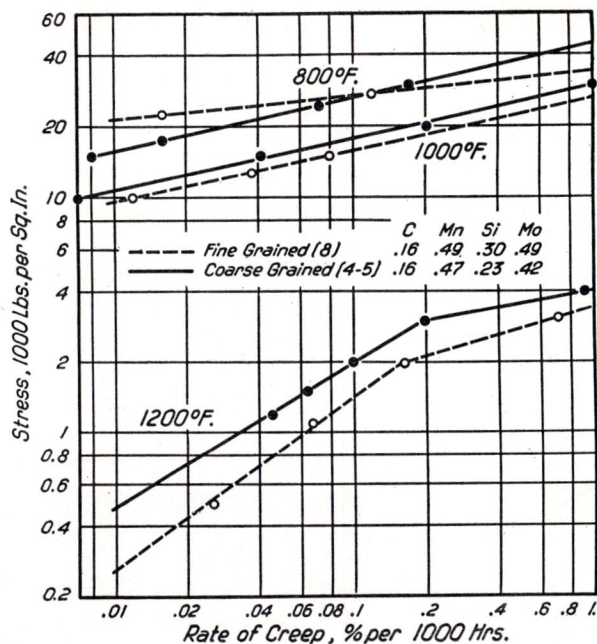

FIG. 198. Effect of grain size on the creep of molybdenum steel (see Table **XXX**). (*Clark and White.*[381])

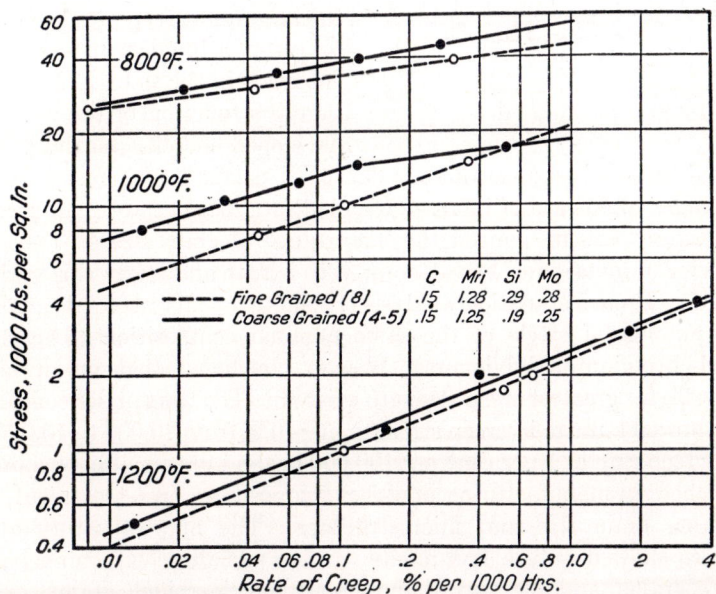

FIG. 199. Effect of grain size on the creep of manganese-molybdenum steel (see Table **XXX**). (*Clark and White.*[381])

Hanson and Wheeler[383] studied the creep characteristics of aluminum having grain-size differences ranging from the relatively small size ordinarily encountered to single crystals, and although their efforts were primarily concerned with the mechanism of flow and fracture, some limited data relative to the influence of grain size on creep strength were obtained. Most of the tests were conducted at 480°F. Failure of ·aggregates was always intercrystalline at 480°F under creep conditions, whereas the single crystals failed by shear along slip planes. Specimens containing mixed coarse and fine grains were observed to be weaker in creep than when the grains were all uniformly small; however, the authors' experiments in this regard were not extensive.

McKeown[384] has studied the influence of grain size on creep at room temperature in virgin leads of high purity. For the high-purity lead studied, the recrystallization temperature of extruded samples was below room temperature. McKeown's results are summarized in Fig. 200, which shows the minimum creep rate and the total creep in 100 days of four different leads in the as-extruded condition as a function of the grain size developed on self-annealing. The several tests fall on a continuous curve; of particular interest is the increasingly rapid rate of increase of creep rate in going to small grains.

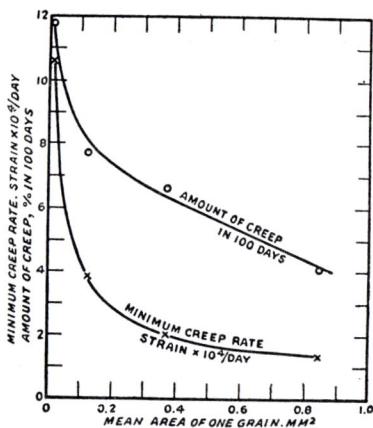

Fig. 200. Effect of grain size on the creep of high-purity lead at room temperature under 500 psi. (*McKeown.*[384])

Weaver[368] has recognized the importance of grain size on the creep behavior of metals and has attempted to isolate and study this variable in steel. From a statistical analysis of some 30 creep tests made at 840°F on a number of steels of the same nominal composition (SAE 4330, nickel-chromium-molybdenum), Weaver concluded that an optimum grain size for greatest creep strength existed. The tests under consideration showed a range in creep strength at 840°F from 40,000 to 10,000 psi for a creep rate of 1 per cent per 100,000 hr, and presumably encompass differences in manufacturing practice, composition, heat-treatment, and therefore grain size and microstructure. The microstructure of all samples showed only a fine ferrite carbide structure with no separate ferrite grains, and the size of these so-called "carbide" grains, or the actually existing grains as defined by the grain boundaries revealed on etching, was measured by Weaver and related to the creep strength, with results (Fig. 201) which apparently show an optimum. These results represent heat-treatments including oil quenching and tempering, normalizing and drawing, and annealing. Weaver states that these tests also represent a uniform microstructure, but by this he apparently means type of microstructure, for it is to be expected, and his accompanying photomicrographs show, that the microstructure was far from strictly uniform so far as carbide particle size and probably other characteristics are concerned. The grain size of the test labeled "315" on the plot is admitted to be in some question. Because of the simultaneous varia-

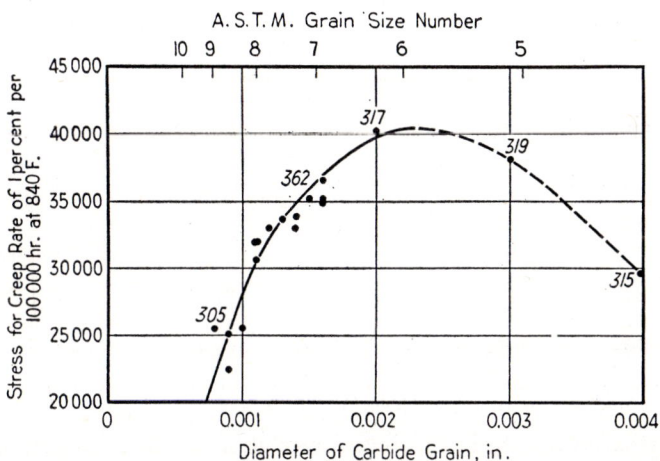

Fig. 201. Effect of carbide grain size on the creep of SAE 4340 steel at 840°F. (*Weaver.*[368]) The dotted portion beyond grain size 6 is in some question (see text).

tion of several variables, some of which are known to exert profound influences on creep strength, it is somewhat questionable, as several discussers of this paper point out, whether the results shown in Fig. 201 really represent what they purport to show, particularly in view of the admittedly uncertain nature of the grain size of Test 315. It should also be pointed out that Test 315 differs from all the others in that the steel was slow-cooled and not reheated. Thus it appears that the results at best can be only taken to show that increasing grain size results in increased creep strength; but further and more careful investigation of this question is necessary. It would seem that the influence of grain size per se could most readily be studied in a single-phase metal rather than in the complex structures of heat-treatable ferritic steels.

Weaver[385] in a subsequent paper again considers the influence of grain size and again concludes that an optimum grain size for best creep strength exists.   In this case, 1 per cent molybdenum steel, 1 per cent molybdenum–1.5 per cent chromium steel, 0.5 per cent molybdenum–5 per cent chromium steel, and 1.7 per cent tungsten–1.7 per cent chromium–0.3 per cent nickel steel are considered, with most attention being devoted to the plain molybdenum steel.   In this latter case, the microstructure consists of ferrite and "carbide" (pearlitic) grains and Weaver employs a "structural" grain size which includes both the ferrite and "carbide" grains.   Variation in grain size was obtained by heating different samples to successively higher temperatures.   By employing the same steel in each series, the variables of composition and of manufacturing practice were eliminated, and presumably the only remaining variables were grain size and microstructure as the result of the different heat-treatments employed.   Unfortunately, these necessarily varied simultaneously, and this, coupled with the fact that the results did not show well-developed optimum grain sizes, again makes it somewhat uncertain that Weaver's claim of an optimum is justified by his experimental results.

In an investigation of the influence of manufacturing variables on creep behavior of steels, Cross et al.[361–363] have also attempted to isolate the influence of grain size in ferritic-carbidic steels and, although not completely successful because of the multiplicity of variables, have gathered some data of interest.   The grain size considered in this study was the actual austenitic grain size, which seems a poor choice since it is nonexistent in the steel as tested. However, since the actual grain size is related to the austenitic grain size for these annealed or normalized steels, it may be expected that a second-order correlation may be observed.   In one instance of a 0.35 per cent carbon steel tested at 850°F, Cross and Lowther[361] found that steel with a grain size of ASTM 0 to 4 showed a creep rate about one-fifth of that for the same steel with a grain size of ASTM 7 to 8.   However, it should be pointed out that with different austenitic grain size and similar rate of cooling a different microstructure is developed.   Similar improvement in creep strength was observed for other steels when the austenitic grain size was coarsened. An exception was a steel with 0.37 per cent carbon–0.18 per cent vanadium, which having relatively high creep strength in the fine-grained condition was improved only slightly by coarsening.   Tests of some of the steels at 750 and at 950°F also revealed marked superiority for coarsened steel except in one instance at 750°F in which the two structures showed similar strength.

In a second paper, Cross and Lowther[362] report further data relative to the influence of austenite grain size on creep behavior of steels. Some of these results have been earlier summarized in Table XXI, and inspection of these data will show for any of the particular steels included a superiority of the coarse-grained condition. It might be noted in Table XXI, however, that the superiority of the coarse-grained over the fine-grained rimmed steel is hardly significant. Also tested were a pure iron (0.003 per cent carbon) and a pure iron-silicon alloy (0.003 per cent carbon, 0.5 per cent silicon), both showing a rather pronounced in-

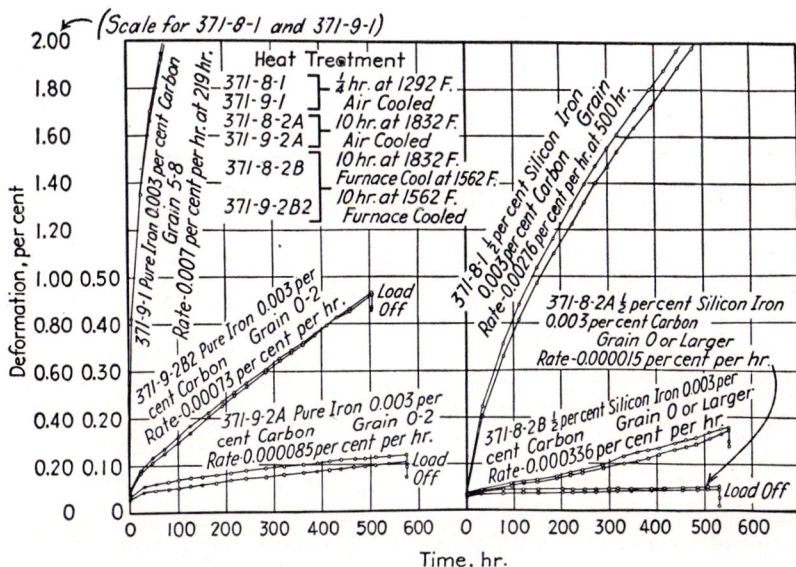

Fig. 202. Effect of grain size on creep of pure iron and pure iron with 0.5 per cent silicon at 850°F under 6,000 psi. (*Cross and Lowther.*[362])

fluence of grain size in 500-hr comparative tests at 850°F, as revealed in Fig. 202. Since these two materials contain only the single-phase ferrite, the influence of grain size per se has presumably been isolated. There is, however, an effect of the rate of cooling, as indicated by comparison of the furnace-cooled and air-cooled conditions, also included in Fig. 202.

Clark and White[388] have made short-time creep-rupture tests of several of the steels tested by Cross *et al.*[361–363] and determined that an improvement was effected in the 10-hr rupture strength if the materials were coarsened by heat-treatment.

Hanson and Sandford[336] showed that increased grain size resulted in increased life in creep-rupture tests of alloys of tin containing cadmium and antimony. Their study of this matter, however, was not very comprehensive, since the principal interest lay with the influence of composition.

Hanson[386], in a general treatment of the subject of creep of metals, recognized the importance of grain size, but pointed out inconsistencies with the concept of equicohesion, noting in particular that the rate of extension must be considered. He stated that "no convincing explanation of the effect of grain size has yet been offered." Hanson also presented some hitherto unreported data (Fig. 203) showing an optimum grain size for minimum creep rate and maximum life in constant stress creep-rupture tests of pure tin at room temperature.

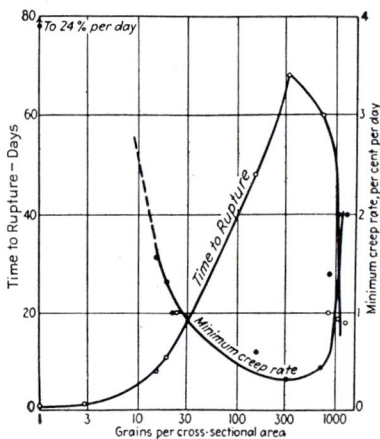

Fig. 203. Effect of grain size on the creep and rupture of pure tin at room temperature under 500 psi. (*Hanson*.[386])

Gillett[387] has also recently given a general treatment of the creep of metals. In summarizing the literature, he noted that in nonferrous metals coarse-grained material is the more creep-resistant at sufficiently high temperatures, while fine-grained material is the superior at low temperatures. However, he related the creep behavior of steels to the austenitic grain size (although he dismisses the carburized grain size) and suggests that the effect of ferritic or actual grain size requires study.

Gillett[387] also considered the theories relating to the influence of grain size, in particular, that postulating an "equicohesive" temperature. He concluded that since this temperature appears to be quite indefinite, being dependent upon strain-rate, its use "tends to muddy our thinking."

In an attempt to develop an explanation for the influence of grain boundaries, Gillett[387] considered, as have others, the existence of lattice imperfections or notches both within the grains and at the grain boundaries. It is suggested that the defects at the grain boundaries, since they presumably represent more violent disregistry of the atoms, should not heal so readily with increasing temperature as those in the interior. Those in the interior should tend to heal because of increased atom mobility. Thus at high temperatures grain boundaries may be relatively more a region of weakness than at low temperatures, and accordingly the beneficial effect of increased grain size results because of the attendant decrease in amount of grain-boundary region and thus simultaneously of the weakening defects. The worth of Gillett's suggestion is difficult to judge owing to lack of experimental or other theoretical support. However, Gillett admits that in a sense the theory merely describes the experimental observations. Too, the theory would seem to lead to the single crystal as the most desirable condition for high-temperature use; this is not supported by actual experimental test.

White and Crocker[360] considered the influence of grain size and structure on creep of 0.15 per cent carbon–0.5 per cent molybdenum steel and properly concluded that earlier investigators have placed too much emphasis on grain size and too little on the actual carbide structure. This latter was indicated to be the more influential variable and to overshadow that of grain size in steels having a structure consisting of ferrite and carbide. This work is reviewed in the preceding section on the influence of heat-treatment, and some of the data are summarized in Table XXVI.

Thielemann[389] has reported that ferritic alloys which in long-time creep-rupture tests fracture through the grains rather than at the grain boundaries contained appreciable amounts of chromium and has suggested the value of a "chromium equivalent," which may be calculated from the chemical composition, as a criterion of susceptibility to intergranular cracking. Elements like tungsten, molybdenum, and silicon are considered to act like chromium, while the elements carbon, nickel, and manganese are considered to act in an opposite fashion. Although such a scheme might be of some practical importance, if further corroborated, the fundamental nature of the reported relation is not evident. It should also be pointed out that materials not liable to intergranular failure at one temperature may become so at a higher temperature, as is well known.

Thielemann[389] also made a few tests which showed an increase in creep-rupture strength at 1100°F with increasing grain size of a steel containing 0.12 per cent carbon, 3 per cent chromium, and 0.5 per cent molybdenum, though it seems probable that some of the effect may be the result of change in microstructure. The results (Fig. 204) show a rather pronounced influence of grain size in this instance; also noteworthy is the longer time for onset of intergranular failure in the coarse-grained material.

Austin and Samans[372] made comparative upstep creep tests of an 18 per cent chromium–8 per cent nickel austenitic steel and observed that coarsening of the grain resulted in improved creep strength at temperatures of 1300 and 1475°F but had no influence at 1100°F. The temperature between 1100 and 1300°F at which the influence of grain size becomes of moment is suggested to be associated with recrystallization.

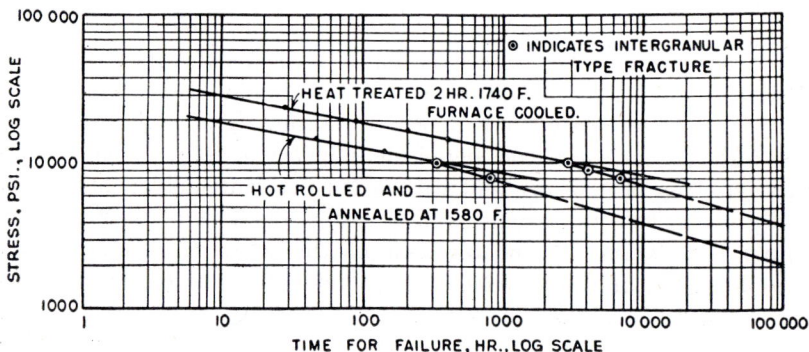

FIG. 204. Showing the pronounced effect of a grain-coarsening heat-treatment, which presumably also effected a change in microstructure, on the creep to rupture of a steel containing 3 per cent chromium, 0.5 per cent molybdenum, and 0.12 per cent carbon at 1100°F. (*Thielemann.*[389])

Because these data were obtained in upstep tests, it seems unwise to place too much reliance upon them in view of the uncertain nature of such tests.

Burghoff et al.[346] have found the creep strength of 70–30 brass to increase with grain size at 300, 400, and 500°F (Fig. 205). These data differ from those of Clark and White[341] who reported that fine-grained 70–30 brass was the superior at 400°F and lower. Pending further study, the data of Burghoff et al. should be given the greater weight because they are the more recent and were apparently obtained with refinements of test procedure and cognizance of variables which have evolved since the earlier work. These investigators also observed that coarse-grained silicon bronze (96.3 per cent copper, 2.8 per cent silicon, 0.8 per cent zinc) had greater creep strength than fine-grained material (Fig. 206) but

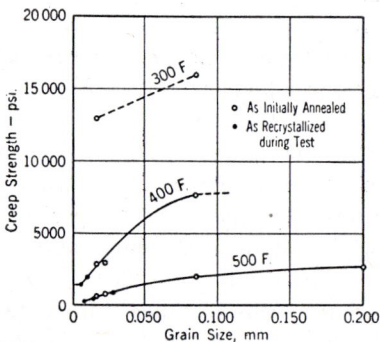

FIG. 205. Effect of grain size on the creep strength, stress to produce creep rate of 0.01 per cent per 1,000 hr, of 70–30 brass. (*Burghoff et al.*[346])

they warn that very coarse-grained metal may become embrittled and subject to sudden failure. This appears to be a general likelihood, and it again emphasizes that very often a gain in one property of a metal is accompanied by a loss in another.

Miller[364] has reported on the influence of grain size on the creep strength of steel containing 0.5 per cent molybdenum. Two such steels, one deoxidized with 0.5 lb and the other with 1.5 lb of aluminum per ton of steel, were studied at 850 and 1000°F with the microstructures shown in Fig. 191. These photomicrographs clearly illustrate the difficulty of a varying microstructure which hampers the study of the influence of grain size on creep of steels. The creep test results for the steel deoxidized with 1.5 lb of aluminum per ton are shown in Fig. 207; the coarse ferrite-pearlite structure (*A* of Fig. 191) is markedly superior to the fine ferrite-pearlite structure (*C* of Fig. 191) at 1000°F but slightly inferior at 850°F. Tests of the ferrite-Widmanstätten structure (*B* of Fig. 191) at 1000°F showed it to have a strength intermediate between that of the other two structures.

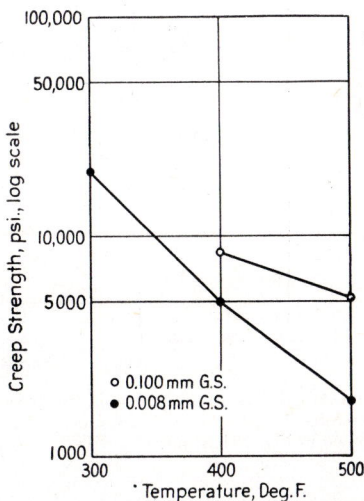

Fig. 206. Effect of grain size on the creep strength, stress to produce creep rate of 0.01 per cent per 1,000 hr, of an alloy containing 96 per cent copper, 3 per cent silicon, and 1 per cent zinc. (*Burghoff et al.*[346])

Parker[391] has discussed the investigations and theories in regard to the occurrence of intercrystalline failure at elevated temperatures and has also offered a few additional data. Grain boundaries are considered to be a source of weakness at high temperatures and of strength at low temperatures in conformity with the concepts of Jeffries.[375] However, the generally assumed agreement between recrystallization temperatures and so-called equicohesive temperatures was held to be merely a coincidence, common to many alloys, but with notable exceptions. One exception was an iron-chromium alloy of 13 per cent chromium which at 1100°F showed only transcrystalline failures in tests out to 17,000 hr, and yet this material will recrystallize at this temperature. In passing, it is of interest to note that the ferritic iron-chromium alloys have generally been observed to be quite resistant to intercrystal-

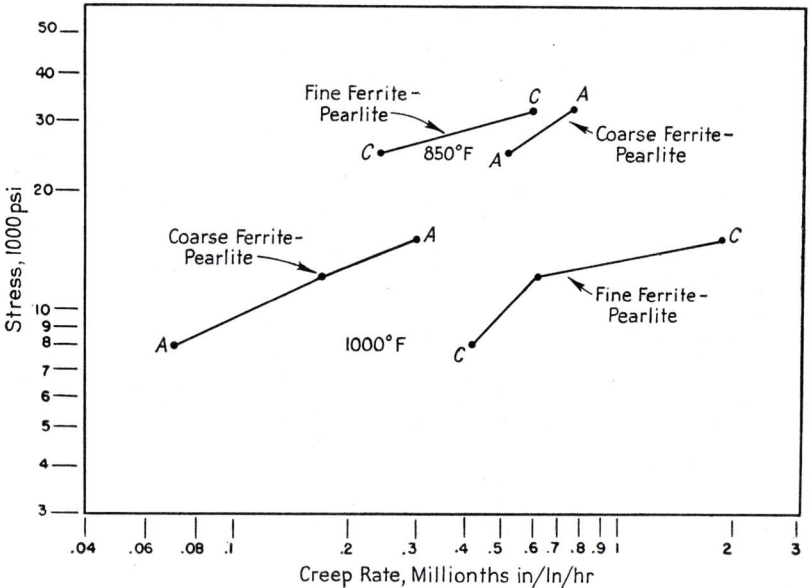

Fig. 207. Effect of grain size on the creep of a steel containing 0.5 per cent molybdenum, deoxidized with 1.5 lb of aluminum per t,n of steel.   Corresponding microstructures are shown in Fig. 191 *A* and *C*.   (*Miller*.[364])

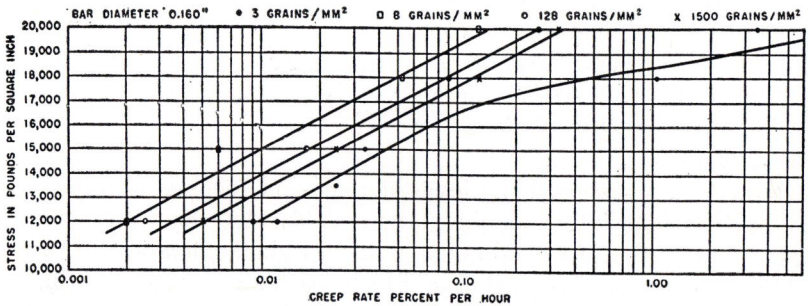

Fig. 208. Effect of grain size on the creep of oxygen-free high-conductivity copper at 400°F.   (*Parker and Riisness*.[392])

line failure.   Another exception was encountered in the aluminum alloy 2S which though it will recrystallize below 400°F required prolonged testing above 750°F to produce intercrystalline failure.   Considering in some detail the nature of the grain boundary in metals, Parker suggested somewhat in line with Gillett[387] that such a region is a site of imperfections from which dislocations propagate across the grains to

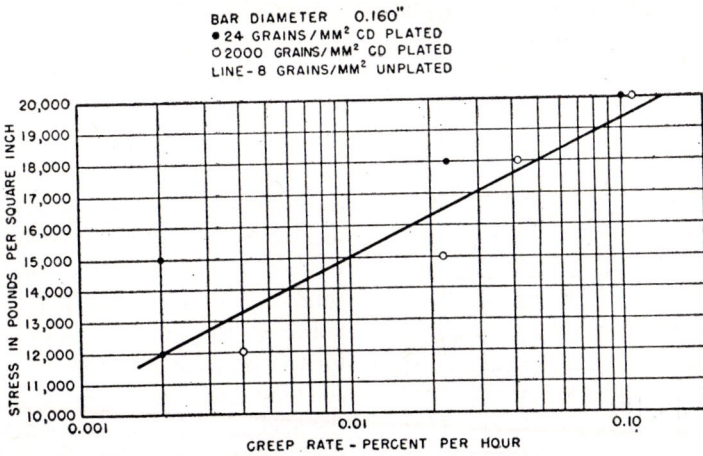

FIG. 209. Showing the effect of reducing oxidation by cadmium plating on the creep of oxygen-free high-conductivity copper at 400°F (compare Fig. 208). (*Parker and Riisness.*[392])

TABLE XXXI.   COMPOSITION AND HEAT-TREATMENT OF THE AUSTENITIC STEELS OF FIGS. 210 AND 211*

Type of steel	C	Mn	Si	Cr	Ni	Cb
18-8 (Q)	0.06	0.50	0.61	17.75	9.25	
18-8 (N)	0.056	0.50	0.47	18.68	10.21	
18-8 Cb (Q)	0.07	1.68	0.55	17.78	12.70	0.88
18-8 Cb (N)	0.08	1.72	0.58	18.25	12.93	0.88
25-20	0.11	0.58	0.75	23.60	20.65	
25-12	0.06	1.55	0.42	24.96	13.40	

Type of steel	Heat-treatment, °F†		Brinell hardness	ASTM grain size
18-8 (Q)	Water-quenched	2000	137	2–5
18-8 (N)	Normalized	1700	143	8+
18-8 Cb (Q₁)	Water-quenched	1900	144	4–6
18-8 Cb (Q₂)	Water-quenched	2250	148	2–4
18-8 Cb (N)	Normalized	1700	163	8
25-20 (Q)	Water-quenched	2150	143	2–4
25-20 (N)	Normalized	1700	159	8+
25-12 (Q₁)	Water-quenched	1900	183	5–7
25-12 (Q₂)	Water-quenched	2200	178	3–5

* Data from Clark and Freeman.[393]
† Bars initially cold-drawn an unstated amount.

result in plastic strain and which at the same time may act as internal notches which under appropriate conditions result in intercrystalline failure. As discussed earlier, this hypothesis appears to be oversimple and incapable of explaining all the associated phenomena. For example, the presence of a sharp mechanical notch in a specimen tested at ordinary temperatures does not cause intercrystalline failure, and therefore a comprehensive theory of intercrystalline failure must account not only for the origin of a notch at the grain boundary but for the propagation of the crack at the boundaries rather than within the grains. Of related interest is the generalized intercrystalline cracking often observed remote from the fracture.

That the influence of grain size cannot be independent of specimen size has long been known, and this question has been considered in some detail by Parker and Riisness.[392] This effect is of particular importance as the grain size approaches the specimen size, and the specimen size is one of the variables requiring attention in any proper evaluation of the influence of grain size on creep strength, except probably when the grain size is relatively fine.

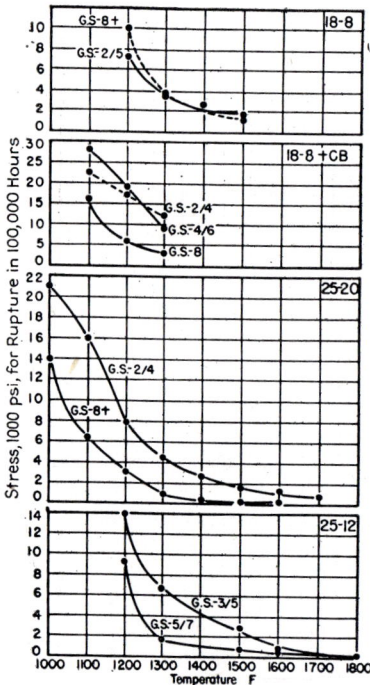

Fig. 210. Apparent effect of grain size on the stress for rupture in 100,000 hr of several austenitic steels (see Table XXXI). *Clark and Freeman.*[390])

Parker and Riisness made creep tests at 400°F on oxygen-free high-conductivity copper specimens of several different diameters. The data obtained on 0.160-in.-diameter bars showed (Fig. 208) an optimum grain size for best creep strength, but tests with 0.375- and 0.500-in. bars showed only a small variation, less than the experimental error in creep rate. The two larger sizes had equal strength, but the small bars were weaker. However, suspecting that oxidation played a role, particularly in the small-diameter specimens, some tests were made of cadmium-plated 0.160-in. bars. The results were held to support the supposition of an influence of oxidation, and the authors concluded that grain size has little effect on the creep rate. The plot (Fig. 209) of their data on plated specimens, which unfortunately were of different grain sizes than the unplated specimens, does not appear to justify the authors' conclusion, although the relative level of strength does appear changed. Furthermore, more extensive testing of this kind is much to be desired, for the conclusions of Parker

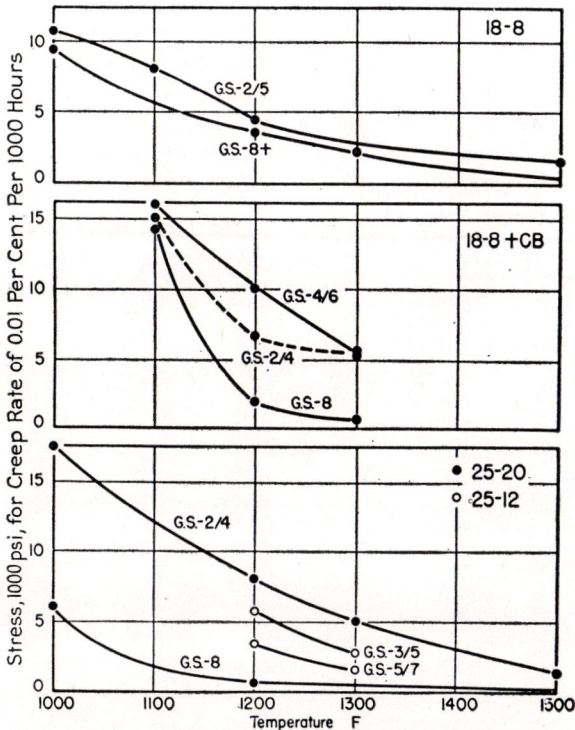

Fig. 211. Apparent effect of grain size on the creep strength, stress to produce creep rate of 0.01 per cent per 1,000 hr, of several austenitic steels (see Table XXXI). (*Clark and Freeman.*[390])

and Riisness, particularly that creep strength was independent of grain size, are somewhat surprising and contradictory of other investigations.

Clark and Freeman[390] have recently shown an apparently profound influence of grain size on the high-temperature properties of austenitic steels. Four different types of steels, 18 Cr–8 Ni, 18 Cr–8 Ni–Cb, 25 Cr–20 Ni, and 25 Cr–12 Ni, described in Table XXXI, were studied in creep and creep-rupture tests in the temperature range 1000 to 1800°F in a fine- and a coarse-grained condition resulting from heat-treatment of cold-drawn bars.   This is also described in Table XXXI.   Since the fine- and coarse-grained conditions were produced by heat-treatments at different temperatures with different modes of cooling and consequently with slight differences in the mode and degree of dispersion of the carbide, it is questionable whether the effect should be termed one of grain size or of heat-treatment.   This point is to be emphasized, for the authors reported the occurrence of an "unknown" phase in the fine-grained materials under certain conditions whose presence appeared to be associated with markedly inferior creep resistance.   Barnett and Troiano[421] later reported that the "unknown" phase is the sigma phase. The test results are summarized in Figs. 210 and 211, and a truly profound influence of grain size, or perhaps better, of heat-treatment, is to be observed in some instances.   Because of their great practical and theoretical interest these phenomena deserve further study.

CHAPTER X

EFFECT OF VARYING TEMPERATURE AND LOAD
AND OF THE STATE OF STRESS

Effect of Varying Temperature

Laboratory creep tests are generally conducted with precise control of temperature, both because the influence of temperature per se is so great and because the extensions which are of interest are so small in magnitude that in order to obtain the rate of extension in a test of only 1,000 to 2,000 hr duration, the measuring instrument must have a sensitivity corresponding with the change in length resulting from 1 to 2°F change in temperature.

In contrast with this, however, service very seldom involves a temperature constant within a few degrees. Rather, the temperature oscillates or cycles between comparatively wide limits, in which, as in intermittent operation, one limit may be atmospheric temperature. The specific conditions depend upon the particular service. In a central-station steam-power generator, the temperature may be expected to be reasonably constant for a relatively long period of time, while in a charge furnace the temperature may range between near-atmospheric and some high value once or more per day.

The matter of the influence of varying temperature is therefore one of great practical import, and one which, unfortunately, has received as yet only very inadequate experimental consideration. If the creep were only a function of time and temperature, it would be a comparatively simple problem to calculate from creep-rate data obtained at constant temperature what average creep strength might be expected for any specific schedule of cycling. Robinson[393] has considered this problem and, assuming a certain specific relation between stress and creep rate and between temperature and creep strength,* presents formulas covering several specific cases, such as when a bar varies uniformly in temperature from one limit to another with an equal part of

---

* The assumed relations were (1) that rate of creep is a power function of the stress and (2) that creep strength is an exponential function of the temperature. These relations have been shown by many tests to be valid over a fairly wide range of stress and temperature.

the time at each temperature.   It is of interest to note that in this case, which is probably a fairly common one, Robinson's calculations for two carbon steels and one austenitic steel show that the temperature range through which cycling may occur and yet not cause more than 10 per cent deficiency in strength from that at the nominal temperature is some 40 to 50°F above and below nominal temperature.

Unfortunately, it appears that in some instances, at least, creep is not a function of temperature and time only, in which case Robinson's analyses will not correctly represent the cases which he examined. Brophy and Furman[394] have reported that a cycling temperature will in some instances result in increased extension, and their finding has been corroborated by others.   Brophy and Furman studied several austenitic stainless alloys in creep test at 1800°F with cycles to lower temperatures and observed an acceleration of creep rate "which may amount to a seventy-fold increase" to result therefrom.   The magnitude of the effect increased with increase in the range of the cycle and with increase of stress.   Other tests showed that as the maximum temperature of the cycle was lowered toward 1700°F the effect diminished to the vanishing point.   Brophy and Furman's tests were not very extensive and their explanation of the phenomenon as caused by thermal stresses resulting from transverse thermal gradients between center and outside of the test bar is in some doubt.

In discussion to the Brophy-Furman paper, Avery[395] confirmed with studies of cast austenitic steels the existence and magnitude of the strain acceleration resulting from cycling temperature.   Avery experimented with two types of cycles: (1) the temperature cycles within rather narrow limits about a mean, and (2) a cycle involving a cooling to room temperature.   The results of the first type of cycle are given in Table XXXII and those of the second in Table XXXIII.

TABLE XXXII.   EFFECT OF CYCLIC HEATING ON CREEP RATE*†

Steel	0.32 C	0.46 Mn	0.45 Si	11.5 Ni	25.9 Cr	0.16 N

Stress, psi	Temp., °F	Duration, hr	Rate, %/hr	Total elong., %	Remarks
3,000	1800	440	0.0025	2.4‡	Constant temp.
3,000	1800	530	0.0039	4.7‡	Constant temp.
3,000	1800	221	0.0260	5.5	Cyclic temp.

* Data from Avery.[395]
† Temperature varied from ±7 to 12°F about 1200°F in 5.4 to 8 min cycles.
‡ Broke during creep test.

The cycling test of Table XXXII showed a 10 times faster rate than the constant-temperature tests, a rather remarkable effect, and if generally true, one of considerable practical significance. Of course, it is to be expected that in a test such as this the creep rate will be more rapid than that corresponding to the average temperature, since creep rate increases exponentially (as a first approximation) with temperature. Preliminary experiments on low-carbon 18 per cent chromium–8 per cent nickel steel at the U. S. Steel Corp. of Del. Research Laboratory indicate that in the range 1100 to 1300°F the creep rate in a test with cycling temperature is not significantly greater than that calculated on the basis of the time at each temperature. A great deal more work must be done in this field with different materials and different temperature ranges in order to develop a proper understanding.

TABLE XXXIII. EFFECT OF CYCLIC HEATING ON CREEP RATE*†

C	Mn	Si	Ni	Cr	N	Creep characteristics in 1,000 hr tests at 1800°F		
						Cycle	Stress, psi	Min. rate %/hr
0.30	1.62	1.28	12.5	28.2	0.09	None	1,050	0.00014
0.30	1.50	0.63	11.7	27.2	0.07	4–20–24	1,000	0.00175
0.30	1.50	0.63	11.7	27.2	0.07	4–20–24	255	0.00029
0.49	1.08	0.74	12.5	27.0	0.12	None	3,000	0.00003
0.49	1.08	0.74	12.5	27.0	0.12	4–20–24	1,000	0.00037
0.49	1.08	0.74	12.5	27.0	0.12	4–20–24	255	0.00005
0.45	0.97	1.32	36.6	17.9	0.06	None	1,250	0.00002
0.45	0.97	1.32	36.6	17.9	0.06	4–20–24	1,000	0.00046

* Data from Avery.[395]

† The cyclic test involved heating to 1800°F in 4 hr, holding there for 20 hr (during which creep measurements were made), and slow cooling to room temperature in 24 hr.

Avery and Matthews[396] report further data on the effect of periodic cycling to room temperature; these are summarized in Table XXXIV. The data in Tables XXXIII and XXXIV apply to periodic cycles to room temperature, and it is readily apparent from inspection that the stress required to produce a specific creep rate is considerably smaller for the cycling than for constant-temperature tests. It is quite difficult or perhaps impossible to analyze this type of test with present knowledge, since creep ceases on cooling below some temperature level and the behavior on reheating into the creep range may be somewhat analogous to the first heating, with a stage of primary creep. This type of test also warrants considerable further investigation.

Foley[418] has reported the results of a cycling creep test in which at intervals the load was removed and the temperature allowed to drop to atmospheric, as shown in Fig. 212. The upper curve A represents creep under constant load and temperature; the lower curve A is merely for easy comparison. The alloy studied was not identified. It is apparent that the rate of creep under these cycling conditions is slightly increased, even if no account is taken of the time at rest. When such account is taken, the creep curve is that given by B.

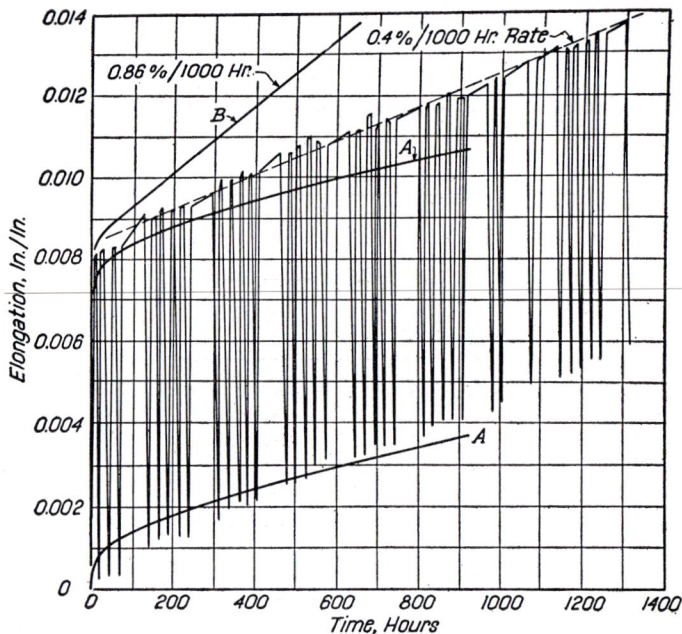

Fig. 212. Effect of interrupted heating and loading on the rate of deformation. Conditions of test: 1500°F.; 6,000 psi stress. Upper curve A is the creep curve for steady load and temperature. Curve B is the summation of elongations in cyclic experiment for the actual time under load. (*Foley.*[418])

Effect of the State of Stress

Most studies of the creep behavior of metals are made in pure tension, but the state of stress in service is seldom so simple. It is the purpose of this section to review the experimental creep investigations made with the stress state other than simple tension, with the particular aim of relating such tests to simple tension tests.

It has been shown that at atmospheric temperature the criterion for plastic flow of isotropic polycrystalline metal aggregates is the so-called shear-strain energy (or the so-called octahedral shear stress, which is proportional to the square root of the shear-strain energy). This criterion was first proposed by von Mises when it became clear that the maximum shear-stress criterion, which governs flow in single crystals, was inadequate. It should be pointed out, however, that the difference between the maximum-shear-stress and the shear-strain-energy theories is at the most only some 15 per cent, an inappreciable difference in many

TABLE XXXIV. COMPARISON OF CYCLIC AND CONSTANT-TEMPERATURE CREEP TESTS*

Steel	Chemical composition, %					
	C	Mn	Si	Ni	Cr	N
A	0.45	0.97	1.32	36.6	17.9	0.06
B	0.21	1.11	1.21	34.2	18.0	0.03

Steel	Temp., °F	Cycle†	Stress, psi	Duration, hr	Min. rate, %/hr	Elong., %
A	1800	4–20–24	255	1,010	0.0001	0.150
	1800	4–20–24	1,000	1,008	0.00046	0.487
	1800	None	1,250	1,060	0.00002	0.046
	1800	None	2,100	1,008	0.00016	0.205
B	1800	4–20–24	1,000	1,030	0.00013	Not reported
	1800	5–1	1,000	1,056	0.00011	0.124
	1800	None	1,500	1,056	0.00003	0.039
	1800	None	2,100	1,273	0.0001	0.340

* Data from Avery and Mathews.[396]
† The cyclic test involved heating to 1800°F in 4 hr, holding at 1800°F for 20 hr (during which creep measurements were made), and slow cooling to room temperature in 24 hr, the cycle being repeated continuously. In one case, designated the 5–1 cycle, the specimen was heated to 1800°F in 4 hr, held at 1800°F for 68 hr, furnace-cooled to 70°F in 4 hr, and held at 70°F for 20 hr.

instances. At creep temperatures, the shear-strain-energy criterion might be thought to govern the onset of flow also, but most investigations have been concerned with the maximum-shear-stress theory.

Bailey[397 –399, 403] was probably the first to consider experimentally the problem of creep under multiaxial stress. Steel tubes were tested in axial tension, torsion, and combined axial tension and torsion at 900 and 1020°F, while thin- and thick-walled lead pipes were subjected to internal pressure and to combined internal pressure and axial loading at atmospheric temperature.   Basing consideration on the uniform rate of creep attained during the second stage of creep, Bailey set out to determine the relation between creep in simple tension and creep under combined stresses, in particular whether creep is dependent only upon the maximum shear stress.   The torsion test of thin-walled tubing corresponds to pure shear and the maximum shear stress equals the maximum normal stress, while in the tension test, the maximum shear stress is one-half the maximum normal stress.   In the case of a thin-walled tube under internal pressure, the axial tensile stress is one-half the circumferential, or "hoop," tensile stress, while the radial stress is of negligible magnitude.   In this case the maximum shear stress is one-half the maximum normal stress.   Bailey observed no creep in the axial direction of such tubes if subjected only to internal pressure, but if an external axial stress was applied, creep in that direction occurred, depending upon the magnitude of the stress.   In the torsion tests, no axial creep nor change in tube diameter or wall thickness was detected.

Bailey observed experimentally that in tests of thin steel tubes the tensile creep rate was about twice the torsional creep rate for the same value of maximum shear stress at 900°F, while at 1020°F the ratio was about 3; for lead at atmospheric temperature the ratio was about 5. Similar nonconformance with theory was observed in the case of combined internal pressure and axial tension.   These results indicated that creep was dependent not only upon maximum shear stress but also upon some other factor, and Bailey was led to consider shear-strain energy as the criterion of flow, but with little better success.   It should be emphasized that the studies of Bailey were concerned only with secondary creep and that possible anisotropy of the test samples may have been an important factor.

Everett[400] presented a mathematical analysis for the relation between shear stress and shear creep rate and temperature.   Torsion creep tests at 750 and 930°F of thin-tube specimens of carbon steel were shown to support the relation.   Additional tests were made on lead tubing under tension, torsion, and internal pressure, either separately or together. For the same maximum shear stress in tension and torsion, it was observed that the shear creep rates on the planes of maximum shear stress were in the ratio of 2.5 to 1.   This suggested that creep in tension tests may be the result of shear on all shear planes, not solely on that of maximum shear stress.

Tapsell and Johnson[401] have made creep tests in bending of commercially pure lead at atmospheric temperature.   Comparative tensile creep tests were also made.   It was concluded that (1) plane sections remain plane, that is, the rate of strain is proportional to the distance from the neutral axis; (2) the redistribution of stresses resulting from creep is complete in a very short time, and the stresses then remain constant with time; (3) the behavior of a material under bending may be determined from its behavior in tension since similar power functions define the relation between stress and creep rate in tension and between stress and distance from neutral axis in flexure. How general these conclusions may be is uncertain; it should be pointed out that Tapsell and Johnson's tests were few in number and of relatively short duration.

Marin[402] has interpreted the results of torsion creep tests of lead tubes, and of some additional data of other investigators of lead under combined stresses, in terms of theories advanced by Bailey and by St. Venant. It was shown that little difference existed between the creep behavior demanded by each theory and that both represented the experimental data considered with a fair degree of adequateness.

Moore, Betty, and Dollins[319] have considered, for lead at atmospheric temperature, the relation between tension creep tests and creep tests of cable sheaths under internal pressure. It was observed that the sheaths required a longer time than the tension specimens to establish a constant creep rate. Irregularities in the data obtained on the sheaths were considered to make it impractical to attempt an extensive comparison, in terms of Bailey's formulas,[403] between creep under simple and combined stresses. These irregularities, or variation of creep behavior at different positions along the cable sheath, were attributed to irregularity of stress distribution resulting from imperfections or varying wall thickness and to cold-working effects. For four of the cable sheaths, an average circumferential creep rate was determined, and the ratio between this rate and the rate of tensile creep under a tensile stress identical with the circumferential stress of the sheaths computed. This ratio was 0.86, 0.74, 0.42, and 0.52 for the four cases. If the maximum shear stress held, the ratio should be about 0.5. Some very few measurements of axial creep were made for sheaths under internal pressure and none was detected. This is in conformity with Bailey's analysis.

Everett and Clark[404] made creep tests in shear and in tension at 800 and 1050°F on a commercial steel containing 0.15 per cent carbon and 0.50 per cent molybdenum. The tests in shear were made by subjecting thin-walled tubular specimens to torsion. The results obtained are shown in terms of second-stage creep rate in Fig. 213 and are summarized in Table XXXV.

It is to be noted that except for the 0.01 per cent per 1,000 hr rate at 1050°F, the ratio of the torsional to the tension creep strength is about

0.6. This ratio should be 0.5 if the maximum-shear-stress criterion of plastic flow is valid since the maximum shear stress in a tension test is one-half the maximum normal or axial stress. The authors state that the ratio of the yield stress in shear to that in tension for steels at atmospheric temperature is generally about 0.6. Theoretically, by the shear-strain-energy theory, the ratio should be 0.577.

Norton[406] made creep tests of 5 per cent chromium–0.5 per cent molybdenum steel and 0.5 per cent molybdenum steel in the form of $\frac{3}{8}$-in. wall tubes subjected to internal pressure. The plain molybdenum steel, which was identical with that studied by Everett and Clark[404] was tested at 800 and 1050°F, while the chromium-molybdenum steel

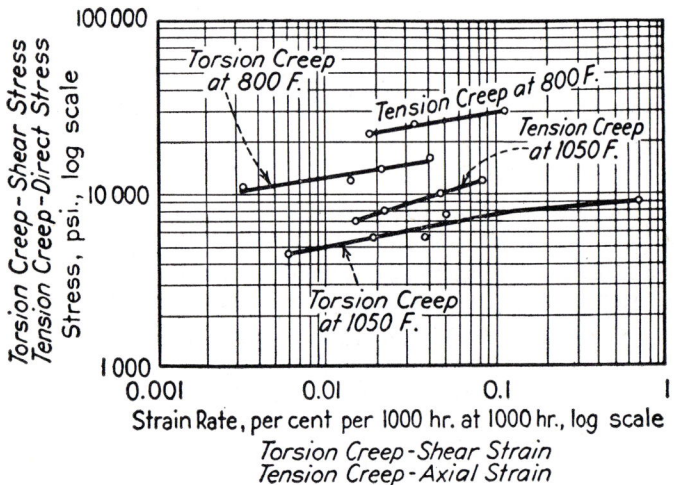

FIG. 213. Comparison of torsion and tension creep tests of a steel containing 0.5 per cent molybdenum and 0.15 per cent carbon at 800 and 1050°F. (*Everett and Clark.*[404])

was tested at 1200°F. Comparison specimens were cut from the walls of the same batch of tubing, with their lengths parallel to the tube axis, and were tested in tension. The longitudinal creep of the internal-pressure tests was quite low or immeasurable, as would be expected, and the authors conclude that it is probably safe to assume no such creep in any design involving tubes so stressed. In agreement with the results of Moore *et al.*[319] on lead, Norton observed that longer time was needed to reach the steady-state condition of the second stage of the creep curve for the circumferential creep of tubes than for tension tests.

Davis[405] has collated the data obtained by Everett and Clark[404] and by Norton [406] on the 0.5 per cent molybdenum steel, and this is summarized

TABLE XXXV. CREEP CHARACTERISTICS IN TORSION AND TENSION AT 800 AND 1050°F OF 0.15 PER CENT CARBON–0.5 PER CENT MOLYBDENUM STEEL*

Type	Temp., °F	Stress†, 1,000 psi, for designated creep rate		Ratio of torsion to tension creep strength	
		0.01%/ 1,000 hr	0.10%/ 1,000 hr	0.01%/ 1,000 hr	0.10%/ 1,000 hr
Torsion	800	12.2	17.8	0.63	0.60
Tension	800	19.2	29.7		
Torsion	1050	4.9	7.5	0.80	0.59
Tension	1050	6.2	12.8		

* Data from Everett and Clark.[404]
† Maximum shear stress for torsion; maximum normal stress for tension. Torsion creep in terms of shear strain; tension creep in terms of axial strain.

in Fig. 214. The basis of comparison employed is that of Nadai's octahedral shear stress and strain rate, the octahedral shear stress being proportional to the von Mises shear-strain energy. The transformation equations necessary to convert Everett and Clark's and Norton's data had earlier been developed by Nadai.[407, 408] As evident in Fig. 214, the data at 800°F are in fair agreement, while at 1050°F there is considerable scatter. Davis points out, however, that this scatter is not all attributable to the difference in types of tests, since there is considerable difference between the tension creep results obtained by the two investigators.

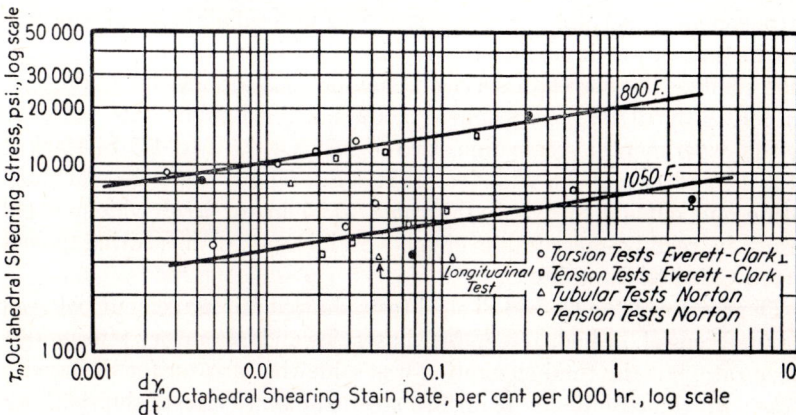

FIG. 214. Comparison of different types of creep tests on a steel containing 0.5 per cent molybdenum and 0.15 per cent carbon at 800 and 1050°F. (*Davis.*[405])

Norton's tests of the 5 per cent chromium–0.5 per cent molybdenum steel at 1200°F showed a slightly lesser creep rate in the circumferential direction of the tubular specimen than for the identical stress in the tension test. The difference was probably not significant in view of the few tests made. Further tests of this sort are desirable.

Norton[409] reported further data on the creep of tubular test specimens of the same molybdenum steel tested earlier, but employing tubes with thinner walls. Comparison specimens removed from the tube wall were tested in tension for comparison. The test temperatures were 900 and 1050°F. The tubular test specimens under internal pressure showed substantially no longitudinal creep. The circumferential creep in these tubes was slightly less than in the tensile specimens with a stress equivalent to that in the circumferential direction of the tube. Soderberg[410] considered Norton's[409] experimental results in the light of mathematical relations developed to relate creep under multiaxial stresses to creep in simple tension. Soderberg's treatment requires that the ratio of circumferential creep rate to the creep rate of the tensile test should be 0.867. The experimental ratios obtained were considered by Soderberg to be as close to the theroretical as could be expected. Variations in temperature, dimensions, and other factors and possible anisotropy were considered to be possible reasons for divergence. It is interesting to note that Soderberg's theory predicts zero axial creep, in comformity with experimental observation.

Van Duzer and McCutchan[411] have reported the results of creep measurements made during service of a 1000°F turbogenerator and of a small experimental 1100°F superheater and piping system. In the turbogenerator set up, creep was found to be negligible in all except a few instances, one involving the turbine stop valve and another bolted pipe joints. To correlate service behavior with laboratory creep tests on conventional tensile specimens, four machined tubes were installed in the experimental steam line, two of 1.25 Cr–0.5 Mo–1.5 Si steel at 1100°F, and two of 0.5 Mo steel at 925°F. The tubes were machined inside and outside to a wall thickness (0.25 in. or less) which would result in readily measurable creep. Stainless steel measuring points were welded to the tubes.

The results of the Cr-Mo-Si steel tests showed fair agreement between circumferential, or hoop, creep rate in service and laboratory tension test creep rate, but the total elongation was somewhat greater for the service tests. In the case of the plain Mo steel, the service tests showed both greater elongations and somewhat greater creep rates than the laboratory tests. These tests seem to disprove the widely held theory that the creep of tubes subjected to internal pressure is materially less than that to be expected on the basis of laboratory tests. Further tests relating service performance to laboratory test data are much needed.

Phelps, Gates, and Kahn[412] have made creep tests of lead cable sheathing under internal hydraulic pressure, but have not attempted a correlation of the results with similar results for creep tests in tension.

Marin and Zwissler[413] have related the creep at atmospheric temperature of an aluminum alloy under bending and under tension. The alloy was that designated 3S (aluminum containing 1.2 per cent manganese and normal impurities) and had been cold-worked to "half-hardness." The tension creep rates were found to be related, within the range of rates studied, to the stress by means of the usual power function. Then, assuming that plane sections remain plane during bending, for which there is some basis in experimental fact,[401] that is, that the creep deflections are proportional to the distances from the neutral axis, the constants of the power function defining the tension data were employed to predict the actual creep deflections in bending. Comparison, then, with the measured deflections showed that for two of the four specimens tested in bending the experimental values were about 10 per cent less than the theoretical, while for the remaining two specimens the differences were about 40 per cent, but in one case positive, in the other negative. Further work of this nature is to be desired to explain the observed differences, presuming that they are beyond the experimental error.

Kelton and Grissinger[330] made both bend and tension creep tests at atmospheric temperature of an alloy of zinc with about 4 per cent aluminum. The analysis made of the data was not very extensive in regard to the interests of this section, but it was reported that if the redistribution of stresses which takes place in the bend test was taken into consideration, the tension and bend creep-test results were in fair agreement.

Davis[414] has developed a theory of creep in bending and reported the results of several creep tests in bending and tension of a chromium-nickel cast alloy at 1500 and 1650°F designed to check the theory. Davis assumed that the stress was proportional to both a power function of the strain and a power function of the strain rate, rather than simply the latter as is more commonly done (Tapsell and Johnson[401] have employed such a treatment for bending). The experimental results appeared to support the assumptions.

Moore, Dollins, and Craig[320] made tension creep-rupture tests of specimens from the same lead cable sheathing which Phelps, Gates, and

Kahn[415] tested in internal-pressure creep-rupture tests. Each tension specimen was cut with its axis in the circumferential direction of the sheathing and contained the weld of the sheathing across the reduced section. The specimens necessarily had to be flattened prior to test. A comparison of the results of the two types of tests is afforded by Fig. 215, which shows quite good agreement. The hoop, or circumferential, stress in the bursting tests was computed by the thin cylinder formula $S = PD/2t$, where S is the hoop stress, P is the internal pressure, and t

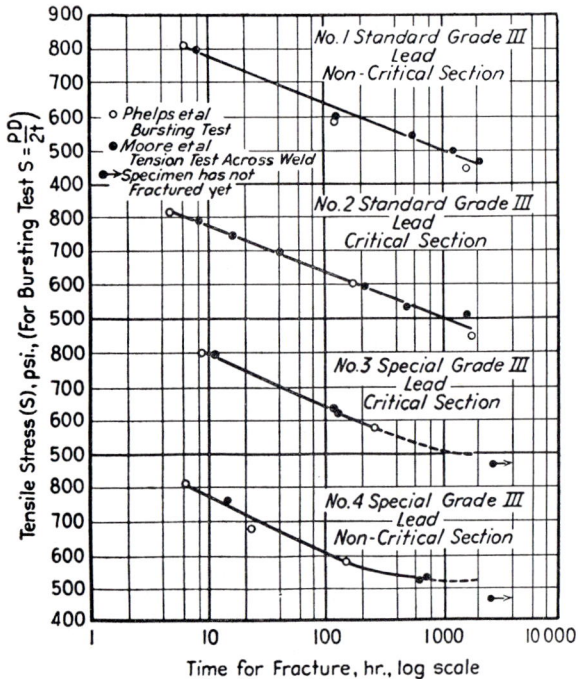

Fig. 215. Comparison of tension and internal pressure creep to rupture tests of lead at 110°F. (*Moore et al.*[320])

is the wall thickness. The good agreement observed in this comparison is probably attributable in part to the fact that the comparison is on the basis of rupture time on which the straightening of the tensile specimens exerted little influence, rather than on the basis of creep rate. In other words the creep-rupture strength is probably less structure sensitive than the creep-rate strength.

Siegfried[416] has made creep-rupture tests out to 10,000 hr of notched and unnotched tin-cadmium alloys loaded in tension at room temperature.   Notches of different depth, angle, and radius were studied.   The triaxial state of stress at the base of a notch is quite complicated and not well known, and undoubtedly changes quite markedly with only slight plastic deformation.   Siegfried apparently made no attempt to analyze the stress state in his tests.   For each type of notch, the plot of nominal stress versus time to rupture lay somewhat higher and to the right for the notched bars than for the unnotched bars, but tended to approach one another at very long times for rupture.   The type of notch appeared to play a minor role in these tests.   Presumably deformation altered the shapes of the notches and they tended to one form.   After completion of the tin-cadmium tests at room temperature, tests on both notched and notch-free bars of a 30 per cent nickel–15 per cent chromium steel and a 12 per cent nickel–15 per cent chromium steel were made at 1200°F.   The results were quite similar to those of the tin-cadmium alloys, the notched bars requiring the longer time to rupture under the same nominal stress.   However, in the case of the higher nickel steel the two plots merged at what was considered a relatively short time of 1,000 hr.   Further experimental work on the influence of stress concentrations on the creep and rupture of metals at high temperatures is greatly to be desired.

Effect of Varying Stress

Not a great deal is known about the influence of variables such as the speed of application of loading and the cyclic or interrupted loading, although they are of some considerable interest to those who must apply laboratory creep data to service.   For example, there is seldom a service application that does not involve interruptions to the loading, and the engineer generally lacks knowledge of the effects of such interruptions on the creep rate and on the time for rupture.

The marked influence of rate of strain on the ordinary tensile properties of metals at elevated temperatures (or on lead at atmospheric temperature) is well known, and it should be apparent that the similarly marked influence of stress on creep rate or rupture time is an analogous phenomenon.   Accordingly it should not be difficult to imagine an influence of interruptions of loading and at least a minor influence of the rate at which the load is applied.   Both the effects have been observed experimentally.

One of the most striking examples of the influence of load interruption has been shown by Chaston[417] for commercially pure lead.   By interrupting a tension test of such material at intervals of 13 per cent strain and allowing the specimen to remain free of stress for 5 min, an elongation of 320 per cent was observed which was about 7 times that observed, 45 per cent, on continuous straining. The rate of straining during loading was identical in the two instances. Chaston also studied the influence of time at rest in this instance and found that even as short a time as 30 sec resulted in a definite small increase in final strain, but that the most marked influence was found only after a rest time of 4 min, as shown in Fig. 216. This would suggest recrystallization or self-annealing, as would the fact that the effect was not observed in lead hardened by the addition of other elements; however, no microscopic or

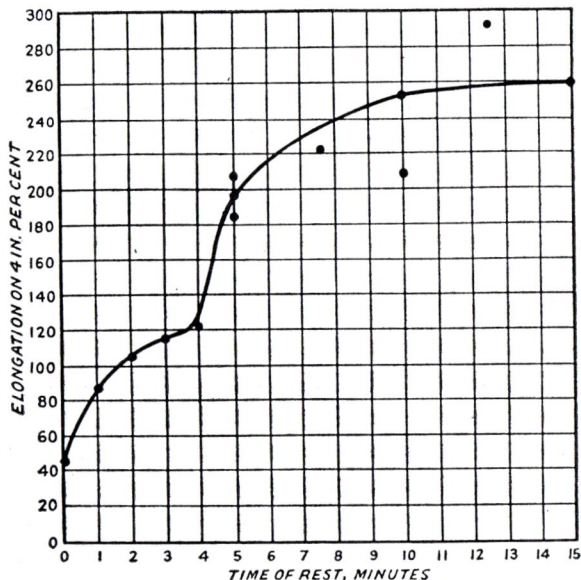

Fig. 216. Effect of time of interruption of straining in a tension test on the elongation at fracture of commercially pure lead at atmospheric temperature. (*Chaston.*[417])

X-ray diffraction study was made to check this point. It should be pointed out that the elongations considered by Chaston greatly exceed those generally encountered in the service of metals at elevated temperatures, and therefore these studies do not necessarily relate to service. It seems very probable, however, that similar phenomena may occur under service conditions, since recrystallization has been occasionally observed during creep tests.

Phelps, Gates, and Kahn[415], in studying the behavior of lead cable sheathing under internal-pressure bursting tests, made a cyclic loading test between partial vacuum and some positive value in an effort to determine what influence the nonconstancy of load encountered in service might exert. The pressure was built up at an approximately uniform rate during a period of 1 hr, held 2 hr at constant pressure, and then decreased to maximum vacuum in 5.5 hr. Two cycles per day

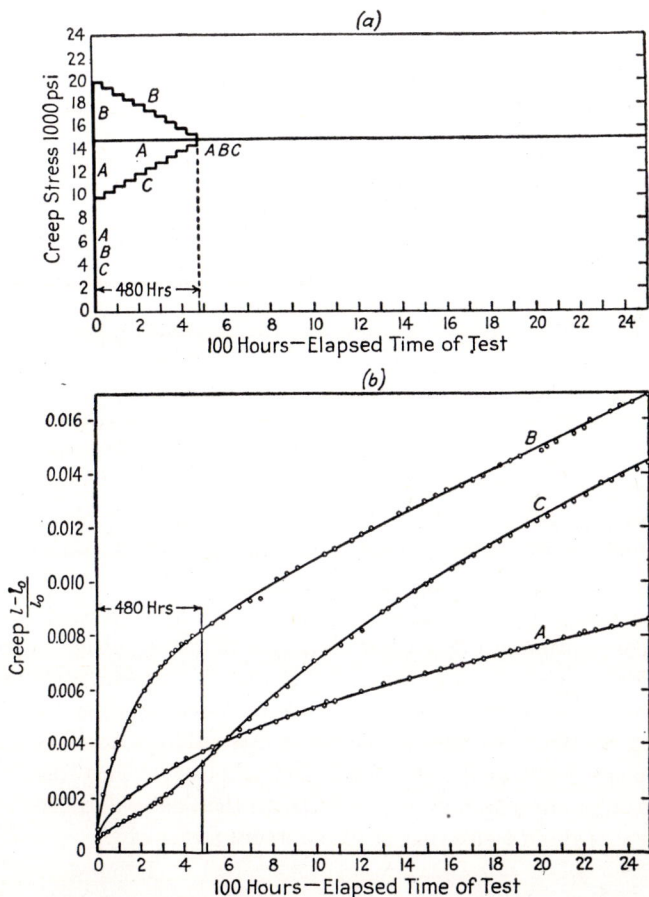

FIG. 217. Effect of mode of loading (a) on the creep-time curve (b) of steel containing 2.25 per cent chromium and 1 per cent molybdenum at 1000°F. (*U. S. Steel Corp. of Del. Research Laboratory.*)

were employed. When the time during which the specimen was at maximum stress was summated, this value of the bursting time agreed reasonably well with the constant-pressure tests. Further tests of this nature are greatly to be desired.

In reply to discussion of their paper, Brophy and Furman[394] stated that they had investigated the effect of varying load at a constant temperature (their paper had considered varying temperature at constant load as reviewed earlier) and observed a "normal response," that is, shrinkage on unloading and extension on loading, as would be expected. No details were given, and it seems probable that their consideration of the problem was brief.

Jenkins, Bucknall, and Jenkinson[343] reported that in an investigation of the creep characteristics of an alloy of 3 per cent nickel and silicon in copper they had found it possible by gradual loading over a period of 2 to 3 hr to apply at 390°F to an initially slow-cooled specimen a stress in excess of the tensile strength observed in an ordinary test lasting about 7 min. This is not simply an effect of speed of testing on the strength, since the effect would be of opposite sign, but rather indicates a precipitation-hardening phenomenon. This was also indicated by another test in which, although the short-time tensile strength was 13.5 to 13.8 tons/sq in., a specimen loaded gradually to 14.0 tons/sq in. required 2,100 hr for rupture. These tests thus bear out an influence of the manner of loading, aside from the usual speed effect, upon the strength of metals at elevated temperatures, at least for the special case in which microstructural changes may be expected to occur.

Results obtained at the U. S. Steel Corp. of Del. Research Laboratory, summarized in Fig. 217, indicate a slight influence of initial mode of loading on the creep curve of a steel in which structural changes are presumed to be a minimum. In this instance, a steel containing nominally 2.3 per cent chromium and 1 per cent molybdenum, initially air-cooled from 1650°F, then drawn 4 hr at 1380°F, and furnace-cooled, was tested in upstep and downstep fashions, and at constant stress, at 1000°F, according to the schedules indicated in Fig. 217a. As shown in Fig. 217b, the creep rate at the end of test for either of the two tests in which the stress was initially raised or lowered to the final value over a period of 480 hr was about twice that of the constant stress test.

CHAPTER XI

CHANGES DURING SERVICE — SCALING AND MICROSTRUCTURAL CHANGES

During service at elevated temperatures, two important types of phenomena occur which affect the load-carrying ability of a metal and must therefore be considered in choosing metals for such service. The first of these is the corrosive attack of the environment upon the surface of the metal (sometimes termed "surface instability") which results in oxidation (scaling) or other loss of effective metal. This loss of metal results in an increase in the unit stress on the remaining metal. In some cases, attack occurs preferentially at the grain boundary, giving rise to notch effects. A somewhat related surface phenomenon is the absorption by the metal of carbon, nitrogen, and other elements, resulting in changes in properties.

The other general class of phenomena may be grouped under the heading of microstructural changes. Many such changes may occur, as we shall see, all as a result of a striving for equilibrium or minimum free energy. These changes, which depend on time and especially temperature, result in changes in the strength and ductility of the metal, which in some cases are quite marked.

Scaling

The resistance of metals to oxidation or other corrosive attack is a very complex subject, especially in the case of alloys. Consideration will be given here only to the scaling type of attack, which may be expected to occur in the large majority of all applications of metals at elevated temperatures. Most of the available data pertain to an air atmosphere, but some discussion of the effects of other atmospheres is included. The purely chemical solution type of attack is outside the scope of this book.

Scaling of Pure Metals. Most studies of oxidation have been made with pure metals, and understanding of the scaling process is most advanced for this class of material. The scaling of a pure metal at a constant temperature may be considered to be the resultant of two processes, one a chemical combination of the oxygen with the metal to form an oxide or oxides and the other a process of diffusion of the oxygen inward (a relatively minor effect) and the metal outward through the scale already formed.   According to the nature of the oxide which forms, one or the other of these processes may be the controlling factor.

The rate of conversion of a pure metal to oxide in terms of either increase in thickness or weight has been experimentally observed to be either constant or to decrease parabolically with time (Fig. 218).* These may be expressed mathematically as follows:

Linear:

$$X = ct \qquad (49)$$

Parabolic:

$$X^2 = kt \qquad (50)$$

where X is the thickness or weight of oxide, t is the time, and c and k are, respectively, the linear and parabolic rate constants.   The linear type of scaling will, in general, occur when the oxide has a smaller specific volume than the metal, and the parabolic type of scaling may be expected when the scale is adherent and has a specific volume equal to or greater than the underlying metal.   This general relation was first pointed out by Pilling and Bedworth.[423]   Among metals which show linear rates of oxidation are calcium and lithium, while metals like chromium and iron form dense adherent scales.   Metals of the linear rate type have little if any, application for extended service at elevated temperatures.

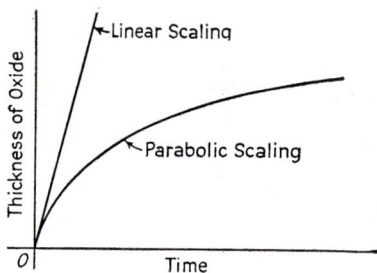

FIG. 218. Schematic representation of linear and parabolic scaling.

The linear type of scaling is a direct consequence of the smaller specific volume of the oxide; the scale is thus porous and offers little obstruction to the inward flow of oxygen to the metal surface.   The scale also has a tendency to spall and fall off from the metal.   The parabolic type of scaling of metals forming dense adherent oxides results from the fact that the process of diffusion is the controlling factor—in effect, with increasing thickness of oxide, increasing resistance is offered to the inward diffusion of oxygen and outward diffusion of metal.   The parabolic relation evolves directly from the theory of diffusion.   Certain deviations

* A logarithmic relation is observed during the very initial stages in the oxidation of some metals, that is, where the oxide is of temper-film order of thickness.

from the parabolic law occur, especially in the very early stages of scaling where the oxide is a mere film; in such cases oxidation seems to be dependent primarily upon the chemical process of solution of the oxygen. Deviations also may occur after scaling has proceeded to an advanced state, since owing to the difference in specific volumes of metal and oxide, interface stresses arise which may result in cracking and loosening of the scale.

When the scaling is of parabolic nature, the variation of rate of oxidation with temperature, as with other processes controlled by diffusion, is exponential in nature. This may be expressed in terms of the parabolic rate constant k of Eq. (50) as

$$k = Ae^{-Q/RT} \tag{51}$$

where T is the absolute temperature, R is the gas constant, and A and Q are constants.

The scale which forms by diffusion in a pure metal will show various layers corresponding to the various solid-solution phases which exist in the metal-oxygen equilibrium diagram corresponding to the existent oxygen pressure. No two-phase layers, except those which may form during cooling from the scaling temperature, will be observed. This is nicely illustrated for the scaling of iron by Fig. 219, after Heindlhofer and Larsen.[424] This illustration shows a portion of the iron-oxygen equilibrium diagram, below which is a photomicrograph showing in cross section the three layers of oxide which form on iron at temperatures above about 550°C; also indicated is the concentration gradient of oxygen across each of the individual oxide layers as well as the discontinuous concentration change at the interfaces between layers. Next to the metal lies the oxide least rich in oxygen, namely, FeO,* while most remote from the metal is the oxide most rich in oxygen, namely, Fe_2O_3; between these lies the intermediate oxide Fe_3O_4. Below about 550°C only two oxide layers will be found to form on iron, since FeO does not exist in the range. The nature of the oxide layers also depends on the oxygen pressure; if, for example, this is sufficiently low, the oxygen richest layer may be missing.

Scaling of Alloys. When alloying elements are added to a metal, its scaling behavior may become quite complex; the effects of time and temperature and even of the amount of alloying additions on rates of

---

* The photomicrograph shows this layer to be two-phase; the single-phase layer FeO which existed at the oxidizing temperature was not preserved unchanged during cooling to atmospheric temperature. Iron and Fe_3O_4 precipitated in the FeO layer during cooling.

scaling are not simple, and behavior is not readily predictable. In addition, new phenomena such as selective oxidation and precipitation of phases from solution may occur. This may take place within the metal itself and it is then called subscaling or internal oxidation; for example, aluminum or silicon in solid solution in iron will combine with inward-diffusing oxygen and precipitate as alumina or silica. On the other hand,

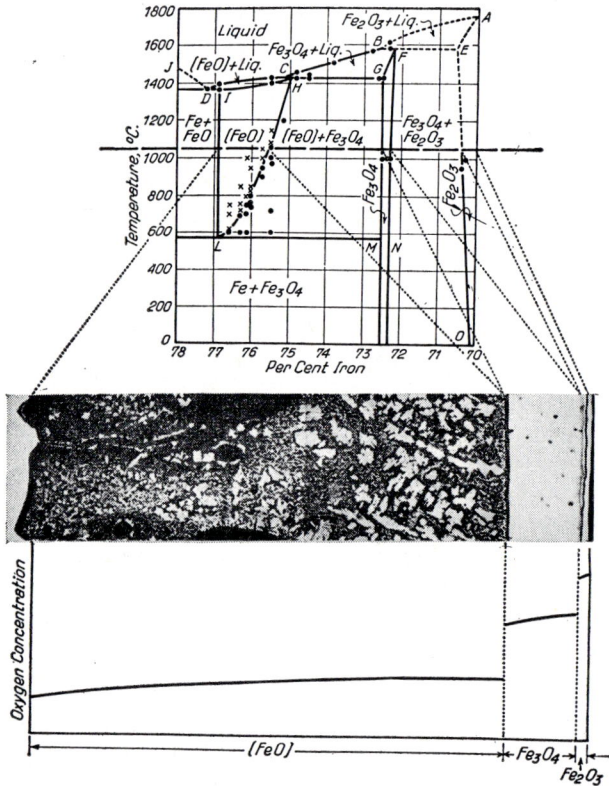

FIG. 219. Showing the relation of the several oxide layers which form on iron to the iron-oxygen constitution diagram. Also indicated schematically is the decreasing oxygen concentration from the outer surface inward. (*Heindlhofer and Larsen.*[424])

if the added element is less oxidizable than the base metal, particles of the added element may be found unoxidized in the scale itself; thus particles of metallic nickel may be observed embedded in the scale of a nickel-containing steel.

The formation of so-called "protective" oxide films is of considerable practical importance as well as theoretical interest. In such cases, the oxide which forms is relatively impervious to further diffusion and scaling ceases. Metals may be made to develop protective oxides or increased resistance to oxidation by proper alloying. The marked effect of such elements as chromium, aluminum, and silicon on the scaling of iron is of this nature. The addition of chromium to iron actually results in an initially faster rate of scaling, which is not generally recognized, but owing to a selective attack of the readily oxidizable chromium, an oxide rich in chromium is formed which is impervious to further diffusion. Whether a protective scale will form on an alloy depends in a complex way on the nature of the scale formed, the diffusion rates in the scale and the metal, and the temperature and time. In extreme instances it may be observed that an alloy may actually show a decreasing rate of scaling with increasing temperature over a limited range of temperature. The complexity of scaling in alloys is so great that few generalities can be stated, necessitating an experimental study of individual alloys under the exact conditions of interest. Accordingly, we shall briefly summarize the results of several investigations of the scaling behavior of alloys, generally of commercial type.

Experimental Investigations of Scaling of Alloys in Air and Other Atmospheres. Before proceeding to a consideration of the results of actual studies of scaling in alloys, it may be well to consider the means by which resistance to scaling may be determined. Two general methods have been widely employed. In the first of these the scale is removed from a specimen after a period of exposure at elevated temperatures, and the loss in weight of metal determined. Since scaling is generally not linear with time, a study of the effect of time requires the testing of a number of samples. In the other commonly employed technique, the gain in weight resulting from oxidation of a specimen is determined; the same specimen may be employed for a continuous series of measurements, thus effecting a considerable saving in experimental effort. Of course, at the end of test, the scale may be removed and the weight loss determined.

It may be of interest to describe an apparatus which has been successfully employed in the U. S. Steel Corp. of Del. Research Laboratory for making scaling measurements of the continuous weight-gain type. The apparatus, shown in the photograph of Fig. 220 and the sketch of Fig. 221 consists of an annular furnace in which a large number of specimens may be tested simultaneously in an air atmosphere. The specimens slowly rotate in the annular muffle, and the gain in weight is determined while the specimen remains at temperature, by stopping the rotation underneath an analytical balance and weighing the specimen.

The results of tests of a number of steels employing the apparatus of Figs. 220 and 221 are given in Table XXXVI and in Fig. 222. Included are many of the commercial steels used at elevated temperatures, ranging from plain low-carbon steel to the highly resistant 27 Cr steel. The effect of both time and temperature and of alloy content may be observed.

Several points of interest demonstrating the complexity of the scaling process in alloys may be noted. For example, it is generally impossible to predict the scaling behavior of a given alloy at longer times or at

FIG. 220. Apparatus employed for scaling tests at the U.S. Steel Corp. of Del. Research Laboratory.

other temperatures from a short-time test at one temperature. In respect to time, the relation between weight gain and time is roughly parabolic in form, but curves for different alloys may cross; as an example of this behavior, alloy 31 (0 Cr–2 Mo) is more resistant at 1500°F than alloy 32 (2 Cr–0 Mo) for a day or week, but at 6 weeks the higher chromium alloy is considerably better. It is quite common for alloys containing chromium to show an initially fast rate of scaling owing to the ready oxidizability of chromium; but the scale which forms is protective and the rate may rapidly decelerate.

The effect of temperature is quite pronounced, but irregularities are apparent. The most striking of these and apparently real is that alloy No. 15 (5 Cr–5 Mo) scaled more in 1,000 hr at 1100°F than at 1300°F.

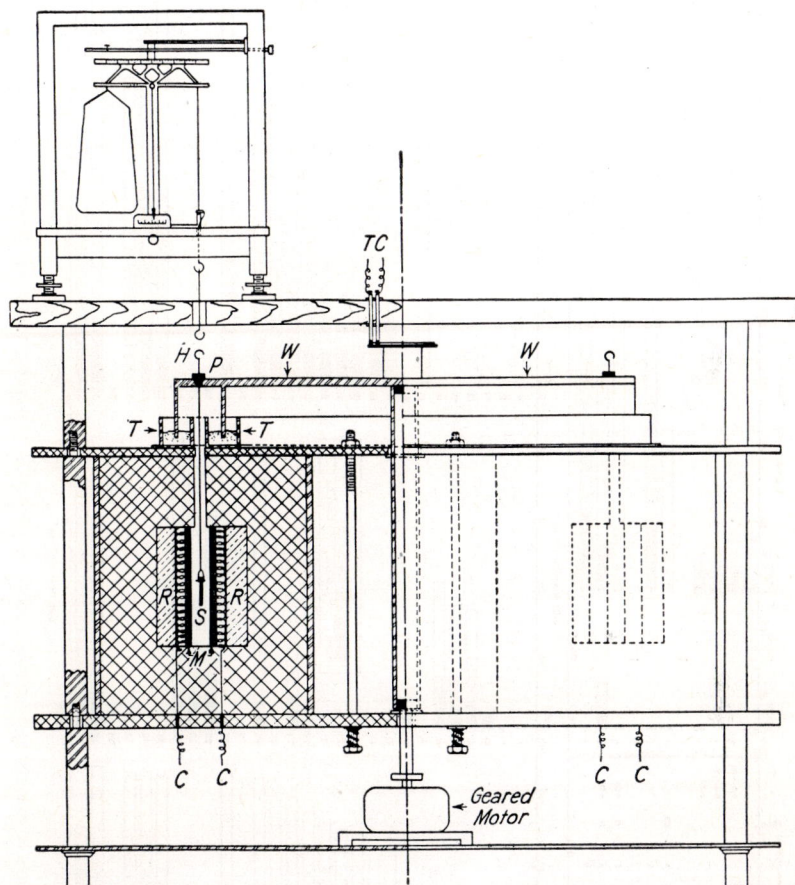

Fig. 221. Sketch of annular furnace, capacity 39 specimens simultaneously. *M*, annular muffle in which specimens *S* are moved slowly by rotating member *W*, circumference of which dips into annular trough *TT* containing sand as a seal; *CC*, current supply to heating coils; *R*, refractory brick; *H*, hook to attach specimen to balance; *P*, keyed plug; *TC*, leads through a commutator on axis to thermocouple occupying one of the 40 specimen locations. (*Day and Smith.*[425])

These tests reported in Table XXXVI and Fig. 222 were made at a constant temperature and, as Brasunas *et al.*[426] have shown, more rapid scaling may occur in some instances when the samples are intermittently heated and cooled. Presumably such an effect is a consequence of

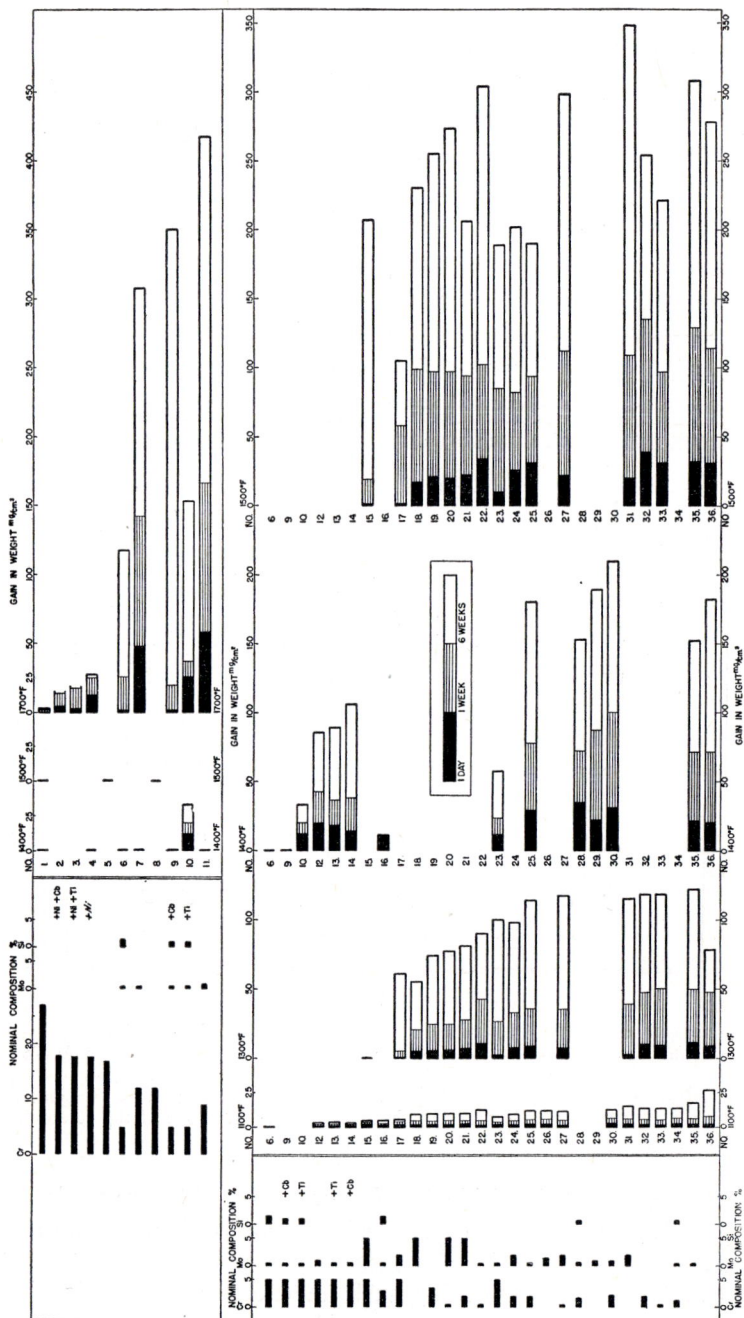

FIG. 222. Relative resistance to oxidation of various steels in air at 1100, 1300, 1400, 1500, and 1700°F.   (*Day and Smith.*[425])

spalling of the scale owing to a difference in thermal expansion coefficient of scale and metal.

The effect of the composition of the atmosphere is of considerable practical importance, since metals in service are subjected quite often to an environment of air contaminated with combustion products of fuels, steam, etc. Under certain conditions the resistance to scaling may be critically dependent upon the exact nature of the atmosphere and accordingly it is sometimes hazardous to predict the resistance of a metal to a specific atmosphere. Not only does the atmosphere affect the scaling behavior but in some cases one or more elements of the atmosphere may dissolve in and diffuse into the base metal, producing embrittlement or other changes in properties of the metal.

The corrosion of various steels in steam, which is of importance in steam-turbine power generation, has been studied by a number of investigators, including in recent years Hawkins[427-429] and Rohrig *et al.*[430]. Preece and Riley[431] and Stauffer and Kleiber [432] have studied the scaling of steels in combustion gases, while Nicholson and Kwasney[433] have studied the effect of sulfur dioxide, oxygen, and nitrogen. In general, the effect of adding oxygen, steam, and especially sulfur to the testing atmosphere is to accelerate the rate of attack. The effect becomes of increasing importance with increasing temperature. Nickel-base alloys seem to be particularly susceptible to sulfur-containing atmospheres, in which they become embrittled.

Microstructural Changes During Service at High Temperatures

Engineering structures used for prolonged service at elevated temperatures are generally designed according to certain allowable working stresses imposed by some such code as the ASME Boiler Code[434] or the API Construction Code[434] on the basis of creep-rate and creep-rupture data (and, to some extent, actual service experience). These properties are determined in tests of generally short duration, relative to the service life. As discussed earlier, the strength of a metal or alloy at high temperatures depends upon its microstructure just as at ordinary temperatures. With some notable exceptions, such as strain or quench-aging of steel and similar precipitation phenomena in nonferrous alloys, metals do not undergo a change of microstructure at ordinary temperatures. However, metals do undergo changes of microstructure at high temperatures. Since these changes are largely controlled by diffusion, they depend upon temperature and time, and are influenced by certain other factors, the principal one of which is stress (or the attendant strain).

Since changes in microstructure occur at high temperatures, bringing

TABLE XXXVI. RELATIVE RESISTANCE TO OXIDATION OF VARIOUS STEELS IN AIR, AT 1100, 1300, 1400, 1500, AND 1700°F*†

No.	Steel	1100°F weight, mg/cm²				1300°F weight, mg/cm²				1400°F weight, mg/cm²				1500°F weight, mg/cm²				1700°F weight, mg/cm²			
		(a)	(b)	(c)	(d)	(a)	(b)	(c)	(d)	(a)	(b)	(c)	(d)	(a)	(b)	(c)	(d)	(a)	(b)	(c)	(d)
1	27 Cr	0	0	0	0	0	0	0	0	0.03	0.06	0.12		0.12	0.4	1.0	1.8	0.1	1.9	2.1	
2	18 Cr–8Ni + Cb																	4.4	13.5		
3	18 Cr–8Ni + Ti																	2.9	17.3		
4	18 Cr–8Ni	0	0	0	0	0	0	0	0	0.09	0.15	0.18	0.5	0.06	0.3	1.0	1.2	12.7	24.8	27.0	
5	17 Cr																				
6	5 Cr–0.5 Mo–1.5 Si									0.18	0.23	0.35	0.5					0.5	25.7	117	
7	12 Cr–0.5 Mo									0.12	0.18	0.35	0.9					48.0	142	307	
8	12 Cr	0	0	0	0	0	0	0	0	0.55	0.67	0.73	1.1	0.03	0.2	0.9	1.6	0.44	19.6	350	
9	5 Cr–0.5 Mo–1 Si + Cb									12.0	20.0	33.0	84					26.0	37.1	153	
10	5 Cr–0.5 Mo–1 Si + Ti																				
11	9 Cr–1 Mo	1.2	2.3	3.1	8.1					0.20	0.26	0.41	0.8					58.5	166	417	
12	5 Cr–1 Mo	1.2	2.3	3.8	9.3					19.8	42.5	85	340								
13	5 Cr–0.5 Mo + Ti	1.2	2.3	2.9	7.7					18.0	36.5	89	230								
14	5 Cr–0.5 Mo + Cb									14.0	38.0	106	293								
15	5 Cr–5 Mo	2.4	3.9	4.6	11	0	0	0	0					0.06	19	207	485				
16	3 Cr–0.5 Mo–1.5 Si	1.8	2.7	4.9	15	0.3	5.0	61	154	9.3	10.2	10.5	28	0.6	58	105	285				
17	5 Cr–2 Mo	2.0	4.0	5.5	13	4.8	20.2	55	155					17	99	230	620				
18	5 Mo	2.0	4.7	9.2	28	5.4	24.1	74	207					21	97	255	720				
19	3.5 Cr	2.0	4.4	9.9	27	5.7	24.3	77	204					20	97	273	760				
20	0.5 Cr–5 Mo	2.0	4.6	10.0	27																

320

No.	Steel																
21	2 Cr–5 Mo	2.3	4.8	10.0	28	7.0	27.9	81	213					21	94	206	595
22	0.5 Cr–0.5 Mo	1.7	4.9	12.6	41	10.5	42.7	90	255					34	102	304	900
23	5 Cr–0.5 Mo	2.0	4.8	9.7	24	2.5	26.3	100	245					10	85	189	545
23	5 Cr–0.5 Mo	1.8	2.7	4.9	13					11.7	23.4	57	156	26	82	202	535
24	2 Cr–2 Mo	1.9	4.5	9.2	24	7.6	32.0	98	249								
25	2 Cr–0.5 Mo	1.9	4.7	10.2	25	8.8	35.2	114	306					31	94	190	585
25	2 Cr–0.5 Mo	2.3	5.9	13.9	36					29.2	77.5	180	500				
26	1.4–Mo	2.3	5.9	11.9	32												
27	0.5 Cr–2 Mo	1.8	4.7	11.3	29	7.6	35.1	117	300					22	112	298	760
28	1.8 Cr–0.7 Mo–0.6 Si									35.0	72.0	153	450				
29	1 Mo	3.0	6.6	12.6	32					22.2	87.0	189	520				
30	2.2 Cr–1 Mo									31.0	100	210	670				
31	2 Mo	2.4	5.6	16.2	44	2.6	38.9	115	293					20	109	348	930
31	2 Mo	2.5	6.6	14.1	39												
32	2 Cr	2.1	5.5	13.5	36	10.0	47.6	118	326					39	135	254	760
33	0.5 Cr	1.9	5.3	13.7	37	9.4	50.6	118	367					31	97	221	640
34	1.3 Cr–0.5 Mo–0.8 Si	2.5	6.6	13.9	36	11.4	50.0	122	349					32	129	308	935
35	0.5 Mo	2.2	5.9	17.6	49												
35	0.5 Mo	2.2	6.1	17.7	45												
35	0.5 Mo	2.5	6.6	16.2	44					21.6	71	152	432				
36	Carbon	2.1	7.8	26.6	67	8.8	47.8	78	252					31	114	278	835
36	Carbon									20.5	71	182	510				

* Data after Day and Smith.[425]

† Gain in weight (in mg per sq cm surface) after (a) 1 day, (b) 1 week, (c) 6 weeks, interpolated from the mean curve representing duplicate observations on 36 steels, and (d) the observed weight loss after pickling one of each pair of specimens after 6 weeks exposure.

about concurrent changes in strength, most often a loss, the engineer must know about and provide for them in his design. It should be emphasized that these changes are distinct from those brought about by oxidation (scaling) or corrosion (including caustic embrittlement), which effect changes in load-carrying ability primarily through loss in effective cross section or by stress concentration.

Over the years, considerable knowledge has accumulated concerning the properties of the various engineering alloys employed in elevated-temperature service. However, considerably less is known about how these properties change during service. It is the purpose of this section to bring together and interpret such information of this kind as is avail-

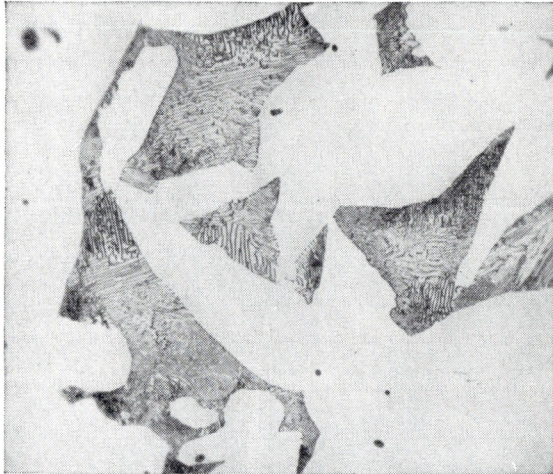

FIG. 223. Ferrite and pearlite in low-carbon steel; ×1,000.

able. For the purpose of discussion, the various changes which might occur have been arbitrarily classified into the following categories: (1) spheroidization of carbide; (2) graphitization of carbide; (3) precipitation effects and phase changes; (4) recrystallization. The first two of these apply only to certain kinds of steel, but the vast majority of alloys used in service at high temperatures fall into this category.

Spheroidization. Low alloy steels used in elevated-temperature service are generally employed in an annealed or normalized condition, the microstructure then consisting of proeutectoid ferrite (since all such steels are hypoeutectoid) and an eutectoid aggregate of ferrite and carbide called pearlite (Fig. 223). When held at temperature during service, the structure of the aggregate tends to change, depending on the actual temperature and on the time, from its initial lamellar, or platelike, form to a more stable form in which the carbide is dispersed in a globular or spheroidal manner—thus, spheroidization (Fig. 224). In those instances where low alloy steel is applied in a condition other than annealed or normalized, this condition is one of quench and temper,* and in this case the microstructure at the beginning of service is already one in which the carbides are distributed as globules like, but smaller than, those in Fig. 224. The end product of long service, however, tends to be the same in both cases, the small globules of the quench and temper treatment tending to agglomerate.

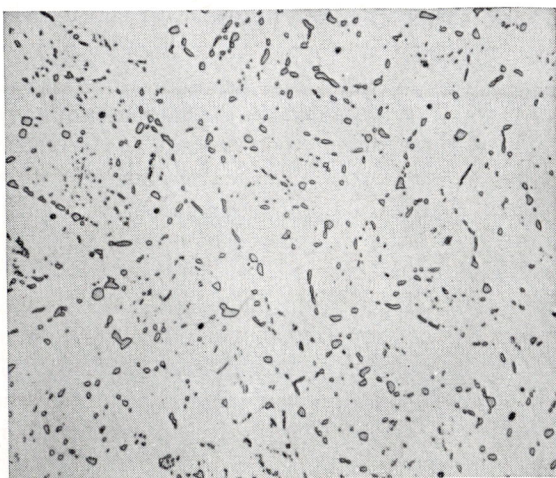

FIG. 224. Ferrite and spheroidized carbide; ×1,000.

It is less generally recognized that when alloying elements are present in the steel changes in composition and nature of the carbide may occur concurrently with spheroidization, since in general the carbide can then no longer be considered to be simply Fe_3C as in plain carbon steel. This sort of behavior, which is of obvious importance, has only recently received attention. Bowman, Parke, and Herzig[435] have studied the partition of molybdenum between matrix and carbide in steels. Crafts and Offenhauer[436, 437] have reported on the types of carbide existing in low chromium-molybdenum steels which had been quenched and tempered. Smith, Miller, and Tarr[438] have recently briefly reviewed this subject.

Investigation of the spheroidization which occurs during holding at

* This treatment is commonly used in steels used for bolting applications.

elevated temperatures has not been very intensive, and the studies which have been made have largely dealt with steels having initially a martensitic structure. Engel[440] studied the softening rates of a 0.94 per cent carbon steel when tempered from different initial structures, and found, as would be expected, that the smaller the initial carbide particle size, the faster the rate of softening. Bain[441] has devoted attention to the tempering reactions of quenched steels. However, except for bolting applications, steels subjected to service conditions involving creep are not generally applied in the quenched condition.

Austin *et al.*[442–448] have studied both spheroidization and graphitization in hypereutectoid steels of different compositions, particularly when priorly quenched. They observed a semilogarithmic relation between hardness and tempering time except when graphitization occurred, in which case the hardness dropped more rapidly.

Smith, Miller, and Tarr[438] studied the changes in both normalized and annealed samples of three plain carbon steels (0.15 per cent carbon) and six molybdenum steels (0.1 to 0.2 per cent carbon–0.5 per cent molybdenum) of different deoxidation practices and found a slight but definite tendency for spheroidization to proceed at a more rapid rate in steels deoxidized with aluminum than in those deoxidized with silicon. The decline in hardness on tempering the plain carbon steels approximated a semilogarithmic relation as reported above. However, hardness tests on the molybdenum steels showed a precipitation-hardening phenomenon which was related to the appearance of a fine precipitate earlier reported by Miller *et al.*[449] (Fig. 225). This will be discussed further in a later portion of this chapter.

Some investigators have recorded observations of microstructural changes encountered during creep or creep-rupture test at elevated temperatures. Jenkins, Mellor, and Jenkinson[450] studied the changes in carbon steels of 0.17 to 1.14 per cent carbon during creep-rupture tests at elevated temperatures. They reported that deformation accelerated spheroidization and graphitization. White, Clark, and Wilson[451] described the progressive spheroidization in SAE 1015 steel of coarse-grain deoxidation practice during creep tests at 1000°F. Miller *et al.*[452,453] have reported microstructural changes in a wide variety of steels when held at elevated temperatures in creep test.

The work of Weaver[454, 455] has shown the quantitative changes in creep strength that may be expected to occur concurrently with spheroidization. In the first of these papers,[454] Weaver developed an equation for the elongation-time curve in creep and concluded that departure from the calculated elongation-time curve is to be attributed to change in microstructure during creep test, in particular, to the slow spheroidization of carbide. He then summarized (as in Fig. 226) the carbide-spheroidization study of Bailey and Roberts,[456] which shows a logarithmic relation between temperature and time for a specific degree of spheroidization. Bailey and Roberts report that the spheroidization changes are not influenced by stresses of the magnitude used in creep tests,* and that complete spheroidization resulted in an approximately tenfold increase in

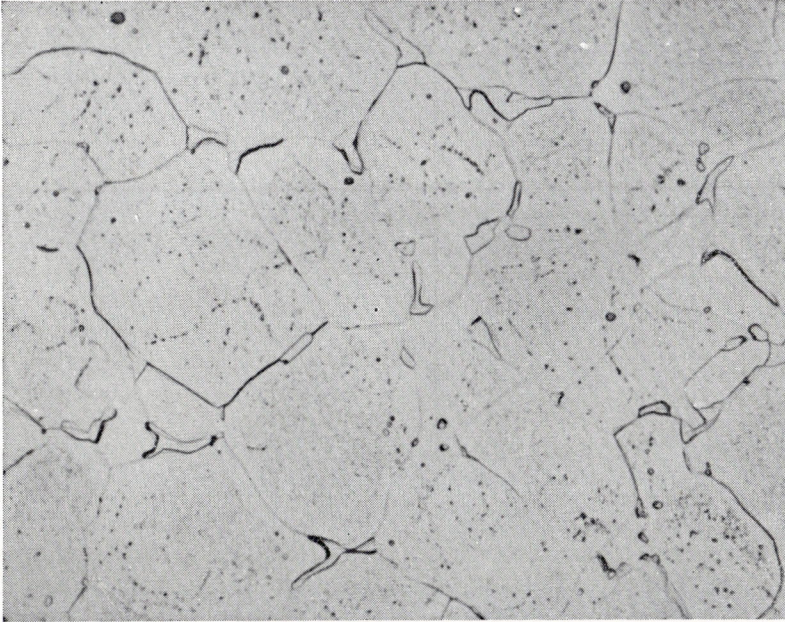

Fig. 225. Iron-molybdenum-carbon precipitate and spheroidized carbide in 0.11 per cent carbon–0.54 per cent molybdenum steel, initially air-cooled from 1650°F, then heated 1 week at 1300°F, and finally tested in creep for 3,000 hr at 1100°F under 3,500 psi; ×1,000. (*Miller et al.*[449])

creep rate (which, however, is a far cry from a tenfold decrease in creep strength).

In a second investigation[455, 480] Weaver studied the creep and rupture strength at 900 and 1000°F of a heat of 0.17 per cent carbon–0.42 per cent molybdenum steel in four different initial structural conditions: (1) fine-

* This does not conflict with the work of Jenkins, Mellor, and Jenkinson[450] discussed earlier, for these investigations were concerned with deformation to fracture, while the deformation in a creep test alluded to by Bailey and Roberts probably does not exceed 1 to 2 per cent.

grained, annealed; (2) fine-grained, normalized; (3) coarse-grained, annealed; (4) coarse-grained, normalized. Each was prespheroidized at 1292°F (700°C) to three degrees or stages of spheroidization. By spheroidizing for relatively a short time at 1300°F, presumably the same changes are effected as would occur in a considerably longer time at service temperatures. Weaver determined the relation between spheroidization and time at higher than service temperatures, and extrapolated to service temperatures. The temperature and time for spheroidization relation was reported to be exponential, as would be expected for a process governed by diffusion. However, because he had to extrapolate several hundred degrees and because his creep tests were made by the downstep method, Weaver's numerical values are open to some question. However, these results, summarized in Fig. 227, provide an indication of what may be expected. For example, the data in Fig. 227 show that a coarse-grained, normalized (CN) molybdenum steel may be expected to decrease in creep strength from about 24,000 psi to about 16,000 psi during 100,000 hr at 900°F without stress. But as Bailey and Roberts[456] report, it seems unlikely that creep stresses will affect to any significant extent the spheroidization rate.

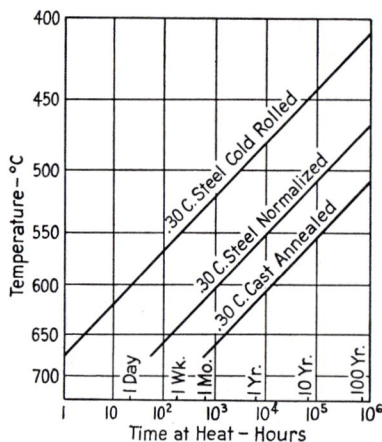

FIG. 226. Influence of temperature on time for spheroidization of carbon steel in three initial conditions. (*Curves drawn by Weaver*[454] *from data published by Bailey and Roberts.*[456])

Graphitization. The other main type of microstructural change occurring in steel is the decomposition of metastable carbide to graphite (Fig. 228). Comparatively little was known until recently about this phenomenon in low-carbon steel, such as that used in high-temperature service, especially when alloying elements are present. Wells[457] established that the carbide Fe_3C is not a stable phase in iron-carbon alloys, at least at temperatures below about 2050°F. However, it must be said that even though graphite is the stable phase, carbide will in some cases persist indefinitely even at a temperature at which in another instance it will readily invert to graphite. The breakdown of carbide to graphite can, like other reactions, be divided in two separate processes: (1) nucleation and (2) growth. It seems rather certain that the failure of carbide to transform to graphite in certain cases must be attributed to an inability of the new phase to nucleate and that conversely the ease with which the reaction occurs in other cases is to be attributed to the presence of factors promoting nucleation. The growth of graphite appears to be a relatively simple process, governed, like spheroidization, principally by the diffusion of carbon to the nuclei. In the past graphitization has not been a problem to users of steel at elevated temperatures.

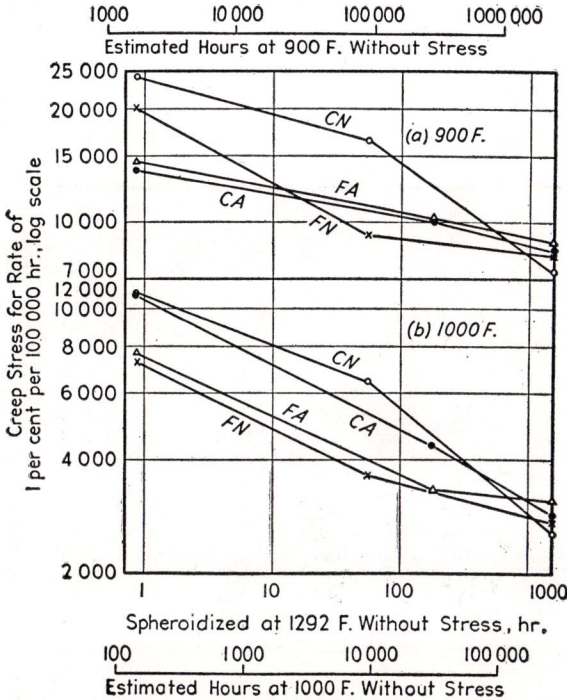

Fig. 227. Log plot of creep stress at 900 and 1000°F versus spheroidizing time without stress for 0.5 per cent molybdenum steel. *FN* and *CN* refer to fine- and coarse-grained normalized steel, while *FA* and *CA* refer to fine- and coarse-grained annealed steel. (*Weaver.*[455])

The problem of graphitization during service at elevated temperatures was first recognized as a result of a failure of a welded steam pipe in a central power-generating station. The fracture, which has been described in some detail by Emerson,[459] occurred suddenly around the whole periphery of the wall of an aluminum-killed 0.5 per cent molybdenum steel pipe, such as was commonly used in this type of service, at a distance of approximately 1/16 in. from the fusion zone of a weld by which it was joined to a main steam header. The pipe had been in service for $5\frac{1}{2}$ years at a nominal steam temperature and pressure of 935°F and 1,300 psi. Metallographic examination revealed a profuse amount of graphite in a narrow region on both sides of the fracture; this graphite formed an almost continuous plane of weakness, providing a ready path for fracture, and was clearly the reason for failure. The region of graphitization occurred near the lower limit of the "heat-affected" zone of the base metal in a portion of the pipe which had apparently reached,

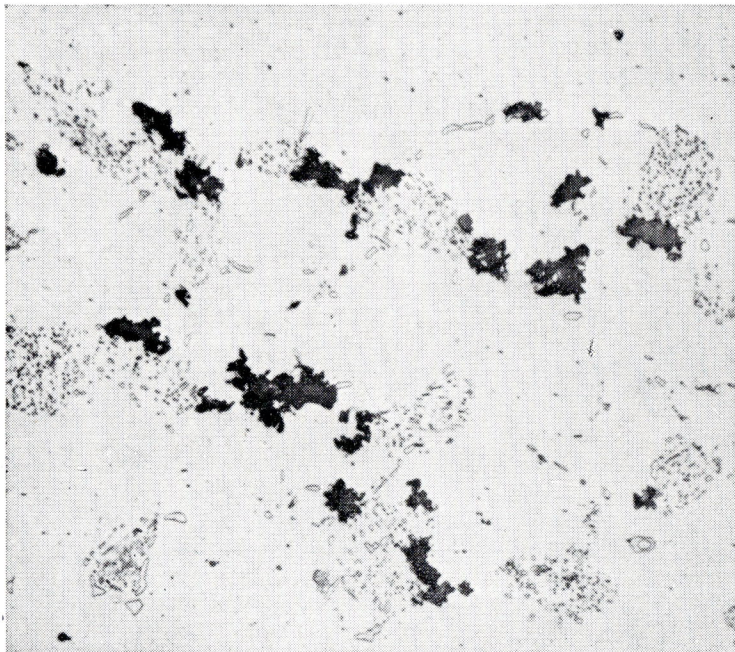

FIG. 228. Graphite and spheroidized carbide in 0.20 per cent carbon steel after 1,000 hr at 1100°F; ×1,000.

during welding, a temperature slightly above the lower critical temperature A_1, or 1350 to 1400°F. Furthermore, the width of the graphitized region was so narrow that the path of fracture closely conformed to the 1350 to 1400°F isothermal line of the individual weld passes. There were occasional graphite nodules in the base metal, unaffected by welding, but these were scattered and therefore of little concern.*

* It is only when graphite is localized that it can become dangerous, for if all the carbide were to graphitize *in situ* it would occupy only slightly greater volume than the carbide and would affect the properties in nearly the same way as well-

This failure caused great concern in the power industry, and examination of other generating stations also showed graphitization, although seldom to such a pronounced degree or with such a dangerous distribution. Accordingly, a great deal of effort has been expended in attempting to determine the cause of the peculiar formation of graphite, how affected pipes might be rehabilitated, and how its occurrence might be prevented.

Review of the literature showed few recorded instances of graphitization during elevated-temperature service. In 1935, Kinzel and Moore[458] reported complete graphitization of the carbide of a 0.15 per cent carbon steel that had been in service for about 26,000 hr at a temperature of about 1100 to 1200°F. In discussing this paper, both Mathews and Sauveur reported graphitization in slightly hypereutectoid steels. In an extensive investigation of graphitization of iron-carbon alloys of high purity, Wells[457] succeeded in forming graphite in a steel containing as little as 0.13 per cent carbon.

Jenkins, Mellor, and Jenkinson[450] determined the microstructural changes in carbon steel, ranging from 0.17 to 1.14 per cent carbon, tested in creep rupture. They found graphite in an aluminum-killed 0.40 per cent carbon steel after rupture in 4,300 hr at a stress of 18,000 psi at 840°F and also in many of the other steels after test at 1200°F. Unstressed samples of 0.60, 0.86, and 1.14 per cent carbon steels graphitized almost completely in 360 hr at 1200°F, and samples of 0.90 and 1.10 per cent carbon steels showed partial graphitization, but steels containing 0.24, 0.40, and 0.57 per cent carbon showed no sign of graphite. The results indicated that graphite precipitated more readily the higher the carbon content, although this tendency was influenced by deoxidation practice and the rate accelerated by plastic deformation.

The effect of manufacturing practice and in particular of deoxidation practice has been considered by Austin *et al.* in a series of investigations[442-448] of the spheroidization and graphitization of slightly hypereutectoid steels. Among their more important conclusions were that graphitization is facilitated by (1) the use of aluminum in deoxidizing the steel and (2) by providing the samples with an initially martensitic structure.

Hughes and Cutton,[460] in a study of the graphitization of 0.4 to 0.6

---

spheroidized carbides. However, when graphite is localized, carbon atoms diffuse through the ferrite from the carbide particles to the graphite because of the solubility difference between stable and unstable phase; thus sufficient graphite can form in one region to create a continuous or near-continuous distribution of the phase.

per cent carbon-steel strip, found that graphite appeared in 72 hr at 1200°F in aluminum-killed but not in silicon-killed steel and that the rate of graphitization was accelerated by slow cooling from 1600°F and by cold working prior to subcritical annealing.

Abundant evidence has accumulated in the investigations* conducted since the occurrence of the power-generating station failure described earlier to prove that carbon or molybdenum steels deoxidized with a large amount of aluminum, $1\frac{1}{2}$ lb or more per ton of steel, are quite susceptible to carbide instability, while those deoxidized with silicon and only $\frac{1}{2}$ lb or less of aluminum per ton of steel are extremely resistant to graphitization. Associated with the addition of a large amount of aluminum for deoxidation is a fine grain size and a so-called abnormal structure in the carburizing test,[461] and Kerr[462] has suggested that specifications for steel to be used under conditions which may give rise to graphitization should require coarse grain size and "normal" structure. The "normality" specification seems unnecessarily restrictive since (1) experimental studies have shown that "normal" steels occasionally graphitize and many "abnormal" steels do not, and (2) it is quite difficult to produce a strictly "normal" steel even when no aluminum is used in deoxidation. Furthermore, it is very desirable economically, both for better product and better yield, to use up to 0.5 lb of aluminum per ton of steel.

The other principal means suggested for preventing graphitization is the addition of a carbide-stabilizing element such as chromium in an amount ranging from 0.5 to 1.0 per cent. A number of investigators[463] have examined this possibility and determined that something in excess of 0.5 per cent chromium is probably necessary. Along with the addition of chromium, it seems desirable to add no more aluminum for deoxidation than necessary.

Other Precipitation Effects and Phase Changes. There are four general ways† of increasing the strength of a metal: (1) by solid-solution strengthening; (2) by the formation of an additional phase or phases; (3) by the development of a finely dispersed precipitate (in reality, this

---

* A thorough review of these investigations is beyond the scope of this book, and therefore only the important findings will be summarized. The reader is referred, for more complete details, to a series of symposia held during the past several years and published[463] by the American Society of Mechanical Engineers under the sponsorship of the Joint ASME-ASTM Research Committee on the Effect of Temperature on the Properties of Metals, and to a general review of these by Smith.[483]

† There is some question of whether the martensitic hardening in steels falls into any of these groups.

is part of method 2); (4) by deformation. The first three methods have been widely employed for improvement of strength in creep service, but the last has had as yet only limited application. The general subject of the effect of alloying elements, which are responsible for the improvement in strength of the first three categories, has been discussed in earlier chapters. As pointed out there, not a great deal is yet known about the influence of alloying elements on creep resistance, but it is generally considered that precipitation-hardening effects are desired; Parker[466] has discussed this matter, with primary reference to steel. Heat-treatments to effect these changes are generally applied prior to service installation.

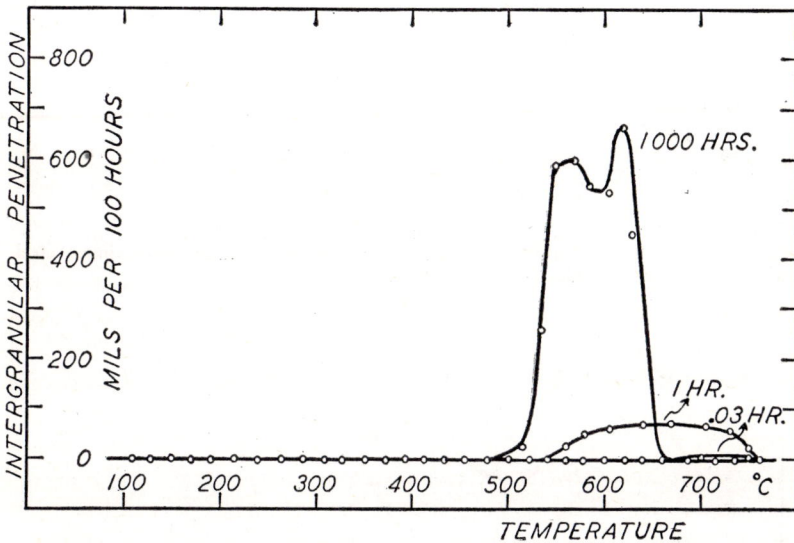

Fig. 229. Effect of time and temperature on the intergranular attack of austenitic 18 per cent chromium–8 per cent nickel steel. (*Bain, Aborn, and Rutherford.*[482])

In the present section, precipitation effects and other phase changes will be discussed as they occur during service. Among these are carbide precipitation in austenitic stainless steels, sigma phase formation in high-chromium ferritic or austenitic steels, temper embrittlement in low and intermediate alloyed steels, and strain aging in mild steel.

Carbide Precipitation in Austenitic Stainless Steels. When the austenitic chromium-nickel-iron alloys are heated in the temperature range of 850 to 1600°F, after first being rapidly cooled from a high temperature, carbide precipitation or "sensitization" occurs.[467] The carbide which precipitates is rich in chromium, according to generally accepted theory, and there results a decrease of this element from the immediately adjacent

Fig. 230a. Annealed 18 per cent chromium–8 per cent nickel austenitic stainless steel. Showing freedom from carbide precipitation; × 1,000.

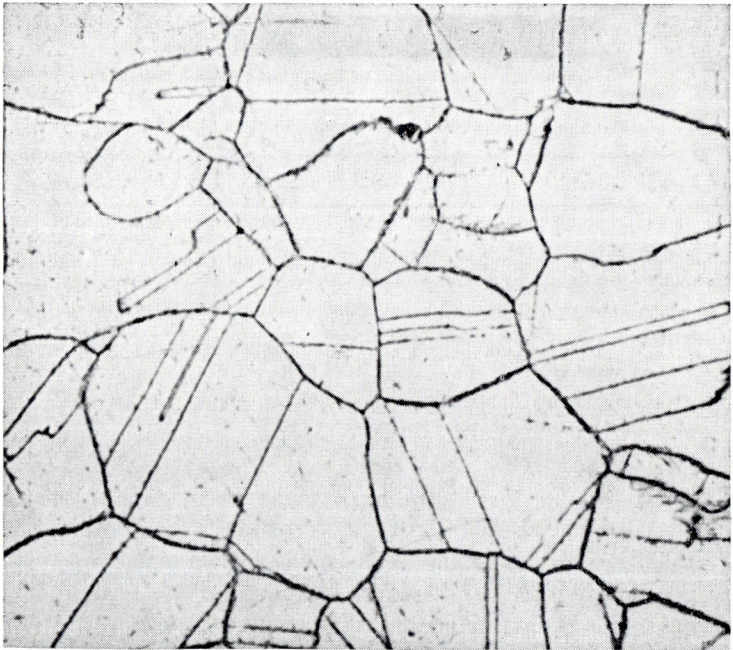

Fig. 230b. Same steel shown in Fig. 230a after carbide precipitation, principally at grain boundaries; × 1,000.

matrix. If the time and temperature conditions are appropriate, this deficiency is repaired by diffusion of chromium from the surrounding matrix. However, if this does not occur, the depleted portion of the matrix adjacent to the carbide is susceptible to corrosive attack. If the precipitate were randomly dispersed, this would be of no serious consequence since these steels have quite low carbon content. However, the usual mode of precipitation is at the grain boundaries, and with such a limited location, there is sufficient carbide (and thus presumably chromium depletion in localized areas) to provide a continuous or near-continuous path; thus the phenomenon of intergranular corrosion and embrittlement occurs. Figures 229 and 230 illustrate the characteristics of this phenomenon.

There are several ways of ameliorating the difficulties of carbide precipitation:

1. By avoiding sojourn in the susceptible temperature range.
2. By lowering the carbon content to a sufficiently low value, 0.03 per cent or less, so that this element is completely soluble in austenite over the complete temperature range. Urban[468] has obtained a patent for a method of doing this commercially.
3. By precipitating the carbide at a sufficiently high temperature, 1500 to 1600°F, so that the loss in chromium adjacent to the carbide particles is replenished by diffusion. This treatment is called "stabilizing."
4. By adding an element, titanium or columbium, which, because it has greater affinity than chromium for carbon, effectively ties up the carbon. This procedure is also called stabilizing, and is commonly employed where service requires heating into the "sensitizing" range of temperature.
5. By cold working the metal prior to precipitating the carbide, in which case the carbides precipitate more randomly.

For elevated-temperature service in the temperature range of carbide precipitation, all the various austenitic grades have been employed, though the stabilized (with titanium or columbium) grades have been more widely used. Few instances have been reported in the literature of failure directly traceable to carbide precipitation, and nonstabilized material has been used successfully for oil-cracking still tubes in the susceptible temperature range. The specific effect of the carbide precipitation is difficult to evaluate in as much as the sigma phase forms in many of the austenitic stainless steels in the same temperature range. The over-all effect of these changes is often an increase in strength and a loss in ductility or toughness at ambient temperature; at elevated temperatures the loss in toughness is somewhat less.

Clark and Freeman[469] examined 18 Cr–8 Ni cracking-still tubes which had been in service for times ranging from 35,000 to 100,000 hr at a maximum operating temperature of 1200 to 1250°F. Some of these tubes had actually failed while others were in various stages of deterioration. The authors report, however, that in general this type of steel has performed satisfactorily in service. The room-temperature tensile strength and elongation of these samples were quite good, the service embrittlement being detected only in a flattening test. From metallographic examination, the authors concluded that the embrittlement of the material was attributable to microstructural alterations. The authors, however, gave no clear explanation of the structure changes, but suggested that a precipitation of ferrite particles in the grain boundaries probably occurs first and is followed by carbide precipitation. Why the authors suspected the ferrite to precipitate first, if ferrite were present, is not made clear; it seems more probable that carbide precipitation would occur first and that ferrite formed then owing to the loss of carbon in the immediately adjacent austenite.

Kahn, Oster, and Wachtell[470] report upon a type of elevated-temperature failure occurring in 18 Cr–8 Ni stainless steel stabilized with titanium, and presumably also with columbium, such as that used in aircraft exhaust systems. Under certain conditions, the exhaust gases are carburizing to such steel, and the absorption of carbon, particularly at grain boundaries, is more than sufficient to combine with the stabilizing element, titanium or columbium, and deterioration occurs as though no stabilizing element were present. Samples taken at the fracture show a heavy carbide precipitation at the grain boundaries and a general darkening within the grains. Samples removed from service and also samples pack-carburized in the laboratory showed embrittlement when tested in the standard Strauss solution (boiling $CuSO_4$–H_2SO_4), which is commonly used for detecting "sensitization."

It seems probable that carbide precipitation in the austenitic stainless steels during elevated-temperature service is a common occurrence, but that the embrittlement resulting therefrom is not in sufficient degree to cause failure, unless the service conditions, including the corrosiveness of the atmosphere, are severe. This seems to be the only interpretation that can be given to the dearth of service failures reported. However, an apparent exception is the difficulties encountered in the exhaust manifolds of the reciprocating-engine airplane, which must contain incompletely combusted exhaust gases at very high temperatures, and which therefore become carburized.

Sigma Phase Formation in High-chromium or High-chromium–Nickel Alloys. The sigma phase is a hard, brittle, nonmagnetic, intermetallic compound occurring in high-chromium iron alloys and corresponding to the formula FeCr (or nearly 50 per cent chromium and 50 per cent iron). However, this phase can be found in iron-chromium alloys containing as little as perhaps 25 per cent chromium (Fig. 231), and when

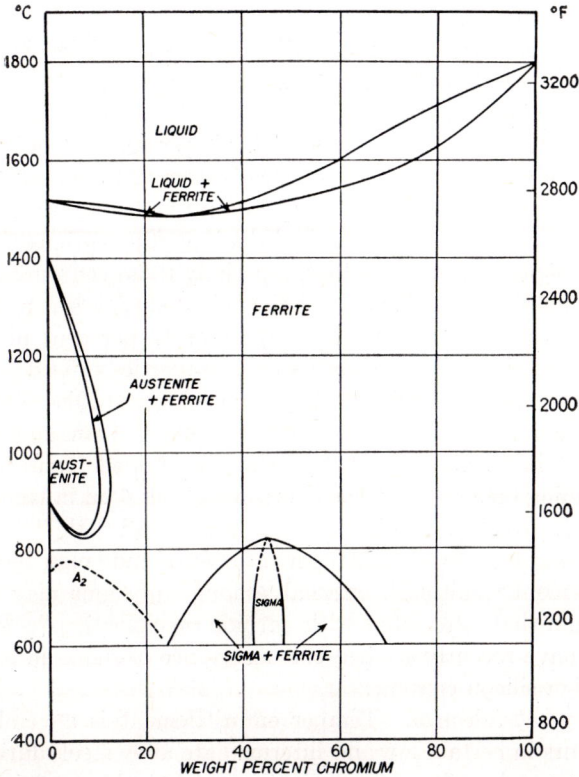

FIG. 231. The iron-chromium constitution diagram. (*"ASM Handbook,"* 1948.)

other elements like nickel, molybdenum, silicon, and manganese are present, the range of occurrence is broadened even more. The sigma phase is stable below some 1600°F, transforming to ferrite or austenite at higher temperatures. There has been some controversy as to whether sigma can form only from ferrite or whether it can also precipitate directly from austenite. Recent work[481] indicates that the latter is true and this is indicated by the generally accepted equilibrium diagram for the iron-chromium-nickel system. Foley[471] has recently reviewed the literature on sigma occurrence.

The transformation to sigma, at temperatures below some 1600°F, is relatively sluggish when it occurs in an austenitic matrix and is relatively rapid when it forms from ferrite. However, long-time holding, as in service at elevated temperatures (especially if preceded or accompanied by deformation) permits sigma to form, even in alloys which are initially all austenite; and its occurrence may be the cause of embrittlement at ambient temperature and to a lesser degree at elevated temperatures,[481] particularly when it occurs at the grain boundaries. Few, if any, instances of this nature have actually been reported in the literature, though it is not improbable that service failures attributable to this cause have occurred.

The formation of sigma takes on added importance when it is realized, as Foley[471] points out, that many of the commercial high-chromium alloys fall within or near the range of composition for the occurrence of sigma. These include plain 27 per cent chromium, the various 18 per cent chromium–8 per cent nickel alloys, especially those containing molybdenum or columbium, the 25 per cent chromium–20 per cent nickel with or without silicon, and 25 per cent chromium–12 per cent nickel alloys. The effects of sigma on the mechanical properties of cast 25 per cent chromium–12 per cent nickel alloys have been studied by Gow and Harder[472] and by Avery, Cook, and Fellows.[473] Gow and Harder reported that in 25 Cr–12 Ni steel, which contained ferrite as a minor phase, holding below 1600°F, as in creep test, resulted in transformation of the ferrite to sigma, which is "both weak and brittle." Avery *et al.* also found sigma to form from ferrite at 1600°F and below but state that "embrittlement resulting from small amounts of sigma may be no more serious than that associated with carbide precipitation." Payson and Savage[481] have recently studied the occurrence of sigma in 25 Cr–20 Ni steel of high silicon content.

Temper Embrittlement. Temper embrittlement is an embrittlement which occurs in certain low and intermediate alloy steels during tempering, or slow cooling from tempering, in a particular temperature range which depends on the composition of the steel. The embrittlement is detected only in the notch-impact test at atmospheric or a lower temperature, not at high temperatures, and does not affect the other mechanical properties materially. It occurs particularly in steels containing chromium, nickel, and manganese. The embrittlement is generally attributed to a precipitation phenomenon, but there is no substantial agreement among metallurgists as to the exact nature of the precipitation reaction. Hollomon[474], in reviewing this subject, suggested that the precipitate may be iron nitride; others have suggested that it is a carbide.

The brittleness is alleviated by one of several means: (1) rapid cooling through the embrittling temperature range; (2) thorough deoxidation; (3) by the addition of molybdenum.

Temper brittleness is no longer of more than minor concern to users of steel at elevated temperatures, except in bolting applications where quenched and tempered steels are generally used. In these latter applications, the embrittlement has caused service failure, presumably when the metal is cooled to a lower temperature during a shutdown, as at the base of threads (which act as natural notches), but none of these appear to have been described in the literature. In the normalized or annealed steels generally applied for most of the other high-temperature uses, molybdenum is now almost always present, primarily for improvement of creep strength, but a secondary effect is its palliative action on brittleness. It is to be emphasized that this type of embrittlement does not exist at elevated temperatures.

A type of embrittlement which in some respects is similar to temper brittleness occurs in plain high-chromium–iron alloys, the maximum brittleness occurring on tempering or slow cooling through the temperature range of 850 to 900°F. The embrittlement is lessened by rapid cooling through the temperature range of 1100 to 750°F. Newell[475] has recently reviewed this subject; experimental studies, particularly metallographic, of this phenomenon have been quite scarce.

Strain Aging. Strain aging is a phenomenon occurring in mild steel and in some nonferrous alloys whereby an increase in strength and a loss in ductility and notch toughness is encountered on aging after plastic straining. Thus mild steel which has been plastically deformed will gain in strength and lose in toughness if permitted to age. The time required is of the order of several days at room temperature, but at the temperature of boiling water a period of only hours suffices. The optimum temperature is 400 to 600°F, the blue-brittle range, which corresponds to a maximum in hot strength in an ordinary tension test. In contrast to temper embrittlement, the property changes resulting from strain aging are evident at the aging temperature as well as at lower temperatures. This effect is of great commercial importance in certain branches of metallurgy,* but is of only limited importance in the use of steel at elevated temperatures except in the fabrication for certain uses. It is of some importance in such uses as locomotive fireboxes and boilers and other relatively low-temperature installations for which mild steel or

---

* For example, one of the effects of strain aging is recovery of the sharp yield point in mild steel, which is temporarily eliminated by temper rolling, and this produces undesirable "stretcher strains" in deep drawing.

other low alloy steels also susceptible to strain aging have been used, where thermal changes produce deformation at operating temperatures in the range up to 600 to 800°F and accordingly strain aging results.

Sensitivity to strain aging is reduced by normalizing, as compared to the as-rolled condition, but most particularly, by thorough deoxidation, as with a relatively large amount of aluminum. Aluminum presumably acts in two ways: (1) in reducing the grain size and (2) by eliminating or reducing elements responsible for strain aging, among which are reputed to be nitrogen, oxygen, and carbon. Low and Gensamer[476] have recently reviewed this subject.

Recrystallization. When a cold-worked metal is heated, recrystallization occurs. This term describes the formation and growth of new, undistorted, and generally equiaxed grains in and at the expense of the cold-worked and distorted original grains. The rate at which recrystallization occurs in any metal depends upon the degree of deformation and upon time and temperature. With increasing deformation, the process occurs at a lower temperature or a shorter time.

The formation of these new grains is accompanied by changes in the physical and mechanical properties. It is convenient to remember that the recrystallization process represents a return to the properties prior to cold working; with respect to the mechanical properties, this entails a decrease in strength and an increase in ductility.

When the deformation which is necessary for recrystallization occurs at a high temperature, much the same sort of behavior must occur as that described for cold deformation, and it is possible to imagine a threshold value of deformation for a particular metal, temperature, and time* which when exceeded will result in recrystallization. This is exactly what occurs, as illustrated in Fig. 232. These photomicrographs were taken at the fracture of a 0.15 per cent carbon–0.5 per cent molybdenum steel strained at a series of constant rates. At the fast rates, the grains are severely distorted in the direction of pull, and no recrystallization is apparent. At somewhat slower rate, however, small equiaxed grains, representing recrystallization appear, and at the slowest rate the grains are comparatively large again for the most part. An identical behavior is found in creep-rupture tests. However, in ordinary creep tests, in which the greatest strain is only some 1 to 2 per cent, the deformation is insufficient to cause recrystallization, and generally no apparent change in size or shape of the grains can be noted. Few experimental data are available to define quantitatively the phenomena described, and this

---

* It would be quite difficult to consider time quantitatively since the deformation occurring at temperature is also a function of time.

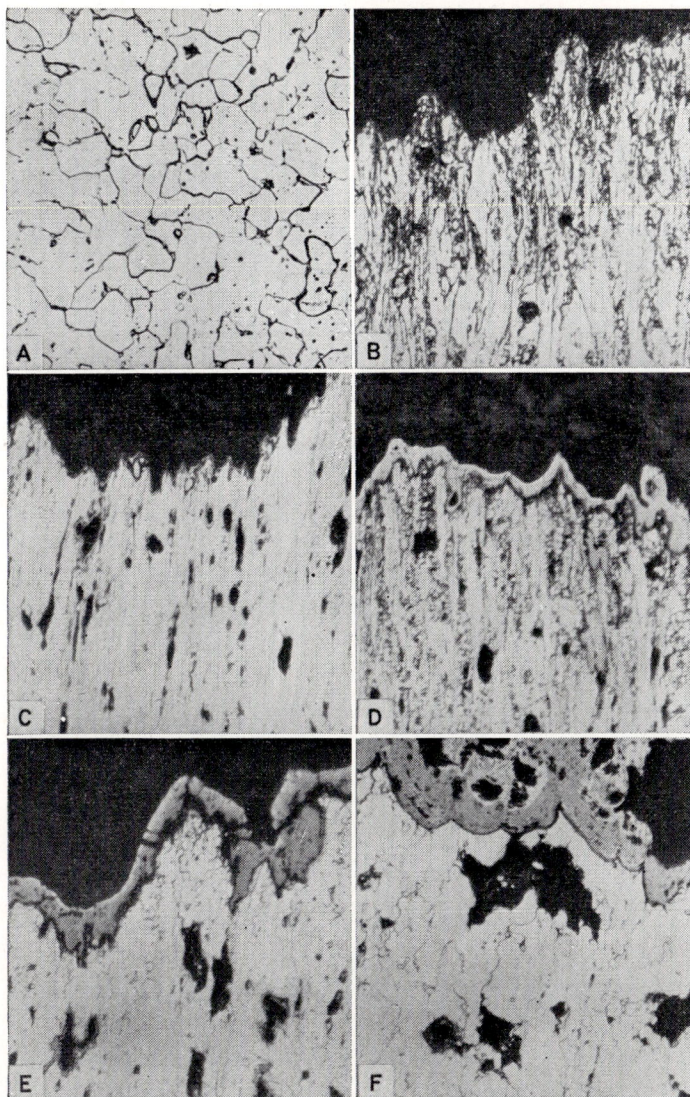

A. Original microstructure............................... 106 VPN
B. 7.5 in./in./hr....................................... 166 VPN
C. 1.0 in./in./hr....................................... 158 VPN
D. 0.1 in./in./hr....................................... 150 VPN
E. 0.01 in./in./hr...................................... 113 VPN
F. 0.001 in./in./hr..................................... 110 VPN

FIG. 232. Longitudinal section through fracture of controlled-strain-rate tensile specimens of spheroidized C–Mo steel at 1100°F, ×250, showing the occurrence of recrystallization while straining at elevated temperatures. (*Miller, Smith, and Kehl.*[101])

should be a fruitful field for research aimed at better understanding of creep behavior.

White, Clark, and Wilson[477] studied the fracture of carbon steels in creep-rupture tests at 1000, 1200, 1300, and 1400°F, and photomicrographs taken at the fracture show how the grain shape and size change with test conditions. Smith,[478] in studying the creep and recrystallization of lead, reported recrystallization to occur during creep test at relatively high stresses, but not to occur in low-stress tests. Gohn, Arnold, and Bouton[479] described structural changes occurring during creep-rupture tests of various lead alloys, one of the changes being recrystallization. Incidentally, these authors also describe several instances, among the very few in the literature, of other types of structural changes in nonferrous alloys. In lead-antimony alloys, the antimony particles coalesced, while a similar effect was observed in the case of the tin-rich solid solution needles in lead-tin alloys. Both of these changes are quite analogous to the spheroidization and agglomeration of carbide in steels, described earlier.

CHAPTER XII

DESIGN FOR ELEVATED–TEMPERATURE SERVICE

Many properties of a metal or alloy must be taken into consideration in designing a structural element for long-time operation at elevated temperatures. Foremost among these for most applications is, of course, the load-carrying ability, which must be defined in somewhat different terms than in design at atmospheric temperature, namely, in terms of a limiting permissible creep as well as freedom from fracture. Besides the strength, however, the engineer designing for elevated-temperature service must, in the general case, also be concerned with such characteristics as resistance to scaling or other corrosive attack, moduli of elasticity, damping capacity, thermal expansivity, and thermal conductivity. Structural changes during service with consequent change in strength and possible embrittlement are of interest, although these may be considered as a special aspect of the load-carrying problem. Some attention must also be paid to the ordinary ambient-temperature characteristics, both before and after exposure at elevated temperatures; these determine how readily the part may be fabricated by mechanical deformation, machining, or welding prior to service, and the likelihood of failure resulting from mechanical abuse during shutdown periods.

Such properties as thermal conductivity and expansivity, moduli of elasticity, etc., do not vary rapidly with composition and heat-treatment, that is, they are not structure sensitive, and therefore are not generally controlling factors in design. Often it is merely desired to know the specific value of the property so that design may allow for sufficient expansion owing to the temperature change or to the elastic strain corresponding to the applied stress. These structure-insensitive properties, moreover, may be determined in short-time tests by comparatively simple means. Figures 233 and 234 are included to show the linear thermal expansion and thermal conductivity of various ferrous alloys employed at high temperatures.

Resistance to scaling or corrosion at high temperatures depends primarily on chemical composition and in some few cases on the structure. As we noted in the previous chapter, resistance to scaling or corrosion cannot generally be evaluated in relatively short-time tests. Fortunately, however, scaling and corrosion can be effectively limited to tolerable amounts by alloying additions, especially of chromium and in some cases of silicon, or by protective coatings for the large majority of applications at moderate temperatures; in such service, overdesign is so easily and so economically accomplished that scaling or corrosion is of little concern. In some cases of very severe attack, as at very high temperatures, scaling may be so excessive that it is the controlling fac-

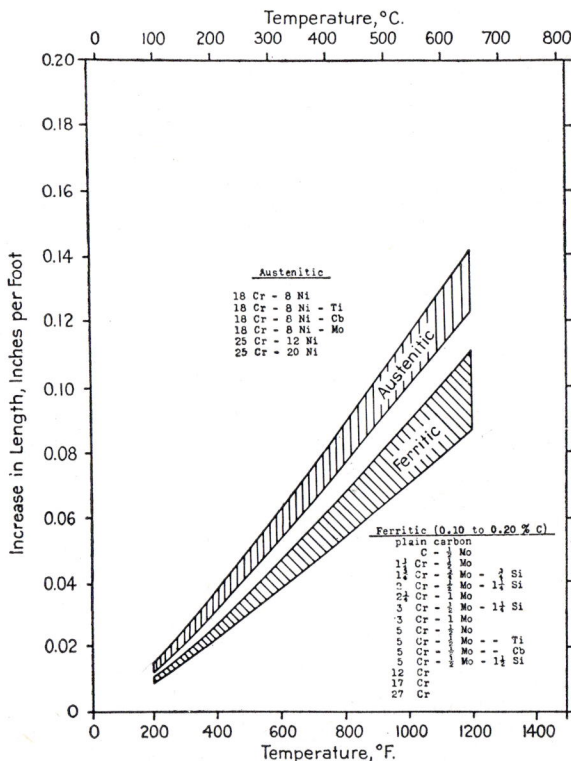

FIG. 233. Linear thermal expansion of various steels (increase in length in inches per foot in going from 70°F to any temperature between 200 and 1200°F). (*U. S. Steel Corp. data.*)

tor. Parts in such service are then replaced periodically according to a schedule which experience or periodic examination dictates.

Working Stresses

By far the most difficult problem in designing for service at elevated temperatures is that of the working stresses which should be employed. This is primarily a consequence of the fact that continuing creep necessitates an extrapolation beyond the time which can generally be em-

ployed in making a laboratory test. For those applications where the
contemplated service life is relatively short, no great problem* exists,
since laboratory tests can be made to encompass the service time. The
problem of extrapolation beyond the test time or of prediction of long-

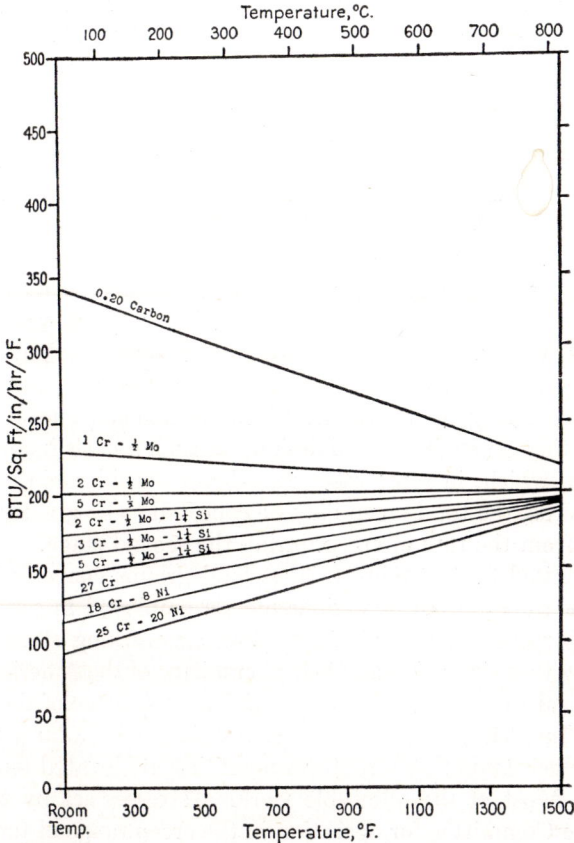

Fig. 234. Thermal conductivity of various steels at temperatures between room temperature and 1500°F. (*U. S. Steel Corp. data.*)

time behavior is a difficult one and the longer the test time which may
be employed, the better is the estimation which can be made.

As we have attempted to make clear in earlier discussion, tests of only
several days duration, such as have been employed abroad, cannot be
expected to bear any close relation to long-time behavior. We shall

* Aside from the general problem of applying laboratory data obtained in
uniaxial test to the complex stress states of actual structures.

therefore not consider such data as being of value in setting working stresses for other than relatively short-time service. The large majority of creep-strength data reported in the literature, in the United States, has been in terms of the stress to produce a secondary (minimum) creep rate of 1 per cent per 10,000 hr or of 1 per cent per 100,000 hr. More properly, of course, these should be termed 0.0001 and 0.00001 per cent per hour, since this rate was determined not in a test of 10,000 or 100,000 hr duration, but rather at most in 2,000 to 3,000 hr. In recent years, an increasing quantity of creep-rupture data has been reported; these data are generally stated in terms of the stress to produce rupture in 1,000 hr, or 10,000 hr, or some other arbitrary period of time. As indicated by the literature, many engineers fail to appreciate fully the significance of creep-rupture data, regarding it as a possible substitute for the more commonly reported creep strength defined in terms of creep rate. In reality the two types of data are distinct, being related in only a very general way. Both are needed for intelligent design.

Although creep-strength data defined in terms of the stress to produce a specific secondary creep rate are of unquestioned value, it should be recognized that an engineer who designs on such a basis ignores the primary creep, which, in some cases may be of considerable importance. In other words, the total creep may be expected to be greater than that calculated from the rate of creep during the second stage.

In the United States, there exist several groups concerned with the appraisal of the strength of various metals employed in service at elevated temperatures, and which set allowable working stresses. Foremost among these is the Boiler Code Committee of the American Society of Mechanical Engineers, as well as a similar committee of the American Petroleum Institute, under whose construction codes a large number of pressure vessels and other structures operating at elevated temperatures are built. Most of the allowable working stresses set by the ASME Boiler Code Committee for operation in the creep range of temperature, above about 700 to 800°F, have been based on a certain fraction of a conservative average of reported data for the stress to produce a creep rate of 1 per cent per 100,000 hr (0.00001 per cent per hour), although in recent years some consideration has been paid to creep-rupture data; below the creep range of temperature, the allowable working stress is based on a certain fraction of the short-time tensile strength at atmospheric temperature.

The setting of a fixed maximum allowable working stress, common to all construction, has been found unsatisfactory for certain applications, since creep may be expected to continue throughout service, and design should therefore be based on a definite life interval and a limiting total creep. For example, within a contemplated life of 20 years, a certain structure must not creep more than a given amount, depending upon the application, and, of course, within this limitation, actual fracture must not occur. Thus the same stress might not be used for equipment designed for a life of 5 years as for equipment designed for a life of 20 years or more.

Basis for Working Stresses

Since creep may be expected to occur throughout the period of service at elevated temperatures, design should be based, as stated before, on (1) a definite life period and (2) a maximum permissible creep. Implicit in these limitations is that fracture does not occur. In some cases, especially when the amount of creep is of little consequence, it may be desirable or even necessary to plan for no specific life. However, in this type of design, fracture should be guarded against by proper consideration of creep-rupture data, as described below. Periodic examination may show whether and to what extent creep is occurring, but not necessarily whether fracture is imminent, since this may occur at quite small strains for most metals in long-time service. In other words, the engineer should not assume that the absence of significant creep is an indication that fracture will not occur.

The choice of working stresses for service in the creep range of temperature may be considered in terms of two methods, depending upon whether, in one case, little or no extrapolation of the available data is required, or in the other, whether extensive extrapolation is required. The two methods are not entirely different, however, and the distinction is to some extent an arbitrary one. By the first method, a plot is prepared of stress versus time for various degrees of total deformation as well as time for rupture, all on the same chart and sometimes referred to as "design curves." Such plots were introduced a number of years ago, and have been rather widely employed in recent years for the design of relatively short-lived equipment such as in jet-propelled aircraft and similar service. An example of such a plot is reproduced in Fig. 235, after Freeman et al.,[486] for one of the so-called "superalloys" developed during the Second World War. In the example shown, plotted to semilogarithmic coordinates, the relation between the stress and time for a specific total deformation does not depart far from linearity and therefore might be considered suitable for extrapolation. However, many similar plots reported in the literature do not show this linearity, and could be extrapolated only with considerable trepidation.

From a plot such as that shown in Fig. 235, the design engineer, knowing the total deformation which his structural part may be permitted to undergo in a specific time interval, may readily choose the permissible working stress. Or, conversely, knowing the stress, he can readily estimate the time interval in which the part will not have exceeded the permissible deformation, that is, he can estimate the life of the part. Necessarily the choice of a working stress in this manner will

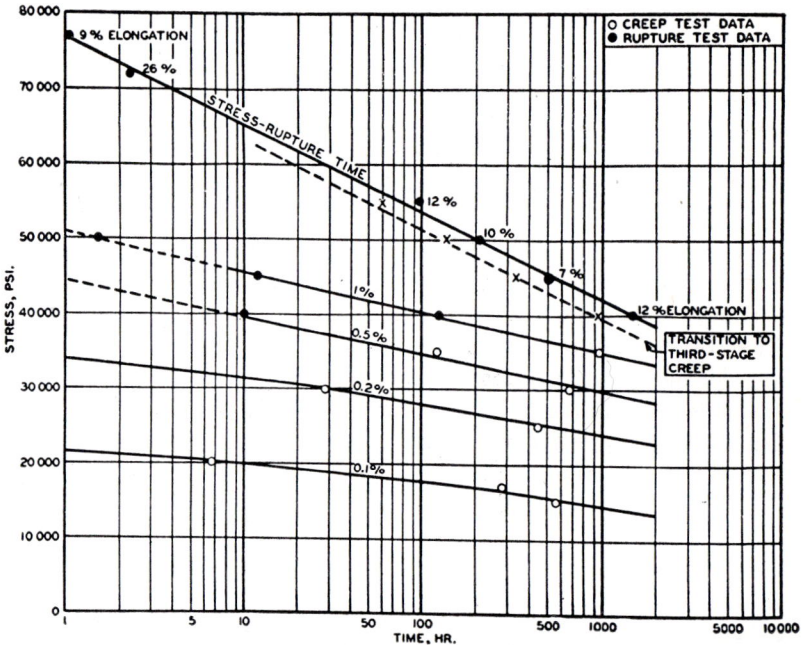

FIG. 235. Relation between stress and time for various specified total creep strains as well as for the beginning of third-stage creep and for rupture. Low-carbon N 155 alloy (20 Cr, 20 Ni, 20 Co, with small amounts of Mo, Cb, and W, balance iron) at 1200°F. Samples from a forged gas-turbine disk. (*Freeman et al.*[486])

preclude actual fracture; moreover the factor of safety relative to fracture is readily apparent by inspection.

If extensive extrapolation of laboratory data is required as when the intended life is in terms of years rather than hours, it would appear that a better way (than the design chart of Fig. 235) for selecting working stresses is in terms of an analysis of the creep-time curve originally suggested by McVetty,[487] ensuring by consideration of creep-rupture data that fracture will not occur. As discussed earlier, the creep curve may be considered to consist of four distinct stages: (1) the strain occurring immediately, or nearly so, on application of the load; (2) a period of decelerating creep rate, often called primary creep; (3) a period of substantially constant as well as minimum creep rate, often called secondary creep; (4) a period of accelerating creep, ending in fracture of the specimen, and sometimes called tertiary creep.   These various stages are illustrated by the schematic sketch of Fig. 236, which has appeared earlier but is now repeated for convenience.

It will also be recalled that the two limitations which must be considered in selecting working stresses are (1) that the total deformation shall not exceed a specific limit and (2) that fracture shall not occur.   It is the first of these limitations that involves the greatest difficulty in extrapolation.   In terms of the creep curve of Fig. 236 it is apparent by

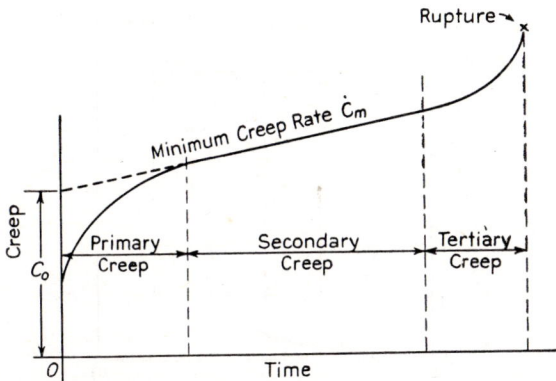

Fig. 236. Creep curve plotted to cartesian coordinates; schematic.

inspection that the total creep C_t at some time t short of that at which tertiary or accelerating creep begins is given by

$$C_t = C_0 + \dot{C}_m t \qquad (52)$$

where C_0 is the intercept on the strain axis of the slope $\dot{C}_m$ of the secondary creep rate.   To calculate the total creep at some time t before tertiary creep begins for any specific stress thus requires knowledge of the relation between C_0 and stress and between $\dot{C}_m$ and stress.   Fortunately the latter relation seems to be rather simple, being represented by a power function (and perhaps in some cases by a hyperbolic sine function) over a relatively wide range of creep rates.   The relation between the intercept C_0 and stress is, however, not so simple but may be conveniently expressed in graphic fashion.

To define the limit beyond which the calculation does not hold, namely, when tertiary creep begins, it is necessary to have the relation between stress and this time.   This relation appears to parallel that between stress and the time for rupture.   This latter relation may be expressed mathematically by a power function,* and is thus suited to extrapolation.

To illustrate how the procedure which has just been described may be applied, we shall consider an actual example, using the experimental data recorded in Figs. 237 and 238.   Thus let us estimate the total creep

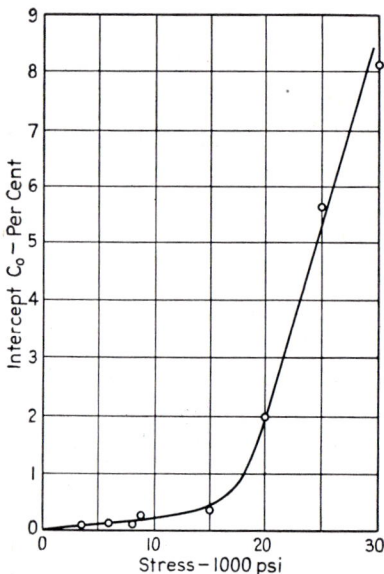

Fig. 237. Variation with stress of the intercept C_0 of the tangent to the minimum creep-rate portion of the creep curve; austenitic 18 Cr–8 Ni stainless steel at 1300°F. (*U. S. Steel Corp. data.*)

which may be expected at the beginning of tertiary creep for austenitic 18 Cr–8 Ni steel at 1300°F, under a stress of 5,000 psi.   Under this stress the intercept C_0 is 0.06 per cent and by extrapolation the time at which tertiary creep begins is 25,000 hr.   Also, by extrapolation, the time for rupture under 5,000 psi is about 40,000 hr.   The minimum creep rate under 5,000 psi by interpolation is 0.00006 per cent per hour.   Accordingly the total creep at 25,000 hr is given by substitution in Eq. (52)

$$C_{25,000 \text{ hr}} = 0.06 + (0.00006)(25,000) = 1.56 \text{ per cent}$$

In this case, little error would have resulted from disregarding C_0, but this may not be assumed to be generally true.   As the total permissible creep becomes less, the fraction represented by C_0 becomes greater.

* Plotting linearly on double logarithmic coordinates.

It will be of interest to estimate the total elongation which may be expected at fracture, employing the technique described in Chap. V. It will be recalled that the relation between initial stress and the "average creep rate" (ratio of total elongation at fracture to time at fracture) is linear on double logarithmic coordinates, and is therefore suited to extrapolation. Such a plot is also recorded in Fig. 238, and by extrapolation it may be determined that the "average creep rate" under 5,000 psi

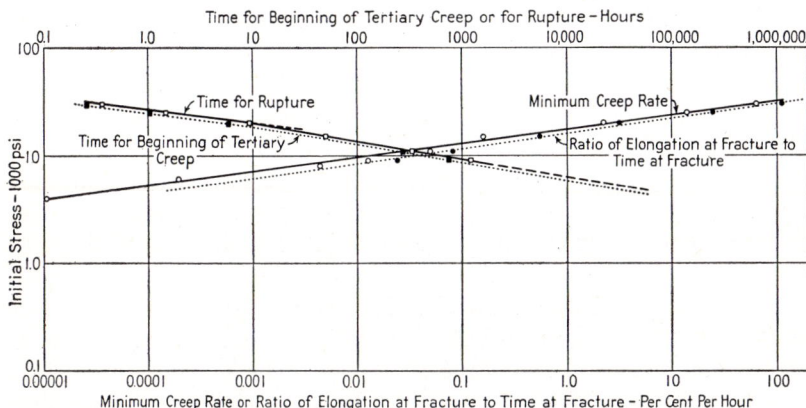

Fig. 238. Variation of (1) time for rupture; (2) time for beginning of tertiary creep; (3) minimum creep rate; and (4) ratio of elongation at fracture to time of fracture, with initial stress; austenitic 18 Cr–8N; steel at 1300°F. (*U. S. Steel Corp. data.*)

is 0.0002 per cent per hour. Since under 5,000 psi the time for rupture is 40,000 hr, the total elongation to be expected at fracture is given by

$$(40,000)(0.0002) = 8 \text{ per cent}$$

Equation (52) may obviously be employed in various ways other than in the example shown, as, for example, to calculate the stress which will not give more than a certain permissible total creep. In practice, the engineer would, of course, apply a factor of safety in accordance with the degree of information concerning actual conditions of service.

It is interesting to note that the use of the initial stress rather than the true stress throughout plots such as Figs. 237 and 238 introduces no significant error into the final result inasmuch as the total creep is of small magnitude.

Practical Considerations

The example which has just been considered represents perhaps the simplest case possible, namely, constant temperature and stress and simple tension, conditions which are seldom realized in actual service.

Elevated-temperature service represents a greatly more complex problem in design, for a number of reasons which will be briefly noted.

Service quite frequently involves complex states of stress which in some cases are as yet indeterminate. Elastic theory which has been developed for stress design at ordinary temperatures cannot be expected to apply simply to creep which is plastic deformation. Several investigators have studied the creep of metals under combined stresses. The results of these studies, although far from satisfactory, indicate that, to a first approximation, creep under combined stresses may be related to the maximum shear stress in the metal.

Observations of creep of parts in service have been reported to indicate less creep than would be expected from laboratory tests,[488] although carefully obtained data reported by Van Duzer and McCutchan[485] for steam pipes would appear to refute this generally held concept. Steam-pipe service, however, involves rather constant temperatures and stress, while many other applications involve variation in these conditions, as well as frequent shutdowns, all of which may well affect the total creep and the rupture strength of metals. In fact, the greatest single lack of information regarding creep behavior lies in the effect of variations in temperature and stress and of the effect of periodic interruptions. This should be a fruitful field of research. It is especially important that observations be made and reported of the behavior of metals in actual service.

REFERENCES

1. ANDRADE, E. N.: On the Viscous Flow in Metals and Allied Phenomena, *Proc. Roy. Soc. (London)*, (A) **84**, 1, 1911. See also The Flow in Metals under Large Constant Stresses, *Proc. Roy. Soc. (London)*, (A) **90**, 329, 1914.

2. CHEVENARD, P.: Sur la viscosité des aciers aux températures élevées, *Compt. rend.*, **169**, 712–715, 1919.

3. DICKENSON, J. H. S.: Some Experiments on the Flow of Steels at a Low Red Heat with a Note on the Scaling of Heated Steels, *J. Iron Steel Inst.*, **106**, 103, 1922.

4. LEA, F. C.: Effect of Low and High Temperatures on Materials, *Proc. Inst. Mech. Engrs.*, Part II, 1053–1096, 1924.

5. TAPSELL, H. J., and J. BRADLEY: Mechanical Tests at High Temperatures on a Nonferrous Alloy of Nickel and Chromium, *Engineering*, **120**, 614, 1925.

6. FRENCH, H. J., and W. A. TUCKER: Flow in a Low-carbon Steel at Various Temperatures, *Natl. Bur. Standards Technol. Paper* 296, 1925.

7. FRENCH, H. J.: Methods of Test in Relation to Flow in Steels at Various Temperatures, *Proc. ASTM*, **26**, Part II, 7–32, 1926.

8. SCHMID, E., and W. BOAS: "Kristallplastizität," Springer, Berlin, 1935.

9. ELAM, C. F.: "Distortion of Metal Crystals," Oxford, New York, 1935.

10. BARRETT, C. S.: "Structure of Metals," McGraw-Hill, New York, 1943.

11. HANSON, D., and M. A. WHEELER: The Deformation of Metals Under Prolonged Loading, Part I, The Flow and Fracture of Aluminum, *J. Inst. Metals*, **45**, 229–264, 1931.

12. MILLER, R. F., and W. E. MILLIGAN: Influence of Temperature on Elastic Limit of Single Crystals of Aluminum, Silver and Zinc, *Trans. AIME*, **124**, 229–251, 1937.

13. BURGHOFF, H. L., and C. H. MATHEWSON: Time and Temperature Effects in the Deformation of Brass Crystals, *Trans. AIME*, **143**, 45–56, 1941.

14. MILLER, R. F.: Creep and Twinning in Zinc Single Crystals, *Trans. AIME*, **122**, 176–191, 1936.

15. BAKARIAN, P. W., and C. H. MATHEWSON: Slip and Twinning in Magnesium Single Crystals at Elevated Temperature, *Trans. AIME*, **152**, p. 226–254, 1943.

16. BARRETT, C. S.: A New Microscopy and Its Potentialities, *Trans. AIME*, **161**, 15–64, 1945.

17. BETTY, B. B.: Making and Testing Single Crystals of Lead, *Proc. ASTM*, **35**, Part II, 193–203, 1935.

18. BOAS: W., and E. SCHMID, Zur Temperaturabhängigkeit der Kristallplastizität, *Z. Physik.*, **100**, 463, 1936.

19. CHALMERS, B.: Micro-plasticity in Crystals of Tin, *Proc. Roy. Soc. (London)*, **156**, 427–443, 1936.

20. CHALMERS, B.: Precision Extensometer Measurements on Tin, *J. Inst. Metals*, **61**, 103–122, 1937.

21. BAKER, J. B., B. B. BETTY, and H. F. MOORE: Creep and Fracture Tests on Single Crystals of Lead, *Trans. AIME*, **128**, 118–142, 1938.
22. GENSAMER, M., and R. F. MEHL: Yield Point of Single Crystals of Iron under Static Loads, *Trans. AIME*, **131**, 372, 1938.
23. KARNOP, R., and G. SACHS: Kordinaten der Verfestigungskurve, *Z. Physik.*, **41**, 116, 1927.
24. CARPENTER, H. C. H., and C. F. ELAM: The Production of Single Crystals of Aluminum and Their Tensile Properties, *Proc. Roy. Soc. (London)* **100**, 1921.
25. BASSETT, W. H., and C. H. DAVIS: A Comparison of Grain Size Measurements and Brinell Hardness of Cartridge Brass, *Trans. AIME*, **60**, 428, 1919.
26. BEILBY, G. T.: The Hard and Soft States in Metals, *J. Inst. Metals*, **6**, 5–43, 1911.
27. BENGOUGH, G. D.: Study of Properties of Alloys at High Temperatures, *J. Inst. Metals*, **7**, 123–190, 1912.
28. ROSENHAIN, W.: See discussion of reference 27.
29. ROSENHAIN, W., and D. EWEN: Intercrystalline Cohesion in Metals, *J. Inst. Metals*, **8**, 149–185, 1912.
30. JEFFRIES, Z.: The Amorphous Metal Hypothesis and Equi-cohesive Temperatures, *J. Am. Inst. Metals*, **11**, 300–324, 1917.
31. JEFFRIES, Z.: Effect of Temperature, Deformation, and Grain Size on the Mechanical Properties of Metals, *Trans. AIME*, **60**, 474–576, 1919.
32. ZENER, C.: Anelasticity of Metals, *Trans. AIME*, **167**, 155–191, 1946.
33. ROSENHAIN, W., and J. HUMFREY: The Crystalline Structure of Iron at High Temperatures, *Proc. Roy. Soc. (London)*, **83**, 200, 1909.
34. MOORE, H. F., B. B. BETTY, and C. W. DOLLINS: The Creep and Fracture of Lead and Lead Alloys, *Univ. Illinois Bull.* 272, 1935.
35. ZENER, C., D. VAN WINKLE, and H. NIELSON: High-temperature Internal Friction of Alpha Brass, *Trans. AIME*, **147**, p. 98, 1942.
36. SEITZ, F., and T. A. READ: Theory of the Plastic Properties of Solids, *J. Applied Phys.*, **12**, 100, 170, 470, 538, 1941.
37. ASTON, R. L.: Tensile Deformation of Large Aluminum Crystals at Crystal Boundaries, *Proc. Cambridge Phil. Soc.*, **23**, 549, 1927.
38. MILLER, R. F.: Influence of a Grain Boundary on the Deformation of a Single Crystal of Zinc, *Trans. AIME*, **111**, 135, 1934.
39. CHALMERS, B.,: The Influence of the Difference in Orientation of Two Crystals on the Mechanical Effect of Their Grain Boundary, *Proc. Roy. Soc. (London)*, **162**, 120–127, 1937.
40. CHALMERS, B.: Crystal Boundaries in Tin, *Proc. Roy. Soc. (London)*, **175**, 100–110, 1940.
41. MOHR, O.: Welche Umstände bedingen die Elastizitätsgrenze und den Bruch eines Materials? *Z. Ver. Deut. Ing.* **44**, 1524–1530, 1572–1577, 1900.
42. GUEST, J. J.: The Strength of Ductile Materials under Combined Stress, *Phil. Mag.*, **50**, 69–132, 1900.
43. MOHR, O.: "Abhandlungen aus dem Gebiete der technischen Mechanic," 2d ed., W. Ernst und Sohn, Berlin, 1914.
44. TRESCA, H.: Sur l'écoulement des corps solids soumis à de fortes pressions, *Compt. rend.* (Paris) **59**, 754–758, 1864, **54**, 809–812, 1867.

45. NADAI, A.: "Plasticity," McGraw-Hill, New York, 1931.
46. VON MISES, R.: Mechanik der festen Körper im plastisch-deformablen Zustand, *Nachr. Ges. Wiss. Göttingen*, 1913, p. 582.
47. HENCKY, H.: Zur Theorie plastischer Deformationen, *Z. ang. Math. Mech.*, **4**, 323, 1924.
48. NADAI, A.: Plastic Behavior of Metals in the Strain Hardening Range, *J. Applied Phys.*, **8**, 205–213, 1937.
49. LODE, W.: Versuche über den Einfluss der mittleren Hauptspannung auf das Fliessen der Metalle Eisen, Kupfer, und Nickel, *Z. Phys.*, **36**, 913, 1926; also Dissertation Göttingen, published in *Mitt. u. Forschungsarb*, V.D.I. Verlag 363, Berlin, 1928.
50. TAYLOR, G. I., and H. QUINNEY: The Plastic Distortion of Metals, *Trans. Roy. Soc. (London)*, (A) **230**, 323–362, 1931.
51. SACHS, G.: Zur Ableitung einer Fliessbedingung, *Z. Ver. deut. Ing.*, **72**, 734–736, 1928.
52. LUDWIK, P.: "Elements der technologischen Mechanik," Springer, Berlin, 1909.
53. BRIDGMAN, P. W.: Effects of High Hydrostatic Pressure on the Plastic Properties of Metals, *Rev. Mod. Phys.*, **17**, 3–14, 1945.
54. TAYLOR, G. I.: Plastic Strain in Metals, *J. Inst. Metals*, **62**, 307–324, 1938.
55. MacGREGOR, C. W.: Relation between Stress and Reduction in Area for Tensile Tests of Metals, *Trans. AIME*, **124**, 208–228, 1937.
56. GENSAMER, M., E. B. PEARSALL, and G. V. SMITH: The Mechanical Properties of the Isothermal Decomposition Products of Austenite, *Trans. ASM*, **28**, 390–398, 1940.
57. MacGREGOR, C. W., and L. E. WELCH: True Stress-Strain Relations at High Temperatures by the Two-load Method, *Trans. AIME*, **154**, 423–437, 1943.
58. HOLLOMON, J. H.: Effect of Heat-treatment and Carbon Content on the Work-hardening Characteristics of Several Steels, *Trans. ASM*, **32**, 123–133, 1944.
59. HOLLOMON, J. H.: Tensile Deformation, *Trans. AIME*, **162**, 268, 1945.
60. GENSAMER, M.: The Yield Point in Metals, *Trans. AIME*, **128**, 104–117, 1938.
61. BRIDGMAN, P. W.: The Stress Distribution at the Neck of a Tension Specimen, *Trans. ASM*, **32**, 553–572, 1944.
62. JELINEK, J. J., A. J. LATTER, E. G. THOMSEN, and J. E. DORN: Plastic Flow in Metals, War Production Board Report W-200, Washington, D. C., 1945.
63. JACKSON, L. R.: Work Hardening and Rupture in Metals, *Trans. AIME*, 1947.
64. LANKFORD, W. T., J. R. LOW, and M. GENSAMER: The Plastic Flow of Aluminum Alloy Sheet under Combined Loads, *Trans. AIME*, **171**, 574, 1947.
65. DAVIS, E. A.: Plastic Behavior of Metals in the Strain-hardening Range, Part II, *J. Applied Phys.*, **8**, 213–219, 1937.
66. DAVIS, E. A.: Increase of Stress with Permanent Strain and Stress-strain Relation in the Plastic State for Copper under Combined Stresses, *Trans. ASME*, **65**, A187–A196, 1943.
67. SEITZ, F.: "The Physics of Metals," p. 114, McGraw-Hill, New York, 1943.
68. BARRETT, C. S., and L. H. LEVINSON: The Structure of Aluminum after Compression, *Trans. AIME*, **137**, 112–127, 1940.

69. BAUSCHINGER, J.: Changes of the Elastic Limit and the Modulus of Elasticity in Various Metals, *Zivelingenieur*, **27**, 289–347, 1881.

70. WEBER, W.: Uber die Elastizität der Seidenfaden; *Ann, Poggend*. **34**, 247, 1834, and Uber die Elastizität fester Korper, *Ann., Poggend.* 1, 1841.

71. HEYN, E.: "Festband Kaiser Wilhelm Gesellschaft," p. 131, 1921.

72. MASING, G.: *Wiss. Siemens-Konzern*, **3**, 231, 1924, with W. Mauksch, *ibid.*, **4**, 244, 1925; **5**, 135, 142, 1926.

73. JOHNSON, A. E.: The Creep Recovery of a 0.17% Carbon Steel, *Proc. Inst. Mech. Engrs.*, **145**, 210–220, 1941.

74. SACHS, G., and H. SHOJI: Zug-Druck-Versuche an Messingkristallen, *Z. Physik*, **45**, 776–796, 1927.

75. WARTENBURG, H. V.: Keine Nachwirkung bei W- und Zn-Kristallen, *Verhandl. deut. physik. Ges.*, **20**, 113, 1918.

76. DALBY, W. E.: "Strength and Structure of Steel and other Metals," Arnold, London, 1923.

77. READ, T. A.: Internal Friction of Single Crystals of Copper and Zinc, *Trans. AIME*, **143**, 30, 1941.

78. ZENER, C., H. CLARKE, and C. S. SMITH: Effect of Cold-work and Annealing upon Internal Friction of Alpha Brass, *Trans. AIME*, **147**, 90, 1942.

79. FOUND, G. H.: Internal Friction of Single Crystals of Brass, Copper and Aluminum, *Trans. AIME*, **161**, 120–139, 1945.

80. SIEGEL, S.: The Hardness of Metals as Affected by Alloying Agents, *J. Applied Phys.*, **13**, 84–89, 1942.

81. SACHS, G., and J. WEERTS: Zugversuche an Gold-Silberkristallen, *Z. Physik*, **62**, 473–493, 1930.

82. O'NEILL, H.: "The Hardness of Metals and Its Measurement," Chapman & Hall, London, 1934.

83. LUDWIK, P.: *Z. anorg. Chem.*, **94**, 161, 1917.

84. HUME-ROTHERY, W.: Structure of Metals and Alloys, *Inst. Metals (London)*, 1939.

85. NORBURY, A. L.: The Volumes Occupied by the Solute Atoms in Certain Metallic Solid Solutions and Their Consequent Hardening Effects, *Trans. Faraday Soc.*, **19**, 586–600, 1924.

86. BRICK, R. M., D. L. MARTIN, and R. P. ANGIER: Effect of Various Solute Elements on the Hardness and Rolling Textures of Copper, *Trans. ASM*, **31**, 675, 1943.

87. FRYE, J. H., JR., and J. W. CAUM: The Hardness of Certain Primary Copper Solid Solutions, *Trans. AIME*, **152**, 75–82, 1943.

88. FRYE, J. H., JR., and W. HUME-ROTHERY: The Hardness of Primary Solid Solutions with Special Reference to Alloys of Silver, *Proc. Roy. Soc. (London)*, **181**, 1–14, 1942.

89. FRYE, J. H., JR., J. W. CAUM, and R. M. TRECO: Hardness and Lattice Stress in Solid Solutions, *Trans. AIME*, **152**, 83–93, 1943.

90. AUSTIN, C. R.: Effect of Elements in Solid Solution on Hardness and Response to Heat Treatment of Iron Binary Alloys, *Trans. ASM*, **31**, 321–339, 1943.

91. LACY, C. E., and M. GENSAMER: The Tensile Properties of Alloyed Ferrites, *Trans. ASM*, **32**, 88–110, 1944.

92. Nabaro, N. F. R.: *Proc. Roy. Soc. (London)* , **175**, 519, 1940; *Proc. Phys. Soc.*, **52**, 90, 1940; N. F. Mott and N. F. R. Nabarro: *Proc. Phys. Soc.*, **52**, 86, 1940.

93. Gensamer, M., E. B. Pearsall, W. S. Pellini, and J. R. Low, Jr.: The Tensile Properties of Pearlite, Bainite and Spheroidite, *Trans. ASM*, **30**, 983–1020, 1942.

94. Gensamer, M.: Strength and Ductility, *Trans. ASM*, **36**, 30–60, 1946.

95. Hollomon, J. H.: The Effect of Heat Treatment and Carbon Content on the Work Hardening Characteristics of Several Steels, *Trans. ASM*, **32**, 123–133, 1944.

96. Hollomon, J. H., L. D. Jaffe, D. E. McCarthy, and M. R. Norton: The Effects of Microstructure on the Mechanical Properties of Steels, *Trans. ASM*, **38**, 807–844, 1947

97. Manjoine, M., and A. Nadai: High-speed Tension Tests at Elevated Temperatures, *Proc. ASTM* **40**, 822–837, 1940.

98. Nadai, A., and M. J. Manjoine: High-speed Tension Tests at Elevated Temperatures, Parts II and III, *J. Applied Mechanics*, **8**, A–77–91, 1941.

99. Gensamer, M.: Strength of Metals under Combined Stresses, *Am. Soc. Metals*, 1941.

100. Hollomon, J. H.: The Problem of Fracture, *J. Am. Welding Soc. Suppl.*, **11**, 534s, 1946.

101. Miller, R. F., G. V. Smith, and G. L. Kehl: Influence of Strain Rate on Strength and Type of Failure of Carbon-Molybdenum Steel at 850, 1000 and 1100F, *Trans. ASM.*, **31**, 817–848, 1943.

102. Zener, C. and J. H. Hollomon: Plastic Flow and Rupture of Metals, *Trans. ASM* **33**, 163–235, 1944.

103. Hollomon, J. H., and C. Zener: High Speed Testing of Mild Steel; *Trans. ASM*, **32**, 111–122, 1944.

104. Tapsell, H. J.: "Creep of Metals," Oxford, New York, 1931.

105. Mcvetty, P. G.: The Interpretation of Creep Tests, *Proc. ASTM*, Part II, **34**, 105–122, 1934.

106. Greenwood, J. N., and C. W. Orr: Influence of Composition on the Properties of Lead, *Proc. Australasian Inst. Mining & Met.*, 1938, pp. 1–24.

107. Hollomon, J. H.: The Mechanical Equation of State, *Trans. AIME*, **171**, 535, 1947.

108. Karnop, R., and G. Sachs: Versuche über die Rekristallisation von Metallen, *Z. Physik.*, **42**, 283–301, 1927.

109. Hanffstengel, K., and J. Hanemann: Der Kriechvorgang in belastetem Blei, *Z. Metallkunde*, **30**, 41–46, 1938.

110. Zener, C., and J. H. Hollomon: Problems in Non-elastic Deformation; *J. Applied Phys.* **17**, 69–82, 1946.

111. Robinson, E. L.: 100,000 Hour Creep Test; *Mech. Eng.*, March, 1943, pp. 166–168.

112. Bailey, R. W.: Note on the Softening of Strain Hardened Metals and Its Relation to Creep, *J. Inst. Metals*, **35**, 27, 1926.

113. Bailey, R. W., and A. M. Roberts: Testing of Materials for Service in High-temperature Steam Plant, *Engineering*, **133**, 261, 1932.

114. Gillett, H. W.: Some Things We Don't Know about the Creep of Metals, *Trans. AIME*, **135**, 15, 1939.

115. CROSS, H. C., and J. G. LOWTHER: Report on Long-time Creep Tests of 18% Cr 8% Ni Steel K19 and 0.35% C Steel K 20, *Proc. ASTM*, **37,** Part I, 178–186, 1937; *ibid.*, **38,** 121–129, 1938.

116. TAPSELL, H. J., and L. E. PROSSER. High Sensitivity Creep Testing Equipment at the National Physical Laboratory, *Engineering*, **137,** 212, 1934.

117. CHEVENARD, P.: Étude experimentalle de la déformation visqueuse des fils de fer et de nickel, *Rev. mét.*, 1934, p. 473.

118. BAILEY, R. W.: The Utilization of Creep Test Data in Engineering Design, *Engineering*, **140,** 595, 1935.

119. JOHNSON, A.: The Creep Recovery of a 0.17 per cent Carbon Steel, *Proc. Inst. Mech. Engrs.*, *(London)*, **146,** 187, 1941.

120. KANTER, J. J.: Interpretation and Use of Creep Results, *Trans. ASM*, **24,** 870–912, 1936.

121. CLARK, C. L., and A. E. WHITE: Influence of Recrystallization Temperature and Grain Size on the Creep Characteristics of Non-ferrous Alloys, *Proc. ASTM*, **32,** Part II, 492–516, 1932.

122. McVETTY, P. G.: Working Stresses for High Temperature Service, *Mech. Eng.*, March, 1934, pp. 149–154.

123. KÊ, T. S.: Experimental Evidence of the Viscous Behavior of Grain Boundaries in Metals, *Phys. Rev.*, **71,** 533–546, 1947.

124. KÊ, T. S.: Stress Relaxation across Grain Boundaries in Metals, *Phys. Rev.*, **72,** 41–46, 1947.

125. WEAVER, S. H.: The Creep and Stability of Steels at Constant Stress and Temperature, *Trans. ASME*, **58,** 745–751, 1936.

126. STURM, R. G., C. DUMONT, and F. M. HOWELL: A Method of Analyzing Creep Data, *J. Applied Mech.*, **58,** A–62–66, 1936.

127. SODERBERG, C. R.: The Interpretation of Creep Tests for Machine Design, *Trans. ASME*, **58,** 733–743, 1936.

128. KANTER, J. J., and L. W. SPRING: Some Long-time Tension Tests of Steel at Elevated Temperatures, *Proc. ASTM*, **30,** Part I, 110, 1930.

129. MARIN, J.: A Comparison of the Methods Used for Interpreting Creep Test Data, *Proc. ASTM*, **37,** Part II, 258–268, 1937.

130. GENTNER, F.: The Interpretation of Creep Tests, *Archiv. Eisenhüttnw.*, **9,** 441–450, 1936.

131. SODERBERG, C. R.: Plastic Flow and Creep in Polycrystalline Materials, *Proc. Intern. Congr. Applied Mech.*, *5th Congr.*, 1938.

132. McVETTY, P. G.: Interpretation of Creep Test Data, *Proc. ASTM*, **43,** 707–734, 1943.

133. ANDRADE, E. N.: On the Viscous Flow in Metals, and Allied Phenomena, *Proc. Roy. Soc.* *(London)*, (A), **84,** 1, 1910.

134. MOORE, H. F., and B. B. BETTY: Discussion, *Trans. ASM*, **24,** 913, 1936.

135. SODERBERG, C. R.: Working Stresses, *Trans. ASME*, **55,** 131, 1933.

136. NORTON, F. H.: "Creep of Steel at High Temperatures," McGraw-Hill, New York, 1929.

137. Compilation of Available High-temperature Creep Characteristics of Metals and Alloys, ASME-ASTM Joint Research Committee on Effect of Temperature on the Properties of Metals, 1938.

138. NADAI, A.: "The Influence of Time upon Creep. The Hyperbolic Sine Creep Law," Stephen Timoshenko Anniversary Volume, Macmillan, pp. 155–170 New York, 1938.

139. NADAI, A.: "The Creep of Metals under Various Stress Conditions," Theodore von Kármán Anniversary Volume, Applied Mechanics, 1941.
140. McVETTY, P. G.: Creep of Metals at Elevated Temperature—The Hyperbolic Sine Relation between Stress and Creep Rate, *Trans. ASME*, **65**, 761–767, 1943.
141. NADAI, A., and P. G. McVETTY: Hyperbolic Sine Chart for Estimating Working Stresses of Alloys at Elevated Temperatures, *Proc. ASTM*, **43**, 735–745, 1943.
142. KANTER, J. J.: The Problem of the Temperature Coefficient of Tensile Creep Rate, *Trans. AIME*, **131**, 385–418, 1938.
143. KANTER, J. J., and E. A. STICHA: Creep Rates from Tests of Short Duration, *Trans. ASM*, **28**, 257–276, 1940.
144. MacGREGOR, C. W., and J. C. FISHER: A Velocity Modified Temperature for the Plastic Flow of Metals, *J. Applied Mechanics*, **13**, 11–16, 1946.
145. MacGREGOR, C. W., and J. C. FISHER: Tension Tests at Constant True Strain Rates, *Trans. ASME*, **67**, A217, 1945.
146. KAUZMANN, W.: Flow of Solid Metals from the Standpoint of the Chemical-rate Theory, *Trans. AIME*, **143**, 57–81, 1941.
147. MANJOINE, M. J.: Influence of Rate of Strain and Temperature on Yield Stresses of Mild Steel, *Trans. ASME*, **66**, A211, 1944.
148. DUSHMAN, S., L. W. DUNBAR, and H. HUTHSTEINER: Creep of Metals, *J. Applied Phys.*, **15**, 108–124, 1944.
149. GLASSTONE, S., K. J. LAIDLER, and H. EYRING: "The Theory of Rate Processes," McGraw-Hill, New York, 1941.
150. EYRING, H.: Viscosity, Plasticity, and Diffusion as Examples of Absolute Reaction Rates, *J. Chem. Phys.*, **4**, 283–291, 1936.
151. CONDON, E. U.: Discussion, *Trans. AIME*, **131**, 410, 1938.
152. NOWICK, A. S., and E. S. MACHLIN: Dislocation Theory as Applied by N.A.C.A. to the Creep of Metals, *J. Applied Phys.*, **18**, 79–87, 1947.
153. HOLLOMON, J. H., and J. D. LUBAHN: The Flow of Metals at Elevated Temperatures, *Gen. Elec. Rev.*, February, April, 1947.
154. FISHER, J. C., and C. W. MacGREGOR: Tempering Effects and the Mechanical Equation of State, *Trans. ASM*, **40**, 302, 1948.
155. BOYD, J.: The Relaxation of Copper at Normal and at Elevated Temperature, *Proc. ASTM*, **37**, Part II, 218–234, 1937.
156. ROBINSON, E. L.: A Relaxation Test on 0.35 C Steel K 20, *Trans. ASME*, **59**, 451–452, 1937.
157. ROBINSON, E. L.: The Resistance to Relaxation of Materials at High Temperature, *Trans. ASME*, **61**, 543–554, 1939.
158. DAVIS, E. A.: Creep and Relaxation of Oxygen-free Copper, *J. Applied Mechanics*, **10**, A101–A105, 1943.
159. GEORGIEFF, M., and E. SCHMID: Uber die Festigkeit und Plastizität von Wismutkristallen, *Z. Phys.*, **36**, 759, 1926.
160. FAHRENHORST, W., and E. SCHMID: Uber die Temperaturabhängigkeit der Kristallplastizität, Part II, *Z. Phys.*, **64**, 895, 1930.
161. SEIGLE, L., and R. M. BRICK: Mechanical Properties of Metals at Low Temperatures; A Survey, *Trans. ASM*, **40**, 813, 1948.
162. BARRETT, C. S., G. ANSEL, and R. F. MEHL: Slip, Twinning and Cleavage in Iron and Silicon Ferrite, *Trans. ASM*, **25**, 702, 1937.

163. GOUGH, H. J.: Crystalline Structure in Relation to Failure of Metals—Especially by Fatigue, *Proc. ASTM*, **33**, Part II, 1933.
164. HEINDLHOFFER, K.: Plasticity of Iron at Low Temperatures, *Trans. AIME*, **116**, 232–238, 1935.
165. DAVIDENKOV, N., and F. WITTMAN: Mechanical Analysis of Impact Brittleness, *Tech. Phys. U.S.S.R.*, **4**, 3–17, 1937.
166. HOLLOMON, J. H., and C. ZENER: Conditions of Fracture in Steel, *Trans. AIME*, **158**, 283, 1944.
167. GENSAMER, M., E. SAIBEL, and J. T. RANSOM: Report on the Fracture of Metals, *J. Am. Welding Soc. Supp.*, **12**, 443-s–484-s, 1947.
168. MAIER, A. F.: Stress Reversal in Tubes under Internal Pressure, *Stahl u. Eisen*, **54**, 1289, 1934.
169. McADAM, D. J.: The Technical Cohesive Strength of Metals, *Trans. ASME*, **63**, A156–A165, 1941.
170. McADAM, D. J., and R. W. MEBS: An Investigation of the Technical Cohesive Strength of Metals, *Trans. AIME*, **162**, 474–537, 1945.
171. McADAM, D. J.: Fracture of Metals under Combined Stresses, *Trans. ASM*, **37**, 538, 1946.
172. SACHS, G., and J. D. LUBAHN: Notched Bar Tensile Tests on Heat Treated Low Alloy Steels, *Trans. ASM*, **31**, 125–157, 1943.
173. SACHS, G., J. D. LUBAHN, and L. J. EBERT: The Effects of Notches of Varying Depth on the Strength of Heat Treated Low Alloy Steels, *Trans. ASM*, **34**, 517–539, 1945.
174. KUNTZE, W.: The Cohesive Strength of Previously Stretched and Compressed Tensile Specimens, *Z. Metallkunde*, **22**, 264–268, 1930.
175. KUNTZE, W.: "Cohesive Strength," Springer, Berlin, 1932.
176. McADAM, D. J., G. W. GEIL, and R. W. MEBS: Influence of Plastic Deformation, Combined Stresses, and Low Temperatures on the Breaking Stress of Ferritic Steels, *Trans. AIME*, **172**, 323, 1947.
177. HOLLOMON, J. H., and C. ZENER: Problems in Fracture of Metals, *J. Applied Phys.*, **17**, 82–90, 1946.
178. SWIFT, A. W.: Tensional Effects of Torsional Overstrain in Mild Steel, *J. Iron Steel Inst.*, **140**, 205, 1937.
179. KÖRBER, F., A. EICHENGER, and H. MÖLLER: The Behavior under Tensile Stress of Metals Deformed by Compression, Mitt. *Kaiser-Wilhelm-Inst. Eisenforsch. Düsseldorf*, **23**, 123–133, 1941; **26**, 71–89, 1943.
180. GOUGH, H. J., and N. V. POLLARD: Strength of Metals under Combined Alternating Stresses, *Inst. Mech. Eng. (London)*, **131**, 3–103, 1935.
181. MAIER, A. F.: Stress Reversal in Tubes under Internal Pressure, *Stahl u. Eisen*, **54**, 1289, 1934.
182. MORIKAWA, G. K., and L. GRIFFIS: The Biaxial Fatigue Strength of Low-carbon Steels, *Research Supp.*, *Welding J.*, **24**, 167s–179s, 1945.
183. WHITE, A. E., C. L. CLARK, and R. L. WILSON: Fracture of Carbon Steels at Elevated Temperatures, *Trans. ASM*, **25**, 863, 1937.
184. WHITE, A. E., C. L. CLARK, and R. L. WILSON: Rupture Strength of Steels at Elevated Temperatures, *Trans. ASM*, **26**, 52, 1938.
185. JEFFRIES, Z.: Effect of Temperature, Deformation and Grain Size on the Mechanical Properties of Metals, *Trans. AIME*, **60**, 474, 1919.

186. DICKENSON, J. H. S.: Some Experiments on the Flow of Steels at a Low Red Heat with a Note on the Scaling of Heated Steels, *J. Iron Steel Inst.*, **106**, 103, 1922.

187. ROSENHAIN, W.: Discussion of Paper by Bengough, *J. Inst. Metals*, **1**, 123–190, 1912.

188. ROSENHAIN, W., and D. EWEN: Intercrystalline Cohesion in Metals, *J. Inst. Metals*, **2**, 149–185, 1912.

189. ROSENHAIN, W., and J. C. W. HUMFREY: The Tenacity, Deformation and Fracture of Soft Steel at High Temperature, *J. Iron Steel Inst.*, **87**, 219–314, 1913.

190. BLEAKNEY, H. H.: Intercrystalline Cohesion and the Stress-rupture Test, *Proc. ASTM*, **47**, 1947.

191. JENKINS, C. H. M., and G. A. MELLOR: Investigation of the Behavior of Metals under Deformation at High Temperatures, Part I, *J. Iron Steel Inst.*, **132**, 179–236, 1935.

192. JENKINS, C. H. M., G. A. MELLOR, and E. A. JENKINSON: Investigation of the Behavior of Metals under Deformation at High Temperatures, Part II, *J. Iron Steel Inst.*, **145**, 51–86, 1942.

193. THIELEMANN, R. H., and E. R. PARKER: Fracture of Steels at Elevated Temperatures after Prolonged Loading, *Trans. AIME*, **135**, 559–575, 1939.

194. AGNEW, J. T., G. A. HAWKINS, and H. L. SOLBERG: Stress-rupture Characteristics of Various Steels in Steam at 1200 F, *Trans. ASME*, **68**, 309–314, 1946.

195. SMITH, G. V., E. J. DULIS, and E. G. HOUSTON: Unpublished Research, U.S. Steel Corp. of Del. Research Laboratory.

196. PARKER, E. R., H. E. DAVIS, and A. E. FLANIGAN: A Study of the Tension Test, *Proc. ASTM*, **46**, 1159–1174, 1946.

197. McADAM, D. J., G. W. GEIL, and D. H. WOODARD: Influence of Strain Rate and Temperature on the Mechanical Properties of Monel Metal and Copper, *Proc. ASTM*, **46**, 902–950, 1946.

198. WOOD, W. A., and H. J. TAPSELL: Mechanism of Creep in Metals, *Nature*, **158**, 415, 1946.

199. OROWAN, E.: Notch Brittleness and the Strength of Metals, *Inst. Engrs. Shipbuilders Scotl. Paper* 1063, 1945.

200. ZWICKY, F.: Die Reissfestigkeit von Steinsalz, *Z. Physik*, **24**, 131, 1923.

201. DE BOER, J. H.: Influence of van der Waals' Forces and Primary Bonds on Binding Energy, Strength and Orientation, *Trans. Faraday Soc.*, **32**, 10, 1936.

202. GRIFFITH, A. A.: Phenomena of Rupture and Flow in Solids, *Proc. Roy. Soc. (London)*, (A), **221**, 163, 1920.

203. GRIFFITH, A. A.: Theory of Rupture, *Proc. Intern. Congr. Applied Mech., 1st Congr., Delft*, 1924, p. 55.

204. JOFFE, A., M. W. KIRPITSCHEWA, and M. A. LEWITSKY: Deformation und Festigkeit der Kristalle, *Z. Phys.*, **22**, 286, 1924; also A. JOFFE, "The Physics of Crystals," McGraw-Hill, New York, 1928.

205. FISHER, J. C., and J. H. HOLLOMON: A Statistical Theory of Fracture, *Trans. AIME*, **171**, 546, 1947.

206. BORN, M., and R. FURTH: Stability of Crystal Lattices, III, Attempt to Calculate the Tensile Strength of a Cubic Lattice by Purely Static Consideration, *Proc. Cambridge Phil. Soc.*, **36**, 454, 1940.

207. FURTH, R.: A Thermodynamic Theory of the Tensile Strength of Isotropic Bodies, *Proc. Roy. Soc. (London)*, (A) **177**, 217, 1940–1941.
208. BORN, M.: Thermodynamics of Crystals and Melting, *J. Chem. Phys.*, **7**, 591–603, 1939.
209. SAIBEL, E.: A Thermodynamic Theory of Fracture of Metals, *Trans. AIME*, **171**, 639, 1947.
210. SAIBEL, E.: Effect of Prior Strain on Fracture, *Trans. AIME*, **172**, 363, 1947.
211. MACHLIN, E. S., and A. S. NOWICK: Stress Rupture of Heat-resisting Alloys as a Rate Process, *Trans. AIME*, **172**, 386, 1947.
212. SMEKAL, A.: *Phys. Z.*, **26**, 707, 1925; *ibid.*, **34**, 633, 1933.
213. ZWICKY, F.: *Proc. Natl. Acad. Sci., U.S.*, **15**, 253, 816, 1929.
214. BECKER, R.: *Phys. Z.*, **26**, 919, 1925.
215. OROWAN, E.: *Z. Physik*, **89**, 605, 1934.
216. OROWAN, E.: Zur Kristallplastizität III. Uber den Mechanismus des Gleit-vorganges, *Z. Physik*, **89**, 634, 1934.
217. POLANYI, M.: *Z. Physik*, **89**, 660, 1934.
218. TAYLOR, G. I.: The Mechanism of Plastic Deformation of Crystals, *Proc. Royal Soc. (London)*, **145**, 362–388, 1934.
219. SCHMID, E., and G. SIEBEL: *Z. Elektrochem*, **37**, 447, 1931.
220. ROSBAUD, P., and E. SCHMID: *Z. Physik*, **32**, 197, 1925.
221. SACHS, G., and J. WEERTS: *Z. Physik*, **62**, 473, 1930.
222. GÖLER, V., and G. SACHS: *Z. Physik*, **55**, 581, 1929.
223. BOAS, W., and E. SCHMID: *Z. Physik*, **61**, 767, 1930.
224. SCHMID, E., and H. SELIGER: *Metallwirtschaft*, **11**, 409, 1932.
225. FAHRENHORST, W., and E. SCHMID: *Z. Physik*, **64**, 845, 1930.
226. BOAS, W., and E. SCHMID: *Z. Physik*, **71**, 703, 1931.
227. HAASE, O., and E. SCHMID: *Z. Physik*, **33**, 413, 1925.
228. OROWAN, E.: The Creep of Metals, *West Scotl. Iron Steel Inst.*, February, 1947.
229. GEISLER, A. H., C. S. BARRETT, and R. F. MEHL: Mechanism of Precipitation from Solid Solutions of Zinc in Aluminum, Magnesium in Aluminum, and of some Magnesium-base Alloys, *Trans. AIME*, **152**, 201–222, 1943.
230. BIRCHENALL, C. E., and R. F. MEHL: Self-diffusion in Iron, *J. Applied Phys.*, **19**, 217, 1948.
231. DORN, J. E., A. GOLDBERG, and T. E. TIETZ: The Effect of Thermal-mechanical History on the Strain-hardening of Metals, *Metals Technol.*, September, 1948.
232. JANITZKY, E. J., and M. BAEYERTZ: The Marked Similarity in Tensile Properties of Several Heat Treated SAE Steels, "ASM Handbook," 515, 1939.
233. BRINELL, J. A.: Researches on the Comparative Hardness of Acid and Basic Open Hearth Steel at Various Temperatures by Means of Ball Testing, *J. Iron Steel Inst.*, **9**, 16–19, 1905.
234. FETZ, E.: Dynamic Hardness Testing of Metals and Alloys at Elevated Temperature, *Trans. ASM*, **30**, 1419–1462, 1942.
235. BISHOP, E. C., and M. COHEN: Hardness Testing of High Speed Steel at High Temperatures, *Metal Progress*, March, 1943, p. 413.
236. BENS, F. P.: Hardness Testing of Metals and Alloys at Elevated Temperature, *Trans. ASM*, **38**, 505–513, 1947.

237. ASTM Recommended Practice for Short-time Elevated-temperature Tension Tests of Metallic Materials: Designation E21-43, ASTM Standards.

238. TAPSELL, H. J.: "Creep of Metals," Oxford, New York, 1931.

239. MANJOINE, M., and A. NADAI: High-speed Tension Tests at Elevated Temperatures, Part I, *Proc. ASTM*, **40**, 822–837, 1940.

240. JENKINS, C. H. M., and G. A. MELLOR: Investigation of the Behavior of Metals under Deformation at High Temperatures, Part I, *J. Iron Steel Inst.*, **132** 179–236, 1935.

241. HATFIELD, W. H.: The Application of Science to the Steel Industry, *Trans. ASST*, **15**, 474, 1929.

242. DIN Tentative Standards, DVM Test Method A117–118, September, 1937.

243. BARR, W., and W. E. BARDGETT: An Accelerated Test for the Determination of the Limiting Creep Stress of Metals, *Proc. Inst. Mech. Engrs. (London)*, **122**, 285–377, 1932.

244. ROBINSON, E. L.: A Relaxation Test on 0.35 C Steel K 20, *Trans. ASME*, **59**, 451–452, 1937.

245. ROHN, W.: Creep Limit of Metals at Elevated Temperatures and Influence of Heat Treatment, *Z. Metallkunde*, **24**, 127–131, 1933.

246. KANTER, J. J.: The Problem of the Temperature Coefficient of Tensile Creep Rate, *Trans. AIME*, **131**, 385, 1938.

247. SMITH, G. V., R. F. MILLER, and W. G. BENZ: Creep and Creep-rupture Testing, *Proc. ASTM*, **47**, 615–638, 1947.

248. NORTON, F. H., and J. A. FELLOWS: A New Device for Creep Testing, *Metal Progress*, October, 1933.

249. McVETTY, P. G.: New Equipment for Creep Tests at Elevated Temperatures, *Proc. ASTM*, **37**, Part II, 235–257, 1937.

250. THIELEMANN, R. H., and E. R. PARKER: Fracture of Steels at Elevated Temperature after Prolonged Loading, *Trans. AIME*, **135**, 559–582, 1939.

251. THIELEMANN, R. H.: Correlation of High Temperature Creep and Rupture Test Results, *Trans. ASM*, **29**, 355–369, 1941.

252. FELLOWS, J. A., E. COOK, and H. S. AVERY: Precision in Creep Testing, *Trans. AIME*, **150**, 358–372, 1942.

253. MANJOINE, M. J.: New Machines for Creep and Creep-rupture Tests, *Trans. ASME*, **67**, 111–116, 1945.

254. McCULLOUGH, G. M.: Experimental and Analytical Investigation of Creep in Bending, *Trans. ASME*, **55**, APM 55-9-55, 1933.

255. TAPSELL, H. J., and A. E. JOHNSON: An Investigation of the Nature of Creep under Stresses Produced by Pure Flexure, *J. Inst. Metals*, **57**, 121–137, 1935.

256. MARIN, J., and L. E. ZWISSLER: Creep of Aluminum Subjected to Bending at Normal Temperatures, *Proc. ASTM*, **40**, 937–947, 1940.

257. DAVIS, E. A.: Creep of Metals at High Temperatures in Bending, *Trans. ASME*, **60**, A-29, 1938.

258. EVERETT, F. L.: Strength of Materials Subjected to Shear at High Temperatures, *Trans. ASME*, APM 53-10, 1931.

259. PHELPS, H. S., A. M. GATES, and F. KAHN: Internal Hydraulic Bursting Tests of Lead Cable Sheathing, *Proc. ASTM*, **40**, 885–903, 1940.

260. NORTON, F. H.: Creep in Tubular Pressure Vessels, *Trans. ASME*, **61**, 239–245, 1939.

261. Report of Joint Research Committee on Effect of Temperature on Properties of Metals, *Proc. ASTM*, **38**, Part I, 112, 1938.
262. BOYD, J.: The Relaxation of Copper at Normal and at Elevated Temperatures, *Proc. ASTM*, **37**, Part II, 218–232, 1937.
263. MOCHEL, N. L.: Relaxation Tests on 0.35 C Steel K20 at 850F, *Trans. ASME*, **59**, 453–455, 1937.
264. KANTER, J. J.: Interpretation and Use of Creep Results, *Trans. ASM*, **24**, 870–912, 1936.
265. ROBINSON, E. L.: The Resistance to Relaxation of Materials at High Temperature, *Trans. ASME*, **61**, 543–554, 1939.
266. NADAI, A., and J. BOYD: Relaxation of Steels at Elevated Temperatures— A New Automatic Relaxation Machine, *J. Applied Mech.*, **60**, A-118, 1938.
267. MOORE, H. F.: Corrosion-fatigue of Metals; "ASM Handbook," 147, 1939.
268. WELCH, W. P., and W. A. WILSON: A New High Temperature Fatigue Machine, *Proc. ASTM*, **41**, 733–745, 1941.
269. HOWELL, F. M., and E. S. HOWARTH: A Fatigue Machine for Testing Metals at Elevated Temperatures, *Proc. ASTM*, **37**, Part II, 207, 1937.
270. MOORE, H. F., and N. T. ALLEMAN: Progress Report on Fatigue Tests of Low Carbon Steel at Elevated Temperatures, *Proc. ASTM*, **31**, Part I, 114, 1931.
271. KINNEY, J. J.: An Investigation of the Effects of Elevated Temperatures on the Fatigue Properties of Two Alloy Steels, *Proc. ASTM*, **38**, Part II, 197–201, 1938.
272. HEMPEL, M., and H. KRUG: Fatigue Diagrams for Steels at High Temperatures, *Archiv. Eisenhüttenw.*, **16**, 261–268, 1943.
273. EVERETT, F. L., and J. MIKLOWITZ: Poisson's Ratio at High Temperatures, *J. Applied Phys.*, **15**, 592–598, 1944.
274. ROBERTS, M. H., and J. NORTCLIFFE: Measurement of Young's Modulus at High Temperatures, *J. Iron Steel Inst.*, **157**, 345–348, 1947.
275. SAUVEUR, A.: Steel at Elevated Temperatures, *Trans. ASST*, **17**, 410–448, 1930.
276. EVERETT, F. L., and C. L. CLARK: Report on Torsion Creep Tests for Comparison with Tension Creep Tests on a Carbon-Molybdenum Steel, *Proc. ASTM*, **39**, 215, 1939.
277. IHRIG, H. K.: The Effect of Various Elements on the Hot Workability of Steel, *Trans. AIME*, **167**, 749–777, 1946.
278. CLARK, C. L., and J. RUSS: A Laboratory Evaluation of the Hot Working Characteristics of Metals, *Trans. AIME*, **167**, 736–748, 1946.
279. FLANIGAN, A. E., L. F. TEDSEN, and J. E. DORN: Compressive Properties of Aluminum Alloy Sheet at Elevated Temperatures, *Proc. ASTM*, **46**, 951, 1946.
280. QUICK, G. W.: The Resistance to Impact of Rail Steels at Elevated Temperatures, *Trans. AIME*, **100**, 1932.
281. KINNEY, W. F., I. A. ROHRIG, and H. S. WALKER: Notch Toughness Tests of Carbon-Molybdenum Pipe Material, *Trans. ASME*, **66**, 421–431, 1941.
282. SAWYER, C. F.: Bend Tests above Room Temperature, *Metal Progress*, **46**, 714, 1944.
283. SCHABTACH, C., and R. O. FEHR: Measurement of the Damping of Engineering Materials during Flexural Vibration at Elevated Temperatures, *J. Applied Mech.*, **11**, A86–A92, 1944.

284. TOOLIN, P. R., and N. L. MOCHEL: The High Temperature Fatigue Strength of Several Gas Turbine Alloys, *Proc. ASTM*, **47**, 677–694, 1947.

285. LEA, F. C.: The Effect of Temperature on Some of the Properties of Metals with Particular Reference to Limiting Creep Stress, *J. Soc. Chem. Ind. (London)*, **46**, 238, 1927.

286. TAPSELL, H. J., and W. J. CLENSHAW: Mechanical Properties of Armco Iron, 0.17 Per Cent Carbon Steel, and 0.24 Per Cent Carbon Steel, with Special Reference to Creep, *Eng. Res'ch. Special Rep.* 1, H. M. Stationery Office, London, 1927; Mechanical Properties of 0.51 Per Cent Carbon Steel and 0.53 Per Cent Carbon Cast Steel, *Eng. Res'ch. Special Rep.* 2, H. M. Stationery Office, London, 1927.

287. POMP, A., and A. DAHMEN: Entwicklung eines abgekürtzten Prüfverfahrens zur Ermittlung der Dauerstandfestigkeit von Stahl bei Erhöhten Temperaturen, *Mitt. Kaiser-Wilhelm-Inst. Eisenforsch.*, **9**, 38–52, 1927.

288. COURNOT, J., and K. SASAGAWA: Sur la viscosité à chaud de quelques alliages, *Compt. rend.*, **181**, 661, 1925.

289. TAPSELL, H. J.: "Creep of Metals," Oxford, New York, 1931.

290. NORTON, F. H.: "Creep of Steels at High Temperature," McGraw-Hill, New York, 1929.

291. WHITE, A. E., C. L. CLARK, and R. L. WILSON: Influence of Carbon Content on High Temperature Properties of Steels, *Trans. ASM*, **23**, 995–1015, 1935.

292. JENKINS, C. H. M., G. A. MELLOR, and E. A. JENKINSON: Investigation of the Behavior of Metals under Deformation at High Temperatures, II, Structural Changes in Carbon Steels Caused by Creep and Graphitization, *J. Iron Steel Inst.*, **145**, 51–86, 1942.

293. AUSTIN, C. R., C. R. ST. JOHN, and R. W. LINDSAY: Creep Properties of Some Binary Solid Solutions of Ferrite, *Trans. AIME*, **162**, 84–105, 1945.

294. MILLER, R. F., W. G. BENZ, and W. E. UNVERZAGT: The Creep Strength of 17 Low-alloy Steels at 1000F, *Proc. ASTM*, **40**, 771–787, 1940.

295. CLARK, C. L., and A. E. WHITE: Creep Characteristics of Metals, *Trans. ASM*, **24**, 831–869, 1936.

296. U.S. Steel Corp. Research Laboratory data.

297. CROSS, H. C., and J. G. LOWTHER: Progress Report on Study of Effects of Manufacturing Variables on the Creep Resistance of Steels, *Proc. ASTM*, **38**, Part I, 149–171, 1938.

298. JENKINS, C. H. M., H. J. TAPSELL, G. A. MELLOR, and A. E. JOHNSON: Some Aspects of the Behavior of Carbon and Molybdenum Steels at High Temperatures, *Trans. Chem. Eng. Congr. World Power Conf.*, London, **1**, 122–162, 1936.

299. BAILEY, R. W.: Steel at Elevated Temperatures, *J. West. Scot. Iron Steel Inst.*, **45**, 11–12, 1937–1938.

300. BULLENS, D. K.: "Steel and Its Heat Treatment," 4th ed., Vol. II, pp. 336–395, Wiley, New York, 1939.

301. BARDENHEUER, P., and W. A. FISCHER: Influence of Titanium upon Creep Limit of Steel, *Archiv. Eisenhüttenw.*, **16**, 31–38, 1942.

302. HOUDREMONT, E., and G. BANDEL: Influence of Titanium upon the Creep Limit of Steels, *Archiv. Eisenhüttenw.*, **16**, 85–97, 1942.

303. WEVER, F., and W. PETER: Precipitation Hardening and Creep Limit of Iron-Columbium Alloys and Columbium Alloyed Steel, *Archiv. Eisenhüttenw.*, **15**, 357–361, 1942.

304. CROSS, H. C., and D. E. KRAUSE: Phosphorus as an Alloying Element in Steels for Use at Elevated Temperature, *Metals & Alloys*, **8**, 53–58, 1937.
305. NEWELL, H. D., and F. E. OLZAK: Effect of Phosphorus in 5 Per cent Chromium 0.5 Per Cent Molybdenum Steel, *Metals & Alloys*, **11**, 106–111, 1940.
306. NEWELL, H. D.: Effect of Silicon on Chromium-Molybdenum Steels for High-temperature Service, with a Note on the Effect of Copper, *Trans. AIME*, **131**, 419–440, 1938.
307. COMSTOCK, G. F., and C. L. CLARK: Effect of Titanium on Some Properties of 17.5 Per Cent Chromium Steel, *Metals & Alloys*, **8**, 42–46, 1937.
308. PARKER, E. R.: The Development of Alloys for Use at Temperatures Above 1000F, *Trans. ASM*, **28**, 797–810, 1940.
309. HOLTMANN, W.: Influence of Alloy on Tensile Strength and Creep Limit of Heat-treated Steels, *Mitt. Kohle-u. Eisenforsch.*, **3**, 1–46, 1941.
310. COMSTOCK, G. F.: Effect of Variations in Composition and Heat Treatment on Some Properties of 4 to 6 Per Cent Chromium Steel Containing Molybdenum and Titanium, *Trans. ASM*, **36**, 81–110, 1946.
311. GRÜN, P.: Die Dauerstandfestigkeit von Stählen in Abhängigkeit von Legierung, und Wärmebehandlung, *Archiv. Eisenhüttenw.*, **8**, 205–211, 1934–1935.
312. BAIN, E. C.: "Functions of the Alloying Elements in Steel," American Society for Metals, Cleveland, Ohio, 1939.
313. AUSTIN, C. R., L. A. LUINI, and R. W. LINDSAY: Annealing Studies on Cold Rolled Iron and Iron Binary Alloys, *Trans. ASM*, **35**, 446, 1945.
314. TAMMANN, G.: Die Folgen der Kaltbearbeitung und ihr Verschwinden durch Temperatursteigerung, *Z. Metallkunde*, **28**, 6, 1936.
315. HOUDREMONT, E., and V. EHMCKE: Warmfeste Stähle, *Archiv. Eisenhüttenw.*, **3**, 49–60, 1929–1930.
316. ARCHBUTT, S. L.: Failure of the Lead Sheathing of Electric Cables, *Trans. Faraday Soc.*, **17**, 22, 1921–1922.
317. MOORE, H. F., and N. J. ALLEMAN: The Creep of Lead and Lead Alloys Used for Cable Sheathing, *Univ. of Ill., Eng. Exp. Sta., Bull.* 243, 1932.
318. MOORE, H. F., B. B. BETTY, and C. W. DOLLINS: The Creep and Fracture of Lead and Lead Alloys, *Univ. of Ill., Eng. Exp. Sta., Bull.* 272, 1935.
319. MOORE, H. F., B. B. BETTY, and C. W. DOLLINS: Investigation of Creep and Fracture of Lead and Lead Alloys for Cable Sheathing, *Univ. of Ill., Eng. Exp. Sta.*, Bull. 306, 1938.
320. MOORE, H. F., C. W. DOLLINS, and W. J. CRAIG: Bursting Tests and Tension Tests for Lead Cable Sheathing, *Proc. ASTM*, **40**, 904–909, 1940.
321. MOORE, H. F., and C. W. DOLLINS: Fracture and Ductility of Lead and Lead Alloys for Cable Sheathing; *Univ. of Ill., Eng. Exp. Sta., Bull.* 347, 1943.
322. PHILLIPS, A. J.: Some Creep Tests on Lead and Lead Alloys, *Proc. ASTM*, **36**, Part II, 171–193, 1936.
323. GREENWOOD, J. N.: The Influence of Impurities on the Properties of Lead, *Proc. Australasian Inst. Mining & Met.*, No. 95, 79–124, 1934.
324. GREENWOOD, J. N., and H. K. WORNER: The Influence of Impurities on the Properties of Lead—The Influence of Tellurium on the Creep Rate of Commercial Lead, *Proc. Australasian Inst. Mining & Met.*, No. 101, 57–87, 1936.
325. GREENWOOD, J. N., and H. K. WORNER: Influence of Elements on the Properties of Lead—The Influence of Composition on the Creep Rate of Industrial Lead, *Proc. Australasian Inst. Mining & Met.*, No. 104, 385, 1936.

326. BASSETT, W. H., and C. J. SNYDER: The Testing of Lead Cable Coverings, *Proc. ASTM*, **40,** 910–929, 1940.

327. GOHN, G. R., S. M. ARNOLD, and G. M. BOUTON: Creep Tests on Some Extruded Lead and Lead-alloy Sleeves and Tapes, *Proc. ASTM*, **46,** 990, 1946.

328. SMITH, A. A., JR., and H. E. HOWE: Creep Properties of Some Rolled Lead-Antimony Alloys, *Trans. ASME*, **161,** 472–477, 1945.

329. RUZICKA, J.: Equipment for Routine Creep Tests on Zinc and Zinc-base Alloys, and an Example of Its Application, *Trans. AIME*, **124,** 252–270, 1937.

330. KELTON, E. H., and B. D. GRISSINGER: Creep Data on Die-cast Zinc Alloy, *Trans. AIME*, **161,** 466–471, 1945.

331. HANSON, D., and E. J. SANDFORD: The Creep of Tin and Tin Alloys, Part I, *J. Inst. Metals*, **59,** 159–178, 1936.

332. LEONTIS, T. E., and J. P. MURPHY: Properties of Cerium-containing Magnesium Alloys at Room and Elevated Temperatures, *Trans. AIME*, **166,** 295, 1946.

333. MOORE, A. A., and J. C. McDONALD: Tensile and Creep Strengths of Some Magnesium—Base Alloys at Elevated Temperature, *Proc. ASTM*, **46,** 970, 1946.

334. WELTER, G.: Statisck Dauerfestigkeit von Metallen and Legierungen, *Z. Metallkunde*, **18,** 75, 1926; Ermüdung durch kritische statische Dauerbelastung, *Z. Metallkunde*, **20,** 51, 1928.

335. FLANIGAN, A. E., L. F. TEDSON, and J. E. DORN: Stress Rupture and Creep Tests on Aluminum-alloy Sheet at Elevated Temperatures, *Trans. AIME*, **171,** 213, 1947.

336. HANSON, D., and E. J. Sandford: The Creep of Tin and Tin Alloys, Part II, *J. Inst. Metals*, **62,** 215–237, 1938.

337. BROWN, J. S.: Influence of the Time Factor on Tensile Tests Conducted at Elevated Temperatures, *J. Inst. Metals*, **34,** 21, 1925.

338. COURNOT, J., and R. PAGÈS: Suite à l'étude de la viscosité à température élevée, *Rev. mét.*, **23,** 701, 1926.

339. BOLTON, J. W., and F. H. HEHEMANN: Discussion, ASTM-ASME Symposium on Effect of Temperature on the Properties of Metals, 1931, p. 361–363.

340. KANTER, J. J.: Discussion, ASTM-ASME Symposium on Effect of Temperature on the Properties of Metals, 1931, p. 361–363.

341. CLARK, C. L., and A. E. WHITE: Influence of Recrystallization Temperature and Grain Size on the Creep Characteristics of Non-ferrous Alloys, *Proc. ASTM*, **32,** Part II, 492–516, 1932.

342. JENKINS, C. H. M., and E. H. BUCKNALL: The Inter-relation of Age-hardening and Creep Performance, Part I, The Age Hardening of Nickel-Silicon-Copper Alloys, *J. Inst. Metals*, **57,** 141–171, 1935.

343. JENKINS, C. H. M., E. H. BUCKNALL, and E. A. JENKINSON: The Inter-relation of Age-hardening and Creep Performance, Part II, The Behavior in Creep of an Alloy Containing 3 Per Cent Nickel and Silicon in Copper, *J. Inst. Metal,* **70,** 57–79, 1944.

344. PARKER, E. R.: The Effect of Impurities on Some High Temperature Properties of Copper, *Trans. ASM*, **29,** 269–284, 1941.

345. PARKER, E. R., and C. FERGUSON: Rupture Tests at 200 Degrees Centigrade on Some Copper Alloys, *Trans. ASM*, **31,** 699–715, 1943.

346. BURGHOFF, H. L., A. I. BLANK, and S. E. MADDIGAN: The Creep Characteristics of Some Copper Alloys at Elevated Temperatures, *Proc. ASTM*, **42,** 668–691, 1942.

347. JENKINS, C. H. M., H. J. TAPSELL, C. R. AUSTIN, and W. P. REES: Alloys for Use at High Temperatures, Part II, *J. Iron Steel Inst.*, **121,** 237–314, 1930.

348. BETTY, B. B., E. C. MACQUEEN, and CARL ROLLE: Relaxation Resistance of Nickel-alloy Springs, *Trans. ASME*, **64,** 465, 1942.

349. KENNEDY, R. R.: Creep Characteristics of Aluminum Alloys, *Proc. ASTM*, **35,** Part II, 218–232, 1935.

350. BOLTON, J. W.: Some Tests on Tin Bronzes at Elevated Temperatures, *Proc. ASTM*, **35,** Part II, 204–217, 1935.

351. HILDORF, W. G., C. L. CLARK, and A. E. WHITE: Characteristics of 5.0 and 7.0 Per Cent Chromium Steels with Varying Molybdenum and Vanadium Content, *Trans. ASM*, **27,** 1090–1117, 1939.

352. CROSS, H. C.: High-temperature Tensile, Creep and Fatigue of Cast and Wrought High and Low Carbon, 18 Cr–8 Ni Steel from Split Heats, *Trans. ASME*, **56,** 533–553, 1934.

353. TAPSELL, H. J., and A. E. JOHNSON: The Properties of Copper in Relation to Low Stresses. The Effect of Cold-work, Heat Treatment, and Composition, Part II, Creep Tests at 300 C and 350 C of Arsenical Copper and Silver-arsenical Copper, *J. Inst. Metals*, **48,** 89–96, 1932.

354. MARTIN, D. L., and E. R. PARKER: Effect of Cooling Rate and Minor Constituents on the Rupture Properties of Copper at 200°C, *Trans. AIME*, **156,** 126–141, 1944.

355. BETTY, B. B., H. L. EISELSTEIN, and F. P. HUSTON: Creep Properties of Cold-drawn Annealed Monel and Inconel, *Trans. AIME*, **161,** 441–454, 1945.

356. MONTGOMERY, H. E.: Properties of Some Cast Copper-base Alloys at Elevated Temperatures, *Trans. AIME*, **161,** 455–465, 1945.

357. Compilation of Available High-temperature Creep Characteristics of Metals and Alloys (1938), issued under the auspices of the Joint ASTM–ASME Committee on the Effect of Temperature on the Properties of Metals.

358. KINZEL, A. B.: Discussion, ASTM–ASME Symposium on Effect of Temperature on the Properties of Metals, 1931, p. 389.

359. GILLETT, H. W.: Discrepancies in the Load-carrying Abilities of Carbon Steels at 850 F, *Proc. ASTM*, **37,** 187, 1937.

360. WHITE, A. E., and SABIN CROCKER: Effect of Grain Size and Structure on Carbon-Molybdenum Steel Pipe, *Trans. ASME*, **63,** 749–764, 1941.

361. CROSS, H. C., and J. G. LOWTHER: First Progress Report on Study of Effects of Manufacturing Variables on the Creep Resistance of Steels, *Proc. ASTM*, **38,** Part I, 149, 1938.

362. CROSS, H. C., and J. G. LOWTHER: Second Progress Report on Study of Effects of Manufacturing Variables on the Creep Resistance of Steels, *Proc. ASTM*, **40,** 125, 1940.

363. CROSS, H. C., and W. SIMMONS: Study of Effects of Variables on the Creep Resistance of Steels, *Proc. ASTM*, **44,** 161–185, 1944.

364. MILLER, R. F.: Effect of Deoxidation Practice on Creep Strength of Carbon-Molybdenum Steel at 850 and 1000F, *Trans. ASME*, **65,** 309–316, 1943.

365. KANTER, J. J., and L. W. SPRING: Long Time or Flow Tests on Carbon Steels at Various Temperatures with Particular Reference to Stresses below the Proportional Limit, *Proc. ASTM*, **28,** Part II, 80–116, 1928.
366. WYMAN, L. L.: The Creep of Steels as Influenced by Microstructure, *Mech. Eng.*, October, 1935, pp. 625–627.
367. MILLER, R. F., R. F. CAMPBELL, R. H. ABORN, and E. C. WRIGHT: Influence of Heat Treatment on Creep of Carbon-Molybdenum and Chromium-Molybdenum-Silicon Steel, *Trans. ASM*, **26,** 81, 1938.
368. WEAVER, S. H.: Actual Grain Size Related to Creep Strength of Steels at Elevated Temperature, *Proc. ASTM*, **38,** Part II, 176–196, 1938.
369. WEAVER, S. H.: The Effect of Carbide Spheroidization upon the Creep Strength of Carbon-Molybdenum Steel, *Proc. ASTM*, **41,** 608, 1941.
370. WEAVER, S. H.: The Effect of Carbide Spheroidization upon the Rupture Strength and Elongation of Carbon-Molybdenum Steel, *Proc. ASTM*, **46,** 856, 1946.
371. COMSTOCK, G. F.: Effect of Variations in Composition and Heat Treatment on Some Properties of 4 to 6 Per cent Chromium Steel Containing Molybdenum and Titanium, *Trans. ASM*, **36,** 81–110, 1946.
372. AUSTIN, C. R., and C. H. SAMANS: Effects of Temperature of Pretreatment on Creep Characteristics of 18-8 Stainless Steel at 600 to 800C, *Trans. AIME*, **140,** 459–474, 1940.
373. KANTER, J. J., and L. W. SPRING: Some Long-time Tension Tests of Steels at Elevated Temperatures, *Proc. ASTM*, **30,** Part I, 110–132, 1930.
374. JEFFRIES, Z.: The Amorphous Metal Hypothesis and Equi-cohesive Temperatures, *J. Am. Inst. Metals*, **11,** 300–324, 1917.
375. JEFFRIES, Z.: Effect of Temperature, Deformation, and Grain Size on the Mechanical Properties of Metals, *Trans. AIME*, **60,** 474–576, 1919.
376. ROSENHAIN, W., and D. EWEN: Intercrystalline Cohesion in Metals, *J. Inst. Metals*, **8,** 149–185, 1912.
377. ROSENHAIN, W., and J. C. W. HUMFREY: The Tenacity, Deformation and Fracture of Soft Steel at High Temperature, *J. Iron Steel Inst.*, **87,** 219–314, 1913.
378. BEILBY, G. T.: The Hard and Soft States in Metals, *J. Inst. Metals*, **6,** 5–43, 1911.
379. BENGOUGH, G. D.: A Study of the Properties of Alloys at High Temperatures, *J. Inst. Metals*, **7,** 123–174, 1912.
380. VILELLA, J. R.: The Grain Size of Steel, *Mech. Eng.*, **62,** 293–307, 1940.
381. WHITE, A. E., and C. L. CLARK: Influence of Grain-size on the High Temperature Characteristics of Ferrous and Non-ferrous Alloys, *Trans. ASM*, **22,** 1069–1098, 1934.
382. CROSS, H. C., and E. R. JOHNSON: Creep Properties of 5 Per Cent Chromium, 0.50 Per Cent Molybdenum Steel Still Tubes, *Proc. ASTM*, **34,** Part II, 80–104, 1934.
383. HANSON, D., and M. A. WHEELER: The Deformation of Metals Under Prolonged Loading, Part I, The Flow and Fracture of Aluminum, *J. Inst. Metals*, **45,** 229–264, 1931.
384. MCKEOWN, J.: Creep of Lead and Lead Alloys, Part I, Creep of Virgin Lead, *J. Inst. Metals*, **60,** 201–222, 1937.

385. WEAVER, S. H.: Relation of Grain Size to Creep Strength of Carbon-Molybdenum Steel, *Gen. Elec. Rev.*, **43**, 357–364, 1940.
386. HANSON, D.: The Creep of Metals, *Trans. AIME*, **133**, 15–57, 1939.
387. GILLETT, H. W.: Some Things We Don't Know about the Creep of Metals, *Trans. AIME*, **135**, 15–58, 1939.
388. CLARK, C. L., and A. E. WHITE: Report on Further Experiments with a Proposed Acceptance Test: Effect of Grain Size, *Proc. ASTM*, **39**, 225–233, 1939.
389. THIELEMANN, R. H.: Some Effects of Composition and Heat Treatment on the High Temperature Rupture Properties of Ferrous Alloys, *Proc. ASTM*, **40**, Part II, 788–804, 1940.
390. CLARK, C. L., and J. W. FREEMAN: The Apparent Influence of Grain Size on the High Temperature Properties of Austenitic Steels, *Trans. ASM*, **38**, 148–169, 1947.
391. PARKER, E. R.: Intercrystalline Cohesion of Metals, *Trans. ASM*, **33**, 150–162, 1944.
392. PARKER, E. R., and C. R. RIISNESS: Effect of Grain Size and Bar Diameter on Creep Rate of Copper at 200C, *Trans. AIME*, **156**, 117–125, 1944.
393. ROBINSON, E. L.: Effect of Temperature Variation on the Creep Strength of Steels, *Trans. ASME*, **60**, 253, 1938.
394. BROPHY, G. R., and D. E. FURMAN: The Cyclic Temperature Acceleration of Strain in Heat Resisting Alloys, *Trans. ASM*, **30**, 1115–1138, 1942.
395. AVERY, H. S.: See discussion of reference 394.
396. AVERY, H. S., and N. A. MATTHEWS: Cast Heat Resistant Alloys of the 16% Cr–35% Ni Type, *Trans. ASM*, **38**, 957–1015, 1947.
397. BAILEY, R. W.: Creep of Steel under Simple and Compound Stresses and the Use of High Initial Temperature in Steam Power Plant, World Power Conference, Tokyo, 1929.
398. BAILEY, R. W.: Thick-walled Tubes and Cylinders under High Pressure and Temperature, *Engineering (London)*, **129**, 772, 1930.
399. BAILEY, R. W.: Creep of Steel under Simple and Compound Stresses, *Engineering (London)*, **129**, 265–266, 327–329, 1930.
400. EVERETT, F. L.: Strength of Materials Subjected to Shear at High Temperature, *Trans. ASME*, **53**, 1931; Discussion, ASTM–ASME Symposium on Effect of Temperature on Properties of Metals, 1932, p. 238–242.
401. TAPSELL, H. J., and A. E. JOHNSON: An Investigation of the Nature of Creep under Stresses Produced by Pure Flexure, *J. Inst. Metals*, **57**, 121–137, 1935.
402. MARIN, J.: Design of Members Subjected to Creep at High Temperatures, *Trans. ASME*, **59**, 1937.
403. BAILEY, R. W.: The Utilization of Creep Test Data in Engineering Design, *Proc. Inst. Mech. Engrs. (London)*, **131**, 131–149, 1936; *J. Applied Mech.*, **58**, A-1, 1936.
404. EVERETT, F. L., and C. L. CLARK: Report on Torsion Creep Tests for Comparison with Tension Creep Tests on a Carbon-Molybdenum Steel, *Proc. ASTM*, **39**, 215–224, 1939.
405. DAVIS, E. A.: Correlation of Test Results for Various Types of High-temperature Tests Carried out for the Joint Research Committee, *Proc. ASTM*, **39**, 234–237, 1939.

406. NORTON, F. H.: Creep in Tubular Pressure Vessels, *Trans. ASME*, **61**, 239–245, 1939.

407. NADAI, A.: Plastic Behavior of Metals in the Strain Hardening Range, Part I, *J. Applied Phys.*, **8**, 205–213, 1937.

408. NADAI, A.: On the Creep of Solids at Elevated Temperature, *J. Applied Phys.*, **8**, 418–432, 1937.

409. NORTON, F. H.: Progress Report on Tubular Creep Tests, *Trans. ASME*, **63**, 735–736, 1941.

410. SODERBERG, C. R.: Interpretation of Creep Tests on Tubes, *Trans. ASME*, **63**, 737–748, 1941.

411. VAN DUZER, R. M., JR., and ARTHUR McCUTCHAN: High-temperature Steam Experience at Detroit, *Trans. ASME*, **61**, 383–401, 1939.

412. PHELPS, H. S., A. M. GATES, and F. KAHN: Internal Bursting Tests of Lead Cable Sheathing, *Proc. ASTM*, **40**, 885–903, 1940.

413. MARIN, J., and L. E. ZWISSLER: Creep of Aluminum Subjected to Bending at Normal Temperatures, *Proc. ASTM*, **40**, 937–947, 1940.

414. DAVIS, E. A.: Creep of Metals at High Temperatures in Bending, *Trans. ASME*, **60**, A 29–A 31, 1938.

415. PHELPS, H. S., A. M. GATES, and F. KAHN: Internal Hydraulic Bursting Tests of Lead Cable Sheathing, *Proc. ASTM*, **40**, 885–903, 1940.

416. SIEGFRIED, W.: Brittleness and Ductility of Metal at High Temperatures, *Technische Rundschau Sulzer*, No. 1, pp. 43–79, 1945; see *The Engineers' Digest*, **2**, 391–396, 1945.

417. CHASTON, J. C.: Note on the Effect of Interrupted Straining on the Elongation of Lead, *J. Inst. Metals*, **57**, 109–114, 1935.

418. FOLEY, F. B.: Interpretation of Creep and Stress-rupture Data, *Metal Progress*, **51**, 951–958, 1947.

419. GLEN, J.: Abnormal Creep in Carbon Steels, *J. Iron Steel Inst.*, **155**, 501–512, 1947.

420. ROBINSON, E. L.: Some 1000 F Steam Pipe Materials, *Trans. ASME*, **70**, 855–865, 1948.

421. BARNETT, W. J., and A. R. TROIANO: X-ray Identification of Sigma Phase in 25-20 Cr-Ni Stainless, *Metal Progress*, **35**, 366–367, 1948.

422. GLEN, J.: The Creep Properties of Molybdenum, Chromium-Molybdenum, and Molybdenum-Vanadium Steels, *J. Iron Steel Inst.*, **158**, 37–80, 1948.

423. PILLING, N. B., and R. E. BEDWORTH: The Oxidation of Metals at High Temperatures, *J. Inst. Metals*, **29**, 529–581, 1923.

424. HEINDLHOFER, K., and B. M. LARSEN: Rates of Scale Formation on Iron and a Few of Its Alloys, *Proc. ASST*, **21**, 865–895, 1933.

425. DAY, M. J., and G. V. SMITH: Iron Alloy Scaling, *Industrial and Engineering Chemistry*, **35**, 1098–1103, 1943.

426. BRASUNAS, A. DES., J. T. GOW and O. E. HARDER: Resistance of Iron-Nickel-Chromium Alloys to Corrosion in Air at 1600 to 2200 F, *Proc. ASTM*, **46**, 129, 1946.

427. SOLBERG, H. L., G. A. HAWKINS, and A. A. POTTER: Corrosion of Unstressed Steel Specimens and Various Alloys by High-temperature Steam, *Trans. ASME*, **64**, 303–313, 1942.

428. HAWKINS, G. A., H. L. SOLBERG, J. T. AGNEW, and A. A. POTTER: Corrosion

of Unstressed Specimens of Alloy Steel by Steam at Temperatures up to 1800 F, *Trans. ASME*, **65**, 301–308, 1943.

429. HAWKINS, G. A., J. T. AGNEW, and H. L. SOLBERG: The Corrosion of Alloy Steels by High Temperature Steam, *Trans. ASME*, **66**, 291–295, 1944.

430. ROHRIG, I. A., R. M. VAN DUZER, JR., and C. H. FELLOWS: High Temperature Steam Corrosion Studies at Detroit, *Trans. ASME*, **66**, 277–290, 1944.

431. PREECE, A., and R. V. RILEY: The Scaling Properties of Steels in Furnace Atmospheres at 1150 C, *J. Iron Steel Inst.*, **149**, 253, 1944.

432. STAUFFER, W., and H. KLEIBER: The Scaling Behavior of High-strength Heat-resisting Steels in Air and Combustion Gases, *J. Iron Steel Inst.*, **156**, 181–188, 1947.

433. NICHOLSON, J. H., and E. J. KWASNEY: Scaling at High Temperatures in Sulfur Dioxide, Oxygen, and Nitrogen Containing Atmospheres, *Trans. Electchem. Soc.*, **91**, 681, 1947.

434. ASME Boiler Code, American Society of Mechanical Engineers, New York; API–ASME Code, American Petroleum Institute, New York.

435. BOWMAN, F. E., R. M. PARKE, and A. J. HERZIG: The Alpha Iron Lattice Parameter as Affected by Molybdenum and an Introduction to the Problems of the Partition of Molybdenum in Steel, *Trans. Am. Soc. Metals*, **31**, 487, 1943; see also subsequent papers by Bowman and associates, *Trans. Am. Soc. Metals*, **33**, 481, 1944, **35**, 112, 1945.

436. CRAFTS, W., and C. M. OFFENHAUER: Carbides in Low Chromium Steels, *Trans. Am. Inst. Mining Met. Engrs.*, **150**, 275–287, 1942.

437. CRAFTS, W., and C. M. OFFENHAUER: Carbides in Low Chromium-Molybdenum Steels, *Trans. Am. Inst. Mining Met. Engrs.*, **154**, 361, 1943.

438. SMITH, G. V., R. F. MILLER, and C. O. TARR: Structural Changes in Carbon and Molybdenum Steels during Prolonged Heating at 900 to 1100 F, as Affected by Deoxidation Practice, *Proc. ASTM*, **45**, 486–506, 1945.

439. WELLS, C.: Graphitization of High Purity Iron-Carbon Alloys, *Trans. Am. Soc. Metals*, **26**, 289–357, 1938.

440. ENGEL, E. H.: The Softening Rate of a Steel when Tempered from Different Initial Structures, *Trans. Am. Soc. Metals*, **27**, 1, 1939.

441. BAIN, E. C.: "Functions of the Alloying Elements in Steel," *American Society for Metals*, 1939.

442. AUSTIN, C. R., and B. S. NORRIS: Effect of Tempering Quenched Hypereutectoid Steels on the Physical Properties and Microstructure, *Trans. Am. Soc. Metals*, **26**, 788–845, 1938.

443. AUSTIN, C. R., and B. S. NORRIS: Temperature-gradient Studies on Tempering Reactions of Quenched High-carbon Steels, *Trans. AIME*, **131**, 349–371, 1938.

444. AUSTIN, C. R., and M. C. FETZER: Reactions to Annealing above the Eutectoid Temperature of Quenched Hypereutectoid Steels, *Trans. Am. Soc. Metals*, **27**, 13–39, 1939.

445. AUSTIN, C. R., and M. C. FETZER: Effect of Composition and Steel-making Practice on Graphitization below the A1 of Eighteen One Per Cent Plain Carbon Steels, *Trans. Am. Inst. Mining Met. Engrs.*, **145**, 213–224, 1941.

446. AUSTIN, C. R., and M. C. FETZER: Cementite Stability and Its Relation to Grain Size, Abnormality and Hardenability, *Trans. Am. Soc. Metals*, **29**, 339–354, 1941.

447. AUSTIN, C. R., and B. S. NORRIS: Effects of Small Amounts of Alloying Elements on Graphitization of Pure Hypereutectoid Steels, *Trans. Am. Soc. Metals*, **30,** 425–457, 1942.

448. AUSTIN, C. R., and M. C. FETZER: Factors Controlling Graphitization of Carbon Steels at Subcritical Temperatures, *Trans. Am. Soc. Metals*, **35,** 485–535, 1945.

449. MILLER, R. F., R. F. CAMPBELL, R. H. ABORN, and E. C. WRIGHT: Influence of Heat Treatment on Creep of Carbon-Molybdenum and Chromium-Molybdenum-Silicon Steel, *Trans. Am. Soc. Metals*, **26,** 81–101, 1938.

450. JENKINS, C. H. M., G. A. MELLOR, and E. A. JENKINSON, Investigation of the Behavior of Metals under Deformation at High Temperatures, Part II, Structural Changes in Carbon Steels Caused by Creep and Graphitization, *J. Iron Steel Inst.*, **145,** 51, 1942.

451. WHITE, A. E., C. L. CLARK, and R. L. WILSON: Influence of Time at 1000 F on the Characteristics of Carbon Steel, *Proc. ASTM*, **36,** Part II, 139, 1936.

452. MILLER, R. F., W. G. BENZ, and W. E. UNVERZAGT: The Creep Strength of 17 Low-alloy Steels at 1000 F, *Proc. ASTM*, **40,** 771, 1940.

453. MILLER, R. F., W. G. BENZ, and M. J. DAY: Creep Strength, Stability of Microstructure, and Oxidation Resistance of Cr-Mo and 18 Cr–8 Ni Steels, *Trans. Am. Soc. Metals*, **32,** 381, 1944.

454. WEAVER, S. H.: The Creep Curve and Stability of Steels at Constant Stress and Temperature, *Trans. ASME*, November, 1936, RP 58-16.

455. WEAVER, S. H.: The Effect of Carbide Spheroidization upon the Creep Strength of Carbon-Molybdenum Steel, *Proc. ASTM*, **41,** 608, 1941.

456. BAILEY, R. W., and A. M. ROBERTS: Testing of Materials for Service in High-temperature Steam Plants, *Proc. Inst. Mech. Engr.*, **122,** 209–284, 1932.

457. WELLS, C.: Graphitization of High Purity Iron-Carbon Alloys, *Trans. Am. Soc. Metals*, **26,** 289–357, 1938.

458. KINZEL, A. B., and R. W. MOORE: Graphite in Low-carbon Steel, *Trans. AIME*, **116,** 318–329, 1935.

459. EMERSON, R. W.: Carbide Instability of Carbon-Molybdenum Steel Piping, "Graphitization of Steel Piping," pp. 5–15, American Society of Mechanical Engineers, 1944.

460. HUGHES, M. A., and J. G. CUTTON: Graphite in Cold-rolled Subcritically Annealed Hypoeutectoid Steels, *Trans. ASM*, **37,** 110–135, 1946.

461. McQuaid-Ehn Carburizing Test, E19-39T Austenite Grain Size in Steels, ASTM Standards, p. 1933, 1944.

462. KERR, H. J., and F. EBERLE: Graphitization of Low-carbon and Low-carbon-molybdenum Steels, "Graphitization of Steel Piping," pp. 1–46, American Society of Mechanical Engineers, 1945.

463. "Graphitization of Steel Piping," American Society of Mechanical Engineers, 1944, 1945; *Trans. ASME*, **68,** 571–631, 1946.

464. SMITH, G. V., and R. F. MILLER: A Possible Means of Avoiding Local Graphitization of Steels in Service at Elevated Temperature, "Graphitization of Steel Piping," American Society of Mechanical Engineers, 1944.

465. SMITH, G. V., R. F. MILLER, and C. O. TARR: Precipitation and Reversion of Graphite in Low-carbon Low-alloy Steel in the Temperature Range 900 to 1300 F, *Trans. AIME*, **158,** 387, 1944.

466. PARKER, E. R.: The Development of Alloys for Use at High Temperatures above 1000 F, *Trans. ASM*, **38,** 797–810, 1940.

467. THUM, E. E.: "The Book of Stainless Steels," 2d ed., Amer. Soc. Metals, Cleveland, 1939.
468. URBAN, S. F.: Method of Making Chromium-Nickel Austenitic Stainless Steel, U.S. Patent 2,374,396, April 24, 1945.
469. CLARK, C. L., and J. W. FREEMAN: The Mechanism of Failure of 18 Cr–8 Ni Cracking Still Tubes, *Trans. ASM*, **35**, 298–330, 1945.
470. KAHN, W., H. OSTER, and R. WACHTELL: Investigation of a Type of Failure of 18–8 Stabilized Stainless Steel, *Trans. ASM*, **37**, 567–585, 1946.
471. FOLEY, F. B.: The Sigma Phase; *Alloy Casting Bull.* 5, Alloy Casting Institute, New York, July, 1945.
472. GOW, J. T., and O. E. HARDER: Balancing the Composition of Cast 25 per cent Chromium–12 per cent Nickel Type Alloys, *Trans. ASM*, **30**, 855, 1942.
473. AVERY, H. S., E. COOK, and J. A. FELLOWS: Engineering Properties of Heat-resistant Alloys, *Trans. AIME*, **150**, 373, 1942.
474. HOLLOMON, J. H.: Temper Brittleness, *Trans. ASM*, **36**, 473–542, 1946.
475. NEWELL, H. D.: Properties and Characteristics of 27% Chromium-Iron, *Metal Progress*, May, 1946, p. 977.
476. LOW, J. R., and M. GENSAMER: Aging and the Yield Point in Steel, *Trans. AIME*, **158**, 207–250, 1944.
477. WHITE, A. E., C. L. CLARK, and R. L. WILSON: The Fracture of Carbon Steels at Elevated Temperatures, *Trans. ASM*, **25**, 863–888, 1937.
478. SMITH, A. A.: Creep and Recrystallization of Lead, *Trans. AIME*, **143**, 165, 1941.
479. GOHN, G. R., S. M. ARNOLD, and G. M. BOUTON: Creep Tests on Some Extruded Lead and Lead Alloy Sleeves and Tapes, *Proc. ASTM*, **46**, 990–1024, 1946.
480. WEAVER, S. H.: The Effect of Carbide Spheroidization upon the Rupture Strength and Elongation of Carbon-Molybdenum Steel, *Proc. ASTM*, **46**, 856–869, 1946.
481. PAYSON, P., and C. H. SAVAGE: Changes in Austenitic Chromium-Nickel Steels during Exposure at 1100 to 1700 F, *Trans. ASM*, **39**, 403–452, 1947.
482. BAIN, E. C., R. H. ABORN, and J. J. B. RUTHERFORD: The Nature and Prevention of Intergranular Corrosion in Austenitic Stainless Steels, *Trans. ASST*, **21**, 481–509, 1938.
483. SMITH, G. V.: Graphitization of Low-carbon Low-alloy Steels: An Appraisal of the Literature, *Welding J.*, **27**, 277s–284s, 1948.
484. MILLER, R. F., G. V. SMITH, and P. A. JENNINGS: Alloy Steels for High Temperature Service—Their Properties Compared, *Metals & Alloys*, September, November, 1942.
485. VAN DUZER, R. M., JR., and ARTHUR McCUTCHAN: High Temperature Steam Experience at Detroit, *Trans. ASME*, **61**, 383–401, 1939.
486. FREEMAN, J. W., E. E. REYNOLDS, and A. E. WHITE: High Temperature Alloys Developed for Aircraft Turbo-superchargers and Gas Turbines, ASTM Symposium on Materials for Gas Turbines, 1946, pp. 52–79.
487. McVETTY, P. G.: The Interpretation of Creep Tests, *Proc. ASTM*, **34**, Part II, 105–116, 1934.
488. KANTER, J. J.: Interpretation and Use of Creep Results, *Trans. ASM*, **24**, 870, 1936.

APPENDIX

SUPERALLOYS

by R. F. MILLER

The term "superalloys" has been applied to alloys with the highest available strength at elevated temperatures. While there has been a general trend in the direction of alloys with improved strength for elevated-temperature applications for many years, development work on this subject was greatly accelerated during the Second World War due to the necessity of improving the performance of gas turbines for three different applications. The first of these, and the only one which came into general use during the war, was an exhaust gas turbine for supercharging reciprocating aircraft engines. The second application, which was coming into use just as the war ended, was the jet engine, and the third was the marine gas turbine for ship propulsion. These applications were of such great importance to the war effort that extensive development work was carried out on superalloys by individual manufacturers and by various government agencies such as the War Metallurgy Committee of the National Research Council (Office of Scientific Research and Development) and the National Advisory Committee for Aeronautics. The results of many of these investigations have now been declassified and most of the information has been published in the technical literature. The War Metallurgy Committee work was summarized by Cross and Simmons,[1]* while Freeman, Reynolds, and White[2] have described the investigation sponsored by the National Advisory Committee for Aeronautics. Hundreds of new compositions were developed and tested and the properties of the known alloys were thoroughly explored. The alloys themselves ranged in composition from the familiar iron-base 18 Cr-8 Ni types to the cobalt-base Stellites (Vitallium)† and the nickel-base Hastelloy and inconel alloys.

For gas-turbine applications, the minimum information necessary for each alloy and usually for each condition of each alloy is as follows:

1. Creep strength
2. Rupture strength
3. Amount of extension for specific stresses and times
4. Amount of extension at failure
5. Fatigue strength
6. Damping capacity

---

* See references at end of Appendix.

† The composition of the best known superalloys is shown in Table IA. In order to facilitate the location of any particular alloy, the materials whose designation begins with a letter have been listed alphabetically, and those commencing with a number have been listed numerically.

TABLE IA.   NOMINAL COMPOSITION OF SUPERALLOYS IN THE UNITED STATES, GREAT BRITAIN, AND GERMANY

Alloy	Nominal composition,*								References
	C	Cr	Ni	Co	Mo	W	Cb	Other elements	
United States									
1......................	0.14	19	15	13	2	.....	1	Ta 0.05	2
1M....................	0.22	18	15	11	3	.....	1		2
100 NT-2.............	0.10	20	30	20	3	2	....	Mn 2, Ta 2	30
110 N-2	1.1	21	30	21	3	2	1	Mn 2, N 0.07	30
111VT2-2.............	1.11	23	....	Bal.	6	....	....	Ta 2	30
1073..................	0.32	15	16	16	3	....	....	N 0.05	2
1320..................	0.13	....	55	5	15	5	....	Ti 1.7	1
16-25-6 (Timken).......	0.08	17	25	.....	6	....	....	N 0.07	1, 2, 3, 9, 10, 11, 26, 30, and 33
17W..................	0.49	13	19	.....	0.5	2	....	N 0.03	2
17W (low C).........	0.29	13	19		.5	2	....	....	2
17W-NM.............	0.48	20	20	.....	.5	2	....	N 0.16	2
17W-Cb..............	0.47	12	19	.....	.5	2	1	....	2
18-8..................	0.08	18	8	.....					5, 33
18-8 Mo(18–14S Mo)....	0.06	18	14		3				5
19-9 W-Mo............	0.11	19	9	.....	0.4	1	0.28	Ti 0.45	1, 2, 6, 48
19-9 DL..............	0.30	19	9	.....	1.2	1.2	0.3	Ti 0.21	1, 2, 3, 6, 10, 26, 30, 33, 48
2......................	0.22	19	15	19	2	.....	1	Ta 1, N 0.05, Mn 2	2
2M...................	0.23	19	15	20	2	.....	2	Mn 2	2
2MM..................	0.23	19	15	20	2	.....	2	Mn 2	2
25-20..................	0.35	25	20	....	....	.....	....	Mn 1	6, 33
25-12..................	0.35	25	12	....	....	.....	....	Mn 1	6
2605..................	0.15	13	32	.....	3	2	....	....	2
2606..................	0.15	13	32	2	3	2	....	....	2
2607..................	0.30	13	32	.....	3	2	....	....	2
2608..................	0.30	13	32	2	3	2	....	....	2
31V4..................	0.31	23	....	Bal.	6	....	....	Mn 4	30
35H...................	0.35	23	2	Bal.	6	3	....	Ta 2	30
36J...................	0.36	23	6	Bal.	6	....	....	Ta 2	30
36VT2-3...............	0.36	23	....	Bal.	6	....	....	Mn 2, Ta 2	30
4......................	0.55	14	19	.....	2	.....	1	Ta 0.02	2
422-19 (Stellite 30)......	0.40	25	16	Bal.	6	.....	....		1, 16, 17, 18, 26, 30. 33
4237..................	0.59	26	30	....	....	....	....	Mn 1.5, Ti 2.5	2
4273..................	0.23	18	4	....	3	....	....	Mn 4..........	2
4274..................	1.06	13	13	.....	0.5	2.4	....	....	1, 2
4275..................	0.98	18	4	.....	3	....	....	Mn 4	1, 2
4275-3.................	0.47	18	4	.....	1	2	....	Ti 1.5, Mn 4	1
4275-4.................	0.44	18	5	.....	2.9	2.7	....	Ti 1.5, Mn 4	1
4276..................	0.53	20	....	.....	2	2	....	Mn 12	2
4277..................	1.16	20	....	.....	2	2	....	Mn 12	1, 2
4480..................	0.65	17	4	.....	3	....	....	Mn 4	2
4481..................	0.89	18	4	.....	3	....	....	Mn 4	2
469...................	0.03	60	....	.....	25	....			26
5......................	0.52	14	19	11	3	.....	1	Ta 1.4, Mn 2	2
5M....................	0.53	13	19	11	3	.....	2	....	2
5 Cr-Mo...............	0.15	5	....	.....	0.5				
5MM..................	0.11	13	19	11	3	.....	1	....	2
6......................	0.26	18	25	20	4	.....	2	Ta 1, W 0.07, Mn 2	2
6059 (Stellite 27)........	0.46	26	32	32	6	....	....	....	1, 16, 17, 18 22, 30, 32, 33

* Balance iron unless otherwise indicated.

TABLE IA. NOMINAL COMPOSITION OF SUPERALLOYS IN THE UNITED STATES, GREAT BRITAIN, AND GERMANY.—(*Continued*)

Alloy	Nominal composition,*								References
	C	Cr	Ni	Co	Mo	W	Cb	Other elements	
United States—*Continued*									
6M	0.31	18	24	21	3	....	2	Mn 2.2	2
6MM	0.31	18	24	20	3	....	3	Mn 2	2
61 (Stellite 23)	0.43	24	....	Bal.	3	5	....	....	1, 16, 17, 18, 26, 30, 33
72	0.10	6	52	4	17	6	....	Mn 2	1
73J	0.73	23	6	Bal.	6	....	....	Ta 2	30
8	0.24	18	15	10	6	....	1	Si 1.30	2
8M	0.23	18	15	....	6	....	1	Si 1.36	2
8658-1	0.35	19	15	20	3	....	7	Ta 0.5, Mn 2, Si 2	1, 30
8658-2	0.35	19	15	20	3	....	1.25	Ta 1.0, Mn 2, Si 2	1, 30
8659	0.39	18	25	20	4	....	1.5	Ta 1.0, Mn 2, Si 2	1
9	0.21	13	20	11	6	....	1	....	2
9M	0.21	13	19	....	5	....	1	Si 1	2
AM-BM	0.40	18	4	3	....	....	....	N 0.12	2
ATV-3	0.35	15	27	....	....	4	....	....	1, 30
CM469	0.03	60	....	....	25	....	....	....	30
Co-Cr base (9 W)	0.40	23	3	Bal.	....	9	....	....	30
Co-Cr base (9 Mo)	0.40	23	3	Bal.	9	....	....	....	30
Co-Cr-Ni base (9 Mo)	0.50	23	19	Bal.	9	....	....	....	30
Co-Cr-Ni base (5 Mo-5 W)	0.40	23	18	Bal.	5	5	....	....	30
CSA	0.42	18	5	....	1.5	1.3	0.6	Mn 4	3, 10, 26
Discaloy	0.05	13	25	....	3	....	....	Ti 1.8, Al 0.2	2, 4, 25, 26, 30
EME	0.10	19	12	....	....	3.25	1.25	N 0.15	3, 10, 31
Gamma columbium	0.35	16	25	....	5	....	4	....	1, 2, 11, 30
GT-45	0.08	17	14	....	3	....	0.45	Ti 0.30, Cu 3.0	30, 33
H-350	0.35	15	16	16	3	....	....	....	2
H-351	0.35	15	16	25	3	....	....	....	2
H-353	0.35	15	25	16	2	3	....	....	2
H-354	0.35	15	25	25	2	3	....	....	2
H-355	0.35	20	25	25	3	....	....	....	2, 30
H-357	0.35	15	16	25	5	....	....	....	2
H-359	0.35	20	25	25	2	3	....	....	2
H-412	0.35	15	25	16	2	3	1.5	....	2
H-413	0.35	20	25	25	3	....	1.5	....	2
H-414	0.35	15	25	16	5	....	....	....	2
H-416	0.35	15	35	16	5	....	....	....	2
H-417	0.35	15	35	16	3	2	....	....	2
H-418	0.35	15	35	25	3	2	....	....	2, 30
H-419	0.35	15	35	25	5	....	....	....	2
H-439	0.35	20	30	30	5	....	....	....	2, 30
H-479	0.35	15	20	20	5	....	....	....	2
H-480	0.35	20	20	20	5	....	....	....	2
H-496	0.35	15	25	10	4	....	2	N 0.08	2
H-497	0.35	15	25	20	4	....	2	N 0.08	2
H-624	0.35	15	16	16	5	....	....	....	2
H-625	0.35	15	16	16	5	....	....	....	2
H-626	0.35	15	25	25	5	....	....	....	2
H-627	0.35	15	25	25	5	....	....	....	2
H-628	0.35	15	35	25	5	....	....	....	2
H-629	0.35	15	35	25	5	....	....	....	2
H-630	0.20	15	25	....	4	....	2	N 0.10	2
H-631	0.20	15	25	....	4	....	2	N 0.10	2

* Balance iron unless otherwise indicated.

TABLE IA. NOMINAL COMPOSITION OF SUPERALLOYS IN THE UNITED STATES, GREAT BRITAIN, AND GERMANY.—(*Continued*)

Alloy	Nominal composition,*								References
	C	Cr	Ni	Co	Mo	W	Cb	Other elements	
United States—*Continued*									
H-729	0.25	16	24	....	3	6	....	N 0.10	2
Halcomb 217	0.58	7	....	....	....	....	....	....	2
Hastelloy A	....	....	58	....	20	....	....	Fe 20	12, 13
Hastelloy B	0.12	....	61	....	27	....	....	Fe 5	1, 12, 13, 16, 30, 33
Hastelloy C	0.13	15	53	....	18	4	....	V 0.2	12, 13, 16, 33, 48
Hastelloy D	....	....	85	....	....	....	....	Cu 3, A12, Si 10)	12, 13
Inconel (mod.)	0.03	14	75	....	....	....	....	Cu 0.1, Al 0.6, Ti 2.8	2, 3, 26
Inconel (mod. W)	0.05	14	75	....	....	....	....	Al 0.60, Ti 2.50	1
Inconel X	0.04	15	73	....	....	....	1	Al 0.70, Ti 2.5	10, 14, 30, 48
Inconel W	0.04	15	73	....	....	....	....	Al 0.70, Ti 2.5....	1, 14
Inconel	0.08	13	79	....	....	....	....	Cu 0.2	6, 48
Invar	Low	..	36	....	....	....	....	Bal. Fe	20
K42B (type 5)	0.06	18	42	22	....	....	....	Al 0.59, Ti 2.56	1, 25, 26
K42B	0.02	20	40	22	..	....	....	Al 0.6, Ti 2.3	25, 30, 34
Konel	Low	....	73	17	....	....	....	....	20
L1 (Li T₂)	0.30	13	33	11	4	2	....	....	2, 30
L2	0.12	18	8	....	....	....	2	....	2
L3	0.12	18	8	....	....	....	2	Si 2	2
L4	0.11	13	33	11	4	2	....	N 0.07	2
L7	0.36	12	32	9	4	2	....	N 0.05	2
MT-9-1	0.32	21	31	5	4	4	....	Ta 2, N 0.15, Mn2	20
MT-17	0.06	21	30	21	3	2	....	Mn 2, Ti 2	30
Multimet (low C) (N-155)	0.18	20	20	20	3	2.5	1.25	N 0.10	1, 2, 16, 17, 18, 26, 27, 32, 33
Multimet (med. C) (N-155)	0.40	20	20	20	3	2.5	1.25	N 0.10	1, 6, 10, 16, 17, 18, 26, 27, 33, 48
N-153	0.38	16	15	13	3	2	1	N 0.07	1, 2, 11, 18, 27, 30, 33,
N-153 (Low C)	0.10	15	15	13	3	2	1	N 0.010	1, 2, 26, 27
N-153 (No Co)	0.35	16	15	....	3	2	1	N 0.11, Mn 2	30
N-154	0.32	16	24	21	3	2	1	N 0.07	1, 2, 30
N-154 (low C)	0.10	15	25	21	3	2	1	N 0.10	1, 2
N-155 (multimet)	0.32	21	21	21	3	2	1	N 0.11	1, 6, 10, 16, 17, 18, 26, 27, 33, 48
N-155 (low C)	0.10	20	20	20	3	2	1	N 0.10	1, 2, 16, 17, 18, 26, 27, 32, 33
N-155 (low C, B mod.)	0.12	22	20	20	3	2	....	N 0.12, B .38	1
N-155 (modified)	0.40	21	21	....	3	2	1	N 0.12, Mn 2	30
N-155 (No Co)	0.36	21	21	....	3	2	1	N 0.14, Mn 2	30
N-155 (No Co plus Ta)	0.39	21	21	....	3	2	1	Ta 1	30
N-156	0.33	16	33	24	3	2	1	N 0.04	1, 2, 30
Nichrome	Low	15	70	....	....	....	....	Bal. Fe	20
Nimonic 80	0.04	21	74	....	....	....	....	Cu 0.04, Al 0.63, Ti 2.4	1, 2, 26, 30, 33, 44
Ni-Resist	3.0	2	14	....	....	....	....	Mn 1.25, Si 1.5, Cu 6.25	6
Nonmagnetic	0.73	4	6	....	0.3	0.5	....	V 0.2, Mn 9.3	2
R1038	0.10	14	7	....	3	....	....	....	2
Refractaloy A	0.07	20	50	....	14	....	....	....	1
Refractaloy B	0.07	24	30	....	8	....	....	Mn 2	1, 11, 30

* Balance iron unless otherwise indicated.

TABLE IA. NOMINAL COMPOSITION OF SUPERALLOYS IN THE UNITED STATES, GREAT BRITAIN, AND GERMANY.—(*Continued*)

Alloy	Nominal composition,*								References
	C	Cr	Ni	Co	Mo	W	Cb	Other elements	
United States—*Continued*									
Refractaloy D	0.11	20	20	30	8	4	....	....	26, 30
Refractaloy 26	0.03	18	37	20	3	....	....	Al 0.25, Ti 2.99	1, 25, 26, 30, 33
Refractaloy M284	0.11	20	20	30	8	3.8	....	Mn 2	1
S495	0.50	14	20	....	4	4	5	....	1, 2, 11, 26, 30
S497	0.42	14	19	19	4	4	4	....	1, 2, 11, 30
S588	0.45	20	20	....	4	4	4		29, 33, 45
S590	0.47	19	19	19	4	4	4		1, 6, 10, 26, 29, 30, 33, 45
S816	0.47	19	20	44	4	4	4		1, 10, 26, 28, 29, 30, 33, 45, 47, 48
Stellite 21 (Vitallium)	0.25	28	2	Bal.	6	....	....	....	16, 17, 18, 22, 26, 30, 32, 33, 48
Stellite 23 (61)	0.45	28	2	Bal.	....	6			1, 16, 17, 18, 26, 30, 33
Stellite 27 (6059)	0.45	26	33	33	6				1, 16, 17, 18, 22, 30, 32, 33
Stellite 30 (422-19)	0.45	31	15	46	6				1, 16, 17, 18, 26, 30, 33
Stellite 31 (X-40)	0.48	25	10	55	....	7			1, 16, 17, 18, 26, 30, 33
Stellite 6	0.98	32	....	Bal.	0.6	5			30
TE	0.09	20	30	....	4	4	....	Ta 2, N 0.15	16, 30
TE-O	0.04	20	30	....	4	4	....	Ta 4	20
Ticonium	0.008	23	35	31	6	....	....		1, 2
Timken (16-25-6)	0.06	16	25	....	6	....	....	N 0.07	1, 2, 3, 9, 10, 11, 26, 30, 33
Timken X	0.13	17	29	31	10	....	....	N 0.10	1
Vitallium (Stellite 21)	0.20	27	....	Bal.	6	....		....	1, 10, 26, 28, 29, 30, 33, 45, 47, 48
Vitallium 6059	0.46	26	33	33	6				1, 16, 32
VR	0.43	23	5	....	2.7				2
X-40 (Stellite 31)	0.48	25	10	Bal.	....	7			1, 16, 17, 18, 26, 30, 33
X-41	0.50	25	8	Bal.	....	7.5	....	CrB$_2$ 1.7	1, 26, 30
X-50	0.76	23	20	40	....	12			1, 30
X-63	0.45	25	10	Bal.	6				19
Great Britain									
ATV	....	20	80	....	....	....	....		36
G17	0.4	13	25	....	2	2.5	....	Si 1.5	40
G18 (B), Jessop	0.4	13	13	10	2	2.5	3	Si 1.0	34, 35, 40, 41
G .2	0.4	13	13	....	....	2.5	0.15	Si 1.3	40
H 40	0.2	3	....	....	0.5	0.5	....	V 0.75	42
H. R. crown max	0.22	23	12	....	....	0.5	....	....	35
Immaculate 5	0.14	25	20	....	....	....	....		34
Inconel	0.15	13	80	....	....	....	....		34
Nimonic 80	0.1	20	Bal.	....	....	....	....	Al 1.2, Ti 2.5	34, 35
R.16	0.1	18.5	9.5	....	....	....	....	Ti 0.7, Si 1.2	40
R.18	0.3	19	7.5	....	....	3.5	....	Si 1.7	40
R.20	0.14	19	14	....	....	....	1.7	....	40, 41
Rex 78	0.08	14	18	....	4	....	....	Cu 4, Ti 0.6, V 0.25	34, 35, 37, 39
Stayblade	0.22	20	8.5	....	....	....	....	Al 1.5, Ti 1.0	34, 35, 37
Wex 298	0.4	14	13.7	....	2	2.5	2.9	Si 1.5	40
Wex 299	0.33	22	25.7	....	1.8	2	....	Si 2.3	40

* Balance iron unless otherwise indicated.

TABLE IA.   NOMINAL COMPOSITION OF SUPERALLOYS IN THE UNITED STATES, GREAT BRITAIN, AND GERMANY.—(*Concluded*)

Alloy	Nominal composition,*								References
	C	Cr	Ni	Co	Mo	W	Cb	Other elements	
Germany									
C5T....................	0.13	17	10.5	....	....	....	....	V 1.0, Ti 0.6	38
Cromadur...............	.....	12.5	....	....	....	....	1	Mn 18, V 0.25, N 0.20	35, 36, 38
CM25..................	0.35	1	....	....	....	....	....	V 0.25, Mn 1.7	38
Cr-Mo-V..............	0.2	2.8	....	....	0.4	....	....	V 0.8	34, 35, 36
FK(D)MIO...........	0.25	3	....	....	0.4	0.4	....	V 0.20	36, 38
FK MIO..............	0.25	3	....	....	0.4	....	....	V 1.0 Ti 0.6	36
Tinidur................	0.10	15	30	....	....	....	....	Ti 1.8	34, 35
Vanidur...............	0.10	18	10	....	....	....	....	V 1.0, Ti 0.6	36
8 CrAl 27..............	0.12	6.5	....	....	....	....	....	Al 0.5	38 (wrought)
8 CrSiAl 24...........	0.12	6	....	....	....	....	....	Si 1.5, Al 1.0	38 (wrought)
10 CrSiAl 52..........	0.12	13	....	....	....	....	....	Si 1.5, Al 1.0	38 (wrought)
7 CrAlTi 32...........	0.10	8	....	....	....	....	....	Al 6.0, Ti 1.0	38 (wrought)
10 Mn Cr 72...........	0.15	9	1.8	....	....	....	....	Si 3.0, Mn 18.0	38 (wrought)
15 CrNiSi 38...........	0.15	19.5	9.5	....	....	....	....	Si 2.0	38 (wrought)
15 CrNi 9676..........	0.15	24	19	....	....	....	....	Si 2.0	38 (wrought)
SiCr 13................	0.25	3	....	....	....	....	....	Si 3.25	38 (cast)
CrSi 24...............	0.25	6	....	....	....	....	....	Si 2.5	38 (cast)
CrSi 52...............	0.6	13	....	....	....	....	....	Si 2.5	38 (cast)
Cr 112................	0.6	28	....	....	....	....	....	Si 2.0	38 (cast)
CrAlTi 3222...........	0.15	8	....	....	....	....	....	Al 6.0, Ti 0.85	38 (cast)
CrNi 8838.............	.....	22	9.5	....	....	....	....	Si 2.0	38 (cast)
CrNi 10456............	0.4	26	14	....	....	....	....	....	38 (cast)
C3T....................	0.13	30	15	....	....	....	....	Ti 1.7	38 (wrought)
D2T....................	0.1	16.5	15	....	2	....	....	Si 1.0, Cb 10XC plus N	38 (wrought)
D3T....................	0.15	17	10.5	....	1	....	....	Si 2.3, Cb 1.5, N, 0.11	38 (wrought)
F2T....................	0.10	12	....	....	....	....	....	Mn 18, V 0.65, N 0.2	38 (wrought)
F7T....................	0.18	9.5	....	....	....	....	....	Mn 18.5, V 0.3	38 (wrought)

* Balance iron unless otherwise indicated.

7. Impact strength (notch sensitivity)
8. Thermal expansion
9. Thermal conductivity
10. Density
11. Stability of microstructure
12. Hardness
13. Modulus of elasticity
14. Tensile strength, yield strength, elongation, and reduction of area (with autographic stress-strain curves)
15. Oxidation (corrosion) resistance

All of the foregoing information is available for only a relatively small number of the superalloys.   Even if the foregoing information were available, other important factors must be considered in selecting an alloy for a given application. These factors include the following:

1. Cost
2. Availability of raw materials, particularly in time of national emergency
3. Ease of fabrication
4. Machinability
5. Weldability

It has been found that even quite complete laboratory information is inadequate to qualify a material for service and that actual parts or even complete engines must be built and tested in order to determine the merit of the alloy. Bursting (hot-spin) tests have proved useful in the evaluation of forging and processing methods, heat-treatments, and alloy compositions; the results of extensive tests were described by Fonda[3] who concluded that the most important consideration was ductility, obtained by proper control of grain flow during forging.

The final service demonstration of the value of the material has been termed an "acceptance test" or "proof testing." Only a few of the large number of compositions which have been invented have found their way into such actual service tests. These better known alloys will be mentioned briefly, but a more extensive list of the compositions of the materials which have been described in the literature is appended (Table IA), together with references. Both American and foreign superalloys are listed in the table.

Development of the Superalloys

According to Mochel,[4] some development work was under way in this country on materials for gas turbines in 1939; at that time, it was considered that 1000°F was the safe maximum temperature for uncooled blades of diesel engine gas-turbine superchargers. Reviews of the high-temperature properties of the standard alloys available for gas-turbine applications prior to the development of the superalloys have been presented by Evans.[5, 6]

When the urgent need arose in 1939–1940 for materials with better high-temperature strength, it was found that certain alloys already in existence had fairly good high-temperature properties. These alloys included the iron-base Cr-Ni alloys of the 18–8 Mo type, the nickel-base alloys such as inconel and Hastelloy, the cobalt-base Stellites and Vitallium, and the Ni-Co-Cr-Fe alloy K42B. Modifications of these basic types soon occurred, and alloys containing about 20 per cent each of Co, Cr, Ni, and Fe such as N-155 and S-590 were then developed. Chromium-base materials and the ceramels (mixtures of metals and ceramics) are now under study, as are other materials whose composition and properties have not yet been announced.

The transition of a given composition from the idea stage to laboratory tests and from there to reproducible commercial production is at best a slow and tedious process, usually involving several years. It was not until 1947 that some of the more widely used superalloys were reduced to specifications. This was carried out under the sponsorship of the Society of Automotive Engineers under their Aeronautical Material Specifications. A list of some of these specifications is given in Table IIA. A typical specification (AMS 5532 of Sept. 1, 1947) for low-carbon N-155 describes applications, chemical composition, condition, atmos-

TABLE IIA. HEAT-RESISTANT ALLOYS INCLUDED IN SOCIETY OF AUTOMOTIVE ENGINEERS AERONAUTICAL MATERIALS SPECIFICATIONS*

AMS No.	Specification	Trade designation
AMS 5375	Alloy castings, precision investment, corrosion and heat-resistant cobalt base 25Cr–5W	Stellite 23 (61)
AMS 5378	Alloy castings, precision investment, corrosion and heat-resistant cobalt base 25Cr–32Ni–5Mo	Stellite 27 (6059)
AMS 5380	Alloy castings, precision investment, corrosion and heat-resistant cobalt base 25Cr–15Ni–6Mo	Stellite 30 (422-19)
AMS 5382	Alloy castings, precision investment, corrosion and heat-resistant cobalt base 25Cr–10Ni–7.5W	Stellite 31 (X-40)
AMS 5385	Alloy castings, precision investment, corrosion and heat-resistant cobalt base 27Cr–2Ni–5Mo	Stellite 21 (Vitallium)
AMS 5530	Alloy sheet, corrosion and heat-resistant, nickel base 17Mo–15Cr–6Fe–5W	Hastelloy C
AMS 5532	Alloy sheet, corrosion and heat-resistant, iron base 20Cr–20Ni–20Co–3Mo–2W–1Cb	N-155
AMS 5540B	Plate, sheet, and strip, corrosion and heat-resistant, nickel base 15Cr–7Fe	Inconel
AMS 5542	Alloy sheet, corrosion and heat-resistant, nickel base 15Cr–2.5Ti–1Cb–0.7Al	Inconel X
AMS 5667	Bars and forgings, heat-resistant, nickel base, 15Cr–2.5Ti–1Cb–0.7Al, precipitation	Inconel X
AMS 5668	Bars and forgings, heat-resistant, nickel base, 15Cr–2.5Ti–1Cb–0.7Al, solution and precipitation	Inconel X

* Published Sept. 1, 1947.

pheric-temperature strength and bending properties, quality, tolerances, methods of identification, and details of approval, rejection, and acknowledgment. The specifications do not contain high-temperature requirements.

Iron-base Alloys. According to W. L. Badger[7] and R. B. Johnson,[8] the first material used for gas-turbine rotors for aircraft turbosuperchargers was SAE 2335 (3.5 per cent Ni steel) in 1918. Later, SAE 6150 (1 per cent Cr–0.15 per cent V) was used for the wheel alloy. This was followed by the Silchrome No. 1 (8–9

Cr, 3–3.5 Si, 0.40–0.50 C) an exhaust valve alloy, 17 W (14 Cr, 19 Ni, 2.5 W, 0.5 Mo, 0.50 C), gamma columbium (16 Cr, 25 Ni, 4 Mo, 2 Cb, 0.35 C), and finally by the Timken alloy (16 Cr, 25 Ni, 6 Mo, 0.10 C, 0.10–0.15 N), which became the main production material for the turbosupercharger rotors. The Timken alloy has been discussed at some length by Fleischmann.[9] This material has excellent high-temperature properties up to about 1400°F. It can be successfully hot-formed and welded, and warm-worked at 1200 to 1400°F in small sizes. However, in common with other alloys in this class, some cracking was encountered during warm working of gas-turbine rotors larger than about 15 in. in diameter. Gamma columbium, 17 W, and Timken, among the first to be classed as superalloys, are iron-base chromium-nickel alloys with additions of one or more of the elements Mo, W, Ti, and Cb; 19–9 DL (19 Cr, 9 Ni, 1.2 Mo, 1.2 W, 0.3 Cb, 0.2 Ti, 0.30C) and 19–9 W-Mo (19 Cr, 9 Ni, 0.3 Mo, 2 W, 0.11 C) should also be classed in this category. These alloys are usually employed in rotor wheels for turbosuperchargers and gas turbines with operating temperatures up to about 1200°F, and all of them appear to be better than straight 18 Cr–8 Ni–3Mo (AISI Types 316 or 317).

Early in the development work on these superalloys, it was found that warm working (forging or pressing) in the temperature range 1200 to 1400°F was particularly effective in increasing the yield strength at ordinary temperatures, a requirement thought to be necessary for materials used for rotors of gas turbines, particularly for overspeed spin tests used for inspection and quality control. The warm-working operation also produced a high rupture strength at 1200°F, at least for time periods up to several thousand hours, but this increase of strength is generally accompanied by a decrease of ductility. Improvement of strength by warm working is not so effective in increasing the strength at temperatures above 1350°F, even for time periods as short as 1,000 hr, and may even decrease the strength. At these higher temperatures, solution treatment with or without aging develops the best properties. This effect was well shown in a paper by Freeman, Cross, Reynolds, and Simmons,[10] describing comparative tests on specimens taken from bar stock and from rotor forgings of Timken alloy, CSA, EME, 19–9 DL, low-carbon N-155, S-590, S-816, and inconel X. In the warm-working operation, deformation is not uniform throughout the rotor forging, resulting in nonuniform properties which are usually low at the center of the disk. Considerable effort is now being devoted to the development of rotor materials in which uniformly high strength can be developed by heat-treatment alone.

A recent paper by Leslie and Fontana[11] has called attention to the rapid oxidation of molybdenum-bearing superalloys in still air at temperatures above about 1500°F. This phenomenon has been noted in the Timken alloy (16–25–6), S-497, S-495, and gamma columbium, Refractaloy B, and N-153. All contain iron, 3 to 8 per cent molybdenum, and chromium up to 24 per cent, indicating that iron and molybdenum are required for the reaction and that high percentages of chromium are required to halt it. This type of oxidation does not affect 18–8 Mo, Type 316 stainless steel, which contains 2 to 3 per cent molybdenum.

Nickel-base Alloys. The two nickel-base alloys most widely used for high-temperature applications during the Second World War were Hastelloy and inconel. Hastelloy B (30 Mo, 5 Fe, 0.12 C, balance Ni) was developed for corrosion resistance against hydrochloric acid. According to Badger and Sweeny,[12] it was first described in 1915 but did not become commercially available until 1937. Its high-temperature strength was described by McCurdy[13] in June, 1939. This material has useful properties up to 1400°F, above which its corrosion resistance is not satisfactory. In order to avoid aging during service, the material is customarily heat-treated 72 hr at 1750°F or 24 hr at 1950°F for stabilization. The composition must be closely controlled in order to obtain reproducible properties. This material was standard for rotor blading for the General Electric I-16 gas-turbine engine and it has also been used successfully as a welding electrode for the attachment of the blades to rotors.

Inconel, a nickel-base alloy containing 80 Ni, 14 Cr, and 6 Fe, has found wide application for the combustion liners of jet engines. The age-hardenable inconel alloys, such as inconel W (75 Ni, 14 Cr, 0.60 Al, 2.5 Ti, 0.05 C) and inconel X (same as inconel W, but with addition of 1.0 Cb) have been described by Crawford.[14] These materials show high strength and corrosion resistance up to 1500°F. The Nimonic 80 alloy (74 Ni, 21 Cr, 0.6 Al, 2.4 Ti, 0.04 C) is used extensively by the British for blading in their jet engines. The inconel X alloy appears to offer considerable promise, particularly as a substitute for Nimonic 80.

A series of new nickel-base alloys of high strength has been described by Guy.[15] The alloys contain 6 per cent aluminum, 6 per cent molybdenum, and 20 per cent chromium, the remainder being nickel. The rupture strength of the cast alloys at 1500°F was found to be increased by the addition of 0.5 per cent boron and 2 per cent columbium, and was equivalent to that of the cobalt-base materials.

Cobalt-base Alloys. One of the most widely used superalloys, Vitallium (27 Cr, 5 Mo, 0.20 C, balance Co), was developed before the war as a precision casting alloy for dentures and jewelry. Vitallium is also known as Haynes Stellite 21. Its superior corrosion resistance led to its testing for high-temperature applications and it was found that the material had excellent high-temperature strength.

The cobalt-base alloys are used principally as precision castings and find their chief application in blading in the gas turbines of aircraft superchargers and jet engines such as the General Electric Type B superchargers and I-40 (J-33) jet engines. The Stellites, having been used widely for cutting tools, are usually considered to be hard, brittle materials, but this is true only of the high-carbon variety. The medium-carbon alloys are forgeable and some have been rolled to sheet product. The various Stellite compositions have been described by Badger and Sweeny,[12] Sweeny,[16] Badger and Kroft,[17] and Browne.[18] A number of improvements have been made and Stellite 23 (alloy 61, 26 Cr, 5 W, 1.5 Ni, 0.40 C, balance Co) was used for blading on the Westinghouse 19XB jet engine and was the only one of the modified alloys to be used in service. Two additional investigations should be mentioned. An improved cobalt-base alloy for gas-turbine bucket applications has been developed by Epremian.[19] This alloy was designated as X-63, and contained approximately 25 Cr, 10 Ni, 6 Mo, 0.45 C, balance Co. A second investigation, described in a series of papers by Grant,[20, 21, 22, 23] dealt with modification of Vitallium, 6059, and N-155. Very high strength was developed in some of these alloys, but the materials were found to be quite brittle.

Chromium-base Alloys. An extensive investigation was made of the chromium-base alloys by Parke and Bens.[24] After the elimination of many different compositions, the Cr-Fe-W and Cr-Fe-Mo alloys were selected for further study. On the basis of rupture properties, availability, and cost, the chromium-base-molybdenum system was found to be the most promising. An alloy containing 60 Cr, 15 Fe, and 25 Mo showed rupture strengths in 100 and 1,000 hr of 35,000 and 21,000 psi, respectively, at 1600°F with an average elongation of about 5 per cent and an average reduction of area of about 5 per cent. Recent work at Battelle (private communication, H. C. Cross) has shown that an alloy containing 58 Cr, 15 Fe, 25 Mo, and 2 Ti has a 100-hr rupture strength of about 46,000 psi, and a 1,000-hr rupture strength of about 37,000 psi. These alloys, as they are now made, contain about 0.10 per cent C, 0.60 per cent Si, 0.50 per cent Mn, 0.015 per cent O_2, and 0.030 per cent N_2 (O_2 and N_2 analyzed by vacuum-fusion method). The titanium addition produces a fine uniform grain size in the casting and probably contributes to the deoxidation and the reduction of nitrogen content of the alloy. The alloy is difficult to machine, is brittle at room temperature, and has 2 to 4 per cent elongation in rupture tests at 1600°F. Chromium-base alloys containing 60 Cr, 28 Fe, and 12 Mo have been rolled into sheet form.

Cr-Ni-Co-Fe Alloys. One of the first alloys of the complex Cr-Ni-Co-Fe type was K42B, which has been described by Scott and Gordon.[25] This material contains 42 Ni, 22 Co, 18 Cr, 14 Fe, 0.2 Al, 2.2 Ti, and 0.05 C. It is amenable to precipitation hardening, and shows high strength at temperatures below 1400°F. Refractaloy 26 (37 Ni, 20 Co, 18 Cr, 18 Fe, 0.2 Al, 3 Mo, 2.8 Ti, 0.05 C) and Refractaloy 70 (20 Ni, 30 Co, 20 Cr, 18 Fe, 8 Mo, 3.8 W) show even better properties, and are now being applied commercially.

Recently developed alloys similar to low-carbon N-155 (20 Ni, 20 Co, 20 Cr, 3 Mo, 2 W, 1 Cb, 0.14 N, 0.14 C) described by Binder,[26] and Franks,[27] and S-816 (20 Ni, 34 Co, 18 Cr, 3 Fe, 4 Mo, 4 W, 3 Cb, 0.36 C) described by Wilson[28] and Henry[29] have also shown much promise. All these materials may be strengthened by heat-treatment, and do not require the warm-working operation at 1200 to 1400°F to enhance their strength for service at temperatures in excess of 1350 to 1400°F; indeed, warm working has been found to be undesirable for service temperature above 1350°F.

Comparison of Properties of the Superalloys

As in carbon and low alloy steels, it has been found that the high-temperature properties of the superalloys vary considerably with variation of the following factors:

1. Composition (even within the range of a nominal analysis)
2. Melting and manufacturing practice
3. Heat-treatment
4. Final plastic deformation, if such a step is employed

The factors listed above cause considerable variation in properties, even for such a standard material as Vitallium. For example, at 1500°F, the stress for rupture in 1,000 hr has been reported to vary from 9,000 to 17,000 psi. This represents a spread of nearly 100 per cent, about the same as that found in carbon-molybdenum steel. A complete listing of all of the properties of all the alloys in all conditions of treatment is beyond the scope of this book. Excellent summary comparisons have been prepared by Grant, Frederickson, and Taylor,[30] Badger,[7] Binder,[26] and Knight,[31] but even in these exhaustive articles, the authors did not attempt to present complete information for each material. Such information can best be obtained from the manufacturer or from the original articles describing these materials. In order to facilitate the location of such articles, Table IA has been arranged so that reference numbers appear beside the name and composition of the various materials. Review articles have been omitted from Table 1A, and in general, only articles containing source data are cited.

A comparison of the creep strength of the superalloys with the creep strength of some of the more common materials in use before the superalloys were developed is shown in Fig. 1A. Since the properties of any given alloy vary so greatly, individual values are not shown. The creep strength of the wrought materials is represented by the shaded area within the solid lines, while the cast materials are shown by the lighter band surrounded by dotted lines. For any given temperature, it will be noted that the superalloys have much greater creep strength than the standard austenitic chromium-nickel stainless steels. At 1200°F, for example, the creep strength (stress for creep rate of 0.0001 per cent per hour) of

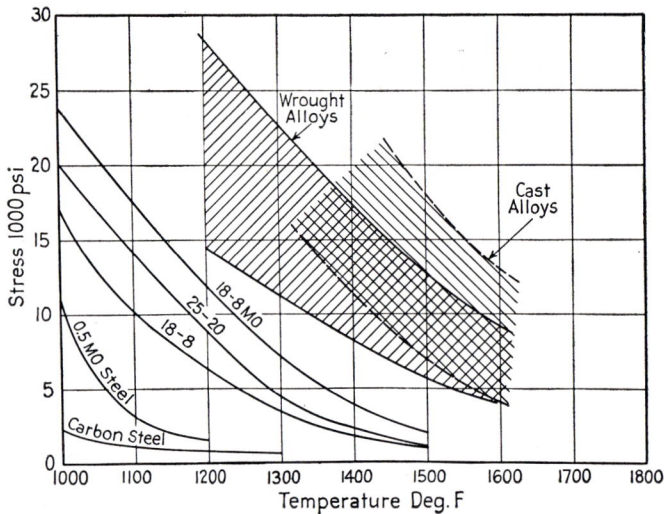

Fig. 1A. Creep strength (stress for creep rate of 0.0001 per cent per hour) of wrought and cast superalloys in comparison with standard materials.

the standard stainless materials is between 6,000 and 12,000 psi, while the superalloys have creep strengths ranging from about 15,000 to 28,000 psi, more than 3 times as high. At 1500°F even a greater increase in creep strength is evident; the stainless steels having a creep strength of about 1,000 to 2,000 psi as compared to 6,000 to 18,000 psi for the superalloys. Speaking in terms of use of the material, this means that parts made of the superalloys can withstand a stress about 3 times as great as the ordinary stainless steels at 1200°F and at least 5 times as high at 1500°F.

The advantage of the superalloys can also be expressed in terms of temperature; a number of the superalloys have the same creep strength at 1500°F as the stainless steels have at 1100 or 1200°F. For the same strength, the superalloys thus permit a working temperature from 300 to 400 degrees higher than was formerly available.

The rupture strength (stress for rupture in 1,000 hr) of these materials is shown in Fig. 2A. The shaded portion again shows the range of strength encountered in the forged superalloys, while the area within the dotted curves shows the rupture strength of the cast materials. It will be seen that at 1200°F the stress for rupture in 1,000 hr for the ordinary stainless steels is from 12,000 psi to 25,000 psi, while the stress for rupture in 1,000 hr of the superalloys ranged from 25,000 to 55,000 psi, a twofold to threefold advantage. At 1500°F, the stress for rupture in 1,000 hr for the stainless steels is from 4,000 to 7,000 psi as compared to 9,000 to 29,000 psi for the superalloys, again a twofold to threefold advantage, somewhat less than noted in Fig. 1A for creep strength. Figure 2A also shows that the superalloys will permit a 300- to 400-deg. increase of temperature for the same stress. High strength, is, of course, not the sole criterion of high-temperature perform-

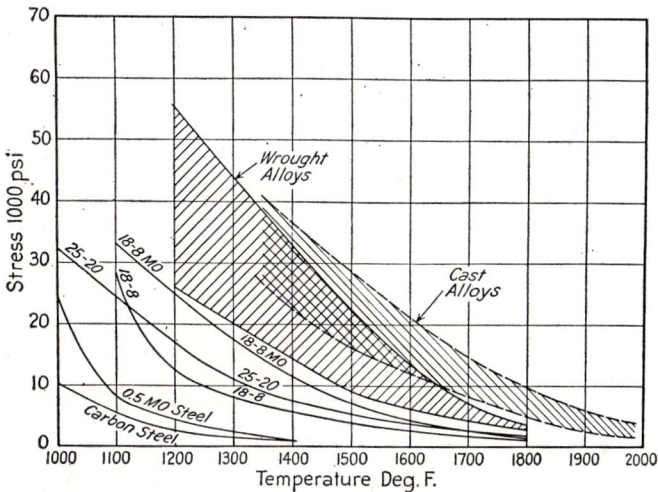

Fig. 2A. Rupture strength (stress for rupture in 1,000 hr) of wrought and cast superalloys in comparison with standard materials.

ance, since the materials should also have the same degree of ductility. In general, the higher the strength, the lower the ductility, and both factors must be given consideration in selecting a material for a given application.

Conclusion

In their summary of the results of the research work on superalloys carried out by the War Metallurgy Committee (Office of Scientific Research and Development) Cross and Simmons[1] concluded that the wrought alloys showed their best and most consistent properties when tested in the solution treated and aged condition rather than in the as-forged or as-rolled and aged condition. The lack of consistency in the results of the tests on as-forged and as-rolled material is probably due to the effects of differences in finishing temperature. Solution annealing not only removes this variable factor but dissolves the complex carbides and intermetallic compounds, the precipitation of which greatly improves the strength of materials upon subsequent aging.

In regard to the effect of composition, Freeman, Reynolds, and White[2] concluded that fabrication procedure and heat-treatment influenced the properties to such a degree that no correlation with composition was possible.

Almost all the superalloys show some change of microstructure during test or service in the temperature range 1200 to 1600°F, usually resulting in an increase of strength and reduction of the ductility. A thorough study of the structural instability and accompanying change of properties of cast Vitallium, N-155 and 6059, was carried out by Grant and Lane.[32] It was found that these alloys were quite stable up to 900 or 1000°F. The first definite precipitation was noted at about 1350°F, and maximum aging occurred between 1550 and 1700°F. In all cases, agglomeration of the precipitate began around 1700°F, and by 2100 to 2200°F practically all of it was back in solution. The microstructure of the superalloys has also been discussed at some length by Franks.[33] Uncontrolled changes of structure or properties are undesirable, and the aim of the present investigators is to develop alloys which will have the desired strength and ductility accompanied by greater structural stability.

Examination of Figs. 1A and 2A shows that while the wrought materials may have superior strength at 1200°F, the cast materials tend to have greater strength at higher temperatures. Cross and Simmons[1] concluded that the best forged alloys at 1500°F are Refractaloy 26, S-816, N-155, Refractaloy 70, and S-590. All these alloys are of the Ni-Cr-Co-Fe class with the addition of one or more of the elements Mo, W, and Cb. The presence of 20 per cent or more cobalt appears to contribute to the strength of these alloys at 1500°F, since none of the Ni-Cr-Fe alloys without cobalt additions, except S-495, approach their strength. The cast alloys of the Co-Cr and Co-Cr-Ni types (Vitallium and its modifications) show better strength at 1500°F than the forged alloys. At 1500°F, the strongest cast alloys were X-40, X-41, X-50, S-816, 422-19, and 61. Even greater difficulty was encountered with the reproducibility of the properties of the cast alloys than with the forged alloys, since in addition to the variables encountered in the wrought alloys, a large variation of grain size is encountered. However, control of mold and pouring temperatures improves the uniformity of grain size and microstructure, and thereby improves the reproducibility of properties.

The best known superalloys, and those for which the most information is available, are as follows:

Forged	Cast
19-9 DL	Vitallium (Stellite 21)
Timken (16-25-6)	61 (Stellite 23)
Low-carbon N-155 (Multimet)	422-19 (Stellite 30)
Refractaloy 26	X-40 (Stellite 31)
Refractaloy 70	S-816
S-590	
S-816	

APPENDIX REFERENCES

General

1. CROSS, H. C., and W. F. SIMMONS: Heat Resisting Metals for Gas Turbine Parts, ASTM Symposium on Materials for Gas Turbines, June, 1946, pp. 3–51.

2. FREEMAN, J. W., E. E. REYNOLDS and A. E. WHITE: High Temperature Alloys Developed for Aircraft Turbo-superchargers and Gas Turbines, ASTM Symposium on Materials for Gas Turbines, June, 1946, pp. 52–79.

3. FONDA, L. B.: Forging High Temperature Alloys, *Trans. ASME*, **70,** pp. 1–12, 1948.

4. MOCHEL, N. L.: Metallurgical Considerations of Gas Turbines, *Trans. ASME,* 1947, **69,** No. 6, 561–568.

5. EVANS, C. T., JR.: Wrought Heat Resistant Alloys for Gas Turbine Service, *Metal Progress*, November, 1945, pp. 1083–1095, 1126.

6. EVANS, C. T., JR.: Materials for Power Gas Turbines, *Trans. ASME*, **69,** No. 6, 601–608, 1947.

7. BADGER, W. L.: Metallurgical Developments of Materials for Superchargers and Aircraft Gas Turbines, *Iron Age*, July 25, 1946, pp. 40–45, and Aug. 1, 1946, pp. 60–66.

8. BADGER, CROSS, EVANS, FRANKS, JOHNSON, MOCHEL, and MOHLING: Super-alloys for High Temperature Service in Gas Turbines and Jet Engines, *Metal Progress*, July, 1946, pp. 97–122.

9. FLEISCHMANN, MARTIN: 16-25-6 Alloy for Gas Turbines, *Iron Age*, Jan. 17, 1946, pp. 44–53, and Jan. 24, 1946, pp. 50–60.

10. FREEMAN, J. W., H. C. CROSS, E. E. REYNOLDS, and W. F. SIMMONS: High Temperature Properties of Rotor Discs for Gas Turbines as Affected by Variables in Processing, *Proc. ASTM*, **48,** 555, 1948.

11. LESLIE, W. C., and FONTANA, M. G.: Mechanism of the Rapid Oxidation of High Temperature, High Strength Alloys Containing Molybdenum, *Trans. ASM*, **41,** 1213, 1949.

12. BADGER, F. S., JR., and W. O. SWEENY, JR.: Metallurgy of High Temperature Alloys Used on Current Gas Turbine Designs, ASTM Symposium on Materials for Gas Turbines, June, 1946, pp. 99–112.

13. McCURDY, F. T.: Nickel-Molybdenum-Iron and Related Alloys—Their Physical and Corrosion-resistant Properties, *Proc. ASTM*, **39,** 698, 1939.

14. CRAWFORD, C. A.: Nickel-Chromium Alloys for Gas Turbine Service, *Trans. ASME*, **69,** (6), 609–612, 1947.

15. GUY, A. G.: Nickel-base Alloys for High Temperature Applications, *Trans. ASM*, **41,** 125, 1949.

16. SWEENY, W.O.: Haynes Alloys for High Temperature Service, *Trans. ASME*, **69,** No. 6, 569–581, 1947.

17. BADGER, F. S., JR., and F. C. KROFT, JR.: Cobalt-base and Nickel-base Alloys for Ultra-high Temperatures, *Metal Progress*, September, 1947, pp. 394–402.

18. BROWNE, L. E.: Cobalt-base High Temperature Alloys, *Steel*, May 27, 1946, pp. 88–91, 132.

19. EPREMIAN, E.: The Development of a Turbosupercharger Bucket Alloy, *Trans. ASM*, **39,** 261–280, 1947.

20. GRANT, N. J.: The Stress Rupture and Creep Properties of Heat Resistant Gas Turbine Alloys, *Trans. ASM*, **39,** 281–334, 1947.

21. GRANT, N. J.: Structural Variation in Gas Turbine Alloys Revealed by the Stress Rupture Test, *Trans. ASM*, **39,** 335–367, 1947.

22. GRANT, N. J.: The Effect of Composition and Structural Changes on the Rupture Properties of Certain Heat Resistant Alloys at 1500 F, *Trans. ASM*, **39,** 368–403, 1947.

23. GRANT, N. J.: The Cobalt-Chromium J Alloy at 1350–1800 F, *Trans. ASM*, **40**, 585–616, 1948.
24. PARKE, R. M., and F. P. BENS: Chromium-base Alloys, ASTM Symposium on Materials for Gas Turbines, June, 1946, pp. 80–98.
25. SCOTT, H., and R. B. GORDON: Precipitation Hardened Alloys for Gas Turbine Service, Parts I and II, *Trans. ASME*, **69**, (6), 583–599, 1947.
26. BINDER, W. O.: Alloys for High Temperature Service, *Iron Age*, Nov. 7, 1946, pp. 46–52, and Nov. 14, 1946, pp. 92–95.
27. FRANKS, R.: The High Temperature N-153 and N-155 Alloys, Electro-Metallurgical Co., New York, 1948.
28. WILSON, THOMAS Y.: High Strength, High Temperature Alloy S-816, *Materials & Methods*, October, 1946, pp. 885–890.
29. HENRY, J. B.: Characteristics of Three High Temperature Alloys, *Iron Age*, June 12, 1947, pp. 58–64.
30. GRANT, N. J., A. F. FREDERICKSON, and M. E. TAYLOR: A Summary of Heat Resistant Alloys from 1200 to 1800 F (in three parts), *Iron Age*, March 18, 1948, pp. 73–78, April 8, 1948, pp. 75–81, April 15, 1948, pp. 84–93.
31. KNIGHT, H. A.: Super Alloys for High Temperature Service, *Materials & Methods*, June, 1946, pp. 1557–1563.
32. GRANT, N. J., and J. R. LANE: Aging in Gas Turbine Type Alloys, *Trans. ASM*, **41**, 95, 1949.
33. FRANKS, R.: On the Structure of the High Temperature Metals, Yearbook, *Am. Iron & Steel Inst.* 1948, pp. 509–539.

Foreign Superalloy Developments

34. TAYLOR, T. A.: Recent Developments in Materials for Gas Turbines, lecture on the Development of the British Gas Turbine Jet Unit, *War Emergency Issue* 12 *Inst. Mech. Eng.* (*London*), republished by ASME, January, 1947. pp. 505–512.
35. GRIFFITHS, W. T.: High Temperature Alloys for Gas Turbines, *Metal Ind.* (*London*) Oct. 31, 1947, pp. 359–362, Nov. 14, 1947, pp. 401–403. (See also *The Aeroplane*, Sept. 6, 1946, and Oct. 31, 1947, p. 577.)
36. ROBINSON, W. J.: "Alloys for Use at High Temperature—Report on Visit to Germany and Austria," Mapleton House, New York, 1947.
37. HALL, C. C.: British High Temperature Steels, *Steel*, June 23, 1947, pp. 101, 132.
38. FEILD, A. L.: German Stainless Steel, *Iron Age*, Dec. 20, 1945, pp. 60–67.
39. SYKES, C.: Steels for Use at Elevated Temperatures, *J. Iron Steel Inst.* (*London*), Part III, **156**, pp. 321–369, 1947 (including bibliography for 1937–1947).
40. OLIVER, D. A., and G. T. HARRIS: A High Creep Strength Austenitic Steel for Gas Turbines, *Metallurgia* (Britain), **35**, 235–238, 1947.
41. OLIVER, D. A., and G. T. HARRIS: Gas Turbine Forgings, *Iron and Steel* (*London*), July, 1947, pp. 329–344.
42. OLIVER, D. A., and G. T. HARRIS: Ferritic Discs for Gas Turbines, *Metallurgia* (Britain), **34**, 293–295, 1946.
43. ZSCHOKKE, H. R., and K. H. NIEHUS: Requirements of Steel for Gas Turbines (Swiss), *J. Iron Steel Inst.* (*London*), June, 1947, pp. 271–283.
44. A New Nimonic Blade Material, *Aeroplane*, **75**, 481–482, 1948 (Nimonic 80 A).

Testing, Processing, and Production Methods

45. Mohling, G.: Problems Involved in the Fabrication of High Temperature Alloys, Yearbook, *Am. Iron Steel Inst.* 1947, pp. 519–527.
46. Smith, Rebecca H.: Selection of High Temperature Materials for Gas Turbines, *Iron Age*, Jan. 22, 1948, pp. 56–60.
47. Guarnieri, G., and J. Miller: Strain Gage for Testing Sheet Metal at High Temperature, *Metal Progress*, Nov., 1948, pp. 692–694.
48. Haythorne, P. A.: Sheet Metals for High Temperature Service, *Iron Age*, Sept. 23, 1948, pp. 89–95.
49. Miller, J., and G. Guarnieri: Short-time High Temperature Deformation Characteristics of Several Sheet Alloys, *Trans. ASM*, **41**, 167, 1949.
50. Birdsall, G. W.: Casting Supercharger Buckets at Allis-Chalmers, *Steel*, Jan. 29, 1945, pp. 72–75, 96, 99–100.
51. Demirjian, S. G.: Precision Drop Forging of High Temperature Alloys, *Materials & Methods*, September, 1947, pp. 68–71.
52. Clauser, H. R.: Alloys Made by Electric Ingot Process Have Improved Properties, *Materials & Methods*, January, 1948, pp. 57–61.
53. Chisholm, C. G.: Welding the Super-alloys, *Steel*, Dec. 29, 1947, pp. 54–56, 58, 60.
54. Price, N. C.: How to Tailor Gas Turbine Parts to Do the Job, *SAE Journal*, Dec., 1946, pp. 52–53.
55. Brams, S. H.: Turbosupercharger Production Details, *Iron Age*, Sept. 6, 1945, pp. 88–93.
56. Focke, A. E.: Supercharger Buckets Mass Produced by Precision Casting, *Metal Progress*, September, 1945, pp. 489–494.
57. Brewer, G.: Use of Stainless Steel as a Structural Material in Jet-propelled Aircraft, *Metal Progress*, July, 1946, pp. 84–87.
58. Smith, C. H., Jr.: Precision Forging of High Temperature Alloys, *Iron Age*, Nov. 28, 1946, pp. 42–46.
59. Willson, R. T.: German Practices in Drawing and Forging Turbine Blades, *Steel Processing*, **34**, No. 10, 545–548, 1948.

NAME INDEX

A

Aborn, R. H., 268–270, 324, 331
Agnew, J. T., 150, 319
Alleman, N. T., 217, 242
Andrade, E. N., 4, 105, 115
Angier, R. P., 72
Ansel, G., 13, 28, 135
Archbutt, S. L., 242
Arnold, S. M., 243, 340
Aston, R. L., 47
Austin, C. R., 75, 223–240, 252, 274, 287, 324, 329
Avery, H. S., 207, 296–297, 336

B

Badger, F. S., Jr., 381, 382
Badger, W. L., 380, 383
Baeyertz, M., 170
Bailey, R. W., 102–103, 226–234, 299–300, 325
Bain, E. C., 240, 265, 324, 331
Bakarian, P. W., 28
Baker, J. S., 34
Bandel, G., 236
Bardenheuer, P., 236
Bardgett, W. E., 191
Barnett, W. J., 294
Barr, W., 191
Barrett, C. S., 8, 12, 13, 23, 28, 61, 64, 79, 133, 135, 157
Bassett, W. H., 243
Bauschinger, J., 64
Becker, R., 166
Bedworth, R. E., 312
Beilby, G. T., 41–42, 277
Bengough, G. D., 43, 277
Bens, F. P., 173–174, 382
Benz, W. G., 193, 226, 229, 271, 324
Betty, B. B., 17, 34, 45, 115, 158, 242, 253, 255, 301
Binder, W. O., 383
Birchenall, C. E., 121n

Birdsall, G. W., 389
Bishop, E. C., 172
Blank, A. I., 252, 288
Bleakney, H. H., 149
Boas, W., 9, 14–21, 26–31, 132, 135
Boer, J. H., de, 161
Bolton, J. W., 249
Born, M., 163
Bouton, G. M., 243, 340
Bowman, F. E., 323
Boyd, J., 129, 211
Bradley, J., 5
Brams, S. H., 389
Brasunas, A. de S., 317
Brewer, G., 389
Brick, R. M., 72–74, 133–135
Bridgman, P. W., 52, 57
Brinell, J. A., 171
Brophy, G. R., 296, 310
Brown, J. S., 249
Browne, L. E., 382
Bucknall, E. H., 275, 310
Bullens, D. K., 234
Burghoff, H. L., 16, 36, 252, 288

C

Campbell, R. F., 268–270, 324
Carpenter, H. C. H., 40
Caum, J. W., 72
Chalmers, B., 31–34, 45–48, 66–67, 103, 115
Chaston, J. C., 307
Chevenard, P., 5, 103, 108
Chisholm, C. G., 389
Clark, C. L., 103, 145, 218, 222, 227–230, 235, 237, 250, 256, 265, 266, 278–280, 284, 293, 301, 324, 334, 340
Clarke, H., 70
Clauser, H. R., 389
Clenshaw, W. J., 221
Cohen, M., 172
Comstock, G. F., 237, 273

SUBJECT INDEX

A

Alloying, effect on creep of, 220–255
  of ferrous alloys, 221–242
    carbon, 221–225
    chromium, 228–230
    general considerations of, 239–242
    manganese and copper, 230–232
    molybdenum, 225–228
    nickel and cobalt, 232–233
    phosphorus, 238
    silicon and aluminum, 232
    tungsten, vanadium, titanium and columbium, 233–238
  of nonferrous alloys, 242–255
    aluminum, 248–249
    chromium, 255
    copper, 249–252
    lead, 242–243
    magnesium, 246–248
    nickel, 252–255
    tin, 244–246
    zinc, 243–244
  effect on flow of polycrystalline metals, 70–84
    in heterogeneous alloys, 77–84
    in homogeneous alloys, 72–76
  effect on, slip, 12, 14
    stress-strain curve of single crystals, 18–19
Aluminum, creep of, 248–249

B

Bauschinger effect of, 64–68
Becker-Orowan theory of flow, 166–167

C

Carbide precipitation in austenitic steels, 331–334

Carbon, effect on creep of steel, 221–225
Chromium, creep of, 255
  effect on creep of steel, 228–230
Compression, hot, test, 218–219
Constant-rate creep (see Minimum creep rate)
Copper, creep of, 249–252
Crack theory of fracture, 161–163
Creep, early investigations on, 4–5
  metallographic characteristics of, 157–161
  of polycrystalline metals, 95–131
  primary, secondary, tertiary (see Creep curve)
  recovery, 66–67, 103
  of single crystals, 28–37
    microcreep, 31–34
    slipless flow, 29
    variation of, with lattice orientation, 30
Creep curve, accelerating creep rate in, 104–105
  at constant load, 96–102
  derivation of, from nominal stress-strain curves, 100–102
  effect of structural instability on, 98–100
  McVetty analysis of, 106–107
  mathematical expressions for, 105–113
  minimum creep rate in, 103–104
  for 100,000-hour test, 102
  period of decreasing rate (primary creep) in, 102–103
  as resultant of strain hardening and temperature softening, 100
Creep-rupture test, 144–146, 186–210
  autographic strain-time recorder for, 203–205
  effect of atmosphere on, 149–150
  specimens of, 202–203
  variation of ductility with time in, 150–151

L

Lattice rotation during slip, 22–24
  deformation bands in, 25
  in polycrystalline metals, 59–61
Lead, creep of, 242–243
Lüders' lines, 50

M

McVetty analysis of creep curve, 106–107
Magnesium, creep of, 246–248
Manufacturing variables, effect on creep, 256–294
  grain size, 277–294
  heat-treatment, 264–277
  melting and deoxidation practices, 256–264
Maximum-shear-stress law for plastic flow, 48–52
Mean ferrite path, 81
Mechanical equation of state, 100–101, 125–127
Melting practice, effect on creep, 256–264
Meyer hardness analysis, 71
Microcreep, 31–34
Microstructural changes, 98–100, 319–340
  carbide precipitation in austenitic steels, 331–334
  graphitization, 326–330
  recrystallizition, 338–340
  sigma phase formation, 335–336
  spheroidization, 322–326
  strain-aging, 337–338
  temper embrittlement, 336–337
Miller indices, $11n$
Minimum creep rate, 103–104
  generalized expressions for, 123–127
  variation of, with stress, 114–119
    exponential and power laws of, 115–118
    hyperbolic sine law of, 118–119
  variation of, with temperature, 119–121
Modulus of elasticity, definition of, 175
  measurement of, 217–218

Mohr theory, 49–52
Molybdenum, effect on creep of steel, 225–228

N

Neumann bands, 11, 25
Nickel, creep of, 252–255
Normal stress, definition of, 49
Notch-impact hot test, 219

O

Octahedral shear stress law, 51
Oxidation (*see* Scaling)

P

Plastic flow, metallographic characteristics, 157–161
  theories of, 164–168
  (*See also* Strain hardening)
Plastic yielding, of single crystals, 9–12
  laws governing, 13–14
  of polycrystalline metals, 48–52
Precipitation hardening, 79–80
Preferred orientation, 59–61
Primary creep, 102–103
  (*See also* Creep curve)
Principle stresses, $50n$
Proportional limit, definition, 175

Q

Quasi-viscous flow, 115
Quasi-viscous flowability, 120

R

Rate of deformation, effect on flow of polycrystalline metal, 84–93
  effect of, on slip, 12, 15
    on stress-strain curve of single crystals, 19
    on twinning, 27
Rate process theory, chemical and physical, 123–124